Newer Methods of
Preparative
Organic Chemistry

Volume II

Newer Methods of
Preparative
Organic Chemistry
Volume II

This volume was originally published
by Verlag Chemie, Weinheim, Germany
as Neuere Methoden Der
Präparativen Organischen Chemie

Newer Methods of Preparative Organic Chemistry

Volume II

Edited by

Wilhelm Foerst

translated by

F. K. Kirchner
Sterling-Winthrop Research Institute
Rensselaer, New York

1963
Academic Press • New York and London

ACADEMIC PRESS INC.
111 Fifth Avenue, New York 3, New York

United Kingdom Edition published by
ACADEMIC PRESS INC. (LONDON) LTD.
Berkeley Square House, London W.1

LIBRARY OF CONGRESS CATALOG CARD NUMBER: 48-6233

PRINTED IN THE UNITED STATES OF AMERICA

Contributors to Volume II

Numbers in parentheses indicate the page on which the author's contribution begins.

R. CRIEGEE (367), *Institute für Organische Chemie der Technischen Hochschule Karlsruhe*

J. EBERSBERGER (227), *Farbenfabriken Bayer A. G., Leverkusen*

HERMANN O. L. FISCHER (253), *Department of Biochemistry, University of California in Berkeley*

WALTER FRANKE (1), *Chemische Werke Hüls A. G., Wissenschaftliches Laboratorium*

R. FUGMANN (361), *Pharmazeutisch-Wissenschaftliche Laboratorien der Farbwerke Hoechst AG*

STEFAN GOLDSCHMIDT (31), *Organisch-chemisches Institut der Technischen Hochschule Munich*

H. HABERLAND (227), *Farbenfabriken Bayer A. G., Leverkusen*

W. HAHN (227), *Farbenfabriken Bayer A. G., Leverkusen*

H. HELLMANN (277), *Chemisches Institut der Universität Tübingen*

K. HEYNS (303), *Chemisches Staatsinstitut, Universität Hamburg*

HELMUT HÖRMANN (213), *Max-Planck Institut für Eiweiss- und Lederforschung, Regensburg*

H. HOFFMANN (163), *Organisch-Chemisches Institut der Universität Mainz*

KURT KOSSWIG (1), *Chemische Werke Hüls.A. G., Wissenschaftliches Laboratorium*

RICHARD KRAFT (1), *Chemische Werke Hüls A. G., Wissenschaftliches Laboratorium*

H. L. KRAUSS (31), *Organisch-chemisches Institut der Technischen Hochschule Munich*

ROLAND MAYER (101), *Institut für Organische Chemie der Technischen Universität Dresden*

W. MEIXNER (361), *Pharmazeutisch-Wissenschaftliche Laboratorien der Farbwerke Hoechst AG*

H. PAULSEN (303), *Chemisches Staatsinstitut, Universität Hamburg*

G. QUADBECK (133), *Max-Planck-Institut für Medizinische Forschung, Institut für Chemie, Heidelberg*

H. RUSCHIG (361), *Pharmazeutisch-Wissenschaftliche Laboratorien der Farbwerke Hoechst AG*

R. SEYDEL (337), *Farbenfabriken Bayer A. G., Leverkusen*

HERMANN STETTER (51), *Chemisches Institut der Universität Bonn**

R. STROH (337), *Farbenfabriken Bayer A. G., Leverkusen*

* Present Address: Institut für Organische Chemie der Technischen Hochschule Aachen.

Preface

New and improved methods in preparative organic chemistry are often scattered throughout the literature. Review articles on these preparative methods are therefore convenient and welcome.

Each chapter in this volume contains several detailed laboratory procedures. Items of both industrial and laboratory interest are included. Numerous references to the original literature and tables of compounds make the chapters more than a mere recounting of synthetic procedures. Since some readers may not have ready access to patents and some foreign journals, reference to *Chemical Abstracts* has been made where possible.

This volume is a collection of articles which appeared originally in *Angewandte Chemie*. The compilation of these articles into one handy volume and its translation should be of value to a wide audience of research workers and graduate students, especially in organic chemistry and biochemistry.

I wish to express my appreciation to the authors who were kind enough to review these articles in translation and to my colleague, Dr. F. C. Nachod, who gave me encouragement and advice during the preparation of this volume.

FRED K. KIRCHNER

Foreword

This volume is intended for all synthetic organic chemists.

The first series of these articles was originally collected in one volume, which went through numerous large editions. (Several editions were reprinted in the United States during the Second World War.)

The reviews in these three volumes are in the form of monographs, and have for that reason not appeared in systematic order. We have selected what seemed to us topical and important. (Reaction mechanisms according to modern theories are postulated only where they allow the prediction of fresh applications of the reaction described.)

The up-to-date character of the reviews is due to the exceptional co-operation of the authors.

W. FOERST

Heidelberg
March 1963

Contents

Syntheses with Acetoacetaldehyde

WALTER FRANKE AND RICHARD KRAFT, IN COLLABORATION WITH KURT KOSSWIG

Preparation of Peptides and Ureas Using Reactive Amides or Imides

STEFAN GOLDSCHMIDT AND H. L. KRAUSS

The Preparation of Long-Chain Carboxylic Acids from 1,3-Cyclohexanediones

HERMANN STETTER

Ethyl 2-Cyclopentanonecarboxylate and Its Importance in Syntheses

ROLAND MAYER

Ketene in Preparative Organic Chemistry

G. QUADBECK

Preparative and Analytical Importance of Phosphines and Related Compounds

L. HORNER AND H. HOFFMANN

Reduction of Carbonyl Compounds with Complex Hydrides

HELMUT HÖRMANN

Alkylation of Aromatic Amines

R. STROH, J. EBERSBERGER, H. HABERLAND AND W. HAHN

Chemical Synthesis of Intermediates of Carbohydrate Metabolism

HERMANN O. L. FISCHER

Amidomethylation

H. HELLMANN

Selective Catalytic Oxidations with Noble Metal Catalysts

K. HEYNS AND H. PAULSEN

Alkylation of Phenols with Alkenes
R. STROH, R. SEYDEL AND W. HAHN

Continuous Preparation of Phenylsodium
H. RUSCHIG, R. FUGMANN AND W. MEIXNER

Newer Investigations on Oxidation with Lead Tetraacetate
R. CRIEGEE

Contents of Volume III

(in preparation)

Syntheses with Acetoacetaldehyde

WALTER FRANKE AND RICHARD KRAFT,

IN COLLABORATION WITH

KURT KOSSWIG

Chemische Werke Hüls A.G., Wissenschaftliches Laboratorium

Acetoacetaldehyde

Free acetoacetaldehyde is as unstable as free acetoacetic acid. The compound was prepared first by Boileau (1) from sodium formylacetone with acetic anhydride in ether, or better, using less than an equivalent of chloroacetic acid (about a 40% yield). A colorless liquid (b.p. 30°/24 mm), having a camphorlike odor, it changes to triacetylbenzene on standing. The violet coloration with $FeCl_3$ is evidence for the enolization (1) which takes place at the aldehyde group as revealed by the IR spectrum.

Bokadia and Deshapande (2) furnished the chemical proof that the aldehyde group is enolized in α-formylketones by the reaction with phenyl isocyanate:

$$C_5H_{11}-CO-CH=CHOH \rightarrow C_5H_{11}-CO-CH=CH-O-CO-NHC_6H_5$$

An α-substituted derivative of the free acetoacetaldehyde was obtained in 17% yield by S. Hünig and O. Boes (3).

$$CH_3-CO-CH=CHONa + O_2N-C_6H_4-\overset{\oplus}{N}_2BF_4^{\ominus} \rightarrow O_2N-C_6H_4-NH-N=C-CO-CH_3$$
$$\underset{HCO}{|}$$

Noteworthy is the formation of 2,2-dimethyl-3-oxo-1-butanal, $CH_3COC(CH_3)_2CHO$, by the epoxidation of mesityl oxide and the isomerization of the epoxide with BF_3-ether in benzene (4). It was not possible to isolate the aldehyde by distillation, but the bis(p-nitrophenylhydrazone) was obtained in 58% yield.

Synthesis of Derivatives

SODIUM FORMYLACETONE (II)

Claisen (5) was the first to obtain the sodium salt of acetoacetaldehyde by the ester condensation of acetone and ethyl formate in the presence of sodium ethoxide in absolute ether:

$$CH_3-CO-CH_3 + HCOOC_2H_5 + NaOC_2H_5 \rightarrow$$
$$CH_3-CO-CH=CHONa + 2\ C_2H_5OH.$$

1

TABLE 1

SUMMARY OF DERIVATIVES AND INTERMEDIATES OF ACETOACETALDEHYDE

Formula[a]	No.	Example	B.p. °C/mm	n_D^{20}	Remarks
$CH_3CX_2CH_2CHX_2$	I	$CH_3COCH_2CH(OCH_3)_2$ Acetoacetaldehyde dimethyl acetal; 3-ketobutyraldehyde dimethyl acetal; 4,4-dimethoxy-2-butanone	70–73°/20	1.4139	Commercial product
$CH_3CX_2CH{=}CHX$	II	$CH_3COCH{=}CHONa$ Sodium formylacetone	—	—	Laboratory preparation
	III	$CH_3COCH{=}CHCl$ β-Chlorovinyl methyl ketone; 1-Chloro-1-buten-3-one	42–43°/20	—	Laboratory preparation
	IV	$CH_3COCH{=}CHOCH_3$ 1-Methoxy-1-buten-3-one	172°	1.4699	—
$CH_3CX{=}CHCHX_2$	V	$CH_3C(OCH_3){=}CHCH(OCH_3)_2$ β-Methoxycrotonaldehyde dimethyl acetal	65°/19	1.4295	—
$CH_3C{\equiv}CCHX_2$	VI	$CH_3C{\equiv}CCH(OCH_3)_2$ 2-Butynal dimethyl acetal	53°/15	1.4278	—
$HC{\equiv}CCX_2CH_3$	VII	$HC{\equiv}CCOCH_3$ 1-Butyn-3-one	83.5–84.5°/752	1.4070	—
$HC{\equiv}CCH{=}CHX$	VIII	$HC{\equiv}CCH{=}CHOCH_3$ 1-Methoxy-1-buten-3-yne	122°	1.475	Technical grade

[a] $X_2 = {>}O$; $X = ONa$, OR, Cl, CN, NR_2.

From acetone, methyl formate, and sodium methoxide the sodium salt was obtained in 80–90% yield (*6–8*).

A flask, evacuated and then filled with nitrogen, is charged with 3.27 gm of alcohol-free sodium methoxide, 4.56 gm of ethyl formate, 3.58 gm of anhydrous acetone, and 150 ml of anhydrous ether. The light yellow reaction mixture is shaken for 10 min, then is allowed to stand at room temperature for 15 hr, care being taken to exclude air from the flask. When the supernatant is suctioned off with a filter stick from the powder-like precipitate, the latter is washed with ether and then dried over potassium hydroxide in a vacuum desiccator. Yield of sodium formylacetone: 6.03 gm (*6*). The substance can be stored for a long time in a well-stoppered flask.

β-CHLOROVINYL METHYL KETONE (III) (1-CHLORO-1-BUTEN-3-ONE)

β-Chlorovinyl methyl ketone is obtained in 50 to 80% yield from acetylene and acetyl chloride with $AlCl_3$ in an inert solvent (*9–13*).

An interesting extension is the reaction of acetyl chloride with vinyl chloride in the presence of $AlCl_3$ to form 1,1-dichloro-3-butanone, from which 1-chloro-1-buten-3-one is prepared using either $NaHCO_3$ or $CaCO_3$ (*14*).

$$CH_3COCl + CH_2=CHCl \rightarrow CH_3-CO-CH_2-CHCl_2 \rightarrow CH_3-CO-CH=CHCl$$

The unpleasant properties of the β-chlorovinyl ketones have hindered the technical application of these syntheses (*10*).

β-Chlorocrotonaldehyde is obtained in 38.5% yield by the reaction of acetone with dimethylformamide and phosphorus oxychloride or phosgene (*15*).

ACETOACETALDEHYDE DIMETHYL ACETAL (I)

The dimethyl acetal is formed from the sodium salt (II) by the action of anhydrous hydrogen chloride in methanol (64% yield) (*16, 17*) or in methyl formate (81% yield) (*7*). The reaction of the sodium salt (II) with ethyl bromide in absolute ethanol gives acetoacetaldehyde diethyl acetal (*18*). The dimethyl acetal (I) is obtained in 70–80% yield by the treatment of β-chlorovinyl methyl ketone with potassium hydroxide in methanol at −15°C (*10, 11, 13, 19, 20*). The most recent technical process (*21*) for dimethyl acetal (I) starts with methoxybutenyne (VIII) which is readily obtained from diacetylene according to Auerhahn and Stadler (*22*). VIII is a stable substance in the cold.

$$HC\equiv C-C\equiv CH + ROH \rightarrow HC\equiv C-CH=CHOR.$$
$$VIII$$

Following the procedure of Franke and Seemann (23), the butynal acetal (cf. VI) is obtained from VIII by the addition of one more molecule of methanol in the presence of alkali. This acetylene derivative is hydrated in boiling aqueous methanol in the presence of an acid catalyst (mercuric sulfate) to the dimethyl acetal (I) in 80% yield. Further experiments have shown that the butynal acetal step can be bypassed. It is possible to add methanol and water to methoxybutenyne (VIII) in the presence of acid catalysts (sulfuric acid, mercuric sulfate, etc.), giving yields of I up to 85%.

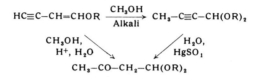

For syntheses of use in the vitamin A series the removal of water and methoxybutenone is required. This is possible by distilling three times or, better, by distillation after the addition of diethanolamine (24).

ACETOACETALDEHYDE BIS-DIMETHYL ACETAL AND β-METHOXYCROTONALDE-
    HYDE DIMETHYL ACETAL (V)

We have also obtained, besides dimethyl acetal, the 1,3-bis-dimethyl acetal from methoxybutenyne or butynal acetal, using the published procedures, but employing anhydrous methanol (21).

$$\text{HC≡C–CH=CHOR} \xrightarrow[\text{H}^+]{\text{CH}_3\text{OH}} \text{CH}_3\text{–C(OR)}_2\text{–CH}_2\text{–CH(OR)}_2$$

Copenhaver (25) prepared the bisacetal by the reaction of ortho-acetic ester with methyl vinyl ether in the presence of acid catalysts:

$$\text{CH}_3\text{–C(OR)}_3 + \text{CH}_2\text{=CHOR} \xrightarrow{\text{BF}_3} \text{CH}_3\text{–C(OR)}_2\text{–CH}_2\text{–CH(OR)}_2$$

The ketal group of the bisacetal is very easily hydrolyzed by an equivalent amount of water to form I. In this manner the mixture of methoxycrotonaldehyde (V) and the bisacetal, formed by the addition of methanol to methoxybutenyne, was converted by Lautenschlager to the dimethyl acetal by careful hydrolysis with water or dilute acid at room temperature (26).

The bisacetal can be obtained by the reaction orthoformic esters with the dimethyl acetal (27).

By passing acetoacetaldehyde bisdimethyl acetal at 250° over a catalyst consisting of 20% barium oxide on 80% silica, methanol is split off to give β-methoxycrotonaldehyde dimethyl acetal in 81% yield (21).

$$CH_3-C(OR)_2-CH_2-CH(OR)_2 \xrightarrow{-ROH} CH_3-C(OR)=CH-CH(OR)_2$$

Viguier (28) has described the synthesis of β-ethoxycrotonaldehyde diethyl acetal by the addition of ethanol to butynal diethyl acetal in the presence of sodium alkoxide in a sealed tube at 140°:

$$CH_3-C\equiv C-CH(OR)_2 + ROH \xrightarrow{NaOR} CH_3-C(OR)=CH-CH(OR)_2 \;.$$

Methoxybutenone (IV)

Methoxybutenone is a frequent by-product with 3-ketobutyraldehyde dimethyl acetal, from which it is derived by splitting off one molecule of methanol upon heating (29), especially in the presence of alkaline substances (30); quantitative conversion occurs in the presence of iron in 5 hr at 150° (31, 31a).

$$CH_3-CO-CH_2-CH(OCH_3)_2 \xrightarrow{-CH_3OH} CH_3-CO-CH=CH-OCH_3 \;.$$

In a 2 liter flask equipped with a column, one liter of 3-ketobutyralde-hyde dimethyl acetal, 10 gm of sodium bicarbonate, and 10 gm of iron turnings (Baustahl St 0037) are slowly heated in an oil bath at 500 mm. Under these conditions methanol distills. After about 5 hr the temperature in the flask reaches the boiling point of methoxybutenone, which is about 160° at this pressure. The temperature of 160° is maintained for 1 hr. The distilled amount of methanol is often somewhat more than calculated. After cooling the mixture is filtered and finally distilled. The yield is 90% (31a).

The compound also is obtained from methoxybutenyne by careful hydration of the triple bond below 50° (32):

$$HC\equiv C-CH=CHOR \xrightarrow[H^+]{H_2O} CH_3-CO-CH=CHOCH_3 \;.$$

Yamada has obtained methoxybutenone (IV) from the sodium salt (II) and dimethyl sulfate (33).

The reactions based on methoxybutenyne and diacetylene are summarized in the diagram; the 1,3-dimethoxybutadiene is not obtainable by these reactions. The "boxed" compounds are available commercially on a large scale.

On the basis of experimental results it is possible to compare the reactivity of acetals of acetoacetaldehyde. The bisacetal and the methoxycrotonaldehyde acetal (V), in which the oxo group is not free, are less reactive than the dimethyl acetal (I) and the methoxybutenone (IV). Especially in an alkaline medium or in reaction with basic reactants, the bisacetal and V react slowly, while I and IV react readily.

Acetals of Acetoacetaldehyde from Diacetylene

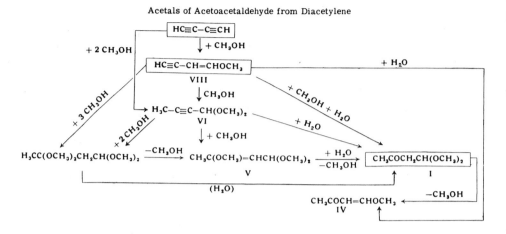

In acid medium the bisacetal and the methoxycrotonaldehyde acetal (V) react like I and IV, because of the rapid hydrolysis of the ketals and enol ethers. I and IV differ only slightly in their reactivity; only the formation of Schiff bases occurs faster with IV than with I.

From the summary it can be seen, that the starting materials methoxybutenyne (VIII) and butynal acetal (VI), used in the preparation of the acetal of acetoacetaldehyde, can be transformed in acid medium to the intermediate, acetoacetaldehyde. In the absence of a suitable reactant, triacetylbenzene is formed. If reactive substances are present in the reaction mixture, then the formation of heterocyclic compounds is possible.

1-AMINO-1-BUTEN-3-ONE

This class of substances can be obtained by the reaction of ammonia or amines, with an alkoxybutenone (*34*) (Procedure 1), or with the acetal I (*34a*) (Procedure 2).

Procedure 1. Ammonia is passed through 1000 gm of freshly distilled methoxybutenone for 5 hr. The temperature is kept at 0–20° by ice cooling. Vacuum distillation yields 85–90% of the aminobutenone, b.p. 95–101°/15 mm.

Procedure 2. The acetal, I, 132 gm, is mixed with 5 ml of a saturated aqueous solution of potassium carbonate and cooled to −35°. At this temperature ammonia is passed in with stirring (within about 3 hr) until the volume is doubled. The temperature is allowed to rise within 2 hr to −10° while stirring and passing in more ammonia. After addition of 125 ml of saturated potassium carbonate solution, the mixture reaches room temperature and should be well mixed. The upper layer is dissolved in ether and dried over potassium carbonate. Distillation yields 67 gm

(79%) of 1-amino-1-buten-3-one, a colorless highly refractive liquid, b.p. 44°/0.5 mm; $n_D^{20} = 1.5585$; $d_4^{20} = 1.022$.

If an aminobutenone is dissolved in benzene, the values of the dielectric constant are lowered (35). This means that the equilibrium which prevailed in the pure liquid is now shifted by the presence of benzene to give a less polar mixture:

$$CH_3-C-CH=CH-\bar{N}-H \rightleftharpoons CH_3-C=CH-CH=\bar{N}-H$$

The investigators A. N. Nesmeyanov and N. K. Kochetkov found that the reaction of 1-chlorobutenone with ammonia and amines leads to aminobutenones in yields up to 90% (36–38). From the fact that the refractive index increases after distillation, the conclusion was drawn that a tautomeric equilibrium sets in favoring RC(OH)=CHCH=NH (39). The IR spectra of some aminobutenones also support this tautomerism (40).

The reaction of chlorovinyl methyl ketone with tertiary amines leads to ammonium salts (41).

$$CH_3COCH=CH-N(CH_3)_3^{\oplus} \ Cl^{\ominus}$$

The reaction of N,N-dimethylamino-1-buten-3-one with methyl iodide gives the corresponding iodide (42). The higher ketobutenyltrialkyl ammonium salts can be converted to the corresponding hydroxymethylene ketones at high temperatures in the presence of water (42). From $CH_3COCH=CHN(CH_3)_3Cl$ and potassium cyanide, $CH_3COCH=CHCN$ is obtained (43).

The aminobutenones react readily; on heating with water triacetyl-benzene is formed (37); on hydrogenation the amino group is split off (44). Our own experimental results confirm the statements of the Russian investigators. The aminobutenones did not react as dienophiles with cyclopentadiene (44); they are suitable for ring closure reactions to form heterocyclic compounds which will be described.

Noteworthy is the reaction of 1-chlorobutenone with aniline: in the molar ratio of 1:1, anilinobutenone (45), $CH_3COCH=CHNHC_6H_5$, is obtained; in the molar ratio of 1:2, the dianil, $CH_3C(=NC_6H_5)CH=CHNHC_6H_5$ (46). The dianils cyclize with sulfuric acid to quinoline derivatives:

If ketobutyraldehyde glycolacetal is treated with a primary amine, the keto group reacts with the formation of (47):

$$CH_3-\underset{\underset{NR}{\|}}{C}-CH_2\underset{\diagdown O-CH_2}{\overset{\diagup O-CH_2}{CH}}$$

Interestingly, in the reaction of aminobutenone with an organometallic compound, the amino group is exchanged for the organic group of the organometallic. Example 1. is from work of Jutz (48) and 2. from Kochetkov (11).

$$CH_3-CO-CH=CH-N(CH_3)-C_6H_5 + C_6H_5Li \rightarrow$$
$$CH_3-CO-CH=CH-C_6H_5$$
$$CH_3-CO-CH=CH-NR_2 + CH_3MgI \rightarrow CH_3-CO-CH=CH-CH_3$$

The aminobutenones act as stabilizers for acrylic acid and its esters (49).

Syntheses in the Aliphatic Series

Plieninger and Müller reacted the acetal (I) with lead tetraacetate in an attempt to prepare the methyl homolog of reductone (50). A 40% yield of A was obtained and only a little of B, although A could be converted to B with methanol.

$$CH_3-CO-\underset{\underset{OCOCH_3}{|}}{CH}-CH(OCH_3)OCOCH_3 \xrightarrow{CH_3OH} CH_3-CO-\underset{\underset{OCOCH_3}{|}}{CH}-CH(OCH_3)_2$$
$$\text{A} \qquad\qquad\qquad\qquad\qquad\qquad\qquad \text{B}$$

B gives $CH_3CHOHCHOHCH(OCH_3)_2$ with $LiAlH_4$.

Kochetkov and Nifant'ev (51) obtained A in a similar manner. The action of bromine on acetoacetaldehyde in the presence of $CaCO_3$ yielded α-bromoacetoacetaldehyde. When the glycol acetal was used the acetal group remained intact and α-bromoacetoacetaldehyde glycol acetal was formed.

$$CH_3-CO-CHBr-CHO \qquad CH_3-CO-CHBr-\underset{\diagdown O-CH_2}{\overset{\diagup O-CH_2}{CH}}$$

Grignard reagents attack the oxo group in the normal manner.

$$C_2H_5O-C\equiv C-MgBr + CH_3COCH_2CH(OCH_3)_2 \rightarrow$$
$$\underset{\underset{C_2H_5O-C\equiv C-C(OH)-CH_2-CH(OCH_3)_2}{|}}{CH_3}$$

As expected, this compound forms the ester, $C_2H_5OCOCH_2C(CH_3)=CHCHO$, with acids at higher temperature (52).

1-Isobutoxy-2-buten-3-one, formed from sodium formylacetone and isobutyl alcohol in the presence of a small amount of *p*-toluenesulfonic acid, gives β-methylcrotonaldehyde in 59% yield when treated with methylmagnesium bromide in absolute ether, followed by hydrolysis (*53*).

A group of investigators at Eastman Kodak carried out work in the carotinoid field using acetoacetaldehyde acetal. The reaction of acetal (I) with propargyl bromide (*54*) in the presence of mercury-activated magnesium occurs in the normal way, at the carbonyl group, leading to a component of the geraniol and phytol series:

$$\underset{}{\overset{\displaystyle CH_3}{HC\equiv C-CH_2-\overset{|}{C}(OH)-CH_2-CH(OCH_3)_2}}.$$

In the vitamin A series the acetal, in four preparative procedures, has been joined in each instance to a different molecule to furnish the necessary intermediates. These procedures are as follows [1. (*55*); 2. (*56*); 3. (*57*); 4. (*58*)]:

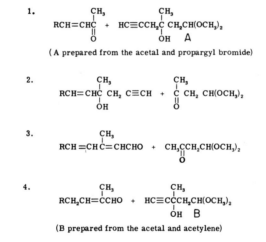

1.
$$RCH=CH\overset{\overset{\displaystyle CH_3}{|}}{C} + HC\equiv CCH_2\overset{\overset{\displaystyle CH_3}{|}}{C}CH_2CH(OCH_3)_2$$
with $\overset{||}{O}$ on the left and $\overset{|}{OH}$ on the right **A**

(A prepared from the acetal and propargyl bromide)

2.
$$RCH=CH\overset{\overset{\displaystyle CH_3}{|}}{C}CH_2 \ C\equiv CH + \overset{\overset{\displaystyle CH_3}{|}}{C}CH_2 \ CH(OCH_3)_2$$
with $\overset{|}{OH}$ and $\overset{||}{O}$

3.
$$RCH=CH\overset{\overset{\displaystyle CH_3}{|}}{C}=CHCHO + CH_3\overset{\overset{||}{O}}{C}CH_2CH(OCH_3)_2$$

4.
$$RCH_2CH=\overset{\overset{\displaystyle CH_3}{|}}{C}CHO + HC\equiv C\overset{\overset{\displaystyle CH_3}{|}}{C}CH_2CH(OCH_3)_2$$
with $\overset{|}{OH}$ **B**

(B prepared from the acetal and acetylene)

In procedure 3 a side-chain methyl group has to be introduced by reaction with methylmagnesium iodide.

The triple bond is hydrogenated to the double bond with Pd/charcoal

$$R-CH=CH-\overset{\overset{\displaystyle HO}{\diagdown}\overset{\displaystyle CH_3}{\diagup}}{C}-CH=CH-CH_2-\overset{\overset{\displaystyle HO}{\diagdown}\overset{\displaystyle CH_3}{\diagup}}{C}-CH_2-CH(OCH_3)_2$$

$$=CH-CH=\overset{\overset{\displaystyle CH_3}{|}}{C}-CH=CH-CH=\overset{\overset{\displaystyle CH_3}{|}}{C}-CH=CHOCH_3$$

$$-CH=CH-\overset{\overset{\displaystyle CH_3}{|}}{C}=CH-CH=CH-\overset{\overset{\displaystyle CH_3}{|}}{C}=CH-CHO$$

Vitamin-A-Aldehyde

TABLE 2
CYCLIZATION REACTIONS OF ACETOACETALDEHYDE, ITS INTERMEDIATES AND DERIVATIVES

Reactant	Reaction product	Bis-acetal	I	II	III	IV	V^a	VI	VII	VIII
	1. Aromatics									
Acetoacetaldehyde	1,3,5-Triacetylbenzene	+	90%	46%	—	85%	+	50%	—	—
Acetoacetic ester	m-Cresotic Acid	—	15%	65%	39%	—	—	—	—	—
	2. Pyrylium salts									
β-Naphthol	2-Methyl-5,6-naphtho(1.2)pyrylium chloride	—	—	—	74%	—	—	—	55%	—
	3. Pyridine ring closure									
Cyanacetamide	3-Cyano-6-methyl-2-pyridone	79%	95%	68%	—	80%	35%	—	—	—
Aminocrotonic ester	Lutidinecarboxylic ester	35%	50%	25%	—	—	40%	—	—	—
Acetylacetone imine	3-Acetyl-2,6-dimethylpyridine	—	47%	—	—	—	40%	—	—	—
Diacetonitrile	3-Cyano-2,6-dimethylpyridine	—	41%	—	—	—	25%	—	—	—
Aminobutenone	5-Acetyl-2-methylpyridine	—	42%	40%	—	—	—	—	—	—
Malonic ester iminoether	2-Amino-6-methylnicotinic ester	—	25%	—	—	—	20%	—	—	—
β-Naphthylamine	6,7-Benzolepidine	—	—	30%	—	—	—	—	—	—

4. Ring closure to 4-methylpyrimidine (= Z)

Reagent	4-Methylpyrimidine	2-Hydroxy-Z	2-Mercapto-Z	2-Amino-Z	2-Hydrazino-Z	2-Cyanamino-Z	Sulfamerazine, Methyldebenal	2-Phenyl-Z	1-Azadehydroquinolinium perchlorate
Formamide	—	70%	—	—	—	—	—	—	—
Urea	86%	85%	—	—	—	—	—	—	50%
Thiourea	95%	95%	—	—	—	—	—	—	95%
Guanidine	—	96%	51%	80%	—	—	—	—	50%
Benzalhydrazinoformamidine	—	—	25%	—	—	—	—	—	—
Dicyandiamide	—	75%	—	—	—	—	—	—	—
Sulfaguanidine	—	82%	—	82%	—	78%	40%	—	—
Benzamidine	—	53%	—	—	—	—	—	82%	—
2-Aminopyrimidine	—	72%	—	75%	—	—	—	40%[b]	—

5. Syntheses of 5-membered rings

Reagent	3-(5-)Methylpyrazole	3-Methyl-1-phenylpyrazole	3-Methyl-1-(p-nitrophenyl)pyrazole	1,3-Dimethylpyrazole	3-Methyl-1-pyrazolecarbonamide	3- and 5-Methylisoxazole	4-Acetyl-1-phenyltriazole
Hydrazine	68%	92%	+	—	—	—	66%
Phenylhydrazine	—	85%	35%	—	—	—	—
p-Nitrophenylhydrazine	—	64%	+	+	—	—	—
Methylhydrazine	—	61%	+	—	—	—	—
Semicarbazide	80%	95%	+	—	—	30%	—
Hydroxylamine	64%	68%	+	+	—	—	—
Phenyl azide	—	—	—	—	44%	—	—

[a] These reactions were carried out with ethoxycrotonaldehyde acetal.
[b] These reactions were carried out with 1-ethoxy-1-buten-3-one.

(quinoline), according to Lindlar. Hydroxyl groups are removed with $POCl_3$ with formation of water, yielding more double bonds; hydrolysis of the acetal group and finally isomerization with alkaline substances leads to vitamin A aldehyde, which is reduced to the alcohol with $LiAlH_4$.

Eiter and Truscheit recently used the acetal (I) to form a vitamin A derivative in 90% yield (58a). Patterned after the Wittig phosphine-methylene method, Pommer and Sarnecki (59) attained similar objectives with the use of 1-methoxy-3-butenone, 1-chlorobutenone, and other oxo compounds.

Ring-closure Syntheses

The ring-closure reactions are the most important transformations of the intermediates and derivatives of acetoacetaldehyde. Table 2 shows the yields obtained by the reaction of acetoacetaldehyde bisacetal and of the substances I–VIII with the compounds named in the first column (+ denotes that the reaction was carried out, but no yield was given).

The reaction procedures are described below; H. Henecka (59a) has dealt with the reaction mechanisms.

Synthesis of Aromatics

1,3,5-TRIACETYLBENZENE

The formation of this compound from the sodium enol salt II by the action of glacial acetic acid was first described by Claisen (5). Fischer and Fink obtained the compound by the treatment of the diethyl acetal with glacial acetic acid (60). Yields of 75–90% are obtained from I or IV by heating with water, as described in a German patent (61) and by Royals and Brannock (8). The preparation of the three semicarbazones is described by F. Mietzsch and H. Schmidt in German patent 922,102 (Farben-Fabriken, Bayer) [Chem. Abstr. 51, 12971 (1957)].

1,3,5-Tris(α-hydroxyethyl) benzene is obtained from triacetylbenzene by hydrogenation. Subsequent splitting out of water forms 1,3,5-trivinyl-benzene which, on addition of styrene, polymerizes to give insoluble resins which swell only a little (62). The entire process for the manufacture of 1,3,5-trivinylbenzene from acetone and methyl formate to form triacetylbenzene, the reduction of the latter to triethylolbenzene and the splitting out of water has been patented (63).

m-CRESOTIC ACID

Prelog, Metzler, and Jeger (*64*) obtained the compound in 55–65% yield from the sodium salt, II, and acetoacetic ester followed by hydrolysis. We obtained only a 15% yield of the ester from I and acetoacetic ester in the presence of sodium alkoxide. Kochetkov, Kudryáskov, and Nesmeyanov (*65*) obtained the compound in 39% yield from acetoacetic ester and 1-chlorobutenone.

2-METHYLNAPHTHALENE

The reaction of acetal I with benzylmagnesium chloride furnishes a route to the naphthalene series (*66*).

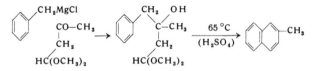

The yields are better (*67*) with glycol acetals,

$$R-CO-CH_2-CH \begin{array}{c} O-CH_2 \\ | \\ O-CH_2 \end{array}$$

Synthesis of Rings Containing Oxygen

An important contribution to the knowledge of β-keto acetals was furnished by Burness (*68*) with his synthesis of 3-methylfuran:

$$(CH_3O)_2CH-CH_2-CO-CH_3 + ClCH_2-COOCH_3$$

$$\downarrow (NaOCH_3)\ 80\ \%$$

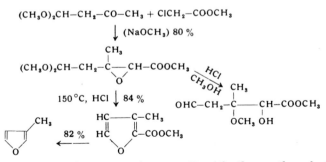

The Darzens reaction proceeds as well with the methoxybutenone, IV; however, neither acetoxybutenone nor sodium formylacetone react with chloroacetic ester.

The ring closure to 3-methylnaphtho[2,1-b]pyrilium chloroferrate (III) from 2-naphthol occurs with 1-butyn-3-one (*69*) and also with chlorovinyl methyl ketone (*70, 71*).

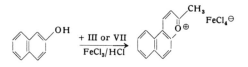

Synthesis of Pyridine Derivatives

3-Cyano-2-hydroxy-6-methylpyridine (R = CN, R′ = OH). This was first obtained by Dornow (*72*) from cyanacetamide and ethoxycroton-aldehyde acetal in 35% yield. Perez-Medina, Mariella, and McElvain (*73*), starting with II and cyanacetamide in the presence of a catalytic amount of piperidine acetate, obtained a 68% yield. From acetoacetal-dehyde bisacetal (*74*) (from VI or VIII) and cyanacetamide in the presence of piperidine acetate, we reached yields of 79–95%. The reaction of cyanacetamide with N,N-dialkylaminobutenones also leads to 3-cyano-2-hydroxy-6-methylpyridine (*75*).

Ethyl 2,6-dimethylnicotinate (R = $COOC_2H_5$, R′ = CH_3). Rabe (*76*) obtained the ester in 25% yield by heating II, acetoacetic ester, and ammonia in alcohol. Dornow (*77*) obtained the ester from ethoxycroton-aldehyde acetal and ethyl aminocrotonate in 40% yield. The preparation of ethyl 2,6-dimethyl nicotinate from I, acetoacetic ester, and ammonia in over 50% yield has been patented (*78*). From acetoacetaldehyde bisac-etal and an ester of aminocrotonic acid, an ester of lutidinecarboxylic acid is obtained. The preparation from I and ethyl aminocrotonate pro-ceeds as follows.

I, 132 gm, 130 gm of ethyl aminocrotonate and 15 gm of ammonium acetate are heated to 40–50° in a water bath and with stirring 30 gm of glacial acetic acid is added. Then water is added and the alcohol removed by steam distillation. The residue is decomposed with dilute sulfuric acid, heated for 20 min on the water bath and, after cooling, extracted with ether. The acid solution is made alkaline with sodium hydroxide and extracted several times with ether. The ether extracts are dried, then concentrated. On distillation the ethyl 2,6-dimethylnicotinate boils at 123–125°/15mm. Yield: 50%. The m.p. of the picrate is 138°.

3-Acetyl-2,6-dimethylpyridine (R = $COCH_3$, R′ = CH_3). Dornow (*77*) obtained this compound from acetylacetonimine and ethoxycroton-aldehyde acetal in 30–40% yields. With I, acetylacetonimine reacts in an analogous manner. A mixture of 9.9 gm of acetylacetonimine, 13.2 gm of I, 1.5 gm of ammonium acetate, and 1 gm of glacial acetic acid is heated for 12 hr in the water bath. The cooled solution is acidified with dilute mineral acid and extracted with ether to remove impurities; finally the solution is made alkaline and extracted several times with ether. The ether extracts are dried; on evaporation an oil is obtained which distills at 110–112°/13 mm. A yield of 7 gm (47%) of 3-acetyl-2,6-dimethyl-pyridine is obtained. Crystals which are volatile are formed from wet ether, m.p. 42° (dihydrate); picrate, m.p. 129°.

3-Cyano-2,6-dimethylpyridine (R = CN, R′ = CH₃). This pyridine derivative is obtained according to Dornow (*77*), from diacetonitrile and ethoxycrotonaldehyde acetal in 25% yields. The compound I reacts in a similar manner.

Diacetonitrile (8.2 gm), 13.2 gm of I, 1 gm of ammonium acetate, and 1 gm of glacial acetic acid are warmed for 8 hr in a water bath. After cooling the reaction mixture is acidified with dilute mineral acid and extracted with ether to remove impurities. The solution is then made alkaline and again extracted with ether. The ether extracts are dried; then the ether is distilled. There remains an oil, which quickly crystallizes (m.p. 83°) and consists of 3-cyano-2,6-dimethylpyridine. Yield: 5.5 gm (41%); picrate, m.p. 180°.

5-Acetyl-2-methylpyridine (R = COCH₃, R′ = H). Benary and Psille (*79*) obtained a 40% yield from the sodium salt II which was treated in ether with a solution of ammonium acetate in glacial acetic acid. Aminobutenone also reacts with I in the presence of glacial acetic acid to form 5-acetyl-2-methylpyridine (from the investigations of D. Tietjen).

A mixture of 38 gm of glacial acetic acid, 11 gm of ammonium acetate, 47 gm of I, and 30 gm of aminobutenone is stirred for 5 hr at 80°. The mixture is cooled, made weakly alkaline with sodium hydroxide, and extracted with ether. After the evaporation of the ether, 5-acetyl-2-methylpyridine remains as an oil, which distills at 103–105°/12 mm. B.p. 231–233°/760 mm. Yield: 20 gm (42%).

Ethyl 2-amino-6-methylnicotinate (R = COOC₂H₅, R′ = NH₂) is obtained, according to Dornow and Karlson (*80*), from ethoxycroton-aldehyde acetal and ethyl β-amino-β-ethoxyacrylate. It is obtained from I in an analogous way. 2-Amino-6-methylnicotinamide was obtained by Dornow and Neuse from sodium formylacetone (II) and 2-aminoaceta-mide in 56% yield (*81*).

6-Butyryl-2-methylpyridine (R = H, R′ = COC₃H₇). Hardegger and Nikles (*82*) obtained a mixture of 6-butyryl-2-methylpyridine (small amount) and 6-butyryl-2-propylpyridine by reaction of III with 1-amino-1-hexen-3-one.

3,5-Diacetyl-1,4-dihydro-1,4-diphenylpyridine was obtained by Inoue

(*83*) in 37% yield by the condensation of 2 moles of 1-anilinobuten-3-one with 1 mole of benzaldehyde in the presence of piperidine.

6,7-Benzolepidine. From β-naphthylamine and sodium formylacetone (II) a 70% yield of 1-(2-naphthylimino)-3-butanone is obtained, which cyclizes with HF to 6,7-benzolepidine (*6*).

Synthesis of Pyrimidine Derivatives

4-Methylpyrimidine (R = H). H. Bredereck and co-workers (*84*) obtained 4-methylpyrimidine in 70% yield from the acetal (I) and formamide at 180° with the addition of NH_4Cl; with 1-ethoxy-1-buten-3-one, 1-dimethylaminobuten-3-one or 1-chlorobuten-3-one a 40% yield is obtained.

A solution of 20 gm of acetoacetaldehyde dimethyl acetal (I) in 50 gm of formamide is added dropwise over a 5 hr period to a solution of 80 gm of formamide, 10 gm of ammonium chloride, and 3 ml of water at 180°. After being heated for an additional 2 hr and then diluted with sodium hydroxide, the mixture is extracted with chloroform for 15 hr. Distillation gives 10 gm (70%) of 4-methylpyrimidine, b.p. 140–142° (*84*).

Yields of 58–66% of 4-methylpyrimidine are obtained by the passage of acetoacetaldehyde acetal and formamide over Al_2O_3 or montmorillonite at 200–240° (*85*).

2-Hydroxy-4-methylpyrimidine hydrochloride (R = OH). Urea and I in an alcohol solution react in the presence of concentrated hydrochloric acid to form 2-hydroxy-4-methylpyrimidine hydrochloride. The bisacetal reacts in the same manner (*74*). The reactions of the bisacetal with amidines have been described by Copenhaver (*86,87*).

2-Mercapto-4-methylpyrimidine hydrochloride (R = SH). This compound is formed in an analogous manner from I or the bisacetal and thiourea (*74*); similarly, methoxybutenyne (VIII) reacts almost quantitatively with thiourea. The methylation of the thiol group with dimethyl sulfate and the removal of the CH_3S-group by reduction leads to 4-methylpyrimidine (*88*). 2-Mercapto-4-methylpyrimidines having a substituent on the sulfur are found to be good vulcanization accelerators (*89*). When morpholine is present as a substituent, the material has an antiscorching effect (*90*).

2-Amino-4-methylpyrimidine (R = NH_2). This pharmaceutically important starting material was obtained by Benary in 51% yield by shaking the sodium salt II and guanidine nitrate in alcohol (*91*). Mauss and Andersag (*92*) used the methoxybutenyne (VIII) and guanidine sulfate, which react in sulfuric acid medium to give a 50% yield. The highest yield (96%) was obtained by the treatment of the acetal (I) with guanidine, utilizing the azeotropic removal of water with xylene (*93*).

2-Hydrazino-4-methylpyrimidine (R = NHNH$_2$). Sodium formylacetone reacts with benzylideneaminoguanidine to give 2-benzylidinehydrazino-4-methylpyrimidine, from which the 2-hydrazino-4-methylpyrimidine is obtained in 25% yield (*94*).

2-Cyanamino-4-methylpyrimidine (R = NHCN). This compound is prepared from dicyandiamide and the acetal (I) in the presence of sodium ethoxide.

Twenty-one grams of dicyandiamide are treated with a solution of 33 gm of I in 150 ml of ethanol. To this mixture is added a solution of 5.7 gm of sodium in 100 ml of ethanol. The mixture is refluxed for several hours and the cooled solution is then neutralized with 15 gm of glacial acetic acid. The crystalline mass is filtered off after 30 min. The product is recrystallized from water. Yield: 25.5 gm (*75%*). It decomposes without definite melting around 200°.

When this compound is heated with dilute mineral acids, the cyano group is attacked to form 4-methyl- 2-ureidopyrimidine (R = NHCONH$_2$). If concentrated hydrochloric acid is used and the mixture heated a short time, 2-amino-4-methylpyrimidine is then the main product.

p-Aminobenzenesulfonamide-4-methylpyrimidine (R = NHSO$_2$C$_6$H$_4$-NH$_2$-*p*). This sulfonamide, known as Methyldebenal, Pyrimal M, and Sulfamerazine, was obtained by the Japanese workers (*17*), as well as by Mauss and Leuchs (*95*), from sulfaguanidine

$$H_2N-\langle\rangle-SO_2-NH-C(=NH)-NH_2$$

and the acetal (I) in 70–80% yield. The resulting monoanil from aniline and the sodium salt (II) was treated with guanidine nitrate by Ishikawa and Kano (*96*) to form 2-amino-4-methylpyrimidine which was converted to Methyldebenal with sulfaguanidine. The same substance is obtained by the reaction of methoxybutenone (IV) (*33*) or chlorovinyl methyl ketone (III) (*97*) with *p*-aminobenzene-sulfaguanidine.

4-Methyl-2-phenylpyrimidine (R = C$_6$H$_5$). This compound had not yet been synthesized directly (*98*). It is prepared from benzamidine and the acetal (I) as follows:

Benzamidine hydrochloride (15.6 gm) is dissolved in 75 ml of ethanol and treated with a solution of 2.5 gm sodium in 75 ml of ethanol. The sodium chloride is filtered off, the filtrate treated with 13.2 gm of (I) and the mixture refluxed for 3 hr. After cooling the solution is neutralized with glacial acetic acid, the ethanol removed by steam distillation, and the residue made alkaline with potassium hydroxide. After extraction with ether and drying over potassium carbonate, distillation follows. At 139–141°/13 mm there is obtained 9 gm (53%) of 4-methyl-2-phenyl-pyrimidine. On cooling crystals are obtained, m.p. 22°. Physical data for 4-methyl-2-phenylpyrimidine obtained in another way are: b.p. 279°/762 mm; m.p. 22.5° (98).

1-Azadehydroquinolizinium perchlorate is formed from I or III with 2-aminopyridine in the presence of perchloric acid in 72 or 75% yield (99).

Synthesis of Nitrogen-Containing Five-Membered Rings

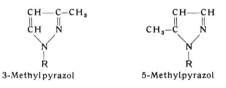

3-Methylpyrazol   5-Methylpyrazol

3-(or 5-)Methylpyrazol (R = H). Rothenburg (100) obtained the compound from the sodium salt (II) and hydrazine acetate. From the bisacetal and hydrazine sulfate a yield of 68% is obtained. It is prepared from I and hydrazine sulfate as follows.

To a suspension of 130 gm of hydrazine sulfate in 160 ml of water 132 gm of the acetal (I) is added slowly and dropwise. The mixture is then heated at 60° for 2 hr, cooled, made alkaline, and extracted with ether. By distilling at 104–106°/18 mm there is obtained 75 gm (92%) of 3-(5-)methylpyrazol.

Methoxybutenyne (VIII) also forms the methylpyrazole with hydrazine sulfate.

A mixture of 130 gm of hydrazine sulfate, 80 ml of water, 250 ml of ethanol, and 2 ml of concentrated sulfuric acid is stirred and heated to 80–85°. Methoxybutenyne (82 gm) is added slowly to the mixture. When the addition is complete, stirring is continued 30 min longer, the alcohol is removed by steam distillation, the residue made alkaline and extracted several times with ether. Evaporation of the ether leaves an oil, which distills at 100–102°/15 mm. Yield: 54 gm (66%).

3-Methyl-1-phenylpyrazole (R = C_6H_5). This compound is formed, according to Claisen and Roosen (*101*), from phenylhydrazine salts and II; von Rothenburg (*100*) obtained the compound from ethoxycrotonaldehyde acetal and phenylhydrazine. Auwers and Hollmann (*102*) obtained an 86% yield by using the enol benzoate. The latter is obtained from the sodium salt (II) and benzoyl chloride. The methylphenylpyrazole is obtained from I as follows.

A solution of 45 gm of concentrated sulfuric acid in 110 ml of water is added dropwise to 108 gm of phenylhydrazine. Neglecting the precipitated sulfate 132 gm of I is added dropwise. The temperature rises; the salt disappears. The mixture is heated at 70° for 2 hr, then made alkaline with sodium hydroxide and extracted with ether. On distillation there is obtained at 138–141°/18 mm a yield of 36 gm (85%) of the methylphenylpyrazole. The largest part (ca. 90%) of this crystallizes on cooling, m.p. 36°.

p-Nitrophenylhydrazine forms with I a 64% yield of the 3-methyl-1-*p*-nitrophenylpyrazole (*103*). The same substance is formed also from III (*104*).

1,3-Dimethylpyrazole (R = CH₃). According to Burness (*93*) the reaction of methylhydrazines with the acetal (I) in acid medium always gives the 1,3-dimethylpyrazole, whereas in an alkaline medium a mixture of the 1,3- and 1,5-isomers is obtained.

Methylhydrazine (3 gm) is added dropwise to 8.6 gm of I. The temperature of the mixture rises to 40°; it is heated for 10 min on the steam bath, 5.5 gm of crude methylhydrazone is dissolved in 5 ml of water, decomposed with 5.3 gm of 6 N hydrochloric acid and heated on the steam bath for 20 min. On addition of 2.4 gm of 50% sodium hydroxide an oil separates which is extracted with ether. After drying and distilling there is obtained a 61% yield of 1,3-dimethylpyrazol (*93*). B.p. 143–145°; n_D^{25} 1.4734. M.p. of picrate: 170–171°.

Auwers and Hollmann obtained a mixture of 1,3- and 1-5-dimethylpyrazole in the reaction of sodium formylacetone with methylhydrazine (*102*). 1-Cyano-3-butenone, which is converted to 1-aminobutenone with secondary amines, also reacts with hydrazine to form 3-methylpyrazole (*105*).

3-Methyl-1-pyrazolecarboxamide (R = CONH₂). This substance is obtained, according to Auwers and Daniel (*106*), from semicarbazide hydrochloride or from the disemicarbazone acetoacetaldehyde on treatment with sulfuric acid. It is also obtained from ethoxycrotonaldehyde acetal and semicarbazide hydrochloride, according to Viguier (*28*). From the acetal (I) and semicarbazide hydrochloride the compound is prepared as follows.

Sixty-six grams of I in 70 ml of water is treated with a solution of

56 gm of semicarbazide hydrochloride in 90 ml of water with ice cooling. After a few minutes an exothermic reaction begins and the methylpyrazole-1-carboxamide precipitates. After several hours the crystals are filtered and washed with a little water. The yield is almost quantitative. The compound melts at 96°, then solidifies, and melts again at 127°, even when the melting point determination is repeated. The compound is probably not the 5-methyl-, but the 3-methylpyrazolecarboxamide.

The corresponding thiocarboxamide is obtained from I and thiosemicarbazide (*93*). By using aminoguanidine the expected pyrazole [R = C (= NH)NH₂] is not obtained; instead 1,3-butanedione-bis(guanylhydrazone) is isolated (*93*).

Methylisoxazole. The mixture of 3- and 5-methylisoxazole is obtained by the reaction of II with hydroxylamine hydrochloride (*107*). This mixture, chiefly the 5-isomer, is also obtained from the acetal (I) and hydroxylamine hydrochloride.

A solution of 69 gm of NH₂OH·HCl in 70 ml of water is added dropwise to 132 gm of I and 60 ml water. The reaction mixture becomes warm (about 50°C). When the addition is complete, the mixture is heated at 60–70° for 2 hr. The mixture is cooled, made alkaline with sodium hydroxide and extracted with ether. After evaporation of the ether an oil remains, which is distilled at atmospheric pressure. The fraction which comes over between 117° and 122° consists of a mixture of 3- and 5-methylisoxazole (the 5-isomer predominating). The yield is 57 gm (68%).

5-Methylisoxazole is also made from 1-dialkylamine-3-butenone or chlorovinyl methyl ketone and hydroxylamine; on treatment with sodium ethoxide it is converted quantitatively to the sodium salt of the enolic acetoacetonitrile (*108*).

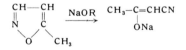

4-Acetyl-1-phenyltriazole was obtained by Kochetkov from chlorovinyl methyl ketone and phenyl azide (*109*).

1-Acetyl-3-methylpyrrole. Plieninger and Bühler (*110*) obtained this compound as follows:

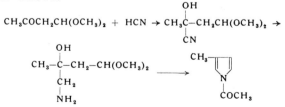

During the reduction of the cyanohydrin with lithium aluminum hydride the hydroxyl group is protected with dihydropyran.

Reaction of Intermediates

Several significant reactions of two important intermediates should be considered. These materials are chlorovinyl methyl ketone (III) and 1-methoxy-1-buten-3-yne (VIII).

A. N. Nesmeyanov and co-workers (*111*) investigated fully the reactivity of chlorovinyl methyl ketone; they obtained, e.g., with $CH_3OC_6H_5$ in the presence of $SnCl_4$ (*111*):

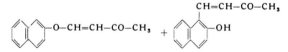

with $CH_3OC_6H_4CH_3$-p in the presence of $SnCl_4$:

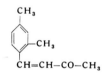

with β-naphthol in the presence of NaOH (*71*):

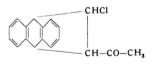

with xylene in the presence of $AlCl_3$ (*112*):

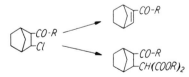

as dienophile with anthracene (*113*):

and as dienophile with cyclopentadiene (*114*):

In the last reaction the chlorine is either exchanged or removed as HCl. Because of the reactivity of the chlorine atom Kochetkov called the introduction of the $CH_3COCH = CH$-group into a molecule, "Ketovinylation"; "ketobutenylation" also occurs in many cases with 1-methoxybutenone (IV), 1-butyn-3-one (VII), or 1-aminobutenone. An example of ketobutenylation with 1-butyn-3-one was carried out by Wenkert and Stevens (115) on 1-methyl-2-naphthol; the following products were obtained:

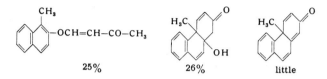

A number of significant syntheses have been carried out with methoxybutenyne (VIII), an important technical starting material for the acetal (I). W. Ried and A. Urschel, in a Merling synthesis, combined VIII with 1,4-cyclohexanediones in liquid ammonia in the presence of lithium amide (116):

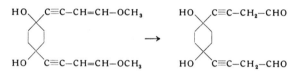

The bisbutynal and the bismethoxybutyl compounds were described as secondary products. Corresponding reactions occur with 1,2-dioxo-cyclohexane; from the substituted 1,2-diol, 1,14-dimethoxy-5,10-dioxo-tetradecane was obtained with lead tetraacetate. By the reaction of benzoquinone with methoxybutenye a 20% yield of 1,4-dihydroxy-1,4-bis(4-methoxy-3-buten-1-ynyl)cyclohexadiene-2,5 (117) was obtained, which, on reduction with SnCl₂ in glacial acetic acid, was converted to 1,4-bis(4-methoxy-3-buten-1-ynyl)benzene (118). Only one mole of methoxybutenyne reacts with anthraquinone or with phenanthraquinone (117).

General directions for the addition of methoxybutenyne to dicarbonyl compounds (116) are as follows.

To a liquid ammonia solution containing the calculated amount of sodium is added about 200 mg of finely powdered ferric nitrate. The conversion of sodium is finished when the blue coloring has disappeared. A toluene solution of the methoxybutenyne in then added dropwise. After 30 min the toluene solution of the dicarbonyl compound is added dropwise and the reaction mixture then stirred at −35° for a whole day. The ammonia is allowed to evaporate overnight, the last traces being removed with a water aspirator. The residue is poured carefully into ice water and immediately neutralized with 4 N sulfuric acid. The mixture is filtered and the toluene layer separated. The residue and the toluene solution are washed well with water and then combined. They are heated and purified with activated charcoal. When the toluene solution is concentrated *in vacuo* the addition product crystallizes.

Marshall and Whitting (*119*) allowed the Grignard reagent of methoxybutenyne to react with *p*-methoxybenzaldehyde to form *p*-methoxyphenyl-4-methoxybutenynyl carbinol, whose triple bond was reduced to the double bond with LiAlH₄; on acidification the hydroxyl group split off and the enol ether hydrolyzed to form the polyene-aldehyde:

$$CH_3O-C_6H_4-\underset{\underset{OH}{|}}{CH}-C\equiv C-CH=CHOCH_3 \longrightarrow$$

$$CH_3O-C_6H_4-CH=CH-CH=CH-CHO.$$

This method, through the reaction of aldehydes, especially unsaturated aldehydes, brings about a lengthening of the carbon chain with four carbon atoms and two double bonds and retention of a terminal aldehyde group.

A solution of 14.6 gm of methoxybutenyne in 20 ml of tetrahydrofuran is added dropwise to a solution of ethylmagnesium bromide (from 3.2 gm Mg) in 90 ml of tetrahydrofuran at 40°. The solution is stirred for 1 hr at 20°, then a solution of 18.1 mg of *p*-methoxybenzaldehyde in 20 ml of tetrahydrofuran is added dropwise over a period of 20 min with ice cooling. After stirring at 20° for 2 hr, the solution is cooled to 0°, 5 ml of ethanol added, and after 20 min a total of 4.0 gm of LiAlH₄ is added in portions. This mixture is stirred at 20° for 3 hr, then ice cooled and successively treated with 6 ml of ethyl acetate, 30 ml of water, 150 ml of 4 N sulfuric acid, and 200 ml of ether. After separation of the ether solution and evaporation of the ether, there remains 5-(*p*-methoxyphenyl)-2,4-pentadienal which is recrystallized from petroleum ether; m.p. 76–78°, yield 13.1 gm (52%). The pure substance melts at 79–80° (*119*).

The carbon chain of methoxybutenyne was increased by one carbon by A. Dornow and E. Ische through the reaction of the Grignard compound with orthoformate ester (*120*) to form 5-methoxy-4-penten-2-yn-1-al acetal (32% yields), from which γ-pyrone may be obtained in 92% yield:

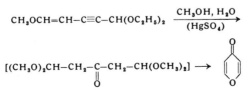

Ten grams of 5-methoxy-4-penten-2-yn-1-al diethyl acetal is dissolved in 20 gm of methanol. Then 1 gm of water and 0.1 gm of mercuric sulfate are added and the mixture stirred for 1 hr at 65°. At the end of the reaction, the mixture is neutralized with soda, filtered, and distilled. There is obtained 4.8 gm (92%) of γ-pyrone, m.p. 31.5° (120).

A lengthening of the methoxybutenyne carbon chain by five carbon atoms is brought about by the reaction with 1-chloro-5-methoxy-1-pentene. The latter is obtained from the reaction of butadiene with chloromethyl methyl ether, the final mixture containing also the isomer, 3-chloro-5-methoxy-1-pentene. The reaction gives a 70% yield of 1,9-dimethoxy-1,6-nonadien-3-yne (120a).

$$CH_3O-CH=CH-C{\equiv}C-CH_2-CH=CH-CH_2-CH_2-OCH_3 .$$

By hydrogenation and oxidation pure azelaic acid is obtained.

The Mannich reaction of methoxybutenyne with formaldehyde and dimethylamine gave a 66% yield (121). 1-Methoxy-5-dimethylamino-1,3-pentadiene and 5-dimethylamino-3-pentanonal dimethyl acetal were obtained as end products.

$$CH_3OH \begin{array}{|l} H_2O \end{array}
\begin{array}{l}
CH_3O-CH=CH-C{\equiv}C-CH_2N(CH_3)_2 \xrightarrow{\quad LiAlH_4 \quad} \\
\qquad CH_3OCH=CH-CH=CH-CH_2-N(CH_3)_2 \\
(CH_3O)_2CH-CH_2-CO-CH_2-CH_2-N(CH_3)_2 .
\end{array}$$

The reaction of the Grignard reagent from methoxybutenyne with diethyl carbonate leads to ethyl 5-methoxy-4-penten-2-ynate (122). Methoxybutenyne itself undergoes a reaction, catalyzed by sodium ethoxide, with diethyl carbonate, in which ethanol is added to form $CH_3OCH=CHC(OC_2H_5)=CHCOOC_2H_5$, the bis enol ether of γ-formylacetoacetic esters,

$$OHC-CH_2-CO-CH_2-COOR.$$

This bis enol ether, after acetalization with ethanol, is transformed to a 1-alkyl-4-amino-2-pyridone by treatment with an amine (122). The condensation of methoxybutenyne with formaldehyde occurs in the presence of caustic alkali and methanol, in which one mole of methanol exothermically adds to the first carbon atom (123).

$$CH_3O-CH=CH-C{\equiv}C-CH_2OH \rightarrow (CH_3O)_2CH-CH_2-C{\equiv}C-CH_2OH$$

In a flask equipped with a stirrer, 150 gm of solid potassium hydroxide, 400 ml of methanol, and 123 gm of 1-methoxy-1-buten-3-yne are heated to 50–55° and then 135 gm of paraformaldehyde is added over a period of 3 hr at the temperature indicated. When the reaction is finished the solution is cooled and neutralized with formic acid. The excess methanol is removed by using a slight vacuum and warming, until potassium formate begins to precipitate in the aqueous layer. The mixture is extracted with ether; the ether extracts are dried. Methoxybutenyne and butynal acetal are distilled off, leaving as a residue 1-methoxy-1-penten-3-yn-5-ol, which boils at 130–133°/22 mm. The yield is over 65%, based on methoxybutenyne.

A mixture of 120 gm of 1-methoxy-1-penten-3-yn-5-ol, 250 ml methanol and 300 gm of caustic alkali is stirred at 60° for 4 hr; after this period the mixture is cooled and neutralized with formic acid, layers being formed. The upper layer (233 gm) is distilled. There is obtained 81 gm of 3-pentyn-5-ol-1-al dimethyl acetal, b.p. 90–110°/1.2 mm. The yield is 65%, based on methoxypentenynol.

Hydration in methanol leads to 5-methoxy-3 pentanon-1-al dimethyl acetal (124).

$$CH_3O-CH_2-CH_2-CO-CH_2-CH(OCH_3)_2.$$

Starting with 5-hydroxy-3-pentynal dimethyl acetal, F. Weygand and H. Leube found a new approach to deoxyribose (125):

$$
\begin{array}{ccccc}
(CH_3O)_2CH & & (CH_3O)_2CH & & (CH_3O)_2CH \\
| & & | & & | \\
CH_2 & & CH_2 & & CH_2 \\
| & \xrightarrow[\text{(Pb)}]{H_2/Pd} & | & \xrightarrow[\text{OsO}_4]{H_2O_2} & | \\
C & & CH & & CHOH \\
||| & & || & & | \\
C & & CH & & CHOH \\
| & & | & & | \\
CH_2OH & & CH_2OH & & CH_2OH \\
\end{array}
$$

The synthesis of very pure suberic dialdehyde is brought about by the oxidation of methoxybutenyne with oxygen in the presence of cuprous salts and pyridine (126) to form:

$$(CH_3O-CH=CH-C{\equiv}C-)_2,$$

f ollowed by the addition of two moles of methanol to give the 1,8-bisdimethyl acetal, followed by hydrogenation to suberic dialdehyde bisacetal and hydrolysis to the final product (127).

Starting with methoxybutenyne, O. Westphal and E. Rüde (Erwin Rüde, Dissertation, Univ. Freiberg/Brsg., 1960) synthesized 3,6-dideoxy-hexoses, which had been found as a natural component in bacterial antigens (128).

REFERENCES

(1) J. Boileau, *Bull. soc. chim. France* [5] **21**, 761 (1954); *Chem. Abstr.* **49**, 6822 (1955).
(2) M. M. Bokadia and S. S. Deshapande, *Agra Univ. J. Research* **6** (Pt. 1), 31 (1957); *Chem. Abstr.* **53**, 194 (1959).
(3) S. Hünig and O. Boes, *Ann. Chem. Liebigs* **579**, 31, 43 (1953).

(4) H. O. House and R. L. Wasson, *J. Am. Chem. Soc.* **78**, 4394 (1956).

(5) L. Claisen and N. Stylos, *Ber. deut. chem. Ges.* **21**, 1144 (1888).

(6) W. S. Johnson, E. Woroch, and F. J. Mathews, *J. Am. Chem. Soc.* **69**, 570 (1947).

(7) D. M. Burness, U.S. Patent 2,760,985 (1953); *Chem. Abstr.* **51**, 2854 (1957); see also French Patent 1,104,438 (1954); *Chem. Zentr.* **129**, 1426 (1958); G. L. Fletcher and J. S. Hull, U.S. Patent 2,760,986 (1956); *Chem. Abstr.* **51**, 2854 (1957); see also French Patent 1,104,439 (1954); *Chem. Zentr.* **129**, 1979 (1958).

(8) E. E. Royals and K. C. Brannock, *J. Am. Chem. Soc.* **75**, 2052 (1953).

(9) J. Nelles and O. Bayer, German Patent 642,147 (1935); *Chem. Abstr.* **31**, 3501 (1937).

(10) C. C. Price and J. A. Pappalardo, *J. Am. Chem. Soc.* **72**, 2613 (1950).

(11) N. K. Kolchetkov, *Chem. Tech. (Berlin)* **7**, 518 (1955); *Chem. Abstr.* **51**, 6506 (1957).

(12) S. Wakayama, S. Itoh, and H. Suginome, *J. Chem. Soc. Japan Pure Chem. Sect.* **76**, 94 (1955); *Chem. Abstr.* **51**, 17727 (1957).

(13) Y. Inoue, *Bull. Inst. Chem. Research Kyoto Univ.* **35**, 49 (1957); *Chem. Abstr.* **52**, 11759 (1958).

(14) V. T. Klimko, V. A. Mikhalev, and A. P. Skoldinov, *Zhur. Obshcheĭ Khim.* **27**, 370 (1957); *Chem. Abstr.* **51**, 15449 (1957); cf. ref. *(11)*.

(15) Z. Arnold and J. Zemlička, *Proc. Chem. Soc. (London)* p. 227 (1958).

(16) H. H. Richmond, U.S. Patent 2,570,713 (1949); *Chem. Abstr.* **46**, 5080 (1952).

(17) S. Sugasawa, Y. Ban, and R. Mochizuki, *J. Pharm. Soc. Japan* **69**, 82 (1949); *Chem. Abstr.* **45**, 3455 (1951).

(18) D. M. Burness, U.S. Patent 2,760,987 (1953); *Chem. Abstr.* **51**, 2854 (1957).

(19) J. Nelles, German Patent 650,359 (1935); *Chem. Abstr.* **32**, 954 (1938).

(20) A. N. Nesmeyanov, N. H. Kolchetkov, and M. I. Rybinskaya, *Izvest. Nauk Akad. S.S.S.R. Otdel. Khim. Nauk* p. 395 (1951); *Chem. Abstr.* **46**, 3007 (1952).

(21) W. Franke, R. Kraft, D. Tietjen, and H. Weber, *Chem. Ber.* **86**, 793 (1953).

(22) A. Auerhahn and R. Stadler, German Patent 601,822 (1932); *Chem. Abstr.* **28**, 7262 (1934).

(23) W. Franke and K. H. Seemann, German Patent 871,006; *Chem. Abstr.* **52**, 19982 (1958); cf. further R. Ströbele, German Patent 817,598 (1949); *Chem. Abstr.* **48**, 7051 (1954); W. Franke and R. Kraft, German Patent 881,941 (1951); *Chem. Abstr.* **52**, 10159 (1958).

(24) G. L. Fletcher, U.S. Patent 2,760,984 (1956); *Chem. Abstr.* **51**, 2854 (1957).

(25) J. W. Copenhaver, U.S. Patent 2,527,533 (1950); *Chem. Abstr.* **45**, 1622 (1951); German Patent 821,201 (1949); *Chem. Abstr.* **49**, 1779 (1955).

(26) W. Lautenschlager, German Patent 870,840 (1951).

(27) S. Sugasawa, Japanese Patent 1526 (1950); *Chem. Abstr.* **47**, 1730 (1953).

(28) P. L. Viguier, *Compt. rend. acad. sci.* **153**, 1232 (1911); *Ann. chim. (Paris)* [8]**28**, 503 (1913); *Chem. Abstr.* **7**, 2214 (1913).

(29) H. Weber and D. Tietjen, German Patent 943,353 (1952); *Chem. Abstr.* **52**, 16204 (1958).

(30) E. E. Royals and K. C. Brannock, *J. Am. Chem. Soc.* **76**, 3041 (1954).

(31) W. Stumpf and W. Franke, French Patent 1,208,917 (1958).

(31a) W. Stumpf and J. Wilck, private communication.

(32) R. Kraft, German Patent 934,824; *Chem. Abstr.* **52**, 19950 (1958).

(33) S. Yamada, *J. Pharm. Soc. Japan* **71**, 1349 (1951); *Chem. Abstr.* **46**, 8033 (1952).

(34) H. Bueren and W. Franke, German Patent 946,137 (1952); *Chem. Abstr.* **53**, 2260 (1959).
(34a) F. Asinger, L. Schroeder, and S. Hoffman, *Ann. Chem. Liebigs* **648**, 83 (1961).
(35) J. Hurwic, J. Radzikowski, and J. Dabrowski, *Roczniki Chem.* **32**, 159 (1958); *Chem. Abstr.* **52**, 16191 (1958).
(36) N. K. Kochetkov, Y. Dombrovskiĭ, R. Trau, and A. V. Shageeva, *Zhur. Obshcheĭ Khim.* **27**, 1626 (1957); *Chem. Abstr.* **52**, 3675 (1958).
(37) M. K. Kochetkov, *Izvest. Akad. Nauk S.S.S.R. Otdel. Khim. Nauk* p. 991 (1953); *Chem. Abstr.* **49**, 2308 (1955).
(38) A. N. Nesmeyanov, N. K. Kochetkov, Y. V. Dombrovskiĭ, *Izvest. Akad. Nauk S.S.S.R. Otdel. Khim. Nauk* p. 179 (1955); *Chem. Abstr.* **50**, 1577 (1956).
(39) N. K. Kochetkov and Y. V. Dombrovskiĭ, *Zhur. Obshcheĭ Khim.* **26**, 3081 (1956); *Chem. Abstr.* **51**, 8644 (1957).
(40) N. Dombrovskiĭ, Y. A. Pentin, Y. Dombrovskiĭ, V. M. Tatevskiĭ, and N. K. Kochetkov, *Zhur. Fiz. Khim.* **32**, 135 (1958); *Chem. Abstr.* **52**, 13619 (1958).
(41) V. T. Klimko, A. Y. Khorlin, V. A. Mikhalev, A. P. Skoldinov, and N. K. Kochetkov, *Zhur. Obshcheĭ Khim.* **27**, 62 (1957); *Chem. Abstr.* **51**, 12084 (1957).
(42) N. K. Kochetkov, M. G. Ivanova, and A. M. Nesmeyanov, *Izvest. Akad. Nauk S.S.S.R. Otdel. Khim. Nauk* p. 676 (1956); *Chem. Abstr.* **51**, 1830 (1957).
(43) A. N. Nesmeyanov and M. I. Rybinskaya, *Doklady Akad. Nauk S.S.S.R.* **115**, 315 (1957); *Chem. Abstr.* **52**, 7158 (1958).
(44) N. K. Kochetkov, *Izvest. Akad. Nauk S.S.S.R. Otdel. Khim. Nauk* p. 47 (1954); *Chem. Abstr.* **49**, 6090 (1955).
(45) M. Julia, *Ann. Chim. (Paris)* [10] **5**, 595 (1950).
(46) A. Y. Yakubovich and E. N. Merkulova, *Zhur. Obshcheĭ Khim.* **16**, 55 (1946); *Chem. Abstr.* **41**, 91 (1947); cited in ref. (*11*).
(47) W. Franke and H. Bueren, German Patent 924,028 (1952); *Chem. Zentr.* p. 5163 (1955).
(48) C. Jutz, *Chem. Ber.* **91**, 1867 (1958).
(49) J.Wilck, W. Stumpf, and W. Franke, German Patent Appl. C 18989 IV b/ 12o (1959).
(50) H. Plieninger and R. Müller, *Angew. Chem.* **68**, 618 (1956); **69**, 561 (1957); German Patent 1,011,874 (1955); *Chem. Abstr.* **53**, 15990 (1959).
(51) N. K. Kochetkov and E. E. Nifant'ev, *Doklady Akad. Nauk S.S.S.R.* **121**, 462 (1958); *Chem. Abstr.* **53**, 1137 (1959).
(52) A. J. Birch, E. Pride, and H. Smith, *J. Chem. Soc.* p. 5096 (1957).
(53) R. P. Gandhi, J. S. Walia, and S. M. Mukherji, *J. Indian Chem. Soc.* **34**, 509 (1957); *Chem. Abstr.* **52**, 5331 (1958).
(54) W. J. Humphlett, British Patent 717,095 (1952); *Chem. Abstr.* **49**, 15955 (1955).
(55) D. M. Burness and C. D. Robeson, U.S. Patent 2,676,994 (1951); *Chem. Abstr.* **50**, 408 (1956).
(56) W. J. Humphlett and D. M. Burness, U.S. Patent 2,676,990 (1951); *Chem. Abstr.* **50**, 408 (1956).
(57) C. D. Robeson and J. K. Lindsay, U.S. Patent 2,676, 988 (1951); *Chem. Abstr.* **50**, 407 (1956).
(58) W. J. Humphlett, U.S. Patent 2,676,992 (1951); *Chem. Abstr.* **50**, 408 (1956).

(58a) K. Eiter and E. Truscheit, German Patent 1,117,570 (1961); *Chem. Abstr.* **56**, 8758 (1962).

(59) H. Pommer and W. Sarnecki, German Patents 1,068,705; 1,068,706; 1,068,710 (1959); *Chem. Abstr.* **55**, 12446 (1961).

(59a) H. Henecka, "Chemie der β-Dicarbonyl-Verbindungen." Springer, Berlin, 1950.

(60) H. Fischer and E. Fink, *Z. physiol. Chem.* **280**, 123 (1944).

(61) W. Franke, R. Kraft, and R. Ströbele, German Patent 912,209 (1951); *Chem. Zentr.* p. 8221 (1954).

(62) D. T. Mowry and E. L. Ringwald, *J. Am. Chem. Soc.* **72**, 2037 (1950); cf. W. Bunge and O. Bayer, German Patent 962,118 (1952); *Chem. Abstr.* **53**, 5739 (1959).

(63) D. T. Mowry, U.S. Patent 2,617,831 (1948); *Chem. Abstr.* **47**, 9360 (1953).

(64) V. Prelog, O. Metzler, and O. Jeger, *Helv. Chim. Acta* **30**, 675 (1947).

(65) N. K. Kochetkov, L. I. Kudryaskov, and A. N. Nesmeyanov, *Izvest. Akad. Nauk S.S.S.R. Otdel. Khim. Nauk* p. 809 (1955); *Chem. Abstr.* **50**, 9335 (1956).

(66) N. K. Kochetkov, E. E. Nifant'ev, and A. N. Nesmeyanov, *Doklady Akad. Nauk S.S.S.R.* **104**, 422 (1955); *Chem. Abstr.* **50**, 11999 (1956).

(67) N. K. Kochetkov, E. E. Nifant'ev, and A. N. Nesmeyanov, *Izvest. Akad. Nauk S.S.S.R. Otdel. Khim. Nauk* p. 949 (1957); *Chem. Abstr.* **52**, 4603 (1958).

(68) D. M. Burness, *J. Org. Chem.* **21**, 102 (1956); U.S. Patent 2,772,295 (1953); *Chem. Abstr.* **51**, 7424 (1957).

(69) A. W. Johnson and R. R. Melhuish, *J. Chem. Soc.* p. 346 (1947).

(70) A. N. Nesmeyanov, N. K. Kochetkov, and M. I. Rybinskaya, *Izvest. Akad. Nauk S.S.S.R. Otdel. Khim. Nauk* p. 479 (1953); *Chem. Abstr.* **48**, 10015 (1954).

(71) N. K. Kochetkov, M. I. Rybinskaya, and A. N. Nesmeyanov, *Doklady Akad. Nauk S.S.S.R.* **79**, 799 (1951); *Chem. Abstr.* **46**, 6102 (1952).

(72) A. Dornow, *Ber. deut. chem. Ges.* **73**, 153 (1940).

(73) L. A. Perez-Medina, R. P. Mariella, and S. M. McElvain, *J. Am. Chem. Soc.* **69**, 2574 (1947); *Org. Syntheses* **32**, 32 (1952).

(74) W. Franke and R. Kraft, *Chem. Ber.* **86**, 797 (1953).

(75) N. K. Kochetkov, *Izvest. Akad. Nauk S.S.S.R. Otdel. Khim. Nauk* p. 991 (1953); *Chem. Abstr.* **49**, 2308 (1955); from ref. (*11*).

(76) P. Rabe, *Ber. deut. chem. Ges.* **45**, 2170 (1912).

(77) A. Dornow, *Ber. deut. chem. Ges.* **72**, 1548 (1939).

(78) J. Boedecker and H. Volk, German Patent 936,448 (1952); *Chem. Zentr.* p. 9579 (1956).

(79) E. Benary and H. Psille, *Ber. deut. chem. Ges.* **57**, 828 (1924).

(80) A. Dornow and P. Karlson, *Ber. deut. chem. Ges.* **73**, 542 (1940).

(81) A. Dornow and E. Neuse, *Chem. Ber.* **84**, 296 (1951).

(82) E. Hardegger and E. Nikles, *Helv. Chim. Acta* **40**, 1016 (1957).

(83) G. Inoue, *J. Chem. Soc. Japan* **79**, 1243 (1958); *Chem. Abstr.* **54**, 24716 (1960).

(84) H. Bredereck, R. Gompper, and G. Morlock, *Chem. Ber.* **90**, 947 (1957).

(85) H. Bredereck, R. Gompper, and H. Herlinger, *Chem. Ber.* **91**, 2832 (1958).

(86) J. W. Copenhaver, German Patent, 822,086 (1948).

(87) J. W. Copenhaver, U.S. Patent 2,515,160 (1950); *Chem. Abstr.* **44**, 8960 (1950).

(88) R. R. Hunt, J. F. W. McOmie, and E. R. Sayer, *J. Chem. Soc.* p. 525 (1959); cf. also J. R. Marshall and J. Walker, *ibid.* p. 1013 (1951).
(89) W. Franke, R. Kraft, R. Hormuth, and W. Ploi, German Patent 957,976 (1957); *Chem. Zentr.* **128,** 10,633 (1957).
(90) W. Franke and W. Ziegenbein, German Patent 1,051,859 (1957); *Chem. Abstr.* **54,** 22690 (1960).
(91) E. Benary, *Ber. deut. chem. Ges.* **63,** 2601 (1930).
(92) H. Mauss and H. Andersag, German Patent 816,700 (1948); *Chem. Abstr.* **47,** 2778 (1953).
(93) D. M. Burness, *J. Org. Chem.* **21,** 97 (1956); U.S. Patent 2,725,384 (1952); *Chem. Abstr.* **50,** 10787 (1956).
(94) D. Shiho and J. Kanai, *J. Chem. Soc. Japan* **73,** 862 (1952); *Chem. Abstr.* **48,** 2070 (1954).
(95) H. Mauss and H. Leuchs, German Patent 871,303 (1951); *Chem. Abstr.* **48,** 2099 (1954).
(96) M. Ishikawa and H. Kano, *J. Pharm. Soc. Japan* **71,** 80 (1951); *Chem. Abstr.* **45,** 8536 (1951); cf. *ibid.* **47,** 9368 (1953).
(97) T. H. Evans, R. W. Mills, and H. R. Chipman, U.S. Patent 2,690,439 (1953); *Chem. Abstr.* **49,** 11726 (1955); U.S. Patent 2,690,466 (1952); *Chem. Zentr.* p. 10070 (1956); H. R. Chipman and T. H. Evans, U.S. Patent 2,688,015 (1952); *Chem. Abstr.* **49,** 11726 (1955).
(98) Beilstein's "Handbuch der organischen Chemie," 4th ed. Vol. 23, p. 202. Springer, Berlin, 1936.
(99) A. N. Nesmeyanov and M. I. Rybinskaya, *Doklady Akad. Nauk S.S.S.R.* **118,** 297 (1958); *Chem. Abstr.* **52,** 10080 (1958).
(100) R. v. Rothenburg, *Ber. deut. chem. Ges.* **27,** 955 (1894); *J. prakt. Chem.* [2] **52,** 49 (1895).
(101) L. Claisen and P. Roosen, *Ann. Chem. Liebigs* **278,** 261 (1894).
(102) K. v. Auwers and H. Hollmann, *Ber. deut. chem. Ges.* **59,** 1282 (1926).
(103) J. L. Finar and R. J. Hurlock, *J. Chem. Soc.* p. 3259 (1958).
(104) N. K. Kochetkov, E. D. Khomutova, O. B. Mikhailova, and A. N. Nesmeyanov, *Izvest. Akad. Nauk S.S.S.R. Otdel. Khim. Nauk* p. 1181 (1957); *Chem. Abstr.* **52,** 6324 (1958).
(105) A. N. Nesmeyanov and M. I. Rybinskaya, *Doklady Akad. Nauk S.S.S.R.* **120,** 793 (1958); *Chem. Abstr.* **52,** 20172 (1958).
(106) K. v. Auwers and W. Daniel, *J. prakt. Chem.* [2] **110,** 235 (1925); cf. ref. *(93)*.
(107) L. Claisen, *Ber. deut. chem. Ges.* **42,** 59 (1909).
(108) N. K. Kochetkov, *Izvest. Akad. Nauk S.S.S.R. Otdel. Khim. Nauk* p. 47 (1954); *Chem. Abstr.* **49,** 6090 (1955); quoted in ref. *(11)*; cf. also ref. *(44)*.
(109) N. K. Kochetkov, *Zhur. Obshchei Khim.* **25,** 1366 (1955); *Chem. Abstr.* **50,** 4924 (1956).
(110) H. Plieninger and W. Bühler, *Angew. Chem.* **71,** 163 (1959).
(111) A. N. Nesmeyanov, N. K. Kochetkov, and L. A. Matov, *Doklady Akad. Nauk S.S.S.R.* **92,** 85 (1953); *Chem. Abstr.* **48,** 10665 (1954).
(112) A. N. Nesmeyanov, M. I. Rybinskaya, and N. K. Kochetkov, *Izvest. Akad. Nauk S.S.S.R. Otdel. Khim. Nauk* p. 1197 (1956); *Chem. Abstr.* **51,** 5726 (1957).
(113) A. N. Nesmeyanov, M. I. Rybinskaya, and N. K. Kochetkov, *Izvest. Akad. Nauk S.S.S.R. Otdel. Khim. Nauk* p. 817 (1955); *Chem. Abstr.* **50,** 9360 (1956).

(114) N. K. Kochetkov and A. Y. Khorlin, *Zhur. Obshcheĭ Khim.* **26**, 3430 (1956);
Chem. Abstr. **51**, 9603 (1957); *Zhur. Obshcheĭ Khim.* **27**, 3182 (1957); *Chem. Abstr.* **52**, 8984 (1958). N. K. Kochetkov, A. Y. Khorlin, and O. S. Chizhov, *Zhur. Obshcheĭ Khim.* **27**, 1045 (1957); *Chem. Abstr.* **52**, 2765 (1958).

(115) E. Wenkert and T. E. Stevens, *J. Am. Chem. Soc.* **78**, 2318 (1956).

(116) W. Ried and A. Urschel, *Chem. Ber.* **90**, 2504 (1957); cf. also W. Ried and H. J. Schmidt, German Patent 1,064,508 (1957); *Chem. Abstr.* **55**, 15447 (1961).

(117) W. Ried and A. Urschel, *Chem. Ber.* **91**, 2459 (1958).

(118) W. Ried, H. J. Schmidt, and A. Urschel, *Chem. Ber.* **91**, 2472 (1958).

(119) D. Marshall and M. C. Whitting, *J. Chem. Soc.* p. 4082 (1956); see also E. L. Pippen and M. Nonaka, *J. Org. Chem.* **23**, 1580 (1958).

(120) A. Dornow and F. Ische, *Angew. Chem.* **67**, 653 (1955); German Patent 953,879 (1955); *Chem. Zentr.* p. 5652 (1957).

(120a) W. Ziegenbein, W. Franke, and A. Striebeck, German Patent 1,073,471 (1958); U.S. Patent 2,937,201; *Chem. Abstr.* **54**, 18366 (1960).

(121) A. Dornow and F. Ische, *Chem. Ber.* **89**, 870 (1956).

(122) A. Dornow and F. Ische, *Chem. Ber.* **89**, 876 (1956).

(123) W. Franke and H. Meister, German Patent 1,019,294; *Chem. Abstr.* **54**, 1320 (1960).

(124) A. Dornow and F. Ische, *Chem. Ber.* **89**, 880 (1956).

(125) F. Weygand and H. Leube, *Chem. Ber.* **89**, 1914 (1956); German Patent 1,010,957 (1956); *Chem. Abstr.* **54**, 3248 (1960).

(126) W. Franke and H. Meister, German Patent 1,015,788 (1954); *Chem. Abstr.* **53**, 15987 (1959).

(127) W. Franke, W. Stumpf, and H. Schlüter, German Patent 1,025,866 (1956); *Chem. Abstr.* **54**, 9772 (1960).

(128) O. Westphal and O. Lüderitz, *Angew. Chem.* **72**, 881 (1960).

Preparation of Peptides and Ureas Using Reactive Amides or Imides

STEFAN GOLDSCHMIDT AND H. L. KRAUSS

Organisch-chemisches Institut der Technischen Hochschule München

Introduction

The union of a carboxyl and an amino group to form an amide group is always a recurring problem in preparative organic chemistry. Next to the synthesis of acid amides and ureas, the formation of peptides from amino acids has kept alive the interest in new solutions of the problem. Many of the usual methods are eliminated because of the sensitivity of the substances.

A rational peptide synthesis must fulfill, in general, the following requirements:

1. Carefully controlled reaction conditions, in which particularly an attack on protective groups is avoided (*1*).

2. Retention of optical activity by introducing optically active amino acids.

3. High yields, which permit repetitive employment for building oligopeptides in a stepwise manner.

4. Analogous applicability to free amino acids and to terminal amino acids of oligopeptides.

For the endergonic reaction:

$$R-COO^- + R'-NH_3^+ \rightarrow R-CO-NH-R' + H_2O$$

to take place, one of the constituent parts must be introduced in an energy-rich "activated" form. Most of the variety of published applications of this reaction are derived from a common principle: they occur through an energetic form of the carboxyl group, in general through mixed anhydrides (*2*) with other acids, according to the following scheme:

Acid (I) + Acid (II) → Mixed Anhydride + H_2O
Amine + Mixed Anhydride → Acid (II)amide + Acid (I)

Acid (II) + Amine → Acid (II)amide + H_2O

Thereby the choice of acid (I) is decisive; the most important syntheses using the above scheme are summarized in Table 1 (*1*).

31

TABLE 1

Author	Year	Acid (I)
T. Curtius	1901	Hydrazoic acid
E. Fischer	1901	Hydrochloric acid
H. Leuchs	1906	⎱ Inner anhydrides of N-carboxylic acids
F. Wessely	1925	⎰ (3)
H. Chantrenne	1949	Phenylphosphoric acid
I. Heilbron	1949	Inner anhydrides of N-dithiocarboxylic acids
J. C. Sheehan and V. S. Frank	1950	Dibenzylphosphoric acid
T. Wieland	1950	Carboxylic acids
R. A. Boissonas, J. R. Vaughan, and T. Wieland	1951	Alkylcarbonic acid
J. R. Vaughan	1951	Arsenious acid derivatives
T. Wieland	1952	Thiophenol
G. W. Kenner and R. I. Stedtman	1952	Sulfuric acid
G. W. Anderson	1952	Derivs. of phosphorous acid (3)

Recently, experiments have been described which differ fundamentally from the above in that it is not the carboxyl component, but the amine component in the activated form, united with a second acid to form an amide linkage, which is transformed.

We then have the following scheme:

$$\text{Amine} + \text{Acid (I)} \rightarrow \text{Acid (I)amide} + H_2O$$
$$\text{Acid (II)} + \text{Acid (I)amide} \rightarrow \text{Acid (II)amide} + \text{Acid (I)}$$

$$\text{Amine} + \text{Acid (II)} \rightarrow \text{Acid (II)amide} + H_2O$$

Outwardly this reaction involves an exchange of two acyl groups, viewed from the nitrogen as an exchange acylation. Again the problem lies in a suitable choice of acid (I).

Peptide syntheses of this type have been described previously using amides or imides of carbonic acids and the acids of trivalent and pentavalent phosphorus.

Synthesis Through Carbonic Acid Imides (4) (Isocyanate Method)

1. Synthesis and Properties of Esters of N-Carbonylamino Acids (5)
(Esters of α-Isocyanatoalkanoic Acids)

Among the procedures most often used, reaction of an ester of α-halogenated fatty acid with a cyanate, Curtius' degradation of the esterazides of C-substituted malonic acids, and the reaction of α-amino acid ester hydrochlorides with phosgene, the first two methods are eliminated because the first takes place at an asymmetric carbon atom and in the second the asymmetric center must be introduced later.

TABLE 2
ETHYL ESTERS OF N-CARBONYLAMINO ACIDS[a]

	B.p. (°C/mm Hg)	Yield (%)	$[\alpha]_D^{20}$
DL-Carbonyl-ala-	69°/11	85–91	—
DL-Carbonyl-α-aminobutyrate	81°/13	92–96	—
DL-Carbonyl-α-aminoisobutyrate	61.5°/12	94	—
DL-Carbonyl-norval	94°/14	94.5	—
DL-Carbonyl-val	87°/11	92–94	—
DL-Carbonyl-norleu	104°/14	91	—
DL-Carbonyl-ileu	94°/11	92–93	—
DL-Carbonyl-leu	97°/11	94–95	—
L-Carbonyl-leu	104.5°/15	91.5	−22.4°
DL-Carbonyl-phgly	127°/12	95	—
DL-Carbonyl-phe	152°/10	90–94	—
L-Carbonyl-SBz-cys	162°/0.8	91	−41.9°
DL-Carbonyl-met	155°/24	97	—
L-Carbonyl-asp (di-ester)	130°/10	89–91	−34.5°
L-Carbonyl-glu (di-ester)	151°/10	92	−46.3°

[a] For key to symbols used see Table 5.

The third reaction leads to the desired compounds without racemization in yields of about 90% (Table 2) (6).

$$HCl \cdot H_2N - \overset{\overset{\displaystyle H}{|}}{\underset{\underset{\displaystyle R}{|}}{C}} - COOR' + COCl_2 \rightarrow ClCONH - \overset{\overset{\displaystyle H}{|}}{\underset{\underset{\displaystyle R}{|}}{C}} - COOR' + 2\,HCl\uparrow$$

$$ClCONH - \overset{\overset{\displaystyle H}{|}}{\underset{\underset{\displaystyle R}{|}}{C}} - COOR' \xrightarrow{120\,°C} O = C = N - \overset{\overset{\displaystyle H}{|}}{\underset{\underset{\displaystyle R}{|}}{C}} - COOR' + HCl\uparrow$$

An example of this synthesis follows.

DL-*N-carbonylalanine ethyl ester (ethyl* DL-*α-isocyanatopropionate.* Dry toluene, 50 ml, is added to DL-alanine ethyl ester hydrochloride (15 gm) which has been dried *in vacuo* at 50° over P_2O_5, and the mixture placed in a three-necked flask fitted with a mechanical stirrer, gas-inlet tube, and reflux condenser. It is heated to 130–150° in an oil bath and phosgene is introduced quickly for 1.5 hr while stirring vigorously. HCl escapes and the hydrochloride gradually goes into solution. When this is accomplished, the toluene is distilled *in vacuo* at 45° using a good column. The residue is purified by distillation to give DL-N-carbonyl-alanine ethyl ester, b.p. 69°/11 mm. Yield: 12–13 gm (85–91%).

The other isocyanates may be obtained in an analogous manner; for dibasic amino acids the following procedure is used.

L-*N-carbonylaspartic diethylester.* L-Aspartic acid diethyl ester hydrochloride (22.5 gm) and 100 ml of dry xylene are mixed and phosgene introduced during 1 hr at 80° as described above. Then the temperature is raised until the mixture boils vigorously and the passage of phosgene is continued for 2 hr longer. Finally the xylene is distilled *in vacuo* and the isocyanate purified by distillation. At the beginning of the distillation some hydrogen chloride is sometimes evolved, since apparently the intermediate carbonyl chloride splits off HCl relatively slowly. B.p. 130°/10 mm, 139°/13 mm; 160°/24 mm; $[\alpha]_D^{24}$—34.5° (no solvent). Yield: 19–19.6 gm (89–91%).

The method cannot be used with dipeptide esters; the reaction goes quantitatively to hydantoin:

$$[O=C=N-CH_2-CO-NH-CH_2-COOR] \rightarrow HN \underset{CO}{\overset{H_2C-\!\!\!-\!\!\!-CO}{\diagdown}} N-CH_2-COOR$$

The α-isocyanato fatty acid esters are colorless liquids, have a stinging odor, and are lachrymators. They may be distilled without decomposition and, with the exclusion of moisture, are indefinitely stable. With amines they are converted to carbamylamino acid esters, which react readily with HCl to give the corresponding hydantoins.

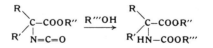

By reaction of α-isocyanato fatty acid esters with alcohol it is possible to prepare the N-carbalkoxyamino acids, important in peptide chemistry, via the N-carbalkoxyamino acid esters and saponification.

$$\underset{R'}{\overset{R}{\diagdown}}C\underset{N=C=O}{\overset{-COOR''}{|}} \xrightarrow{R'''OH} \underset{R'}{\overset{R}{\diagdown}}C\underset{HN-COOR'''}{\overset{-COOR''}{|}}$$

N-Carbethoxyalanine ethyl ester. A mixture of 1.5 gm of ethyl α-isocyanatopropionate, 10 ml of absolute alcohol, and 2 ml of carefully dried pyridine is refluxed for 2 hr with exclusion of moisture. After distillation of the alcohol and the pyridine *in vacuo*, the residual oil is distilled at 123°/11 mm.

The distillate crystallizes when triturated in the cold (−20°) with absolute petroleum ether. M.p. 26°. Yield 1.9 gm (96.5%). The substance is identical with the reaction product obtained from alanine ethyl ester and ethyl chloroformate.

According to Wurtz (7) carboxylic acids react with the elimination of CO_2 and the formation of the corresponding amides (8).

$$R-N=C=O \xrightarrow{\text{R'COOH}} \left[R-NH-C\overset{\displaystyle O}{\underset{\displaystyle OCOR'}{\Big<}} \right] \rightarrow R-NH-C\overset{\displaystyle O}{\underset{\displaystyle R'}{\Big<}} + CO_2$$

2. Peptide Synthesis

If the above reaction is carried out with N-acylamino acids as the carboxyl components, N-acylpeptide esters are formed:

$$\underset{R}{Ac-NH-\overset{H}{C}-COOH} + \underset{R}{OCN-\overset{H}{C}-COOC_2H_5} \xrightarrow[\text{Tol. } 110°\text{C}]{\text{Pyr. } 60°\text{C}}$$

$$\underset{R}{Ac-NH-\overset{H}{C}-CO-NH-\underset{R}{\overset{H}{C}-COOC_2H_5}} + CO_2 \uparrow$$

Under the catalytic influence of pyridine the reaction is finished in 1 hr at 50–60°. Without pyridine it is necessary to heat at 110° for several hours.

A large number of peptide esters have been prepared in this manner, retaining optical activity and with average yields of 90% (Table 3).

The following experimental examples may be applied in an analogous manner to other peptide esters.

Carbobenzoxyglycylglycine ethyl ester. (a) Carbobenzoxyglycine (21.5 gm), dried at 100° *in vacuo,* is mixed with 12.9 gm of N-carbonyl-glycine ethyl ester and 20 ml of dry pyridine. The vigorous evolution of carbon dioxide already occurs in the cold and diminishes after 15 min. The mixture is then kept in the water bath at 60° for 1 hr, after which the pyridine is distilled *in vacuo.* When the residue is shaken with 20 ml of 10% sodium carbonate solution, the dipeptide ester becomes crystalline. The ester is purified by crystallization from a large volume of hot water. The yield of carbobenzoxyglycylglycine ethyl ester is 28.2 gm (96%). M.p. 82°.

(b) Amounts as under (a), but without pyridine. The mixture is heated in an oil bath at 110° so long as carbon dioxide is evolved (2–3 hr). After being cooled the reaction mixture is worked up as in (a). Yield: 25 gm (85%).

The formation of the dipeptide ethyl ester can also be carried out with dry toluene, xylene, anisole, or isoamyl ether as solvents.

*Carbobenzoxy-*L-*glutamyl-α,γ-bisglycine ethyl ester.* From 2.8 gm of carbobenzoxyglutamic acid, 2.6 gm of carbonylglycine ethyl ester and 10 ml of dry pyridine according to (a). When the vigorous reaction has subsided, pyridine and the small excess of the carbonylglycine ester are removed *in vacuo*. The resulting white crystalline mass precipitates from ethanol as fine needles, m.p. 153°. Yield: 4.3 gm (95%).

Since it is impossible to obtain isocyanates of peptide esters, it is necessary in the synthesis of higher peptides, that the amino acid ester to be added contain an isocyanate group on the carboxyl end of the peptide chain.

TABLE 3

SYNTHESIS OF PEPTIDES BY THE ISOCYANATE METHOD

Final product—peptide ethyl esters[a]	Amino-component (as N-carbonyl cpd; ethyl ester)	Acid component	Yield (%)	$[\alpha]_D^{20}$
Dipeptides as Ethyl esters				
Cbzo-gly-gly	Gly	Cbzo-gly	96	—
Cbzo-DL-ala-gly	Gly	Cbzo-DL-ala	91	—
Cbzo-gly-DL-ala	DL-Ala	Cbzo-gly	94	—
Cbzo-gly-DL-leu	DL-Leu	Cbzo-gly	94	—
Cbzo-gly-DL-phe	DL-Phe	Cbzo-gly	84	—
Cbzo-gly-DL-aminobutyric acid	DL-aminobutyrate	Cbzo-gly	93	—
Cbzo-gly-DL-phgly	DL-Phgly	Cbzo-gly	94	—
Cbzo-gly-DL-met	DL-Met	Cbzo-gly	94	—
Cbzo-gly-DL-ileu	DL-Ileu	Cbzo-gly	95	—
Cbazo-gly-DL-val	DL-Val	Cbzo-gly	95	—
Cbzo-gly-DL-norleu	DL-Norleu	Cbzo-gly	92	—
Cbzo-DL-phgly-gly	Gly	Cbzo-DL-phgly	88	—
Cbzo-gly-L-SBz-cys	L-SBz-cys	Cbzo-gly	90	−45.9°
Phth-gly-gly	Gly	Phth-gly	92	—
Phenacetyl-gly-gly	Gly	Phenacetyl-gly	95	—
Tripeptides as Ethyl Esters				
Cbzo-gly-gly-gly	Gly	Cbzo-gly-gly	93	—
Cbzo-gly-DL-ala-gly	Gly	Cbzo-gly-DL-ala	87	—
Cbzo-L-glu-(α,γ)-bisgly	Gly	Cbzo-glu	95	−27.8°
Tetrapeptide as Ethyl Ester				
Cbzo-gly-gly-gly-gly	Gly	Cbzo-gly-gly-gly	95	—

[a] For key to symbols used see Table 5.

Carbobenzoxytetraglycine ethyl ester. A 3.4 gm portion of carbobenzoxytriglycine, and 1.3 gm of carbonylglycine ethyl ester are reacted as in (b) in 5 ml of toluene for 1.5 hr. After being recrystallized from hot water, the compound has a melting point of 185°. The yield: 3.7 gm (85%).

The resulting acylpeptide ester—substances which crystallize well after the removal of unchanged acylamino acid—are saponified to the N-acylpeptides in the usual manner using a slight excess of 2 N aqueous sodium hydroxide in the cold (9).

Carbobenzoxyglycylglycine. Carbobenzoxyglycylglycine ethyl ester,

29.4 gm, is stirred with 50 ml of 2 N sodium hydroxide at room temperature until all the solid has gone into solution (about 1 hr). On acidifying with concentrated hydrochloric acid the carbobenzoxyglycylglycine precipitates. After being recrystallized from methanol the compound melts at 178°, which agrees with the value given by Bergmann and Zervas. Yield: 25.2 gm (91%).

Synthesis with Imides and Amides of P³⁺ and P⁵⁺ Acids (Phosphorazo- and Phosphite Ester Methods)

1. Reactive Amides (Imides)

The trivalent and pentavalent phosphorus amides or imides were systematically explored around 1900 by Michaelis (10). These compounds are commonly prepared by the reaction of suitable phosphorus halides with amines (11). The reactivity of the various types toward the carboxyl group (12) is shown in Table 4.

Accordingly, the derivatives of trivalent phosphorus are in general more reactive than derivatives of phosphoric acid. We encounter, therefore, in those peptide syntheses used for preparative purposes, trivalent phosphorus amides or imides as intermediates, and especially compounds II and VII (13).

The "phosphorazo" compounds (14) (II), substituted by aliphatic groups, form undistillable resins, which have not yet been obtained analytically pure. Their part in peptide synthesis (in which they are not isolated) as well as their mode of formation and structure have been explained in the case of the aromatic-substituted crystalline analogs (15), which, handled with specific precautions, may be crystallized as analytically pure samples.

For the preparation of phosphorazo compound II the following reaction scheme may be proposed:

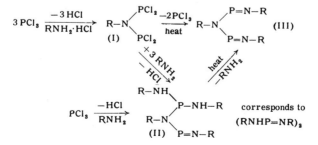

Experimental procedures for the direct preparation from amines and phosphorus trichloride (lower line of reaction scheme) follow.

TABLE 4

Phosphorus Amides and Imides

Parent substance	Amide or Imide	No.	Properties	Reaction with Carboxylic Acids[a]
PCl_3	$R-N(PCl_2)_2$	I	At high temp. forms III	Reactive halogen
	$(R-NH-P=N-R)_2$	II	Over 200°, dec.	+
	$(R-N)_3P_2$	III	Over 300°, dec.	−
	$(R_2N)_3P$	IV	Known only with simple sec. amines	++++
$HO-PCl_2$	$RO-PNR$	V	Stable	++++
	$RO-P(NHR)_2$	Va	Breaks down into II + ROH	++
	$HO-P(NHR)_2$	VI	Stable	+
$(HO)_2PCl$ and $(RO)_2POP(OR)_2$	$(RO)_2PNHR$	VII	Stable	+
$P(O)Cl_3$	$(RNH)_3PO$	VIII	Stable also with prim. amines	(+)
	$RNH\!\!\diagdown\!\! P(O)OH$			
	$R.N\!\!\diagdown\!\! P(O)OH$ with RNH	XIV	Stable	−
$HO-P(O)Cl_2$	$RO-P(O)(Cl)(NHR)$	IX	Stable	Reactive halogen
	$RO-P(O)(NHR)_2$	IXa	Stable	(+)
	$HO-P(O)(NHR)_2$	X	Stable	+
$(HO)_2P(O)Cl$	$(RO)_2P(O)NHR$	XII	Stable	(+)
	$(RO)P(O)(OH)(NHR)$	XIII	Stable	+
	$(HO)_2P(O)NHR$	XI	Changes to $[RNH_3]^+[OPO_2]^-$	Amine salt: −

[a] Key to symbols: + = reacts with carboxylic acids to form amide; (+) = reacts with carboxylic acids to form amide only above 150°; − = does not react with carboxylic acids.

Phenylimino (phenylamino)phosphine   (phosphorazo-compound). A solution of 8.8 ml (13.9 gm; 0.1 mole) of PCl_3 in 50 ml of dry benzene is added dropwise to an ice-cooled and stirred solution of 47 gm (0.505 mole) of freshly distilled, dry aniline in 250 ml of benzene. After standing for 1 hr the precipitated aniline hydrochloride is filtered and washed with 125 ml of dry benzene. After long standing, a white precipitate which is less soluble in cold benzene, is obtained from the filtrate. The amount of solid increases slowly. When recrystallized from toluene, a yield of 16.2 gm (75%) is obtained, decomposition point, 215°. In order to obtain analytically pure phenylimino(phenylamino)phosphine, the compound must be handled in the absence of air or oxygen.

No direct proof has been advanced for the structure of II (16). The close genetic relations to compound III, whose chain structure was proved through dipole measurement, make it seem reasonable that II has the structure designated.

The reactions of II are best indicated through a cryptoionic mechanism: the polar $P^{\delta+}$–$N^{\delta-}$ bond is split in such a way that an electronegative reactant goes to the phosphorus atom, an electropositive to the nitrogen. Carboxylic acids react, in a manner analogous to their esterification, as acyl cation and hydroxyl anion:

$$\frac{1}{2}\, II + 1\, H/OH \rightarrow R-NH-P(OH)-NH-R$$
$$3\, H/OH \rightarrow P(OH)_3 \cdot RNH_2 + RNH_2$$
$$5\, H/Cl \rightarrow PCl_3 + 2\, RNH_2Cl$$
$$2\, Ac/OH \rightarrow (PO_2H)_x + 2\, RNH-Ac$$
$$3\, H/OR' \rightarrow P(OR')_3 + 2\, RNH_2$$

The dialkylphosphite amides (VII) (dialkylphosphoramidites) are prepared by the reaction of the corresponding amine with dialkylchlorophosphite (17) or tetraethyl pyrophosphite (18). Both methods were introduced by Anderson and associates (19) to peptide chemistry.

Diethyl phosphite amide of DL-*phenylalanine ethyl ester.* Two-tenths of a mole of triethylamine is added to a suspension of 0.1 mole of DL-phenylalanine ethyl ester hydrochloride in absolute ether and with cooling a solution of 0.1 mole of diethyl chlorophosphite in absolute ether is added dropwise. The total volume of ether is 300 ml. After standing for ½ hr at room temperature, the triethylamine hydrochloride is filtered and the ether is removed under vacuum. The resulting phosphite amide is distilled at 134–137°/0.05 mm in 48% yield as an analytically pure product.

Since the starting material (diethyl chlorophosphite) is only of limited stability, it is better to start with the stable tetraalkyl pyrophosphite (18).

$$(RO)_2P-O-P(OR)_2 + H_2N-\underset{R'}{\overset{H}{C}}-COOR'' \rightarrow (RO)_2P-NH-\underset{R'}{\overset{H}{C}}-COOR'' + (RO)_2POH$$

TABLE 5

SYNTHESIS OF PEPTIDES USING PHOSPHORAZO COMPOUNDS

Final product[a]	Amine component	Acid component	Yield (%)	$[\alpha]_D$
Dipeptide esters				
Cbzo-gly-gly	Gly-Et	Cbzo-gly	91	—
Cbzo-gly-DL-val	DL-Val-Et·HCl	Cbzo-gly	95	—
Cbzo-gly-DL-leu	DL-Leu-Et	Cbzo-gly	95	—
Cbzo-gly-DL-ileu	DL-Ileu-Et	Cbzo-gly	87	—
Cbzo-gly-L-leu	L-Leu-Et·HCl	Cbzo-gly	89	-30.3[b]
Cbzo-gly-DL-phgly	DL-C-Phgly-Me	Cbzo-gly	98	—
Cbzo-gly-DL-phe	DL-Phe-Et	Cbzo-gly	81	—
Cbzo-DL-ala-gly	Gly-Et·HCl	Cbzo-DL-ala	98	—
Cbzo-DL-ala-DL-ala	DL-Ala-Et·HCl	Cbzo-DL-ala	84	—
Cbzo-DL-val-DL-val	DL-Val-Et·HCl	Cbzo-DL-val	75	—
Cbzo-gly-β-ala	β-Ala-Et·HCl	Cbzo-gly	77	—
α,ε-Bis-cbzo-DL-lys-ε-cbzo-DL-lys	ε-Cbzo-DL-lys-Et·HCl	α,ε-Bis-cbzo-DL-lys	86	—
α,ε-Bis-cbzo-DL-lys-gly	Gly-Et·HCl	α,ε-Bis-cbzo-DL-lys	78	—
Cbzo-gly-ε-cbzo-DL-lys	ε-Cbzo-DL-lys-Et·HCl	Cbzo-gly	78	—
Phth-gly-gly	Gly-Et·HCl	Phth-gly	81	—
Phth-DL-val-gly	Gly-Et·HCl	Phth-DL-val	74	—
Cbzo-α-glu-glu	Glu-Et₂·HCl	Cbzo-glu-γ-Et	85	-35
Cbzo-gluNH₂-glu	Glu-Et₂·HCl	Cbzo-gluNH₂	54	+13.4[b]
Cbzo-γ-glu-glu	Glu-Et₂·HCl	Cbzo-glu-α-Et	85	-22.7
Cbzo-α-glu-gly	Gly-Et·HCl	Cbzo-glu-γ-Et	90	-11.4
Cbzo-gluNH₂-gly	Gly-Et·HCl	Cbzo-gluNH₂	60	+76.3[b]
Cbzo-γ-glu-gly (saponified)	Gly-Et·HCl	Cbzo-glu-α-Et	55	—
Cbzo-α-glu-gly-SBz-cys	SBz-cys-Me·HCl	Cbzo-glu-γ-Et	70	-40
Cbzo-SBz-cys-SBz-cys	SBz-cys-Me·HCl	Cbzo-SBz-cys	77	-58
Cbzo-SBz-cys-gly	Gly-Et·HCl	Cbzo-SBz-cys	88	-26.8
Cbzo-β-ala-SBz-cys	SBz-cys-Me·HCl	Cbzo-β-ala	98	—
C₆H₅CH₂CO-SBz-cys-SBz-cys	SBz-cys-Me·HCl	C₆H₅CH₂CO-SBz-cys	90	—
C₆H₅CH₂CO-SBz-cys-val	Val-Et·HCl	C₆H₅CH₂CO-SBz-cys	90	—

C₆H₅CH₂CO-Gly-SBz-cys	SBz-cys-Me·HCl	C₆H₅CH₂CO-Gly	85	−39
C₆H₅CH₂CO-SBz-cys-gly	Gly-Et·HCl	C₆H₅CH₂CO-SBz-cys-gly	90	—
Cbzo-β-ala-SBz-cysteamine	SBz-cysteamine·HCl	Cbzo-β-ala	82	—
Cbzo-gly-DL-pro	DL-Pro-Et	Cbzo-gly	90	—
Cbzo-DL-try	DL-Try-Me·HCl	Cbzo-gly	93	—
δ-Cbzo-[α-phth-gly]-DL-orn	δ-Cbzo-[α-phth-gly]-DL-orn-Me·HCl	Phth-gly	35	—
Tripeptide esters				
Cbzo-gly-gly-gly	Gly-Et	Cbzo-gly-gly	88	—
Cbzo-gly-gly-gly	Gly-gly-Et	Cbzo-gly	95	—
α,ε-Bis(cbzo-gly)-DL-lys	DL-Lys-Me·2HCl	Cbzo-gly	79	—
Cbzo-α-glu-α-glu-glu	α-Glu-glu-Et₃·HCl	Cbzo-glu-γ-Et	88	—
Cbzo-γ-glu-γ-glu-glu	γGlu-glu-Et₃·HCl	Cbzo-glu-α-Et	92	—
Cbzo-α-glu-gly-gly	Gly-gly-Et·HCl	Cbzo-glu-γ-Et	76	—
Cbzo-α-glu-glu-gly	α-Glu-gly-Et₂·HBr	Cbzo-glu-γ-Et	55	—
Cbzo-γ-glu-gly-gly	Gly-gly-Et·HCl	Cbzo-glu-α-Et	68	—
Cbzo-γ-glu-SBz-cys-gly	SBz-cys-gly-Et	Cbzo-glu-α-Et	90	−18.5[b]
Cbzo-α-glu-SBz-cys-gly	SBz-cys-gly-Et	Cbzo-glu-γ-Et	79	—
Cbzo-SBz-cys-SBz-cys-SBz-cys	SBz-cys-Me·HCl	Cbzo-SBz-cys-cys-SBz-cys	95	—
Tetrapeptide esters				
Cbzo-(gly)₄	(Gly)₂-Et·HCl	Cbzo-(gly)₂	97	—
Cbzo-(γ-glu)₃-glu	(γ-Glu)₃-Et₄·HCl	Cbzo-glu-α-Et	95	—
Cbzo-gly-α-glu-(gly)₂	α-Glu-(gly)₂-Et₂·HBr	Cbzo-gly	65	—

[a] Abbreviations:

Cbzo = Carbobenzoxy
Bz = Benzyl
SBz = S-Benzyl
Phth = Phthalyl
Et = Ethyl ester
Me = Methyl ester
Ala = Alanine
Asp = Aspartic acid
Cys = Cysteine (always L)

Gly = Glycine
Glu = Glutamic acid (always L)
GluNH₂ = Glutamine
Ileu = Isoleucine
Leu = Leucine
Lys = Lysine
Met = Methionine
Norleu = Norleucine
Norval = Norvaline

Orn = Ornithine
Phe = Phenylalanine
Phgly = Phenylglycine
Pro = Proline
Tyr = Tyrosine
Try = Tryptophane
Val = Valine

[b] Optical rotation of free peptide.

Diethyl phosphite amide of DL-*phenylalanine ethyl ester.* Tetraethyl pyrophosphite (10.38 gm; 0.04 mole) is mixed with 7.72 gm (0.04 mole) of freshly distilled DL-phenylalanine ethyl ester. No visible reaction occurs. The distillation through a column gives 5.30 gm (72%) of diethyl phosphite (b.p. 65–70°/11 mm) and 7.61 gm (61%) of the phosphite amide (b.p. 140–150°/1 mm).

With carboxylic acids the P–N bond in VII is broken as in II to form an acid amide and a dialkyl phosphite.

2. Peptide Synthesis

The reaction of phosphite amides and imides with carboxylic acids may be adapted to suitably protected amino acids and leads to synthesis of peptides in very good yields (*20*).

In contrast to the results of Grimmel (*21*), as well as an observation by Anderson (*19*), the "phosphorazo compounds" II had already proved, in initial investigations (*22*), outstanding suitability for the preparation of peptides. The development of this method (*23, 24*) was made more feasible because PCl₃, a commercial product, serves as a "condensation agent." It has proved especially favorable, in that the application is not restricted to esters of amino acids, but that also peptide esters as phosphorazo-components with free carboxyl groups can be reacted. The variations of synthetic possibilities which a combination of larger peptide-building blocks also permits, is restricted only by decreasing solubility brought about by the increasing chain length.

A survey of the peptides prepared by these methods is found in Table 5.

The preparation is illustrated by the following examples.

GENERAL METHODS

Carbobenzoxyglycylglycine ethyl ester. (*a*) To 16.5 gm (0.16 mole) of glycine ethyl ester in 60 ml of dry toluene a solution of 2.8 ml (0.032 mole) of PCl₃ (distilled from dimethylaniline) in 20 ml of toluene is added slowly dropwise with stirring and cooling (0°). Thirty minutes after the end of the reaction the precipitated glycine ester hydrochloride is filtered and washed with toluene. To the combined toluene solution is added 13.5 gm (0.064 mole) of carbobenzoxyglycine and the mixture refluxed for 3 hr. Gradually there is deposited on the walls of the vessel an orange to red-brown precipitate of metaphosphorous acid, from which the reaction mixture can be decanted. The solvent is removed *in vacuo* and the residue is digested with an excess of 10% sodium carbonate solution; during the course of several hours a crystalline mass is obtained. The crystals are suction filtered, washed with water, and dried *in vacuo.* After recrystallization from water or ethyl acetate–petroleum ether, the ester melts at 82° as reported. The yield is 14.1 gm (75%).

(b) To a solution of 3.25 gm of glycine ethyl ester in 30 ml of dry pyridine, a solution of 1.45 ml of PCl_3 in 10 ml of dry pyridine is added as in (a). Pyridine hydrochloride precipitates. After 30 min 6.7 gm of carbobenzoxyglycine is added and the mixture refluxed (calcium chloride drying tube) on the water bath for 3 hr. After working up as in (a), 8.5 gm (91%) of carbobenzoxyglycylglycine ethyl ester, m.p. 82°, is obtained.

(c) Reaction ingredients as in (b). After the addition of 6.7 gm of carbobenzoxyglycine the mixture stands at room temperature (15–16°) for 60 hr. Yield as in (b).

(d) Finely powdered glycine ethyl ester hydrochloride (5 gm) is dissolved in pyridine with brief warming. To the cooled mass, which is completely crystallized, is added 20 ml of pyridine; then at 0° a solution of 1.6 ml of PCl_3 in 20 ml of pyridine is added slowly. Let stand for 30 minutes at room temperature, followed by dropwise addition of 7.5 gm of carbobenzoxyglycine. Finally the mixture is heated for 3 hr on the boiling water bath and allowed to stand at room temperature as in (c). When using pyridine as a solvent the metaphosphorous acid separates mostly as a red-brown film; sometimes there is no visible separation. After distillation of pyridine *in vacuo,* water is added to the residue and the whole is extracted several times with ethyl acetate. The ester extracts are washed successively with dilute hydrochloric acid, water, and two times with 10% sodium carbonate solution. Finally the ethyl acetate solution is washed again with water, dried over sodium sulfate, decolorized with activated charcoal, and concentrated. After cooling in an ice-chest and then adding petroleum ether, 9.1 gm (87%) of carbo-benzoxyglycylglycine ethyl ester, m.p. 82°, is obtained.

(e) Carbobenzoxyglycine (7.5 gm) and 5 gm of finely powdered glycine ethyl ester hydrochloride are dissolved in 50 ml of dry pyridine with shaking and slight warming. Then 1.58 ml of PCl_3 in 10 ml of pyridine are added dropwise with stirring and cooling to 0°. The mixture is allowed to stand at room temperature for 30 min, then heated for 3 hr on the boiling water bath. After working up as in (d) 8.2 gm (78%) of the ester, m.p. 82°, is obtained.

If the carbobenzoxypeptide ester is not difficultly soluble in water— as, for example, the glutamic acid peptide esters—then the following procedure applies:

(f) One proceeds as for (b), then after the reaction distills the pyridine at reduced pressure and water-bath temperature as far as possible. The residue, after addition of 10 ml of water, is extracted several times with ethyl acetate, eventually with slight warming. Then the combined filtered ethyl acetate solutions (about 150 ml) are shaken successively with 2 N hydrochloric acid, water, and 2 or 3 times with 10% sodium carbonate solution, until the last soda extraction remains clear after being acidified. Finally, the ethyl acetate layer is washed again with water and dried over sodium sulfate. The residue, after concentration *in vacuo*, is recrystallized from a suitable solvent or solvent-pair.

β-AMINO ACIDS

Carbobenzoxyglycyl-β-alanine ethyl ester. β-Alanine ethyl ester hydrochloride, 7.5 gm, is allowed to react with 2.2 ml of PCl_3 and then with 10.5 gm of carbobenzoxyglycine as in (*d*). There is obtained 11.6 gm (77%) of oily ester, which gives colorless needles from ether–petroleum ether, m.p. 63° (lit. gives 63–64°).

DIAMINOCARBOXYLIC ACIDS

α,ε-Bis(carbobenzoxyglycyl)-DL-lysine methyl ester. To a suspension of 3 gm of DL-lysine methyl ester bishydrochloride in 100 ml of dry chloroform, 10 ml. of triethylamine is added and the mixture is refluxed for 10 min. Then 100 ml of dry pyridine is added and 60 ml of the solvent mixture is distilled off. After cooling with ice to 0° a solution of 1.23 ml of PCl_3 in 6 ml of dry chloroform is added dropwise. After being allowed to stand for 1 hr at room temperature, 6 gm of carbobenzoxyglycine is added and the mixture is refluxed for 5 hr. After cooling the precipitated hydrochloride is filtered and the filtrate concentrated *in vacuo* to dryness. The resulting oil is triturated with 50 ml of 10% of sodium carbonate solution and the undissolved residue is taken up with ethyl acetate. The ethyl acetate solution is dried over sodium sulfate, cooled to 0°, and petrileum ether is added. The ester precipitates as an oil, which crystallizes on standing for 2 days. Recrystallizing from ethyl acetate–petroleum ether, gives a colorless powder, m.p. 106°. Yield: 5.5 gm (79%).

PEPTIDE ESTERS AS PHOSPHORAZO-COMPONENTS

Carbobenzoxytetraglycine ethyl ester. Diglycine ethyl ester hydrochloride (6 gm) is treated with 1.4 ml of PCl_3, then with 9 gm of carbobenzoxydiglycine, as in (*d*).

The mixture is allowed to stand for 10 days at room temperature (16–17°). (Heated on the water bath the reaction is already complete in about 3 hr.) On working up the mixture white leaflets are obtained, which are recrystallized from water. M.p. 205° (lit. 185°), mixed m.p. with substance from M. Wick: 182° (dimorphism). Yield: 12.0 gm (97%).

AMINODICARBOXYLIC ACIDS

The synthesis of α-glutamyl peptides cannot be accomplished by the methods described. It was found, for example, that α-L-glutamyl-L-glutamic acid triethyl ester hydrochloride, on solution in pyridine, gives the 3,6-bis(2-carbethoxyethyl)-2,5-diketopiperazine by splitting off ethanol. An attempt to isolate the free dipeptide ester from its hydrochloride gave only the diketopiperazine (B):

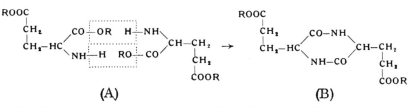

(A)   (B)

To obtain the compounds desired the following method was used.

N-Carbobenzoxy-α-L-diglutamylglutamic acid tetraethyl ester. α-L-Glutamylglutamic acid triethyl ester hydrochloride (1.4 gm) is poured,

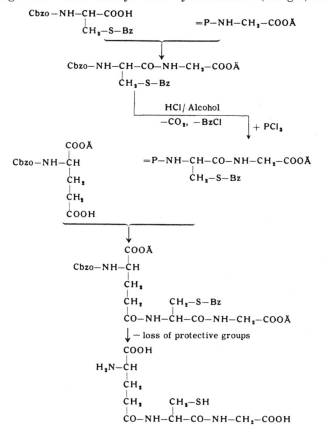

with cooling, directly into a mixture of 0.42 ml of PCl_3 and 20 ml of pyridine. To the clear solution is added 1.3 gm of N-carbobenzoxy-L-glutamic acid α-ethyl ester and an additional 30 ml of pyridine. The mixture is heated on the boiling water bath for 3 hr. Working up according to (f), a yield of 2.1 gm (92%) is obtained, m.p. 114–116° (from ethyl acetate–petroleum ether).

An example of the use of the method in the synthesis of more complicated oligopeptides is the preparation of glutathione (see above).

S-Benzyl-L-cysteinylglycine ethyl ester was obtained by the reaction of N-carbobenzoxy-S-benzyl-L-cysteine with the phosphorazo compound of glycine ethyl ester followed by splitting off the protective group. This phosphorazo compound of S-benzyl-L-cysteinylglycine ethyl ester was then converted by reaction with N-carbobenzoxy-L-glutamic acid α-ester to N-carbobenzoxy-S-benzyl-L-glutathione ethyl ester from which the protective groups may be removed by familiar methods.

Furthermore, β-alanylcysteamine, an important intermediate in the pantetheine synthesis, may be readily obtained in good yield and in few steps, using the phosphorazo method:

$$H_2N-CH_2-CH_2-S-Bz$$
$$\downarrow PCl_3$$
$$Cbzo-NH-CH_2-CH_2-COOH \qquad =P-NH-CH_2-CH_2-S-Bz$$
$$\underbrace{\qquad\qquad\qquad\qquad\qquad\qquad\qquad\qquad}$$
$$Cbzo-NH-CH_2-CH_2-CO-NH-CH_2-CH_2-S-Bz$$
$$\downarrow Na, fl. NH_3$$
$$H_2N-CH_2-CH_2-CO-NH-CH_2-CH_2-SH$$

In all syntheses the configuration of the optically active amino acid is retained, if the carbobenzoxy group serves as the protecting group.

The peptides cited in Table 6 were prepared by the phosphite ester amide procedure according to the following directions.

Carbobenzoxyglycyl-DL-phenylalanine ethyl ester. The solution of 0.1–0.2 mole of carbobenzoxyamino acid and an equivalent amount of suitable phosphite amide in toluene is boiled 1 hr. The solvent is removed *in vacuo* and the residue is crystallized from 50% alcohol. M.p. 90–91°. Yield: 65%.

By using tetraethyl pyrophosphite the following procedures are applicable (25).

(a) AMIDE METHOD

To a solution of 0.010 mole of amino acid (peptide) ester hydrochloride and 0.011 mole of triethylamine in 7 ml of diethyl phosphite as solvent, is added 0.011 mole (2.84 gm) of tetraethyl pyrophosphite. The mixture is heated for 2 min on the steam bath, the acylamino acid (peptide) added, and heating continued for 30 min longer. Then 25–50 ml of water is added, and the mixture cooled to 0° and filtered. The precipitate (acyl-peptide ester) is washed with 10 ml of 5% sodium bicarbonate solution, then two times with 5 ml of water, and finally crystallized from alcohol–water. Yields and melting points are given in Table 6.

(b) STANDARD METHOD

An 0.011 mole portion of tetraethyl pyrophosphite is added to a solution of 0.010 mole of carbobenzoxyamino acid (peptide), 0.010 mole of amino acid (peptide) ester hydrochloride, and 0.011 mole of triethylamine in 7 ml of diethyl phosphite. The reaction mixture is heated on the steam bath for ½ hr and worked up as described above.

TABLE 6
SYNTHESIS OF PEPTIDES USING PHOSPHITE ESTER AMIDES

Peptide ester[a]	Amine component	Acid component	Yield (%)	$[\alpha]_D$
Cbzo-gly-DL-phe-Et	DL-Phe-Et	Cbzo-gly	94	—
Phth-gly-L-leu-Et	L-leu-Et	Phth-gly	78	−26.5°
Cbzo-gly-L-tyr-Et	L-Tyr-Et	Cbzo-gly	65	+19.2°
Cbzo-L-leu-gly-Et	Gly-Et	Cbzo-L-leu	56	−27.2°
Cbzo-L-leu-L-tyr-Et	L-Tyr-Et	Cbzo-L-leu	40	−14°
Cbzo-DL-val-DL-ala-Et	DL-Ala-Et	Cbzo-DL-val	60	—
Cbzo-DL-val-DL-phe	DL-Phe-Et	Cbzo-DL-val	11	—
Cbzo-gly-gly-gly-Et	Gly-gly-Et	Cbzo-gly	78	—
Cbzo-L-tyr-gly-gly-Et	Gly-gly-Et	Cbzo-L-tyr	47	+6.5°
Cbzo-gly-DL-phe-(gly)$_2$-Et	Gly-gly-Et	Cbzo-gly-DL-phe	25	—
Cbzo-gly-L-leu-gly-Me	Gly-Me	Cbzo-gly-L-leu	61	−34.9°

[a] For key to symbols used see Table 5.

3. Urea Syntheses (26)

The resulting unstable N-carboxylic acids, formed from amine and ureas,

$$R-NH_2 + CO_2 \underset{\xleftarrow{\hspace{1.5cm}}}{\overset{Pressure}{\xrightarrow{\hspace{1.5cm}}}} R-NH-COOH$$

react as normal carboxylic acids with phosphorazo compounds (II); ureas are produced in this manner:

$$(R-NHPN-R)_2 + 4CO_2 + 4R'NH_2 \xrightarrow[\sim 100\,°C]{Pressure}$$
$$4R-NH-CO-NH-R' + 2(PO_2H)_x$$

If carbon disulfide is used in place of carbon dioxide, the corresponding thioureas are formed.

In this manner, for example, N,N'-diphenylurea, phenylureidoacetic acid ester, and N,N'-diphenylthiourea have been prepared. The yields are, on the average, 85%.

N,N'-Diphenylurea. A mixture of 17.5 gm of phenylimino(phenyl-amino)phosphine (0.082 mole) in 120 ml of dry pyridine and 15 ml (0.165 mole) of aniline in an autoclave is heated with carbon dioxide at 140 atm pressure at 100–110° for 7 hr with stirring. On cooling over-night, 13.1 gm of thick needles of N,N'-diphenylurea (m.p. 236–237°) precipitate from the cloudy solution. After filtration the mother liquor is evaporated *in vacuo* to dryness. The residue, after solution in hot alcohol, gives an additional 15.4 gm of carbanilide. The total yield is 28.5 gm (83%). A mixed melting point with an authentic sample is unchanged.

N,N'-Diphenylthiourea. Aniline (9.3 gm, 0.1 mole) is dissolved in 60 ml of dry pyridine and a solution of 2.2 ml (0.025 mole) of PCl_3 in 10 ml of pyridine is added dropwise with ice-cooling. After 30 min 20 ml (0.33 mole) of carbon disulfide is added and the red-brown solution is heated on the water bath for 6 hr. The temperature of the solution: 65–70°. After 30 min yellow crystals begin to separate at the brim of the boiling solution. The solution is concentrated *in vacuo* to dryness. The yellow, crystalline residue, recrystallized from 25 ml of alcohol and 50 ml of water, gives light yellow platelets which, recrystallized again from alcohol–water, become colorless and melt at 154°. A mixed melting point with diphenylthiourea is unchanged. From the mother liquor of the first crystallization an additional small amount may be obtained by adding more water. The total yield is 10.8 gm (95%).

Supplement

1. Amides of Tri-valent Phosphorus

The usefulness of the "Phosphorazo Method" for the synthesis of optically active peptides without the occurrence of racemization has been confirmed in several experiments (27). Aside from the compounds already noted, the ester or anhydride of the phosphorus acids I–IV have been proposed for reaction with amino acid esters [I, II, (28); III, (29); IV, (30)].

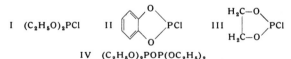

$$I \quad (C_2H_5O)_2PCl \qquad II \qquad III \qquad$$

$$IV \quad (C_2H_5O)_2POP(OC_2H_5)_2$$

The phosphorus ester-amides obtained may react with N-acylamino acids or N-acylpeptides in the same manner as the "Phosphorazo" com-pounds. The use of I–IV offers no preparative advantages, in general, over the phosphorazo method. Compounds having the structure I–IV may be used, however, to proceed from acylamino acids. Under suitable conditions the mixed anhydrides, for example, $CH_3CONHCHRCOOP$ $(OC_2H_5)_2$, are formed; these may then react with amino acid (peptide) esters in the familiar manner (anhydride method).

2. Amides of Pentavalent Phosphorus

Recently Schramm and Wissmann (*31*) have stated that peptides can be obtained when amino acid esters or peptide esters in diethyl phosphite are allowed to react with phosphorus pentoxide in the presence of a tertiary base and then the reaction product is treated with N-acyl-amino acids or N-acylpeptides. This peculiar synthesis apparently takes place in such a manner that from phosphorus pentoxide and diethyl phosphite there is formed the ethyl metaphosphorate V, which produces an acylpeptide according to V–VII.

$$P_2O_5 + (C_2H_5O)_2P(O)H \rightarrow (C_2H_5OPO_2)x + H_3PO_3$$
$$V$$
$$V + H_2N-CHR-CO_2R' \rightarrow C_2H_5OP(OH)-NH-CHR-CO_2R' +$$
$$O$$
$$\underline{Cbzo-NH-CHR''-CO_2H}$$
$$\rightarrow Cbzo-NH-CHR''-CO-NH-CHR-CO_2R' +$$
$$C_2H_5OPO(OH)_2$$

Summary

The range of hitherto useful methods has been enriched by some preparatively favorable procedures. The imides of carbonic acid as well as the imides and amides of phosphorous acid may be used for the preparation of optically active oligopeptides in very good yields under mild reaction conditions. Even though the isocyanate procedure may be subject to certain limitations, the phosphorazo- and phosphite ester procedures allow a successful synthesis of peptides from simple building blocks. The last two syntheses are especially suitable for preparative work because of their simple application and have already shown their serviceability by the preparation of complicated oligopeptides.

REFERENCES

(1) In peptide syntheses the reactive group of the starting substances not expected to take part in the reaction must be blocked by "protective groups." For details see T. Wieland, *Angew. Chem.* **63**, 7 (1951); **66**, 507 (1954).

(2) Concerning different activated carboxyl groups see, e.g., B. H. Lettré and M. E. Fernholz, *Z. physiol. Chem.* **266**, 37 (1940) (oxazolones); J. C. Sheehan and G. P. Hess, *J. Am. Chem. Soc.* **77**, 1067 (1955); H. G. Khorana, *Chem. Ind.* (*London*) p. 1087 (1955) (carbodiimide); R. Schwyzer, B. Iselin, and M. Feurer, *Helv. Chim. Acta* **38**, 69 (1955); R. Schwyzer, M. Feurer, B. Iselin, and H. Kagi, *ibid.*, **38**, 80 (1955); B. Iselin, M. Feurer, and R. Schwyzer, *ibid.*, **38**, 1508 (1955) (active ester).

(3) In that case an amide-like mechanism may also take place.

(4) S. Goldschmidt and M. Wick, *Ann. Chem. Liebigs* **575**, 217 (1952).

(5) Nomenclature according to Beilstein.

(6) It is important to use the completely esterified amino acids. With the exception of alanine ethyl ester hydrochlorides, all the ester hydrochlorides are solids and crystalline. L-Alanine methyl ester hydrochloride, needles, m.p. 105–6°.

(7) C. A. Wurtz, *Ann. chim. (Paris)* [3] **42**, 53 (1854).

(8) The disubstituted ureas formed in a side reaction occur only with aromatic substituted isocyanates.

(9) A large excess of OH⁻ leads to the formation of carbonyl-bis-amino acids. See also F. Wessely and E. Kamm, *Z. physiol. Chem.* **174**, 306 (1928).

(10) A. Michaelis, *Ann. Chem. Liebigs* **326**, 129 (1903)—summarizing paper.

(11) Exceptions: Tetraethylpyrophosphite; see refs. (*18*) and (*30*).

(12) S. Goldschmidt and F. Obermeier, *Ann. Chem. Liebigs* **588**, 24 (1954).

(13) Decisive in this choice were readily available starting materials which were experimentally easy to handle.

(14) Name adopted by A. Michaelis (*10*); more correctly: iminoaminophosphine.

(15) S. Goldschmidt and H.-L. Krauss, *Ann. Chem. Liebigs* **595**, 193 (1955).

(16) Aside from chain-form molecules, ring or cage structures for II and III are conceivable.

(17) Prepared from PCl₃, alcohol, and diethylaniline; yield: 50%; H. G. Cook, J. D. Ilett, B. C. Saunders, G. J. Stacey, H. G. Watson, I. G. E. Wilding, and S. J. Woodcock, *J. Chem. Soc.* p. 2921 (1949).

(18) Prepared from dialkylchlorophosphite, dialkylchlorophosphite and triethylamine in benzene; yield: 41%.

(19) G. W. Anderson, J. Blodinger, R. W. Young, and A. D. Welcher, *J. Am. Chem. Soc.* **74**, 5304, 5309 (1952).

(20) The peptide syntheses described by O. Süs probably follow this scheme; *Ann. Chem. Liebigs* **577**, 96 (1951).

(21) H. W. Grimmel, A. Guenther, and I. F. Morgan, *J. Am. Chem. Soc.* **68**, 539 (1946).

(22) With M. Wick.

(23) S. Goldschmidt and H. Lautenschlager, *Ann. Chem. Liebigs* **580**, 68 (1953).

(24) S. Goldschmidt and C. Jutz, *Chem. Ber.* **86**, 1116 (1953); **89**, 518 (1956).

(25) A synthesis via the mixed anhydride from acylamino acid and diethyl phosphorous acid is also possible; however with this procedure up to 46% racemization occurs (*19*).

(26) H. Lautenschlager, Dissertation, Technische Hochschule München, 1953; O. Sedlmaier, Dissertation, Technische Hochschule München, 1958.

(27) W. Grassmann and E. Wünsch, *Chem. Ber.* **91**, 449 (1958); G. Rosculet, Dissertation, Technische Hochschule München, 1956. For the racemization in the synthesis of a tripeptide, see W. Grassmann, E. Wünsch, and A. Riedel, *Chem. Ber.* **91**, 455 (1958).

(28) G. W. Anderson and co-workers; see ref. (*16*).

(29) R. W. Young, R. H. Wood, R. J. Yoyce, and G. W. Anderson, *J. Am. Chem. Soc.* **78**, 2126 (1956).

(30) G. W. Anderson, *J. Am. Chem. Soc.* **74**, 5309 (1952). H. N. Rydon, Exeter, proposed, that the rather unstable IV be replaced by bis-o-phenylene pyrophosphite in peptide syntheses [*Angew. Chem.* **71**, 741 (1959)].

(31) G. Schramm and H. Wissmann, *Chem. Ber.* **91**, 1073 (1958).

The Preparation of Long-Chain Carboxylic Acids from 1,3-Cyclohexanediones

HERMANN STETTER

Chemisches Institut der Universität Bonn*

Introduction

Dihydroresorcinol (1,3-cyclohexanedione) (I) undergoes a hydrolytic ring opening with alkali to form δ-oxocaproic acid (II). Vorländer had discovered this as far back as 1897 (*1*).

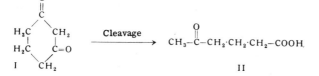

With this reaction dihydroresorcinol proves to be a normal β-diketone, because it gives, on cleavage, the acids characteristic of such diketones.

Proceeding from these observations a new synthetic method for long-chain carboxylic acids was developed by H. Stetter and W. Dierichs (*2, 2a*). This method proceeds in three steps:

The first step consists of introducing organic groups into the 2-position of dihydroresorcinol.

In the second step, the C-alkylated 1,3-cyclohexanedione is treated with alkali, and the δ-oxo acids, which now contain a 6-carbon atom chain plus R, are obtained. By reduction of the carbonyl group in these δ-oxo acids to CH_2, long-chain reduced carboxylic acids are obtained, as the third step.

With this reaction sequence the lengthening of carbon chains by six carbon atoms becomes generally possible, according to the scheme:

The importance of the procedure lies in its wide applicability, which has been confirmed by the synthesis of numerous long-chain carboxylic acids. Dihydroresorcinol, useful in lengthening the chain, in addition contributes its full molecular weight to the final acid. This fact may serve to emphasize the economical nature of the procedure.

* New address: Institut für Organische Chemie der Technischen Hochschule Aachen.

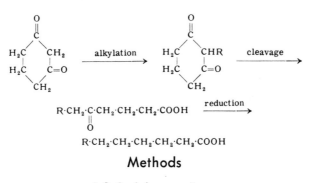

$$R \cdot CH_2 \cdot C \cdot CH_2 \cdot CH_2 \cdot CH_2 \cdot COOH \xrightarrow{\text{reduction}}$$
$$\underset{O}{\|}$$

$$R \cdot CH_2 \cdot CH_2 \cdot CH_2 \cdot CH_2 \cdot CH_2 \cdot COOH$$

Methods

1,3-Cyclohexanedione

Dihydroresorcinol was first obtained by Merling (*3*) by the reduction of resorcinol with sodium amalgam. The yield by this procedure is not satisfactory. Also, the procedure used by Vorländer (*4*), the cyclization of δ-oxocapronate ester, is not suitable for large quantities of dihydroresorcinol. It first became readily available when Klingenfuss (*5*) found that, whereas the catalytic reduction of resorcinol in a neutral or acidic medium leads to an uptake of six hydrogen atoms to form the isomeric resorcitol, in the presence of 1 mole of alkali the reduction stops at the dihydroresorcinol stage.

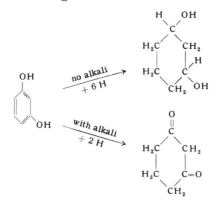

The yield by hydrogenation is over 90%. In the laboratory the procedure of R. B. Thompson (*6*), who used Raney-nickel, has proved to be the best. The procedure can be simplified by reducing at atmospheric pressure at 50° with agitation. With sufficiently intensive shaking the reduction takes 9–10 hr.

The closely related dimedone, 5,5-dimethyl-1,3-cyclohexanedione, is readily obtained by the procedure of Vorländer (*7*), using a Michael addition of malonic ester to mesityl oxide, followed by cyclization of the ester (yield: 80%).

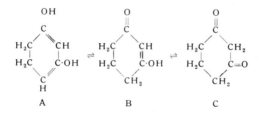

In a similar manner other 5-substituted 1,3-cyclohexanediones, a 5-methyl-1,3-cyclohexanedione (8), and 5-phenyl-1,3-cyclohexanedione (9) are readily obtained.

Dihydroresorcinol may exist in three tautomeric forms.

Actually only the monoenol B and the cyclohexanedione C exist in a solution of dihydroresorcinol (10). According to measurements of Schwarzenbach (11) the enol content in aqueous solution is 95.3%. This strong enolization accounts for the strong acidic character of dihydroresorcinol. Its pK is 5.25 and thus it is an only slightly weaker acid than acetic acid.

Whereas in the open-chain β-diketones the formation of the enol form hinders free rotation and thereby entails an expenditure of energy, in practice this is not the case with 1,3-cyclohexanediones. This explains the great tendency toward enolization in contrast to the open-chain β-diketones (12).

The high acidity is caused by the large resonance energy, which, because of the planar configuration of the ring structure, is produced by the dissociation of a proton (13).

A further characteristic difference between open-chain and cyclic β-diketones was found by Eistert and Reiss (14). The enols of open-chain β-diketones, because of hydrogen bonding, show a chelate structure D, which restricts the possibility of forming the cis-structure of an enol.

These chelates are hydrophobic, as are the corresponding ketones. From this it is evident that such β-diketones show less tendency for enolization in a strongly polar solvent, such as water, than in a nonpolar solvent such as hexane. In the case of cyclic β-diketones the chelate structure of enols is ruled out on steric grounds. In this case the enol form is "transfixed." Therefore it is more hydrophylic than the cyclohexanedione form. Eistert and Reiss could confirm these predictions, finding for such 1,3-cyclohexanediones a higher enol content in the polar solvents than in the nonpolar ones.

On the same steric grounds the cyclohexanediones do not give an enol reaction with ferric chloride in absolute alcohol. The "transfixed" enols cannot form the iron complex necessary for the color reaction (15). Altogether pure and dry dihydroresorcinol is practically stable without limit. Moist or slightly impure dihydroresorcinol undergoes extensive decomposition. Such decompositions are observed in more or less degree with almost all of the alkylated 1,3-cyclohexanediones. The cause is an autooxidation, which Toivonen and associates (16) found to be the case with 2,5,5-trimethyl-1,3-cyclohexanedione. As the first step they postulate the formation of an enol peroxide (E), which, in some unexplainable manner, is converted to β,β-dimethylglutaric acid and acetic acid. More recent investigations with similar peroxides (17) seem to indicate that a keto hydrogen peroxide, formula F, is involved rather than the intermediate E.

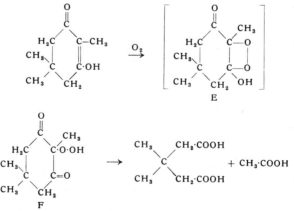

Three-step Procedure

FIRST STEP OF THE REACTION: PREPARATION OF 2-SUBSTITUTED
1,3-CYCLOHEXANEDIONES

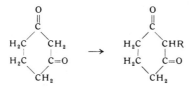

The synthesis of carboxylic acids may be quite varied in the individual reaction steps. This is true especially in the first step which involves the introduction of an organic group into the 2-position of 1,3-cyclohexanedione. As β-diketones these compounds, through their alkali derivatives, are directly alkylated with organic halides. A further possibility for the introduction of an organic group is through addition reactions, which are made possible by the presence of the acidic hydrogen. To the addition reactions belongs also the addition of carbonyl compounds after the manner of an aldol condensation, as well as the Michael addition with β-unsaturated ketones, esters, and nitriles.

Alkylation with Organic Halogen Compounds

As is the case in the alkylation of other β-dicarbonyl compounds, in the reaction of the metal derivatives of 1,3-cyclohexanedione with alkyl halides, the presence of enol ethers and C-alkylated cyclohexanediones must be expected because of the ionic mesomerism:

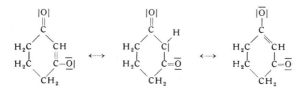

Primarily enol ethers are formed, in keeping with the strong preference for the enol form in such cyclohexanediones. In agreement with this view Merling (*18*) obtained exclusively the enol ethers by treating the silver salt of dihydroresorcinol with alkyl iodides. The compounds could not be isolated in a pure state.

The first C-alkylations of dihydroresorcinol were described in 1936 by Klingenfuss (*19*) and Hewett (*20*). Klingenfuss mentions the preparation of 2-allyl-1,3-cyclohexanedione by the condensation of dihydroresorcinol with allyl bromide. Hewett obtained 2-benzyl-1,3-cyclohexanedione by the reaction of the sodium derivative of dihydroresorcinol with benzyl chloride in absolute alcohol with an 18% yield.

The alkylation of dimedone, 5,5-dimethyl-1,3-cyclohexanedione, was investigated more thoroughly. The methylation of this compound was first described by Toivonen (21). Desai (22) undertook alkylation with methyl iodide, ethyl iodide, n-propyl iodide, n-butyl iodide, isopropyl iodide, allyl iodide, and benzyl iodide; the corresponding C-alkylated dimedones were obtained only in small yields. As by-products enol ethers as well as dialkylated products were obtained.

Stetter and Dierichs (23) systematically investigated the alkylation of dihydroresorcinol from the standpoint of various factors. Alkylation was examined for its dependence upon solvents, salt-formation with various alkali metals, and the concentration and kind of alkyl halide used. The halogen compounds used were n-butyl bromide and n-butyl iodide. The separation of the resulting C-alkylated dihydroresorcinols from the enol ethers were readily achieved, since the C-alkylated dihydro-resorcinols still possess an acidic hydrogen and therefore are soluble in alkali, whereas the enol ethers are insoluble in alkali and can be extracted completely with ether.

The alkylation with n-butyl bromide with different alcohols as solvents showed that the proportion in which the C-alkylated products and

TABLE 1

REACTION OF THE SODIUM DERIVATIVE OF DIHYDRORESORCINOL WITH
n-BUTYL BROMIDE

Solvent	C-alkyl	O-alkyl	Ratio C–O Cpd.
Methanol	15%	36.5%	1:2.4
Ethanol	12%	30%	1:2.5
t-Butyl alcohol	12%	30%	1:2.5

the enol ethers are formed, is independent of the kind of alcohol used (Table 1). Only the higher combined yield in the case of methanol is noteworthy.

A stronger influence on alkylation is shown when different alkali metals are used for salt formation in methanol. In the progression from lithium to potassium a growing promotion of C-alkylation with increasing atomic weight is noted (Table 2). The best yields were obtained with the potassium derivative. This discovery is in good agreement with the investigations of Brändström (24), who observed the same effect in the alkylation of acetylacetone with the series, sodium to cesium.

In order to study the influence of solvent concentration on alkylation, dihydroresorcinol was alkylated with n-butyl bromide in three different concentrations in methanol. The experimental results (Table 3) show definitely that C-alkylation is favored by working in higher concentration.

The closely related investigation of alkylation without a solvent showed that only enol ethers are formed.

TABLE 2

INFLUENCE OF ALKALI METAL ON THE ALKYLATION OF
DIHYDRORESORCINOL WITH n-BUTYL BROMIDE

Metal	C-Alkyl	O-Alkyl	Ratio C:O Cpd
Lithium	6%	21.0%	1:3.4
Sodium	15%	36.5%	1:2.4
Potassium	17.5%	36.4%	1:2.1

It was known from previous work (25) with open-chain β-diketones, that C-alkylation was favorably influenced in proportion to the reactivity of the halogen in the organic halogen compound used. If, in place of an alkyl bromide, the corresponding alkyl iodide is used, the yield of C-alkylated product increases. The same results are observed when under the same conditions n-butyl iodide is used in place of n-butyl bromide

TABLE 3

INFLUENCE OF SOLVENT CONCENTRATION ON THE ALKYLATION OF
POTASSIUM DERIVATIVE OF DIHYDRORESORCINOL WITH n-BUTYL BROMIDE

CH_3OH (ml)	Heating time (hr)	C-Alkyl	O-Alkyl	Ratio C:O Cpd
30	5	18.2%	42.4%	1:2.3
50	5	17.5%	36.4%	1:2.3
200	15	6%	25%	1:4.2

in the alkylation of dihydroresorcinol. The yield of 2-butyl-1,3-cyclohexanedione increases from 18.2 to 28.4%, while the yield of enol decreases from 42.4 to 36.4%.

A totally different picture is presented when n-butyl p-toluenesulfonate is used for alkylation in place of a n-butyl halide. The alkylation proceeds rapidly and gives almost exclusively the enol ether in 80% yield. This exclusive enol ether formation is characteristic when using the esters of sulfonic acids and sulfuric acid for the alkylation of dihydroresorcinol and offers an excellent practical method for obtaining enol ethers.

The investigations just described have shown that the preparation of C-alkylated dihydroresorcinols is most favored when the potassium derivative of dihydroresorcinol is treated with an alkyl halide containing the most active halogen, in the highest concentration possible, using methanol as solvent.

A theoretical interpretation of these investigations of Stetter and Dierichs (*23*), within the scope of a general theory concerning the C- and O-alkylation of β-carbonyl compounds, was presented by A. Bränd- ström (*26*). According to Brändström the alkali salts of dihydroresorcinol exist, in the solvent, in a solvated form, the metal being attached to three solvent molecules and the resonance hybrid of the dihydroresorcinol ion. In this complex one or more of the solvent molecules can be displaced by organic halogen compounds. These bound halides become strongly polarized. In the six-membered ring which is formed, the linkage of the R group can be joined to the carbon atom in position 2 of dihydro- resorcinol. The relations are summarized in the following scheme.

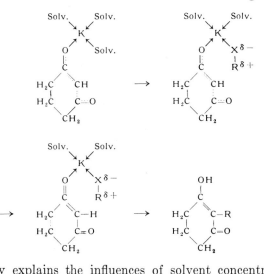

This theory explains the influences of solvent concentration on C- alkylation, since with a lower concentration of the solvent that of the alkyl halide increases, and the formation of the halogen-containing com- plex, and with it C-alkylation, is favored. Similarly the theory explains the increase of C-alkylation with the increasing atomic weight of the alkali metal, since in the open-chain β-carbonyl compounds a reduction in the salt-like character of the alkali compound is also observed with increased atomic weight (*27*). The influence of the strongly polarized halides on the course of C-alkylation may be explained by the greater tendency to form the halogen-containing complex. On the other hand the formation of enol ether is explained by the reaction with the anion with- out the above-mentioned stabilization of the negative charge on the C-atom.

Under the optimum conditions a series of simple alkyl iodides were reacted with dihydroresorcinol by Stetter and Dierichs (*2*). It was shown that in the series from ethyl iodide to cetyl iodide the yields of C-alkylated dihydroresorcinols are largely constant. They are about 27%. Only methyl iodide is an exception, giving 2-methyl-1,3-cyclohexanedione in 51.5% yield. Also, a bromoacetate and allyl bromide gave higher yields (51 and 33%) of the C-alkylated dihydroresorcinol, for in these compounds the halogen is activated by the adjacent double bond.

A significant improvement in C-alkylation was obtained when water or a mixture of water and methanol was used as a solvent in place of methanol. The alkylation with *n*-alkyl iodides under these conditions shows that the reaction velocity is strongly reduced in contrast to the situation in methanol solution. In the case of methylation with methyl iodide the yield of the C-alkylated product increases from 51.5 to 65% (*28*). The reaction with ethyl iodide gives the same yield as when methanol is used (*29*). With higher alkyl iodides the yield is lowered again. The lower yield is attributed to oxidation phenomena and the cleavage reactions by aqueous alkali which are brought about by the longer reaction time made necessary by working in aqueous solution at high concentration. The reaction products are quite impure and are purified with difficulty.

An essential improvement in the yields of C-alkylated compounds results when halogen compounds with strongly activated halogen are used for alkylation in an aqueous medium. In this case the yields of C-alkylated products increase greatly in contrast to working in methanol. Thus the alkylation of dihydroresorcinol with allyl bromide in aqueous solution gives 2-allyl-1,3-cyclohexanedione in 75% yield in contrast to a yield of 33% in methanol solution. In the same manner the yield in alkylating with benzyl chloride increases from 18 to 70%. It is shown that in all cases in which a satisfactory reactive halogen is at hand the yields in C-alkylation in aqueous solution are significantly higher than in methanol.

In special cases aromatically bound halogen may be used for C-alkylation with success. Under consideration here are those halogen compounds in which the halogen is *ortho* to a carboxyl group. It had been found previously (*30*), that such *o*-halocarboxylic acids are useful in alkylations in the presence of copper salts. In this way Stetter and Siehnhold (*31*) have condensed, in aqueous solution, *o*-bromobenzoic acid and 2,5-dibromoterephthalic acid with dihydroresorcinol. Yields of 54 and 42.5% of C-alkylation were readily obtainable. Owing to a very easy intramolecular lactonization with the formation of cyclic enol ester, it was possible to isolate both lactones XXI and XXV.

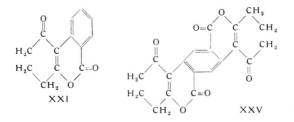

XXI   XXV

Since the 2-alkyl-1,3-cyclohexanediones still have an acidic hydrogen capable of salt formation, the possibility exists of alkylating again to form 2,2-dialkyl-1,3-cyclohexanediones. Stetter and Klauke (*32*) have obtained such dialkyl products through the condensation of 2-alkyl-1,3-

cyclohexanediones with halogen compounds in absolute alcohol. The products differ significantly from the monoalkylated products. Whereas the 2-alkyl-1,3-cyclohexanediones are enolizable because of the available acidic hydrogen, such an enolization is no longer possible with the dialkyl products. Therefore these compounds show a significantly better solubility in nonpolar solvents and in many cases may be distilled without decomposition. Moreover, these compounds prove to be especially sensitive toward aqueous alkali, with which the formation of acids is readily carried out (further details in the section on acid formation). This sensitivity toward alkali leads to a partial cleavage to acid during alkylation in aqueous solvents, therefore the dialkylation is carried out preferably in water-free alcohols.

In one case (*33*) of alkylation in absolute methanol, an alcoholysis resulting in the methyl ester of the δ-oxocarboxylic acid was observed:

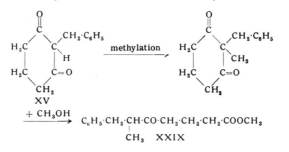

in the methylation of 2-benzyl-1,3-cyclohexanedione, the ester, methyl 6-methyl-7-phenyl-5-oxoheptanoate (XXIX), could be isolated directly.

Essentially, the conditions for alkylation of dihydroresorcinol are suitable for such 1,3-cyclohexanediones which possess alkyl groups in the 4- or 5-position as, for example, dimedone, 5-methyl-1,3-cyclohexane-dione, and 5-phenyl-1,3-cyclohexanedione. Table 4 gives a summary of the 2-alkylated derivatives of 1,3-cyclohexanedione which have been used in the preparation of carboxylic acids.

2. *Alkylation with Carbonyl Compounds*

A simple and important practical method for introducing an organic radical into the 2-position of dihydroresorcinol is shown by the reaction of dihydroresorcinol with aldehydes. The reaction proceeds with the splitting out of 1 mole of water from 2 moles of dihydroresorcinol and 1 mole of aldehyde. Alkylidenedi-1,3-cyclohexanediones having the general formula, G, are formed.

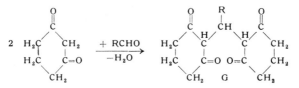

The reaction goes without addition of a condensing agent and in aqueous or alcoholic solution. Since this condensation produces well-crystallized compounds, it is possible to use them for the characterization of aldehydes. The aliphatic aldehydes react most easily, formaldehyde best of all. Methylenedi-1,3-cyclohexanedione (XXXIII) is formed in practically quantitative yield. The reaction proceeds less completely with aromatic aldehydes.

The alkylated 1,3-cyclohexanedione reacts in a manner similar to dihydroresorcinol. It is assumed that both hydrogen atoms are present at the 2-position. With 2 -alkyl-1,3-cyclohexanediones no condensation product with aldehydes could be obtained. The condensation products of dimedone form especially good crystals; for this reason dimedone instead of dihydroresorcinol (*35*) is used for the identification of aldehydes.

Another example of the introduction of an organic radical into the 2-position of dihydroresorcinol was found by H. Stetter and co-workers (*36*). If dihydroresorcinol is heated for 10 hr in an aqueous buffered solution at pH 6, a good crystalline compound is obtained. Analytical data indicate that the molecular weight of the compound is double that for dihydroresorcinol. Apparently it is 1′-hydroxy[bicyclohexyl]-2,3′,6-

TABLE 4

SUMMARY OF 2-SUBSTITUTED 1,3-CYCLOHEXANDIONES PREPARED FROM HALOGEN COMPOUNDS

Halogen compound	β-Diketone	Condensation product	Yield (%)	M.p. (°C)	Ref.
Methyl iodide	Dihydroresorcinol	2-Methyl-1,3-cyclohexanedione (II)	51.5; 65	204°	2, 28
Ethyl iodide	Dihydroresorcinol	2-Ethyl-1,3-cyclohexanedione (III)	27.2	178°	2, 29
n-Propyl iodide	Dihydroresorcinol	2-Propyl-1,3-cyclohexanedione (IV)	26	137°	2
n-Butyl bromide	Dihydroresorcinol	2-Butyl-1,3-cyclohexanedione (V)	18.2	116°	2
n-Butyl iodide	Dihydroresorcinol	2-Butyl-1,3-cyclohexanedione (V)	28.4	116°	2
Cetyl iodide	Dihydroresorcinol	2-Cetyl-1,3-cyclohexanedione (VI)	27.0	73°	2
Allyl bromide	Dihydroresorcinol	2-Allyl-1,3-cyclohexanedione (VII)	75	126°	33
1-Bromo-2-cyclohexene	Dihydroresorcinol	2-Cyclohexenyl-1,3-cyclohexanedione (VIII)	54.5	140°	33
Methyl chloroacetate	Dihydroresorcinol	Methyl 2,6-dioxocyclohexaneacetate (IX)	19	86°	2
Ethyl bromoacetate	Dihydroresorcinol	Ethyl 2,6-dioxocyclohexaneacetate (X)	51	93°	2
Ethyl α-bromopropionate	Dihydroresorcinol	Ethyl 2(2,6-dioxocyclohexane)propionate (XI)	8.7	107°	32
Methyl γ-bromocrotonate	Dihydroresorcinol	Methyl 2,6-dioxocyclohexanecrotonate (XII)	48	158–165°	51
2-Phenoxyethyl iodide	Dihydroresorcinol	2-Phenoxyethyl-1,3-cyclohexanedione (XIII)	11.5	152–3°	54
3-Phenoxypropyl iodide	Dihydroresorcinol	2-(3-Phenoxypropyl)-1,3-cyclohexane-dione (XIV)	17.8	128–130°	54
Benzyl chloride	Dihydroresorcinol	2-Benzyl-1,3-cyclohexanedione (XV)	18; 70	184–5°	33
Phenacyl bromide	Dihydroresorcinol	2-Phenacyl-1,3-cyclohexanedione (XVI)	44	158.5°	51a
p-Methoxybenzyl chloride	Dihydroresorcinol	2-(p-Methoxybenzyl)-1,3-cyclohexane-dione (XVII)	52	69°	2a
o-Nitrobenzyl chloride	Dihydroresorcinol	2-(o-Nitrobenzyl)-1,3-cyclohexanedione (XVIII)	52.2	187° (dec)	55
m-Nitrobenzyl chloride	Dihydroresorcinol	2-(m-Nitrobenzyl)-1,3-cyclohexanedione (XIX)	65.5	192° (dec)	55

p-Nitrobenzyl chloride	Dihydroresorcinol	2-(p-Nitrobenzyl)-1,3-cyclohexanedione (XX)	72.8	238° (dec)	55
o-Bromobenzoic acid	Dihydroresorcinol	Lactone (XXI)	54	172°	31
1,2-Dibromoethane	Dihydroresorcinol	2,2'-Ethylenedi-1,3-cyclohexanedione (XXII)	19	270–1°	51
1,4-Dibromo-2-butene	Dihydroresorcinol	2,2'-(2-Butenylene)di-1,3-cyclohexanedione (XXIII)	69	224° (dec)	33
α,α'-Dichloro-p-xylene	Dihydroresorcinol	2,2'-(p-Phenylenedimethylene)di-1,3-cyclohexanedione (XXIV)	52	300° (dec)	36a, 51
2,5-Dibromoterephthalic acid	Dihydroresorcinol	Dilactone (XXV)	42.5	380° (dec)	31
Ethyl bromoacetate	Dimedone	Methyl 4,4-dimethyl-2,6-dioxocyclohexanecarboxylate (XXVI)	32.5	110.5°	40
Benzyl chloride	Dimedone	2-Benzyl-5,5-dimethyl-1,3-cyclohexanedione (XXVII)	80.4	155°	40
Benzyl iodide	Dimedone	2-Benzyl-5,5-dimethyl-1,3-cyclohexanedione (XXVII)	36	155°	22
Methyl iodide	Dihydroresorcinol	2,2-Dimethyl-1,3-cyclohexanedione (XXVIII)	15	40°	34
Methyl iodide	2-Methyl-1,3-cyclohexanedione	2,2-Dimethyl-1,3-cyclohexanedione (XXVIII)	70.7	40°	34a
Methyl iodide	2-Benzyl-1,3-cyclohexanedione (XV)	Methyl 6-methyl-5-oxo-7-phenylheptanoate (XXIX)	71	b.p. 160°/6 mm	33
n-Butyl iodide	2-Benzyl-1,3-cyclohexanedione (XV)	2-Benzyl-2-butyl-1,3-cyclohexanedione (XXX)	10	89°	32
Allyl bromide	2-Benzyl-1,3-cyclohexanedione (XV)	2-Allyl-2-benzyl-1,3-cyclohexanedione (XXXI)	53.5	69°	32
Benzyl chloride	2-Benzyl-1,3-cyclohexanedione (XV)	2,2-Dibenzyl-1,3-cyclohexanedione (LXV)	69.2	137°	32
Ethyl bromoacetate	2-Methyl-1,3-cyclohexanedione (II)	Ethyl 2,6-dioxo-1-methylcyclohexaneacetate (XXXII)	56.5	67°	32
10-Undecenyl iodide	Dihydroresorcinol	2-(10-Undecen-1-yl)1,3-cyclohexadione (CXXV)	20	—	34b

(continued)

TABLE 4 (*Continued*)

Halogen compound	β-Diketone	Condensation product	Yield (%)	M.p. (°C)	Ref.
Methyl iodide	5-Methyl-1,3-cyclo-hexanedione	2,5-Dimethyl-1,3-cyclohexanedione (CXXVI)	60.7	175.5°	53
Benzyl chloride	5-Methyl-1,3-cyclo-hexanedione	2-Benzyl-5-methyl-1,3-cyclohexanedione (CXXVII)	75	137°	53
Ethyl bromoacetate	5-Methyl-1,3-cyclo-hexanedione	Methyl 2,6-dioxo-4-methylcyclohexane-acetate (CXXVIII)	29.7	94°	53
Phenacyl bromide	2-Methyl-1,3-cyclo-hexandione (II)	2-Methyl-2-phenacyl-1,3-cyclohexane-dione (CXXIX)	44	125-6°	34c
Allyl bromide	2-Allyl-1,3-cyclo-hexanedione (VII)	2,2-Diallyl-1,3cyclohexanedione (CXXX)	70	b.p. 78°/2 mm	34d
Allyl bromide	Dimedone	2-Allyl-5,5-dimethyl-1,3-cyclohexane-dione (CXXXI)	27	147-8°	34d
Benzyl chloride	4,6-Dimethyl-1,3-cyclohexanedione	2-Benzyl-4,6-dimethyl-1,3-cyclohexane-dione (CXXXII)	53	110-20°	34e
—		2,2-Dibenzyl-4,6-dimethyl-1,3-cyclo-hexanedione (CXXXIII)	11	116-8°	34e
Benzyl chloride	4,6-Diethyl-1,3-cyclohexanedione	2-Benzyl-4,6-diethyl-1,3-cyclohexane-dione (CXXXIV)	54	60-3°	34e
Methyl iodide	5-Phenyl-1,3-cyclo-hexanedione	2-Methyl-5-phenyl-1,3-cyclohexane-dione (CXXXV)	53.5	214°	53
Benzyl chloride	5-Phenyl-1,3-cyclo-hexanedione	2-Benzyl-5-phenyl-1,3-cyclohexane-dione (CXXXVI)	62	172.5°	53
Ethyl bromoacetate	5-Phenyl-1,3-cyclo-hexanedione	Ethyl 2,6-dioxo-4-phenylcyclohexane-acetate (CXXXVII)	34	209°	9, 53
Methyl iodide	3,5-Dioxocyclo-hexanecarboxylic acid	3,5-Dioxo-4-methylcyclohexanecarboxylic acid (CXXXVIII)	38	229°	53
Allyl bromide	3,5-Dioxocyclo-hexanecarboxylic acid	4-Allyl-3,5-dioxocyclohexanecarboxylic acid (CXXXIX)	51.8	169°	53

trione (XXXIV) which is formed by an aldol condensation between two molecules of dihydroresorcinol. With concentrated sulfuric acid water is split out intramolecularly. Formulas H and J are possible. This may

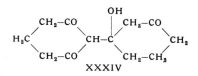

XXXIV

argue for a three-carbon tautomerism. Catalytic hydrogenation converts the compound to [bicyclohexyl]-2,3′,6-trione (XXXV), which is obtained readily in good yield.

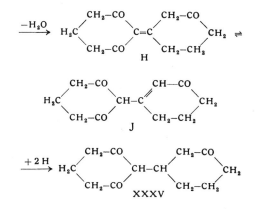

XXXV

Alkylation by Michael Addition

Another simple means for the preparation of 2-substituted dihydroresorcinols exists because dihydroresorcinol, possessing an acidic hydrogen, may undergo Michael addition with α,β-unsaturated ketones, carboxylic esters, and nitriles. A Michael adduct of dihydroresorcinol was first appeared by Mikhailov (37). Mikhailov obtained the expected adduct (XXXVI) by the addition of dihydroresorcinol to benzalacetophenone under the catalytic influence of piperidine.

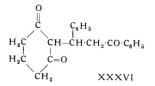

XXXVI

Stetter and Coenen (38) were able to obtain similar adducts with benzalacetone, ethyl acrylate, and acrylonitrile. The addition occurs in absolute alcohols in the presence of alcoholates. Because of the acidity of dihydroresorcinol it is found necessary to use larger amounts of alkali as catalyst than is usual with the Michael addition reaction.

Addition of dihydroresorcinol to benzalacetone gives 1,6-dioxo-4a-hydroxy-8-phenyldecahydronaphthalene, which is formed by cyclic aldol condensation of the primary adduct (XXXVII).

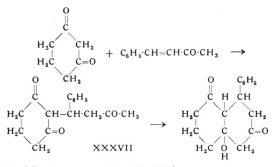

The yields of adducts amount to 40–70%.

Nazarov and Zav'yalov (39), in the Michael addition of dihydroresorcinol with excess methyl vinyl ketone in methanol and with the addition of potassium hydroxide, obtained the adduct XXXIX, formed from 1 mole of dihydroresorcinol and 2 moles of methyl vinyl ketone, as well as the simple adduct XL.

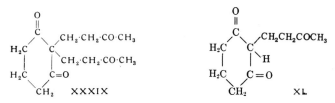

They were able to obtain product XLIII in small yield by the addition of 2 moles of 2-methyl-1,3-cyclohexanedione to 1 mole of divinyl ketone.

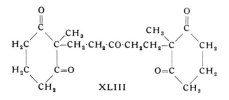

Dimedone also may be used in the Michael addition reaction. Such additions have succeeded with ethyl acrylate (40) and with methyl vinyl ketone (39). In Table 5 are listed the 2-substituted-1,3-cyclohexanediones prepared by Michael addition.

TABLE 5

SUMMARY OF MICHAEL ADDUCTS OF 1,3-CYCLOHEXANEDIONES

Unsaturated compound	β-Diketone	Adduct	Yield (%)	M.p. (°C)	(b.p. °C/mm)	Ref.
1 Mole Methyl vinyl ketone	1 Mole Dihydroresorcinol	XL	39	—	(137–40°/0.2)	39
2 Mole Methyl vinyl ketone	1 Mole Dihydroresorcinol	XXXIX	36	—	(140–3°/0.5)	39
1 Mole Benzalacetone	1 Mole Dihydroresorcinol	XXXVII	50	127°	—	38
1 Mole Benzalacetophenone	1 Mole Dihydroresorcinol	XXXVI	—	—	—	37
1 Mole Methyl vinyl ketone	1 Mole Dimedone	XLI	52	100–1°	—	39
2 Mole Methyl vinyl ketone	1 Mole Dimedone	XLII	43	106–7°	—	39
1 Mole Divinyl ketone	2 Mole 1-Methyl-2,6-cyclohexanedione	XLIII	27	100–1°	—	39
1 Mole Ethyl acrylate	1 Mole Dihydroresorcinol	XLIV	42	128°	—	38
1 Mole Ethyl acrylate	1 Mole Dimedone	XLV	32.5	164.5°	—	40
1 Mole Acrylonitrile	1 Mole Dihydroresorcinol	XLVI	60.5	—	—	38, 38a
1 Mole Acrylonitrile	1 Mole Dimedone	XLVII	44	150–1	—	40a
2 Mole Nitroethylene	1 Mole Dihydroresorcinol	CXL	31.5	146–8° (dec)	—	40b
1 Mole Nitrostyrene	1 Mole Dihydroresorcinol	CXLI	72	165–7° (dec)	—	40b
1 Mole 1-Nitro-1-propene	1 Mole Dihydroresorcinol	CXLII	52	164–6° (dec)	—	40b

The Michael addition could also be realized between dihydroresorcinol and nitroolefins (40b). By using nitroethylene, 2,2-bis(2-nitro-
ethyl)-1,3-cyclohexanedione (CXL) was the only reaction product
obtained. The addition of dihydroresorcinol to β-nitrostyrene and 1-
nitro-1-propene gave crystalline reaction products which contained one
molecule of water less than that of the expected adduct. It is shown that
these compounds are 4-phenyl- and 4-methyl-5-oxo-5,6,7,8-tetrahydro-
1,2,4,-benzoxazine N-oxide (CXLI and CXLII) which are formed from
the initial adducts through spontaneous splitting out of water.

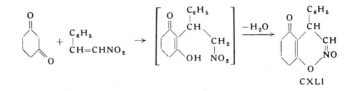

CXLI

Other Methods

In this section reference will be made to other methods for the
preparation of 2-alkyl-1,3-cyclohexanediones, although these methods
have not been used in the synthesis of carboxylic acids.

By reaction of dihydroresorcinol with carboxylic acid anhydrides in
the presence of the alkali salts of the corresponding acid or in the presence of pyridine, the 2-position of dihydroresorcinol is acylated. Such
2-acyl-1,3-cyclohexanediones can be obtained in reasonably good yields
(41).

Smith (42) has subjected 2-acetyl-1,3-cyclohexanedione to catalytic
hydrogenation under a variety of conditions. Hydrogenation with palladium on charcoal furnishes 1-acetyl-2-cyclohexanone as the main
product, along with a small amount of 2-ethyl-1,3-cyclohexanedione
(III). If increasing amounts of sodium hydroxide are added to the
hydrogenation mixture the amount of 1-acetyl-2-cyclohexanone decreases, and the quantity of 2-ethyl-1,3-cyclohexanedione (III) increases.
With a molar quantity of alkali the yield becomes 45% of the
theoretical.

It is assumed that in a similar manner other 2-acyl-1,3-cyclohex-
anediones can be reduced to 2-alkyl-1,3-cyclohexanediones. This offers
another approach to the syntheses of 2-alkyl-1,3-cyclohexanediones.

The preparation of 2-alkylated dihydroresorcinols from the resorcinol
dimethyl ether is also possible. Hydrogenation with sodium and alcohol
in liquid ammonia gives the dimethyl ether of 2,5-dihydroresorcinol. The
latter forms a potassium salt (K) on treatment with potassium amide

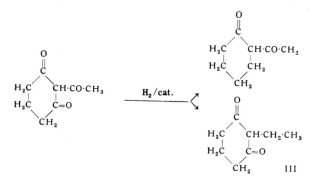

in liquid ammonia; on condensation with methyl iodide in liquid ammonia, followed by hydrolysis, 2-methyl-1,3-cyclohexanedione (II) is obtained in 43.7% yield (*43*).

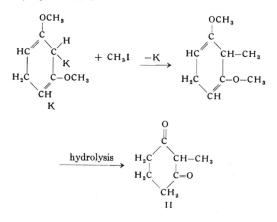

In a similar manner condensation with β-phenethyl bromide and β-(*m*-methoxyphenyl)ethyl bromide yields 2-phenethyl-1,3-cyclohexanedione (*43*) and 2-[β-(*m*-methoxyphenyl)ethyl]-1,3-cyclohexanedione (*44*), respectively. Another method for the preparation of 2-alkyl-1,3-cyclohexanediones is given in the section, "Methods of Lettré and Jahn."

A further interesting possibility for direct alkylation of dihydroresorcinol is offered through the peroxide-catalyzed addition of alkenes to dihydroresorcinol. 2-Octyl-1,3-cyclohexanedione was obtained in 23% yield from dihydroresorcinol and 1-octene in benzene in the presence of diacetyl peroxide (*44a*).

The possibility of introducing organic nitrogen-containing radicals is shown in the condensation of *N*-hydroxymethylphthalimide with dihydroresorcinol and dimedone in the presence of concentrated sulfuric acid

(*44b*). In a smooth reaction 2-phthalimidomethyl-1,3-cyclohexanedione (CXLIII) and the corresponding dimedone derivative are obtained.

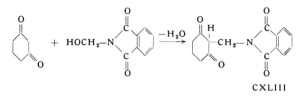

CXLIII

For these amidomethylations other N-methylolamides, such as benzamidomethanol, bis(benzensulfonamido)methane, and α,α-bis(benzamido)toluene are suitable.

The compound CXLIII is well suited for the introduction of the methylenedihydroresorcinol radical into compounds containing an acidic hydrogen (—CH). Thus the condensation of CXLIII with acetamidomalonic ester in the presence of an equivalent amount of sodium alcoholate gives dimethyl 2-dihydroresorcylmethyl(acetamido)malonate (CXLIV) (*44c*).

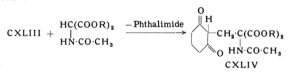

CXLIV

Using CXLIII and 2-(*p*-toluenesulfonamidomethyl)-1,3-cyclohexanedione, analogous condensations were carried out with various compounds containing an acidic hydrogen.

SECOND STEP OF THE REACTION: CLEAVAGE OF
1,3-CYCLOHEXANEDIONES TO ACIDS

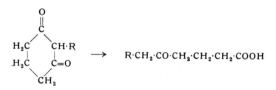

The formation of acid as the second step of the carboxylic acid synthesis could be readily achieved by Stetter and Dierichs (*2*) with all of the 2-alkyl-1,3-cyclohexanediones which they had prepared; this offers a simple procedure for obtaining δ-oxo acids in good yields. Barium hydroxide appears to be the best for the acid cleavage. It is possible to carry out the reaction with sodium or potassium hydroxide. The yields of δ-oxo acids from the simple 2-alkyl-1,3-cyclohexanediones range be-

tween 70 and 80%. The yields are somewhat lower with the unsaturated
δ-oxo acids.

The initially formed oxo acids are not obtained when the acid
cleavage leads to dioxo acids, in which the oxo groups are found in the
1,4- or 1,5-positions. These dioxo acids, by the action of alkali, undergo
a cyclic aldol condensation to form carboxylic acids of the cyclopen-
tenone and cyclohexenone series. Examples are the splitting of 2-phen-
acyl-1,3-cyclohexanedione (XVI) and methylenedi-1,3-cyclohexanedione
(XXXIII). In place of the expected 8-phenyl-5,8-dioxooctanoic acid
(L), 5-oxo-2-phenyl-1-cyclopentene-1-propionic acid [XLVIII] (*31a*),
the product of the cyclic aldol condensation of the expected acid, is
obtained. In a corresponding manner 4-methyl-5-oxo-2-phenyl-1-cyclo-
pentene-1-propionic acid (CL) is obtained from CXXIX (*34c*).

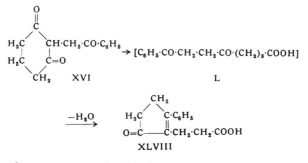

The analogous course of acid cleavage of methylenedi-1,3-cyclohex-
anedione (XXXIII) is discussed in the section on "Reductive Acid
Cleavage."

The acid cleavage of 2,2-dialkyl-1,3-cyclohexanediones goes especially smoothly and leads to formation of δ-oxo acids branched in the
six position.

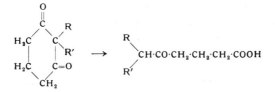

Whereas it is necessary to heat the 2-alkyl-1,3-cyclohexanediones for
30 hr in strong aqueous alkali for complete acid cleavage, the cleavage
of the 2,2-dialkyl-1,3-cyclohexanediones under the same conditions takes
place in a few minutes (*32*). As a result of the facile cleavage, which
requires shorter contact with alkali, the yields of the branched δ-oxo
acids are mostly over 90% of theory.

The ready cleavage also permits the alcoholysis of these compounds to form the corresponding esters of the δ-oxo acids.

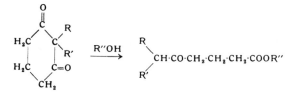

This may be compared with the methylation of 2-benzyl-1,3-cyclo-hexanedione in sections, "Alkylation with Organic Halogen Compounds," and, "Michael Addition with Simultaneous Ring Opening."

Table 6 lists the δ-oxo acids obtained by the cleavage with alkali.

TABLE 6

SUMMARY OF OXO ACIDS OBTAINED THROUGH CLEAVAGE WITH ALKALI

β-Diketone	Oxo acid	Yield (%)	M.p. (°C)	Ref.
I	5-Oxohexanoic acid (XLIX)	—	—	1
II	5-Oxoheptanoic acid (L)	78.2	50°	2
III	5-Oxooctanoic acid (LI)	76	34°	2
IV	5-Oxononanoic acid (LII)	81	40°	2
V	5-Oxodecanoic acid (LIII)	81.9	57–8°	2
VI	5-Oxodocosanoic acid (LIV)	77.5	94°	2
VII	5-Oxo-8-nonenoic acid (LV)	61	28°	33
X	4-Oxooctanedioic acid (LVI)	83	123°	2
XII	5-Oxodecanedioic acid (LVII)	88	116°	51
XV	5-Oxo-7-phenylheptanoic acid (LVIII)	78	58°	33
XXL	6-(2-Carboxyphenyl)-5-oxohexanoic acid (LIX)	96	134°	31
XXIV	δ,δ-Dioxo-p-benzenediheptanoic acid (LX)	81	157°	51
XXV	2,5-Dicarboxy-δ,δ'-dioxo-p-benzenedihexanoic acid (LXI)	53	242°	31
XXVIII	6-Methyl-5-oxoheptanoic acid (LXII)	—	—	—
XXX	6-Benzyl-5-oxodecanoic acid (LXIII)	96	73°	32
XXXI	6-Benzyl-5-oxo-8-nonenoic acid (LXIV)	92.5	40°	32
LXV	6-Benzyl-5-oxo-7-phenylheptanoic acid (LXVI)	97	83°	32

Recently it was discovered that the acid cleavage of 1,3-cyclohexane-diones could be realized in a simple manner and with better yields, if constant boiling hydrochloric acid (see Table 7) is used in place of alkali. The oxo acids prepared in this manner are obtained directly from the reaction mixture in a high degree of purity (44).

A further advantage of the method is that the Michael adduct of dihydroresorcinol (useful in the reductive acid-cleavage procedure) furnishes high yields of δ-oxo acids, while with alkali cleavage these acids

are not formed. The same is true for 2-phthalimidomethyldihydroresor-
cinol (CXLIII). Also, cleavage of this compound to 7-amino-5-oxohep-
tanoic acid (CIL) could be achieved only with hydrochloric acid (44c).
Noteworthy in this connection is the result of the action of hydro-

TABLE 7

SUMMARY OF OXO ACIDS OBTAINED BY CLEAVAGE WITH HYDROCHLORIC ACID

β-Diketone	Oxo acid	Yield (%)	M.p. (°C)	Ref.
X	4-Oxooctanedioic acid (LVI)	89	131–2°	44d
XLIV	5-Oxononanedioic acid (CXLVII)	90.9	110°	44d
XII	5-Oxodecanedioic acid (LVII)	91.9	116°	44d
CXLI	4-Oxo-2-phenyloctanedioic acid (CXLVIII)	26.5	146–8°	40b
CXLIII	7-Amino-5-oxoheptanoic acid (CIL)	75	116–8°	44c

chloric acid on CXLIV. In place of the expected α-amino-δ-oxoazelaic
acid, a mixture of 2,3,4,5,6,7-hexahydro-4-indolone-2-carboxylic acid
(CXLV) and 2-carboxy-Δ²-pyrroline-5-butyric acid (CXLVI) is obtained. This agrees with the tendency of γ-aminoketones to readily
undergo intramolecular loss of water with the formation of a pyrroline
ring system (44c).

The treatment of CXLI with hydrochloric acid eliminates the nitro
group and furnishes 4-oxo-2-phenyloctanedioic acid (CXLVIII) (40b).

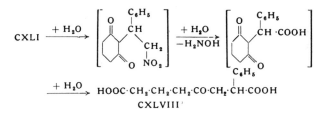

THIRD STEP OF THE REACTION: REDUCTION OF δ-OXO ACIDS

$$R \cdot CH_2 \cdot CO \cdot CH_2 \cdot CH_2 \cdot CH_2 \cdot COOH \rightarrow R \cdot CH_2 \cdot CH_2 \cdot CH_2 \cdot CH_2 \cdot CH_2 \cdot COOH$$

For the third step of the reaction sequence, the reduction of the
carbonyl group in the δ-oxo acids to the methylene group, only two
methods of practical importance are considered: the Clemmensen and
the Wolff-Kishner reduction.

The Clemmensen reduction is basically suited for the reduction
of δ-oxo acids; however, the yields are seldom higher than 50% of
theory.

The Wolff-Kishner reduction, which depends upon the splitting off of hydrazone nitrogen by means of alkali, is significantly better. According to Soffer and Sherk (*45*), as well as Huang-Minlon (*46*), the hydrazone formation and the splitting out of nitrogen take place in a high-boiling solvent, especially diethyleneglycol. In this manner the irksome sealed-tube reactions are avoided. The formation of hydrazones and the splitting out of nitrogen can be accomplished by ordinary heating under reflux.

With these methods it is possible to convert the δ-oxo acids to the reduced carboxylic acids (*2*). The yields are mostly 80–95% of theory. Unfortunately, in the case of δ-oxo acids possessing an alkene double bond, the yields are lower (65–75%). Probably these acids undergo partial decomposition under the influence of the alkali. A particular advantage of the Wolff-Kishner reduction over the Clemmensen reduction lies in the fact that the reduced acid is obtained in a decidedly purer state.

Reductive Acid Cleavage

An important simplification of the original three-step procedure was found by Stetter and Dierichs (*47*). If the C-alkylated 1,3-cyclohexane-diones are subjected to the Wolff-Kishner reduction, the reduced, open-chain carboxylic acids are obtained directly in one operation. The explanation is simple: In the first phase of the Wolff-Kishner reduction in diethyleneglycol, the compound to be reduced is refluxed with an alkali hydroxide and hydrazine. Under these conditions, however, acid cleavage occurs by the action of the alkali. The resulting δ-oxo acid, in the presence of the hydrazine, is immediately converted to the hydrazone, which in the normal manner loses nitrogen to give the reduced carboxylic acid. By this a three-step procedure becomes a two-step one. The synthesis narrows down to alkylation and reductive acid cleavage.

There is, however, yet a further advantage: the yields with the reductive acid-cleavage procedure are higher than when the acid cleavage and reduction are carried out separately. For example, in the case of the simple 1-alkyl-2,6-cyclohexanediones, the over-all yield using separate operations is about 65%, while with the reductive acid cleavage method the yield is 85% of theory. The higher yields can be explained by the fact that in this procedure the synthesized δ-oxo acids are converted

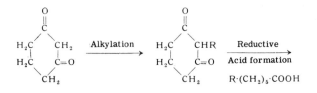

immediately into hydrazone derivatives, and therefore secondary changes are minimized, such changes being unavoidable in a procedure requiring long contact with alkali.

In some cases the reductive acid cleavage procedure was the only way in which the reduced carboxylic acid could be obtained. An illustrative example is the preparation of brassylic acid from methylenedi-1,3-cyclohexanedione (XXXIII). The preparation by acid cleavage from methylenedi-1,3-cyclohexanedione had been investigated by Vorländer (48). Under mild conditions Vorländer opened one of the two dihydroresorcinol rings to form the oxo acid, M. Stronger conditions gave an acid which contained 1 mole of water less than to be found in the expected 5,9-dioxotridecanedioic acid, N. Under the influence of alkali, an intramolecular splitting out of water occurred, in which the acid O was formed. Stetter and Dierichs (47) subjected methylenedi-1,3-cyclohexanedione to the reductive acid-cleavage procedure and obtained a

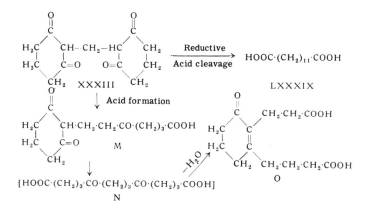

practically quantitative yield of the desired brassylic acid (LXXXIX). Under the conditions of the reductive acid-cleavage procedure, the initially formed diketodicarboxylic acid is immediately converted to the hydrazone and it loses thereby the ability to undergo intramolecular cyclization.

Michael adducts of 1,3-cyclohexanedione can also be converted to long-chain carboxylic acids by the reductive acid-cleavage procedure (38). The attempt to obtain the δ-oxo acids from these adducts by the acid-cleavage procedure using alkali, leads instead to the splitting of the adduct into its original components. For example, the adduct of dihydroresorcinol and benzalacetone (XXXVII) on heating with barium hydroxide, splits to form benzalacetone and dihydroresorcinol, which then is subject to the acid-cleavage reaction to form δ-oxocaproic acid.

The use of the reductive acid-cleavage procedure gives the expected 7-phenyldecanoic acid (LXVII).

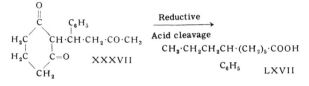

Michael Addition with Simultaneous Ring Opening

Subjecting 2-alkyl-1,3-cyclohexanediones to the Michael addition using α,β-unsaturated carbonyl compounds or nitriles in absolute alcohol in the presence of sodium or potassium alcoholate yields the esters of the open-chain δ-oxo acids and the expected adducts are not obtained (49, 50). This course of reaction is understandable, if one bears in mind that the dialkylated dihydroresorcinols undergo acid cleavage much more readily. Under the conditions of the Michael addition the adducts first formed, which correspond to the dialkylated products, undergo an alcoholysis with ring opening and form the esters of the open-chain δ-oxo acids. The addition of acrylonitrile to 2-methyl-1,3-cyclohexane-dione, which leads to ethyl 8-cyano-6-methyl-5-oxocapric acid (LXVIII) (49) may serve as an example.

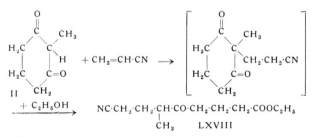

The yields amount to 60–70% and are thus higher than in the case of the true Michael addition. The course of the reaction may be explained by the fact that the equilibrium of the Michael addition is favorably influenced by the alcoholysis of the adduct.

As components of these reactions 2-methyl-1,3-cyclohexanedione (II), 2-ethyl-1,3-cyclohexanedione (III), 2-benzyl-1,3-cyclohexanedione (XV), ethyl acrylate, acrylonitrile, and diethyl maleate have been used.

The same course of action may be observed if dihydroresorcinol is added directly to 2 moles of the reactive component under the reaction conditions described above. An example is the addition of dihydroresorcinol to 2 moles of ethyl acrylate to form the triethyl ester of the oxotricarboxylic acid (LXIX) (50).

TABLE 8

SUMMARY OF OXO ACID ESTERS OBTAINED BY MICHAEL ADDITION AND SIMULTANEOUS RING CLEAVAGE

Unsaturated compounds	β-Diketone	Ester of oxo acids	Yield (%)	Ref.
Ethyl acrylate	2-Ethyl-1,3-cyclohexanedione (III)	Diethyl 4-ethyl-5-oxononanedioate (LXX)	62	50
Ethyl acrylate	2-Allyl-1,3-cyclohexanedione (VII)	Diethyl 4-allyl-5-oxononanedioate (LXXI)	66	49
Ethyl acrylate	2-Benzyl-1,3-cyclohexanedione (XV)	Diethyl 4-benzyl-5-oxononanedioate (LXXII)	61	50
Diethyl maleate	2-Methyl-1,3-cyclohexanedione (II)	Triethyl 3-methyl-4-oxo-1,2,7-heptanetricarboxylate (LXXIII)	62	50
Acrylonitrile	2-Methyl-1,3-cyclohexanedione (II)	Ethyl 8-cyano-6-methyl-5-oxooctanoate (LXVIII)	63	49
Acrylonitrile	2-Allyl-1,3-cyclohexanedione (VII)	Ethyl 6-(2-cyanoethyl)-5-oxo-8-nonenoate (LXXIV)	63	49
Ethyl acrylate (2 moles)	Dihydroresorcinol (2 moles)	Diethyl 4-(2-carbethoxyethyl)-5-oxononanedioate (LXIX)	64.5	50

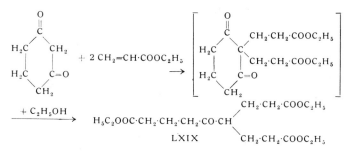

The branched-chain δ-oxo acids, as prepared above, can be converted to the reduced acids through the Wolff-Kishner reduction. This makes it possible to obtain branched-chain acids from a two-step reaction sequence, consisting of the Michael addition, with its simultaneous ring opening, followed by a Wolff-Kishner. This two-step sequence differs from the previously described two-step sequence in that the first two steps of the original three-step reaction are carried out in a single operation.

The esters of oxocyano acids, obtained by the addition of acrylonitrile, are simultaneously reduced and saponified in the Wolff-Kishner to yield branched-chain azelaic acids.

Table 8 summarizes reactions of this type which have been carried out.

Preparation of Straight-Chain Monocarboxylic Acids

Foremost in the preparation of straight-chain, saturated monocarboxylic acids is the reductive acid cleavage of the 2-alkyl 1,3-cyclohexanediones, obtainable through the condensation of alkyl iodides with dihydroresorcinol. The yields with the reductive acid cleavage amount to approximately 85%, while in the three-step procedure they are less. A disadvantage lies in the fact that the first step, the alkylation of dihydroresorcinol with alkyl iodides, furnishes only about a 27% yield of the 2-alkyl-1,3-cyclohexanediones. An exception is the alkylation with methyl iodides, which goes in 65% yields.

The results in the preparation of 7,8-unsaturated monocarboxylic acids are more favorable, for the C-alkylation of dihydroresorcinol with unsaturated halogen compounds (e.g., allyl bromide) occurs with much better yields than with the corresponding saturated halogen compound. The presence of the double bond leads to a somewhat smaller yield in the reductive acid cleavage of the unsaturated condensation products.

The yields of unsaturated carboxylic acids amount to about 65–75% of theory. Unsaturated acids of this type have been prepared from allyl bromide (*33*) and 1-bromo-2-cyclohexane (*33*).

$$\text{H}_2\text{C} \overset{\overset{\displaystyle \text{O}}{\underset{\displaystyle \text{C}}{\|}}}{\diagdown} \text{CH·CH}_2\text{·CH=CHR}$$

$$\text{H}_2\text{C} \quad \text{C=O} \quad \rightarrow \quad \text{R·CH=CH·CH}_2\text{·CH}_2\text{·CH}_2\text{·CH}_2\text{·CH}_2\text{·COOH}$$

$$\underset{\text{CH}_2}{\diagup}$$

The method for the preparation of 7-arylheptanoic acids is especially advantageous, because C-alkylation of dihydroresorcinol by halides of the benzyl chloride type goes very smoothly. With reductive acid cleavage of the condensation product, the yields of 7-arylheptanoic acids are over 90% (*33*).

$$\text{H}_2\text{C} \overset{\overset{\displaystyle \text{O}}{\underset{\displaystyle \text{C}}{\|}}}{\diagdown} \text{CH·CH}_2\text{·C}_6\text{H}_5$$

$$\text{H}_2\text{C} \quad \text{C=O} \quad \longrightarrow \quad \text{C}_6\text{H}_5\text{·(CH}_2\text{)}_6\text{·COOH}$$

$$\underset{\underset{\displaystyle \text{XV}}{\text{CH}_2}}{\diagup} \qquad\qquad\qquad \text{LXXV}$$

Reductive acid cleavage of the condensation products from α-halo-ketones and dihydroresorcinol does not lead to long-chain carboxylic acids. Stetter and Siehnhold (*31a*) attempted to convert 2-phenacyl-1,3-cyclohexanedione, obtained from phenacyl bromide and dihydroresorcinol, to 9-phenylnonanoic acid by the reductive acid-cleavage method. The acid was not obtainable in this manner. The failure is traced to the 1,4-position of the carbonyl groups, which makes dihydrazone formation impossible.

A special case is the preparation of 6-cyclohexylhexanoic acid (LXXXVI) (*36*) from [bicyclohexyl]-2,3′,6-trione (XXXV). The reductive acid cleavage of the trione gives a yield of 96% of the acid through the simultaneous reduction of the two carbonyl groups.

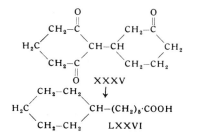

Preparation of Dicarboxylic Acids

Fundamentally there are two possibilities for the preparation of long-chain dicarboxylic acids by the methods described. It is possible to introduce a carboxyl group into the 2-position of dihydroresorcinol, followed by acid formation and reduction. Dicarboxylic acids are formed which are six carbon atoms longer than the acid portion originally introduced.

The second possibility lies in the suitable alkylation of dihydroresorcinol so that two dihydroresorcinol groups are combined in one compound, followed by acid cleavage and reduction. In this manner a chain-lengthening of twelve carbon atoms is attained.

By the first method a 98% yield of suberic acid (LXXXV) can be obtained by the condensation of dihydroresorcinol with ethyl bromoacetate to form ethyl 2,6-dioxocyclohexaneacetate (X), followed by reductive acid cleavage (47).

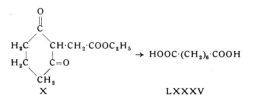

Sebacic acid may be obtained by the condensation of dihydroresorcinol with methyl 4-bromocrotonate to form methyl 2,6-dioxocyclohexanecrotonate (XII) which is catalytically reduced to form the saturated ester (LXXXVI). The latter is subjected to the reductive acid cleavage reaction (51).

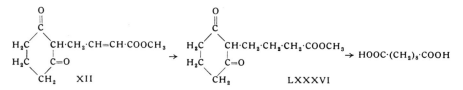

From the Michael reaction adduct, XLIV, of dihydroresorcinol and ethyl acrylate, azelaic acid is obtained by the reductive acid cleavage in 69% yield (38).

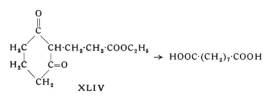

In a similar manner azelaic acid is obtained from the adduct of dihydroresorcinol and acrylonitrile (XLVI); the nitrile group is saponified during the formation of the acid (38).

An especially impressive example of lengthening a chain by twelve carbon atoms is that given in the section on "Reductive Acid Cleavage," in which it was shown that brassylic acid (LXXXIX) was obtained practically in quantitative yield from methylenedi-1,3-cyclohexanedione (XXXIII) (47).

The attempt to form two-ring condensation products from α,ω-dihalogen compounds was successful only in the case of 1,2-dibromoethane. 2,2'-Ethylenedi-1,3-cyclohexanedione (XXII) is obtained in 19% yield. Using the reductive acid cleavage reaction tetradecanedioic acid (XC) is obtained in 85% yield (51).

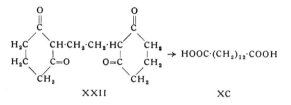

From the statements in the section "Alkylation" it would be expected that the preparation of two-ring condensation products of dihydroresorcinol is more likely if dihalogen compounds are chosen in which the halogen atoms are activated by an adjacent double bond. The simplest compound which fulfills this requirement is 1,4-dibromo-2-butene, which is readily available by the addition of bromine to butadiene. The condensation of this dibromide with dihydroresorcinol gives the product (XXIII) in 69% yield. By reductive acid cleavage 8-hexadecenedioic acid (XCI) is obtained in 79% yield. Catalytic reduction of the unsaturated acid readily furnishes thapsic acid (XCII) (33).

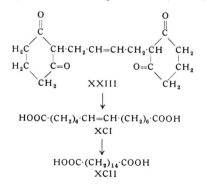

It is possible to obtain a long-chain dicarboxylic acid containing a benzene ring in the middle of the chain by the condensation of α,α'-dichloro-p-xylene with dihydroresorcinol to form 2,2'(p-phenylenedimethylene)di-1,3-cyclohexanedione (XXIV), which is subjected to the reductive acid-cleavage reaction (51).

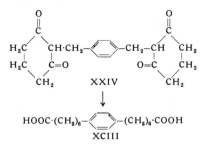

Preparation of Branched-Chain Mono-, Di- and Polycarboxylic Acids

For the preparation of branched-chain carboxylic acids two possibilities are of importance. In the first instance dihydroresorcinol is the starting material and the branched-chain radical is introduced into the 2-position or both hydrogen atoms on the 2-C may be replaced by hydrocarbon radicals. The cleavage and reduction of these condensation products leads to branched-chain carboxylic acids. The second possibility depends on the fact that in place of dihydroresorcinol such 1,3-cyclohexandiones may be used which are substituted in the 4- or 5-position with hydrocarbon radicals. In this case cleavage and reduction of the condensation products also gives branched-chain acids.

Preparation Starting with Dihydroresorcinol

The introduction of a branched-chain hydrocarbon radical into the 2-position of dihydroresorcinol is possible by the condensation of a suitable halogen compound as well as by an addition reaction.

Examples of the preparation of branched-chain acids, starting from such condensation products, are the preparation of α-methylsuberic acid (XCIX) and 7-phenyldecanoic acid (LXVII). α-Methylsuberic acid (XCIX) was prepared by the reductive cleavage of the condensation product (XI) obtained from dihydroresorcinol and ethyl α-bromopropionate (32).

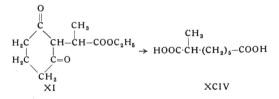

7-Phenyldecanoic acid (LXVII) is obtained by the reductive cleavage of the Michael adduct from dihydroresorcinol and benzalacetone (*38*).

Starting with the two acetones XXI and XXV, obtained by the condensation of dihydroresorcinol with *o*-bromobenzoic acid and 2,5-dibromoterephthalic acid, respectively, the dicarboxylic acid, CXIII, and the tetracarboxylic acid, CXVI, can be obtained (*31*).

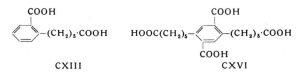

CXIII   CXVI

Cleavage and reduction of the dialkylated products of dihydroresorcinol furnish acids with branching in the 6-position (*32*).

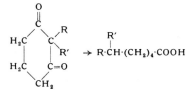

Starting with 2-allyl-2-benzyl-1,3-cyclohexanedione (XXXI), 2,2-dibenzyl-1,3-cyclohexanedione (LXV), and ethyl 2,6-dioxo-1-methyl-cyclohexaneacetate (XXXII), the following acids can be obtained: 6-benzyl-8-nonenoic acid (XCVIII), 6-benzyl-7-phenylheptanoic acid (XCVII), and β-methylsuberic acid (C).

A further excellent possibility for the preparation of acids branched in the 6-position is offered by the simultaneous alcoholysis during the Michael reaction between 2-alkyl-1,3-cyclohexanediones and α,β-unsaturated carbonyl compounds and nitriles. For details see the section, "Michael Reaction with Simultaneous Ring Opening." By saponification and reduction of the δ-oxo acids described in that section, the reduced, branched-chain acids are obtained without difficulty.

Preparation Starting with 4- or 5-Alkylated 1,3-Cyclohexanediones

If in place of dihydroresorcinol such 1,3-cyclohexanediones are used which possess a hydrocarbon radical in the 4- or 5-position, it is to be expected that acids branched in the 2-, 3- or 4-position will be obtained. The cleavage of 4-substituted 1,3-cyclohexanediones can occur in two directions. In one case α-substituted δ-oxo acids are formed, in the other, γ-substituted δ-oxo acids.

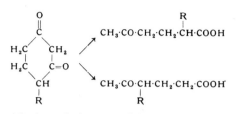

Experiments with 4-methyl-1,3-cyclohexanedione (*52*) show that with cleavage both possible δ-oxo acids are obtained and their complete separation is difficult. The use of 4-substituted 1,3-cyclohexanediones generally offers the possibility of preparing α- and γ-branched-chain acids. Because of the difficulty in separating the isomeric acids this method can hardly be recommended for preparative purposes. It is quite possible that with suitable substitution on the 2- or 4-carbon, one of the two cleavage pathways may be preferred. The results with 5-substituted 1,3-cyclohexadiones are more favorable. Here the cleavage and reduction leads clearly to long-chain acids branched in the β-position. The most familiar compound of this type, 5,5-dimethyl-1,3-cyclohexanedione (dimedone) has been applied to the preparation of β,β-dimethyl acids.

Dimedone itself gives β,β-dimethylcaprylic acid (XCIV). The C-alkylated dimedones such as 2-benzyl-5,5-dimethyl-1,3-cyclohexanedione (XXVII) and methyl 4,4-dimethyl-2,6-dioxocyclohexanecarboxylate (XXVI) also form the corresponding β,β-dimethyl-branched acids, 7-phenyl-3,3-dimethylheptanoic acid (XCVI) and β,β-dimethylsuberic acid (CI).

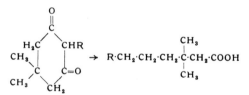

By the reductive cleavage of the easily accessible methylene bisdimedones (from formaldehyde and dimedone), β,β,β′,β′-tetramethylbrassylic acid (CXII) is obtained (*40*).

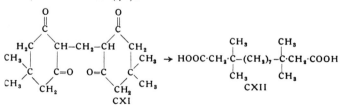

Since dimedone undergoes the Michael reaction, β,β-dimethyl acids may be obtained by the reductive cleavage of the adduct, as in the case of dihydroresorcinol. An example is the reductive cleavage of the adduct (XLV), from dimedone and ethyl acrylate, which gives β,β-dimethyl-azelaic acid (CIII) (40).

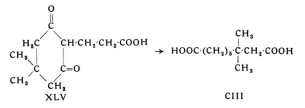

Further examples of the preparation of β-branched acids are the reductive cleavages of 2,2'-methylenebis(5-methyl-1,3-cyclohexane-dione) (CVII) and 2,2'-methylenebis(5-phenyl-1,3-cyclohexanedione) (CIX), both of which are readily obtained by the formaldehyde condensation of 5-methyl-1,3-cyclohexanedione and 5-phenyl-1,3-cyclohex-anedione. As reaction products β,β-dimethylbrassylic acid (CVIII) and β,β-diphenylbrassylic acid (CX) (53) are obtained.

If in place of 4-alkylated dihydroresorcinols, the 4,6-dialkyl (alike) substituted dihydroresorcinols are used, then reductive cleavage uniformly gives α,γ-disubstituted long chain acids.

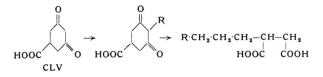

Such syntheses have been carried out with 4,6-dimethyl-1,3-cyclo-hexanedione (CLI) and 4,6-diethyl-1,3-cyclohexanedione (CLII) (34e). These two diones are usually converted through formaldehyde condensation to 2,2'-methylenebis-(4,6-dimethyl-1,3-cyclohexanedione) (CLIII) and 2,2'-methylenebis (4,6-diethyl-1,3-cyclohexanedione) (CLIV); reductive cleavage gives the $\alpha,\alpha',\gamma,\gamma'$-tetraalkylbrassylic acids.

Also 5-carboxy-1,3-cyclohexanedione (CLV), readily obtainable by the catalytic reduction in alkaline medium of 3,5-dihydroxybenzoic acid, may be used for acid syntheses (53a). Alkylated derivatives of succinic acid are obtained by reductive cleavage (53).

The methods developed originally for dihydroresorcinol may be extended considerably through the use of 5-substituted 1,3-cyclohexanediones in place of dihydroresorcinol.

Preparation of Hydroxy and Amino Acids

The preparation of long-chain hydroxy and amino acids is also possible with these methods. For long-chain ether acids, the condensation of halogen ether with dihydroresorcinol, followed by reductive cleavage of the condensation product, leads to the desired acids.

Such condensation products have been obtained by the condensation of dihydroresorcinol with 2-phenoxyethyl iodide, 3-phenoxypropyl iodide, and p-methoxybenzyl chloride. Reductive cleavage of these products gives 8-phenoxyoctanoic acid (CXVII) (54), 9-phenoxynonanoic acid (CXVIII) (54), and 7-(p-methoxyphenyl)heptanoic acid (CXIX)(2a).

There are two possibilities for the preparation of long-chain amino acids. In one case dihydroresorcinol is condensed with halogen compounds which contain an amino group protected by an acyl or sulfonamide group. The resulting substituted dihydroresorcinol then undergoes cleavage and reduction. In the other case, the dihydroresorcinol is condensed with halogenated nitro compounds, followed by reduction of the nitro group. These amino compounds can then be converted to long-chain amino acids by cleavage and reduction.

No amino acids have been prepared according to the first method. Following the second method, 7-(p-aminophenyl)heptanoic acid (CXXI) and 7-(m-aminophenyl)heptanoic acid (CXXIII) have been obtained (55). To prepare these acids p- and m-nitrobenzyl chloride were condensed with dihydroresorcinol. 2-(p-Nitrobenzyl)-1,3-cyclohexanedione (XX) was catalytically reduced to the corresponding amino compound (CXX) (90% yield). The reductive cleavage of this compound furnished 7-(p-aminophenyl)heptanoic acid (CXXI) in 72% yield.

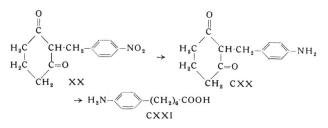

2-(m-Nitrobenzyl)-1,3-cyclohexanedione (XIX) is not reduced under similar conditions. The reduction, using palladium as catalyst in an acetic acid-acetic anhydride mixture, proceeds with simultaneous acetylation to give 2-(m-acetamidobenzyl)-1,3-cyclohexanedione (XXII).

TABLE 9

SUMMARY OF CARBOXYLIC ACIDS PREPARED ACCORDING
TO THE DESCRIBED PROCEDURES

Starting Material	Carboxylic acid	Yield (%)	Ref.
I	Hexanoic acid (LXXVII)	85	47
L	Heptanoic acid (LXXVIII)	86	2
LI	Octanoic acid (LXXIX)	72	2
III	Octanoic acid (LXXIX)	85	47
LII	Nonanoic acid (LXXX)	76.3	2
LIII	Decanoic acid (LXXXI)	80.5	2
LIV	Docosanoic acid (LXXXII)	87.5	2
VII	8-Nonenoic acid (LXXXIII)	64	33
VIII	6-(2-Cyclohexen-1-yl)hexanoic acid (LXXXIV)	73.2	33
XV	7-Phenylheptanoic acid (LXXV)	98	33
XXXV	6-Cyclohexylhexanoic acid (LXXVI)	96	36
X	Octanedioic acid (Suberic acid) (LXXXV)	98	47
LVI	Octanedioic acid (Suberic acid) (LXXXV)	89	2
XLIV	Nonanedioic acid (Azelaic acid) (LXXXVIII)	69	38
LXXXVI	Decanedioic acid (Sebacic acid) (LXXXVII)	quant.	51
XXXIII	Tridecanedioic acid (Brassylic acid) (LXXXIX)	quant.	47
XXII	Tetradecanedioic acid (XC)	85	51
XXIII	8-Hexadecenedioic acid (XCI)	79	33
	(From this obtain hexadecanedioic acid; thapsic acid) (XCII)	quant.	
XXIV	p-Benzenediheptanoic acid (XCIII)	78	51
Dimedone	3,3-Dimethylhexanoic acid (XCIV)	66	40
XXIX	6-Methyl-7-phenylheptanoic acid (XCV)	75	33
XXXVII	7-Phenyldecanoic acid (LXVII)	72	38
XXVII	3,3-Dimethyl-7-phenylheptanoic acid (XCVI)	71	40
LXV	6-Benzyl-7-phenylheptanoic acid (XCVII)	92	32
XXXI	6-Benzyl-8-nonenoic acid (XCVIII)	79.5	32
XI	2-Methyloctanedioic acid (α-Methylsuberic acid) (XCIX)	75	32
XXXII	3-Methyloctanedioic acid (β-Methylsuberic acid) (C)	72.5	32
XXVI	3,3-Dimethyloctanedioic acid) (β,β-Dimethylsuberic acid) (CI)	72	40
LXVIII	4-Methylnonanedioic acid) (γ-Methylazelaic acid) (CII)	63	49
XLV	3,3-Dimethylnonanedioic acid (β,β-Dimethylazelaic acid) (CIII)	70	40
LXX	4-Ethylnonanedioic acid (γ-Ethylazelaic acid) (CIV)	66	50
LXXI, LXXIV	4-Allylnonanedioic acid (γ-Allylazelaic acid) (CV)	58	49
LXXII	4-Benzylnonanedioic acid (γ-Benzylazelaic acid) (CVI)	68	50
CVII	3,11-Dimethyltridecanedioic acid (β,β'-Dimethyl-brassylic acid) (CVIII)	82	53

(continued)

TABLE 9 *(Continued)*

Starting Material	Carboxylic acid	Yield (%)	Ref.
CIX	3,11-Diphenyltridecanedioic acid (β,β'-Diphenyl-brassylic acid) (CX)	71	53
CXI	3,3,11,11-Tetramethyltridecanedioic acid ($\beta,\beta,\beta',\beta'$-Tetramethylbrassylic acid) (CXII)	65	40
XXI	6-(2-Carboxyphenyl)hexanoic acid (CXIII)	67	31
LXXIII	3-Methyl-1,2,7-heptanetricarboxylic acid (CXIV)	52	50
LXIX	4-(2-Carboxyethyl)nonanedioic acid (CXV)	75	50
LXI	2,5-Dicarboxy-*p*-benzenedihexanoic acid (CXVI)	76	31
XIII	8-Phenoxyoctanoic acid (CXVII)	78.8	54
XIV	9-Phenoxynonanoic acid (CXVIII)	79.5	54
XVII	7-(*p*-Methoxyphenyl)heptanoic acid (CXIX)	65.5	2a
CXX	7-(*p*-Aminophenyl)heptanoic acid (CXXI)	72.3	55
CXXII	7-(*m*-Aminophenyl)heptanoic acid (CXXIII)	75	55
CXXV	16-Heptadeceneoic acid (CLVI)	89	34b
5-Methyl-1,3-cyclo-hexanedione	3-Methylhexanoic acid (CLVII)	61	53
CXXVI	3-Methylheptanoic acid (CLVIII)	58	53
CXXX	6-Allyl-8-nonenoic acid (CLIX)	—	34d
CXXXI	3,3-Dimethyl-8-nonenoic acid (CLX)	27	34d
CLI	2,4-Dimethylhexanoic acid (CLXI)	78	34e
CLII	2,4-Diethylhexaneoic acid (CLXII)	70	34e
5-Phenyl-1,3-cyclo-hexanedione	3-Phenylhexanoic acid (CLXIII)	70.6	53
CXXVII	3-Methyl-7-phenylheptanoic acid (CLXIV)	66.4	53
CXXXV	3-Phenylheptanoic acid (CLXV)	75.7	53
CXXXVI	3,7-Diphenylheptanoic acid (CLXVI)	67.6	53
CXXXII	2,4-Dimethyl-7-phenylheptanoic acid (CLXVII)	77	34e
CXXVIII	2-Methyloctanedioic acid (α-Methylsuberic acid) (XCIX)	73	53
CLV	2-Propylbutanedioic acid (CLXVIII)	75	53
CXXXVIII	2-Butylbutanedioic acid (CLXIX)	74.4	53
CXXXIX	(5-Hexenyl)succinic acid (CLXX)	68	53
CLIII	2,4,10,12-Tetramethyltridecanedioic acid (CLXXI)	87	34c
CLIV	2,4,10,12-Tetraethyltridecanedioic acid (CLXXII)	81	34e

Reductive cleavage results in simultaneous hydrolysis of the acetyl group to give the desired 7-(*m*-aminophenyl)-heptanoic acid (CXXIII) (*55*).

The compound, 2-(*o*-nitrobenzyl)-1,3-cyclohexanedione (XVIII), obtained by condensation with *o*-nitrobenzyl chloride, does not give the expected amino compound P on catalytic hydrogenation, but instead 1,2,3,4,9,11-hexahydro-1-acridone (CXXIV), formed by the intramolecular loss of water (55). In this instance the catalytic hydrogenation in the presence of acetic anhydride also failed.

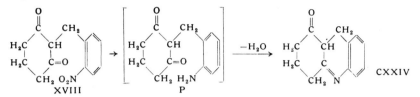

The acids which have been prepared by all of the methods described above are summarized in Table 9.

Ring Opening of Monosubstituted 1,3-Cyclohexanediones with Nitrous Acid and with Aryldiazonium Salts

In place of the simple hydrolytic cleavage of monoalkylated 1,3-cyclohexanediones, it is possible to use a nitrosating cleavage which leads to ε-isonitroso-δ-oxo carboxylic acids (see Table 10).

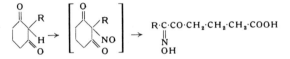

This reaction has been described previously for 2,6-dioxocyclohexanepropionic acid (CLXXIII) (55a). The optimum reaction conditions for this nitrosating cleavage have been ascertained and a series of ε-isonitroso-δ-oxo acids has been prepared (55b). The best yields were obtained by the action of sodium nitrite and hydrochloric acid in a water–tetrahydrofuran mixture. The esters of these acids are obtained by the direct action of ethyl nitrite with sulfuric acid in an alcohol solution.

An exception is the nitrosating cleavage of 2-acylaminodihydroresorcinols. In this case δ-oxo acids of the 1,2,4-oxadiazole series are obtained because of spontaneous cyclization involving the removal of water (55c).

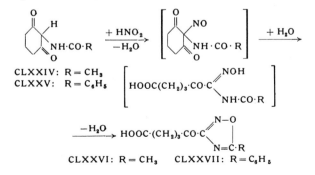

TABLE 10

SUMMARY OF CARBOXYLIC ACIDS OBTAINED BY CLEAVAGE THROUGH NITROSATION

β-Diketone	Nitrosation product (yield)	Dioxocarboxylic acid (yield)	Ref.
II	5,6-Dioxoheptanoic acid 6-oxime (CLXXVIII) (80%)	5,6-Dioxoheptanoic acid (CLXXIX) (44%)	55b
II	Ethyl ester of CLXXVIII (80%)	—	55b
II	5,6-Dioxooctanoic acid 6-oxime (CLXXX) (40%)	5,6-Dioxooctanoic acid (CLXXXI) (44%)	55b
IV	5,6-Dioxononanoic acid 6-oxime (CLXXXII) (45%)	5,6-Dioxononanoic acid (CLXXXIII) (43%)	55b
V	5,6-Dioxodecanoic acid 6-oxime (CLXXXIV) (47%)	5,6-Dioxodecanoic acid (CLXXXV) (42%)	55b
CLXXIII	4,5-Dioxononanedioic acid 4-oxime (CLXXXVI) (73.2%)	4,5-Dioxononanedioic acid (CLXXXVII) (13.8%)	55b
CLXXIV	5-Methyl-3-(1-oxo-4-carboxybutyl)1,2,4-oxadiazole (CLXXVI) (87%)	—	55c
CLXXV	3-(1-Oxo-4-carboxybutyl)-5-phenyl-1,2,4-oxadiazole (CLXXVII) (50%)	—	55c

The previously unknown δ,ε-dioxo carboxylic acids may be obtained from the ε-isonitroso-δ-oxo acids by removal of the isonitroso group with sodium hydrogen sulfite (*55b*).

Analogous to the nitrosating cleavage is the successful application of the Japp-Klingmann reaction (e.g., the action of aryldiazonium salts on monoalkylated β-dicarboxyl compounds) on monoalkylated 1,3-cyclohexanediones, in which 6-arylhydrazones of 5,6-dioxoheptanoic acids are formed in high yields (*55d*) (see Table 11).

TABLE 11

SUMMARY OF CARBOXYLIC ACIDS DERIVED FROM THE JAPP-KLINGEMANN REACTION

β-Diketone	Reaction product (yield)	Ref.
II	5,6-Dioxoheptanoic acid 6-phenylhydrazone (CLXXXIX) (52%)	*55d*
II	5,6-Dioxoheptanoic acid 6-(4-nitrophenyl)hydrazone (CXC) (64%)	*55d*
III	5,6-Dioxononanoic acid 6-(4-nitrophenyl)hydrazone (CXCI) (71%)	*55d*
VII	5,6-Dioxo-8-nonenoic acid 6-(4-nitrophenyl)hydrazone (CXCII) (70%)	*55d*
XV	5,6-Dioxo-7-phenylheptanoic acid 6-(4-nitrophenyl)hydrazone (CXCIII) (72%)	*55d*
CLXXIII	4,5-Dioxononanedioic acid 4-(4-nitrophenyl)hydrazone (CXCIV) (65%)	*55d*
CLXXIV	5-Methyl-δ-oxo-1-phenyl-1H-1,2,4-triazole-3-valeric acid (CLXXXVIII) (75%)	*55d*

$$R\cdot C\cdot CO\cdot CH_2\cdot CH_2\cdot CH_2\cdot COOH$$
$$\underset{HN\cdot C_6H_5}{\overset{N}{\|}}$$

In this instance also, the 2-acylaminodihydroresorcinols become a special case. By the action of benzenediazonium salts on 2-acetamino-dihydroresorcinol (CLXXIV), 5-methyl-δ-oxo-1-phenyl-1H-1,2,4-tri-azole-3-valeric acid (CLXXXVIII) is obtained because of a secondary cyclization reaction (*55d*).

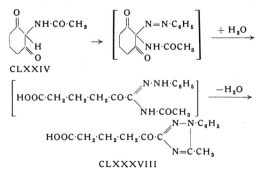

$$HOOC\cdot CH_2\cdot CH_2\cdot CH_2\cdot CO\cdot C\underset{N=C\cdot CH_3}{\overset{N-N\cdot C_6H_5}{<}}$$

CLXXXVIII

Methods of H. Lettré and A. Jahn

Lettré and Jahn (56) devised a method for the preparation of long-chain dicarboxylic acids, which also resembles characteristically the hydrolytic cleavage of 1,3-cyclohexanediones. The method proceeds from the dimethyl ether of resorcinol, which can be metalated on the 2-carbon atom with phenyllithium, according to Wittig (57). The compound, 2,6-dimethoxylithiumphenyl is obtained in 70% yield. By reaction with α,ω-dibromoalkanes it is possible to get α,ω-bis(2,6-dimethoxyphenyl)-alkanes. The condensation goes with 1,3-dibromopropane, 1,4-dibromo-butane, 1,5-dibromopentane, and 1,6-dibromohexane, but not with 1,2-dibromoethane. The yields amount to 50–90% of theory. In the third reaction step the ether linkages of the tetramethoxy compounds are cleaved by hydriodic acid to form the tetrahydroxy compounds in yields of 33–93%. These tetrahydroxy compounds, in a fourth step, are reduced with sodium amalgam. Therefore hydrogenation to the dihydroresorcinol stage and cleavage are attained in one step. The open-ring dioxo dicarboxylic acids are obtained at once. The intermediates in the dihydro-resorcinol stage could not be isolated. The yields with these reaction steps are under 10%. The dioxo dicarboxylic acid could not be obtained from the condensation product with 1,3-dibromopropane. The reduced dicarboxylic acids were obtained in 50–60% yield by the Clemmensen reduction of the dioxo dicarboxylic acids.

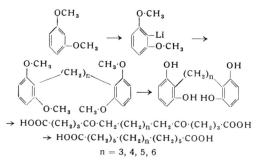

$$\to HOOC \cdot (CH_2)_3 \cdot CO \cdot CH_2 \cdot (CH_2)_n \cdot CH_2 \cdot CO \cdot (CH_2)_3 \cdot COOH$$
$$\to HOOC \cdot (CH_2)_5 \cdot (CH_2)_n \cdot (CH_2)_5 \cdot COOH$$
$$n = 3, 4, 5, 6$$

The over-all yield of this five-step reaction amounts to less than 3% of theory. It is possible to improve the yield if the hydrogenation of the tetrahydroxy compounds is carried out catalytically in the presence of two equivalents of alkali. In this case it is to be expected that the bisdihydroresorcinol derivative can be easily isolated in good yield. The long-chain dicarboxylic acids are attained in better yields by reductive cleavage. The value of this procedure lies in the fact that it is another method for the preparation of 2-alkylated dihydroresorcinols starting with m-dimethoxybenzene.

Experimental Examples

HEPTANOIC ACID (OENANTHIC ACID) (LXXVIII) BY THE
3-STEP PROCEDURE

2-Methyl-1,3-cyclohexanedione (II) *(49)*. To a solution of 10 gm of potassium hydroxide in 55 ml of 50% methanol is added 20 gm of dihydroresorcinol and the whole dissolved with warming. After the addition of 28 gm of methyl iodide, the mixture is refluxed on the water bath for 8 hr. After the solution is cooled, the precipitate is filtered and the filtrate concentrated *in vacuo*. The residue and the filtered residue are dissolved in 180 ml of 3% sodium hydroxide. The solution is extracted with ether. Traces of ether remaining in the aqueous are removed by the passage of air through the solution. The aqueous solution is then ice-cooled and carefully acidified to a pH 4. The precipitate is recrystallized from methanol. Yield: 15 gm (65%). M.p. 204°.

5-Oxoheptanoic Acid (L) *(2)*. A 189 gm (0.6 mole) portion of crystalline barium hydroxide is heated for a short time in 440 ml of distilled water and filtered hot. In this solution 19 gm (0.15 mole) of 1-methyl-2,6-cyclohexanedione (II) is dissolved and refluxed for 30 hr. The reflux condenser is fitted with a drying tube filled with soda lime. The colorless solution gradually becomes yellow. After 30 hr the heating is continued while a stream of carbon dioxide is introduced until the reaction mixture is neutral to litmus. It is found helpful to precipitate initially only a portion of the barium carbonate, filtering, and continuing passage of carbon dioxide through the filtrate. The precipitated barium carbonate is filtered off hot, extracted two times with 100 ml portions of hot water, filtered, and pressed dry. The clear filtrate is concentrated *in vacuo* to a volume of about 80 ml. By careful addition of a 1:10 dilute sulfuric acid solution, the oxo acid is liberated. An unintentional excess of sulfuric acid is neutralized with barium carbonate. The solution is concentrated *in vacuo*. A colorless oil remains which crystallizes on cooling. The acid may be recrystallized from an ether–ligroin mixture. Yield: 17 gm (78.2%). M.p. 50°.

Heptanoic Acid (LXXVIII) *(2)*. A 20 gm portion of finely powdered sodium hydroxide is dissolved with gentle warming in 175 ml of diethyleneglycol. After the addition of 14 gm of 5-oxoheptanoic acid (L) and 12.5 ml of 85% of hydrazine hydrate *(58)* the mixture is refluxed for 2 hr in an oil bath. Then the water which forms and the excess hydrazine are distilled off, until the temperature (thermometer bulb immersed in solution) of the boiling solution reaches 195°. At this temperature the solution is refluxed an additional 20 hr. When the flask is cooled the contents solidify. The contents are diluted with 100 ml of water and made acid with hydrochloric acid. The desired acid precipitates as an oil, which is extracted with a benzene–ether mixture (*31*). After drying over sodium sulfate and removing the solvent, the residue is subjected to fractional ditsillation. Yield: 11.4 gm (86%). B.p. 220°.

7-Phenylheptanoic Acid (LXXV) by the 2-Step Procedure

2-Benzyl-1,3-cyclohexanedione (XV) (*33*). To a solution of 11 gm (0.1 mole) of dihydroresorcinol in 22 ml of 20% potassium hydroxide are added 13.6 gm (0.11 mole) of benzyl chloride and 1 gm of potassium iodide. The reaction mixture is stirred for 2 hr on the water bath. The red-brown oil which forms becomes semisolid on cooling. Dilute sodium hydroxide is added until the oil goes into solution. The solution is extracted with ether. Traces of ether remaining in the aqueous are removed by the passage of air through the solution. The aqueous solution is carefully acidified with dilute hydrochloric acid to a pH of 4. There is obtained 14 gm of XV (70%). After recrystallization from 70% acetic acid or methanol–water, the melting point is 184°.

7-Phenylheptanoic Acid (LXXV) (*33*). To a solution of 11.9 gm (0.29 mole) of finely powdered sodium hydroxide in 89 ml of diethyleneglycol are added 12 gm (0.06 mole) of 2-benzyl-1,3-cyclohexanedione (XV) (crude product), 7.4 ml of 85% hydrazine hydrate (*58*), and 10 ml of absolute methanol. The mixture is then heated under reflux at 125° for 30 hr. The water which forms, methanol, and the excess hydrazine hydrate are distilled off until the inner temperature (thermometer bulb immersed in solution) of the boiling solution reaches 195°. At this temperature the solution is heated an additional 14 hr. When the flask is cooled, the contents solidify to a watery mass. The mass is diluted with an equal volume of water and acidified with hydrochloric acid. The oil which separates is extracted with ether. After the ether is removed, the residue is fractionally distilled. Yield: 12 gm (98%). B.p. 201°/14 mm.

6-Benzyl-7-phenylheptanoic Acid (XCVII) (An Example of Branching in the 6-Position of an Acid)

2,2-Dibenzyl-1,3-cyclohexanedione (LXV) (*32*). To a solution of 2 gm (0.05 gram atom) of potassium in 40 ml of ethanol is added 10.1 gm (0.05 mole) of 2-benzyl-1,3-cyclohexanedione (XV). As soon as a clear solution is obtained by refluxing, 7.6 gm (0.06 mole) of benzyl chloride is added and the mixture is refluxed until the reaction solution is no longer alkaline (about 3 hr). After the solution is cooled, the potassium chloride is filtered, and the filtrate is concentrated *in vacuo*. The residue is taken up in about 80 ml of ether; potassium chloride and unreacted XV remain undissolved. The ether solution is shaken with dilute sodium carbonate solution and with water. The ether is removed *in vacuo* and the residue is crystallized from methanol–water. Yield: 11 gm (69.2%). M.p. 137°.

6-Benzyl-7-phenylheptanoic Acid (XCVII) *(32).* To a solution of 8 gm of finely powdered sodium hydroxide in 60 ml of diethyleneglycol are added 5 gm of 85% hydrazine hydrate *(58)* and 11 gm of 2,2-dibenzyl-1,3-cyclohexanedione (LXV). By the addition of small amounts of methanol the temperature of the boiling solution is maintained at about 115°. The solution is then refluxed for 3 hr. The mixture is distilled until the temperature of the boiling solution reaches 195°. At this temperature heating is continued 12 hr longer. After the solution is cooled, 100 ml of water is added and the mass acidified with hydrochloric acid. After ether extraction, followed by the distillation of the ether, a crystalline mass remains. The acid is recrystallized from methanol–water (1:1). Yield: 11 g. (92%). M.p. 66°.

SUBERIC ACID (LXXXV) AS AN EXAMPLE OF THE PREPARATION OF A DICARBOXYLIC ACID FOLLOWING THE FIRST PROCEDURE (see p. 80)

Ethyl 2,6-dioxocyclohexaneacetate (X) *(2).* In a solution of 7.8 gm (0.2 gram atom) of potassium in 100 ml of absolute ethanol, prepared under nitrogen, 22 gm (0.2 mole) of dihydroresorcinol is dissolved; then 36.8 gm (0.22 mole) of ethyl bromoacetate is added. After heating for 30 min, the reaction is no longer alkaline. The ethanol is distilled *in vacuo,* the residue is cooled and then taken up in 100 ml of 6% sodium hydroxide. This solution is extracted with ether; and after the residual ether in the aqueous is removed, the aqueous is ice-cooled and carefully acidified with 4 N hydrochloric acid to a pH of 5. The solution is concentrated *in vacuo* to about 50 ml and refrigerated overnight. The precipitated crystals are recrystallized from water. Yield: 22 gm (51%). M.p. 93° (the hydrate).

Suberic Acid (Octanedioic Acid) (LXXXV) *(47).* An 11 gm portion of finely powdered sodium hydroxide is dissolved with slight warming in 83 ml of diethyleneglycol. To this solution are added 7 ml of 85% hydrazine hydrate *(58)* and 12 gm of ethyl 2,6-dioxocyclohexaneacetate. Small amounts of methanol are added to the boiling solution until a temperature of 115° is maintained. After refluxing for 30 hr in an oil bath, distillation is begun and continued until the temperature of the boiling solution reaches 195°. At this temperature the mixture is refluxed an additional 17 hr. After the solution is cooled, the precipitated crystalline mass is filtered and dissolved in 100 ml of water. On acidification the suberic acidprecipitates as a fine crystalline powder. After recrystallization from water, the m.p. is 140°. Yield: 9.1 g. (94.5%).

AZELAIC ACID (NONANEDIOIC ACID) AS AN EXAMPLE OF THE PREPARATION OF A DICARBOXYLIC ACID FOLLOWING THE FIRST PROCEDURE, STARTING WITH A MICHAEL ADDUCT (see p. 80)

Adduct of Dihydroresorcinol and Ethyl Acrylate (XLIV) *(38)*. To a solution of 0.5 gm of sodium in in 30 ml of absolute ethanol are added 11 gm (0.1 mole) of dihydroresorcinol and 10 gm (0.1 mole) of freshly distilled ethyl acrylate. The mixture is refluxed for 9 hr on the water bath, the solution becoming cherry red. The solvent is distilled *in vacuo*, the red, sirupy residue taken up in a small amount of 3% sodium hydroxide, and the alkaline solution shaken with ether. After separation, the rest of the ether in the aqueous is removed by the passage of air through the solution. The aqueous is ice-cooled, stirred, and acidified with dilute hydrochloric acid to a pH of 4. The adduct precipitates, is refrigerated for 2 hr, then filtered and dried. The adduct is recrystallized from toluene. Yield: 9.0 gm (42%). M.p. 128°.

Azelaic Acid (Nonanedioic Acid) (LXXXVIII) *(38)*. A 20 gm portion of finely powdered sodium hydroxide is dissolved with slight warming in 150 ml of diethyleneglycol. To this solution are added 12.5 ml of 85% hydrazine hydrate *(58)* and 21.2 gm (0.1 mole) of adduct XLIV. The mixture is refluxed for 30 hr, the temperature being maintained at 115° by the addition of small amounts of methanol. Then the water which is formed, the methanol, and excess hydrazine hydrate are distilled off, until the inner temperature of the boiling solution reaches 195°. At this temperature the mixture is refluxed an additional 15 hr. After the solution is cooled the solidified mass is dissolved with 150 ml of water and made strongly acidic with concentrated hydrochloric acid. The organic acid precipitates as a dark oil, which is extracted with three 100-ml portions of ether. The combined ether extracts are dried over sodium sulfate. After the removal of the ether there remains a light brown crystalline mass, which is recrystallized from water. Yield: 13 gm (69%). M.p. 106°.

BRASSYLIC ACID (TRIDECANEDIOIC ACID) AS AN EXAMPLE OF THE PREPARATION OF A DICARBOXYLIC ACID FOLLOWING THE SECOND PROCEDURE (see p. 75)

Methylenedi-1,3-cyclohexanedione (XXXIII): *(47)*. A 20 gm portion of dihydroresorcinol is dissolved in 300 ml of water and 8 ml of 40% formalin is added. The solution is warmed carefully to the beginning of turbidity. The heating is discontinued and the solution allowed to stand for 12 hr at room temperature. The precipitated crystals are filtered with suction, washed with water and dried at 100°. Yield: quantitative. M.p. 132°.

Brassylic Acid (Tridecanedioic Acid) (LXXXIX): *(47)*. A 16.8 gm portion of finely powdered sodium hydroxide is dissolved with slight warming in 127 ml of diethyleneglycol. After cooling 21.2 gm of 85% hydrazine hydrate *(58)* and 20 gm of methylenedi-1,3-cyclohexanedione (XXXIII) are added. The solution is refluxed in an oil bath; the temperature of the solution is maintained at 125° (bulb immersed in liquid) by the addition of small amounts of methanol. Within 30 minutes the solution becomes clear and gradually assumes a brownish coloration. When, after 30 hr, the heating is completed, water, methanol, and excess hydrazine hydrate are distilled off until the temperature of the boiling solution reaches 195°. At this temperature the mixture is refluxed an additional 10–11 hr. After 1 hr the solution becomes turbid, crystals beginning to separate. The contents of the flask on cooling sets to a crystalline mass. This is dissolved in 600 ml of water and the organic acid is precipitated by acidification with dilute hydrochloric acid. After having been suction-filtered and dried in a vacuum desiccator, the crude product melts at 106–107°. Yield: 22 gm (quantitative). The acid may be recrystallized, using charcoal, from 50% alcohol or carbon tetrachloride. Distinct crystals are obtained when recrystallizing from acetic acid. M.p. 112°.

ETHYL 8-CYANO-6-METHYL-5-OXOOCTANOATE (LXVIII) *(49)* AS AN EXAMPLE OF THE MICHAEL REACTION WITH SIMULTANEOUS RING-OPENING

To a solution of 0.2 gm of sodium in 30 ml of anhydrous ethanol are added 12.6 gm (0.1 mole) of 2-methyl-1,3-cyclohexanedione (II) and 5.8 gm (0.11 mole) of freshly distilled acrylonitrile. The mixture is refluxed, with exclusion of moisture, for 10 hr on the water bath, the oily residue is taken up in ether. The ether solution is washed with soda solution, then two times with water. The ether solution is dried over freshly heated sodium sulfate. The ether is distilled and the residue is fractionated under reduced pressure. Yield: 14.2 gm (63%). B.p. 186–190°/12 mm.

REFERENCES

(1) D. Vorländer, *Ann. Chem. Liebigs* **294**, 253 (1897).
(2) H. Stetter and W. Dierichs, *Chem. Ber.* **85**, 61 (1952).
(2a) H. Stetter and W. Dierichs, German Patent 915,085; *Chem. Abstr.* **52**, 14689 (1958).
(3) G. Merling, *Ann. Chem. Liebigs* **278**, 23 (1893).
(4) D. Vorländer, *Ann. Chem. Liebigs* **294**, 270 (1897); R. v. Schilling and D. Vorländer, *ibid.* **303**, 190 (1899).
(5) M. Klingenfuss, British Patent 416,892; *Chem. Abstr.* **29**, 1104 (1935); French Patent 767,619; *Chem. Abstr.* **29**, 482 (1935).
(6) R. B. Thompson, *Org. Syntheses* **27**, 21 (1947).
(7) D. Vorländer and J. Erig, *Ann. Chem. Liebigs* **291**, 314 (1897); D. Vorländer,

Z. anal. Chem. **77**, 245 (1929); R. L. Shriner and H. Todd, *Org. Syntheses Coll. Vol. II,* p. 200.

(8) A. W. Crossley and N. Renouf, *J. Chem. Soc.* **107**, 605 (1915).

(9) K. W. Rosenmund, H. Herzberg, and H. Schütt, *Chem. Ber.* **87**, 1265 (1954).

(10) B. Eistert and W. Reiss, *Chem. Ber.* **87**, 108 (1954).

(11) G. Schwarzenbach, *Helv. Chim. Acta* **27**, 1059 (1944).

(12) H. Henecka, "Chemie der β-Dicarbonyl-Verbindungen," pp. 27–28. Springer, Berlin, 1950.

(13) H. Henecka, "Chemie der β-Dicarbonyl-Verbindungen," p. 279. Springer, Berlin, 1950.

(14) B. Eistert and W. Reiss, *Chem. Ber.* **87**, 92 (1954).

(15) H. Henecka and B. Eistert, *in* Houben-Weyl-Müller, "Methoden der organischen Chemie," 4th ed., Vol. 2, p. 385. Thieme, Stuttgart, 1953.

(16) N. J. Toivonen, T. Lewison, and H. Kivikoski, *Acta Chem. Fennica (B)* [5] **5**, 31 (1932); *Chem. Zentr.* II, p. 2175 (1932).

(17) R. Criegee, *in* Houben-Weyl-Müller, "Methoden der organischen Chemie," 4th ed., Vol. 8, p. 25. Thieme, Stuttgart, 1952.

(18) G. Merling, *Ann. Chem. Liebigs* **278**, 28 (1893).

(19) M. Klingenfuss, *Festschr. Emil Barell 1936* p. 217 (1936).

(20) C. L. Hewett, *J. Chem. Soc.* p. 50 (1936).

(21) N. J. Toivonen, *Suomen Kemistilehti* **3**, 131 (1930).

(22) R. D. Desai, *J. Chem. Soc.* p. 1079 (1932).

(23) H. Stetter and W. Dierichs, *Chem. Ber.* **85**, 62 (1952).

(24) A. Brändström, *Acta Chem. Scand.* **4**, 208 (1950).

(25) L. Claisen, *Ann. Chem. Liebigs* **442**, 217 (1925); K. von Auwers, *Ber. deut. chem. Ges.* **61**, 408 (1928).

(26) A. Brändström, *Arkiv Kemi* **6**, 185 (1953).

(27) N. V. Sidgwick and F. M. Brewer, *J. Chem. Soc.* p. 2379 (1925).

(28) H. Stetter and M. Coenen, *Chem. Ber.* **87**, 992 (1954).

(29) H. Stetter, C. Büntgen, and M. Coenen, *Chem. Ber.* **88**, 79 (1955).

(30) R. H. Hurtley, *J. Chem. Soc.* p. 1870 (1929); R. Adams, *J. Am. Chem. Soc.* **62**, 2197 (1940).

(31) H. Stetter and E. Siehnhold, *Chem. Ber.* **88**, 1223 (1955).

(31a) H. Stetter and E. Siehnhold, *Chem. Ber.* **88**, 271 (1955).

(32) H. Stetter and E. Klauke, *Chem. Ber.* **86**, 513 (1953).

(33) H. Stetter and W. Dierichs, *Chem. Ber.* **85**, 1061 (1952).

(34) A. Auvinen, A. Hirvimies, T. Rinne, and R. Waris, *Suomen Kemistilehti* **B27**, 88 (1954).

(34a) H. Stetter and H. Spangenberger, Diplomarbeit, Bonn, 1955.

(34b) K. E. Schulte and I. Mleinek, *Arch. Pharm.* **290**, 483 (1957).

(34c) I. N. Nazarov, S. I. Zav'yalov, and M. S. Burmistrova, *Izvest. Akad. Nauk S.S.S.R. Otdel. Khim. Nauk* p. 205 (1956); *Chem Abstr.* **50**, 13762 (1956).

(34d) R. Lukeš and J. Hofman, *Chem. listy* **51**, 2309 (1957); *Collection Czechoslov. Chem. Communs.* **23**, 1110 (1958); *Chem. Abstr.* **52**, 6172 (1958).

(34e) H. Stetter and U. Milbers, *Chem. Ber.* **91**, 374 (1958).

(35) D. Vorländer, *Z. anal. Chem.* **77**, 241 (1927).

(36) H. Stetter, E. Siehnhold, E. Klauke, and M. Coenen, *Chem. Ber.* **86**, 1308 (1953).

(36a) With *p*-xylene dibromide (yield: 63%) J. Clark, *J. Chem. Soc.* p. 2202 (1957).

(37) B. M. Mikhailov, *Zhur. Obshcheĭ Khim.* **7**, 2950 (1937); *Chem. Abstr.* **32**, 5402 (1938).

(38) H. Stetter and M. Coenen, *Chem. Ber.* **87**, 869 (1954); German Patent 1,002,314 (1953); *Chem. Abstr.* **53**, 21819 (1959).

(38a) I. N. Nazarov and S. I. Zav'yalov, *Zhur. Obshcheĭ Khim.* **24**, 469 (1954); *Chem. Abstr.* **49**, 6142 (1955).

(39) I. N. Nazarov and S. I. Zav'yalov, *Zhur. Obshcheĭ Khim.* **23**, 1703 (1953); *Chem. Abstr.* **48**, 13667 (1954).

(40) H. Stetter, H. Kesseler, and H. Meisel, *Chem. Ber.* **87**, 1617 (1954).

(40a) L. Bradford, E. G. Meek, J. H. Turnball, and W. Wilson, *Chem. & Ind. (London)* p. 839 (1951).

(40b) H. Stetter and K. Hoehne, *Chem. Ber.* **91**, 1344 (1958).

(41) N. A. J. Rogers and H. Smith, *J. Chem. Soc.* p. 341 (1955).

(42) H. Smith, *J. Chem. Soc.* p. 803 (1953).

(43) A. J. Birch, *J. Chem. Soc.* p. 1551 (1950).

(44) N. N. Saha and P. Bagchi, *Sci. and Culture (Calcutta)* **18**, 196 (1952); *Chem. Abstr.* **47**, 9281 (1953).

(44a) O. Rosenthal and H. Kosche, German Patent 1,005,508 (1956); *Chem. Abstr.* **53**, 14973 (1959).

(44b) H. Hellmann, G. Aichinger, and H. P. Wiedemann, *Ann. Chem. Liebigs* **626**, 35 (1959); *Angew. Chem.* **70**, 247 (1958).

(44c) H. Hellmann and G. Aichinger, *Chem. Ber.* **92**, 2122 (1959).

(44d) H. Stetter and H. Rauhut, *Chem. Ber.* **91**, 2543 (1958).

(45) M. Soffer and K. Sherk, *J. Am. Chem. Soc.* **67**, 1435 (1945).

(46) Huang-Minlon, *J. Am. Chem. Soc.* **68**, 2487 (1946).

(47) H. Stetter and W. Dierichs, *Chem. Ber.* **85**, 290 (1952).

(48) D. Vorländer and F. Kalkow, *Ann. Chem. Liebigs* **309**, 348 (1899).

(49) H. Stetter and M. Coenen, *Chem. Ber.* **87**, 990 (1954); German Patent 1,005,506 (1954); *Chem. Abstr.* **53**, 18871 (1959).

(50) H. Stetter, C. Büntgen, and M. Coenen, *Chem. Ber.* **88**, 77 (1955).

(51) H. Stetter and W. Dierichs, *Chem. Ber.* **86**, 693 (1953).

(52) H. Kesseler, Diploma work, Bonn, 1953.

(53) H. Stetter and H. Meisel, *Chem. Ber.* **90**, 2928 (1957).

(53a) E. E. von Tamelen and G. T. Hildahl, *J. Am. Chem. Soc.* **75**, 5451 (1953).

(54) H. Stetter and G. Hartmann, unpublished results.

(55) H. Stetter and H. Figge, *Chem. Ber.* **87**, 1331 (1954).

(55a) H. v. Pechmann and N. V. Sidgwick, *Ber. deut. chem. Ges.* **37**, 3816 (1904).

(55b) H. Stetter, R. Engl, and H. Rauhut, *Chem. Ber.* **91**, 2882 (1958).

(55c) H. Stetter and K. Hoehne, *Chem. Ber.* **91**, 1123 (1958).

(55d) H. Stetter, R. Engl, and H. Rauhut, *Chem. Ber.* **92**, 1184 (1959).

(56) H. Lettré and A. Jahn, *Chem. Ber.* **85**, 346 (1952).

(57) G. Wittig, "Neuere Methoden the Präparativen Organischen Chemie," Verlage Chemie, p. 469. Weinheim, 1944.

(58) Hydrazine hydrate (85%) can be obtained from less concentrated aqueous solution by the method of C. D. Hurd and C. W. Bennett, *J. Am. Chem. Soc.* **51**, 268 (1929).

Ethyl 2-Cyclopentanonecarboxylate and Its Importance in Syntheses*

ROLAND MAYER

Institut für Organische Chemie der Technischen Universität Dresden

Preparation

The Dieckmann reaction (*1, 2*), an intramolecular Claisen condensation (*3*) of the diesters of adipic acid leads to esters of 2-cyclopentanonecarboxylic acid (*4–6*). There are considerable difficulties in working with larger amounts especially with respect to the condensing agent. The applications therefore have steadily increased with the discovery of more convenient cyclization agents. Diesters of adipic acid in large quantities may now be cyclized with sodium alcoholate (*7a*) with yields up to 80%. This cyclization is quite superior both to the original Dieckmann procedure, and to the improved procedure of Pinkney (*7*), although a substitute for the ethylate would be desirable.

In older work Neunhoeffer and Paschke (*8*) observed the formation of 2-cyclopentanonecarboxylates during the slow distillation of the monoesters of adipic acid which, however, in the cyclization procedures gave only a minimum yield (<1%) (*9*). Direct condensation of cyclopentanone with formates (*9*) gave yields up to 10%; here, also, a suitable condensing agent is lacking. Likewise, a synthesis of the ester from cyclopentanone and oxalate ester failed because of the stability of the oxalo intermediate (*10*). The action of oxalyl bromide on cyclopentanone with simultaneous splitting out of carbon monoxide was a failure (*10a*). Thus, in contrast to cyclohexanone, the peculiarities of cyclopentanone hinder the reaction with oxalyl bromide. The cyclization of the esters of α-haloadipic acid with magnesium (*11*) (yield: 50%) or of the esters of butanetricarboxylic acid with ethylate (*12*) (yield: 40%), as well as the action of oxalate esters on the monoester of adipic acid (*13*), were uneconomical. The high yields recently attained in the cyclization reaction (*13a*) through the use of sodamide could not be obtained in our group. On the other hand, a thorough investigation of the direct cyclization of the monoester monochloride of adipic acid or of adipyl chloride in alcoholic solution seems promising, since it has been reported that adipyl chloride in benzene, ethanol, and triethanolamine formed, with a trace of hydrogen chloride, a cyclic ester in 40% yield (*13b*).

* Dedicated to the 70th birthday of Dr. W. Treibs.

101

The reaction of solid carbon dioxide with cyclopentanone in the presence of sodamide, and the exchange of the sodium salt with methyl sulfate, gave the methyl ester with a maximum 10% yield (86).

Physical Properties

The colorless, quite fluid, oily, ethyl 2-cyclopentanonecarboxylate is distinguished by its deep blue-violet ferric chloride reaction (alcohol). On shaking with dilute alkali hydroxides, the white alkali salt precipitates; on saponification with alkali, adipic acid is formed, while treatment with acids gives cyclopentanone. The phenylhydrazone (m.p. 93°) or the semicarbazone (m.p. 143°) are formed only under specific conditions and are not suitable for identification. The IR, Raman and UV spectra of the ethyl ester, which is prepared in better yield than the methyl ester and also enters more readily into condensation reactions, have been recorded several times (14, 14a).

Enol

The ester of 2-cyclopentanonecarboxylic acid is enolized only slightly in polar solvents, much more so in nonpolar (14, 15), which is to be considered in the evaluation of the course of the reaction. [The enol content in alcoholic solution at 25° is 4–5% (14, 14a, 15, 15a), in the gaseous state, 27.5% (15b).] For the reaction of the enol hydroxyl with diazomethane and orthoformic ester see ref. (15c).

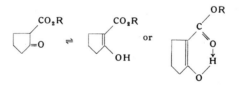

Preparatively important alkali metal salts are formed from the enol:

(1) by dropwise addition of the ester to a hydrocarbon containing "powdered" sodium or potassium (unreacted metal fosters secondary reactions and the danger of explosion);

(2) by dropwise addition of the ester to sodium or potassium ethoxide, dry or dissolved in alcohol (the temperature must be low in order to minimize ring cleavage through alcoholysis);

(3) by dropwise addition of the ester to a water-alcohol solution of potassium hydroxide (16), the potassium salt forming spontaneously. Since this method has been tested in many cases and found satisfactory so far in all requirements (see Example 2 at the end of this chapter), the use of alkali metals or their alkoxides for the conversion of the cyclopentanone carboxylate to its sodium or potassium salt is now

necessary only in special cases. It should be noted, however, when using the methyl ester in methanol solution that the sodium salt is obtained in better yield than the potassium salt. Side reactions can occur here through further condensation.

Condensation with Halides

Halides react with the enol salt to form a C-substituted derivative and the alkali metal halide:

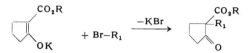

The potassium is split off as a cation (5), the remaining anion (a) is stabilized (b) and serves as the reactive partner for the positive group, R_1^+ (9):

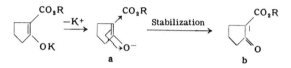

In Table 1 all of the halide condensation reactions which have been published are summarized. It can be seen that as the molecular weight of group R increases, there is greater need for higher boiling solvents and longer heating periods. Deviating from the customary condensation procedure, Weizmann and co-workers (17) used potassium hydroxide in solvents of the acetal type, while Arnold et al. (18) carried out the direct condensation of itaconic ester with cyclopentanone ester in the presence of Triton B. While the substitution reactions recorded in Table 1 are assumed by all investigators to have taken place in the C-1 position and in most cases this has been demonstrated directly through cleavage, the condensation with β-diethylaminoethyl chloride (118) in benzene with sodium hydride or with potassium t-butoxide in t-butyl alcohol furnishes 62% of the O-alkylated product; this is said to occur also in the condensation with 2-chlorocyclohexanone (120). If these particular reactions can be made more general, then quite new possibilities for the synthesis of the oxa-compounds with an attached five-membered ring appear likely. Diethylaminoethyl chloride, however, also was condensed without any indication of O-alkylation (117). The statement (121) that in condensation with bromoacetone in alcohol solution substitution occurs not only on the C-1 position, but also on the C-3 atom, if no cleavage and subsequent cyclization is assumed, cannot be explained at this time.

TABLE 1

CONDENSATION WITH HALIDES

Halide	R	Procedure	Yield (%)	B.p. (°/mm)	Ref.
Methyl iodide	—CH$_3$	NaOC$_2$H$_5$, cooling	60	105°/13	19, 20, 21 22, 23, 24 25
Methyl bromide	—CH$_3$				25
Ethyl iodide	—C$_2$H$_5$	NaOC$_2$H$_5$ or Na, 6 hr, toluene	74	100°/7	20, 23, 26 27, 28
n-Propyl bromide	—C$_3$H$_7$	NaOC$_2$H$_5$	85	136.5°/28	23
i-Propyl iodide	—CH(CH$_3$)$_2$	12 hrs, xylene or Na-K alloy in xylene	59	136-7°/34	20, 29, 30, 31
i-Butyl bromide	—CH$_2$CH(CH$_3$)$_2$	KOH in acetaldehyde dipropylacetal	34	138-42°/15	17
n-Octyl bromide	—(CH$_2$)$_7$CH$_3$	K, 7 hr, xylene	85	157-65°/1	32
n-Decyl bromide	—(CH$_2$)$_9$CH$_3$	K, 10 hr, xylene	50	174°/3	33
4-Phenoxybutyl iodide	—(CH$_2$)$_4$OC$_6$H$_5$	KOC(CH$_3$)$_2$C$_2$H$_5$, xylene, 45 hr at 110° under N$_2$	67	Me ester 178-81°/0.08	34
4-Diethylamino-2-butanone	—CH$_2$CH$_2$COCH$_3$	Direct condensation in benzene	—	115-20°/0.1	35
Benzyl bromide	—CH$_2$C$_6$H$_5$	K, xylene, cold. If warm, ring cleavage takes place (36)	55	154-5°/1	33
Benzyl chloride	—CH$_2$C$_6$H$_5$	KOH in acetaldehyde dipropylacetal at 75°	65	186-90°/14	17
α-Naphthylethyl bromide	—(CH$_2$)$_2$C$_{10}$H$_7$	K in benzene	44	188-9°/0.1	37
3-(m-Methoxyphenyl) n-propyl iodide	—(CH$_2$)$_3$C$_6$H$_4$OCH$_3$	K, 8 hr, xylene	—	165-70°/0.1	38
Allyl bromide	—CH$_2$CH=CH$_2$	Na	—	125°/11	39
Cinnamyl bromide	—CH$_2$CH=CHC$_6$H$_5$	Na, 10 hr, xylene	60	179°/3	33
Methyl chloroformate	—CO$_2$CH$_3$	Na in toluene	95	127-8°/7	40
Methyl bromoacetate	—CH$_2$CO$_2$CH$_3$	—	—	145°/7	40
Ethyl bromoacetate	—CH$_2$CO$_2$C$_2$H$_5$	NaOC$_2$H$_5$, or Na or K in hydrocarbon	60-85	163-7°/15	9, 17, 41-47
Ethyl chloroacetate	—CH$_2$CO$_2$C$_2$H$_5$	—	—	—	9, 46

Compound	Structure	Method	Yield (%)	b.p.	Reference
Ethyl 3-bromopropionate	—CH₂CH₂CO₂C₂H₅	—	75	187–90/18	47, 48
Ethyl 2-bromopropionate	—CH(CH₃)CO₂C₂H₅	—	—	—	49
γ-Bromobutyronitrile	—(CH₂)₃CN	—	—	—	50
Ethyl 5-iodopentanoate	—(CH₂)₄CO₂C₂H₅	Na in toluene	—	180–2°/4	51
Ethyl 11-bromoundecanoate	(—CH₂)₁₀CO₂C₂H₅	K in benzene-toluene, sealed tube	—	Cannot be distilled	52
Diethyl α-bromosuccinate	—CHCO₂C₂H₅ | CH₂CO₂C₂H₅	Na in benzene	—	211–5°/10	53
Diethyl α-bromoadipate	—CHCO₂C₂H₅ | (CH₂)₃CO₂C₂H₅	NaOC₂H₅; better K in toluene	28	216–20°/6	54
Diethyl itaconate	CH₂CO₂C₂H₅ | —CH₂CHCO₂C₂H₅	Direct condensation, Triton B	—		18
γ-Chlorocrotyl chloride	—COCH=CHCH₂Cl	NaOC₂H₅ at 0°	—	81–7°/0.1	55
Ethyl γ-bromo-β-methyl crotonate	—CH₂C=CHCO₂C₂H₅ | CH₃	—	—	—	56
Methylene bromide	—CH₂Br	M — K-cpd in excess CH₂Br₂	6	120–5°/4	16
Ethylene bromide	—CH₂CH₂Br	K-cpd in excess BrCH₂CH₂Br	21–23	143–4°/4	16
1,3-Dibromopropane	—(CH₂)₃Br	NaOC₂H₅	—	134–5°/2	57
1-Bromo-3-chloropropane	—(CH₂)₃Cl	NaOC₂H₅	—	134.5–5.5°/4	57
1,4-Dibromobutane	—(CH₂)₄Br	K-cpd in excess Br(CH₂)₄Br	59	144–7°/2	16
1,6-Dibromohexane	—(CH₂)₆Br	K-cpd in excess Br(CH₂)₆Br	67	160°/2	16
Methyl bromide	—CH₃	Several hr at 20° in alcohol	50	—	102
Methyl iodide	—CH₃	NaOC₂H₅ at −15°, 6 hr stirring, temp to 20°; Powd. Na in benzene, 48 hr reflux	67	116–9°/25	103, 104
Dimethyl sulfate	—(CH₃)₂	Methanol, NaOCH₃	75	—	102

(continued)

TABLE 1 (Continued)

Halide	R	Procedure	Yield (%)	B.p. (°/mm)	Ref.
			(with Me ester low yield)		
n-Propyl iodide	—(CH$_2$)$_2$CH$_3$	K in benzene, 24 hr	75	115–7°/10	106
n-Butyl iodide	—(CH$_2$)$_3$CH$_3$	K in xylene, 120 – 130°	82	127–8°/9	107
n-Pentyl bromide	—(CH$_2$)$_4$CH$_3$	NaOC$_2$H$_5$	44	138–40°/12	108
n-Heptyl halide	–(CH$_2$)$_6$CH$_3$	Na-cpd	65–70	195°/18	109
n-Octyl halide	—(CH$_2$)$_7$CH$_3$	Na-cpd	60	205°/18	109
n-Nonyl halide	—(CH$_2$)$_8$CH$_3$	Na-cpd	60	210°/18	109
n-Decyl halide	—(CH$_2$)$_9$CH$_3$	Na-cpd	55	217°/18	109
Undecyl halide	—(CH$_2$)$_{10}$CH$_3$	Na-cpd	55	225°/18	109
Dodecyl halide	—(CH$_2$)$_{11}$CH$_3$	Na-cpd	50	241°/22	109
2-Iodo-6-methylheptane	—CH(CH$_2$)$_3$CH(CH$_3$)$_2$ —CH$_3$	K in xylene, 43 hr at 130–135°	ca. 30	142–6°/3 165–70°/14	110
2-Bromo-6-methylheptane	—CH(CH$_2$)$_3$CH(CH$_3$)$_2$ —CH$_3$	Na-K alloy	—	—	110
Benzyl bromide	—CH$_2$C$_6$H$_5$	—			111
Phenethyl bromide	—(CH$_2$)$_2$C$_6$H$_5$	K-cpd in toluene, 28 hr	ca. 60	157–63/2	112
β-Nephthylethyl bromide	—(CH$_2$)$_2$C$_{10}$H$_7$	K in benzene	ca. 80	210–15°/1	112
Cinnamyl bromide	—CH$_2$CH=CHC$_6$H$_5$	Na-cpd	48	219°/19	113
Acrylonitrile	—(CH$_2$)$_2$CN	Direct condensation with Na-salt in dioxane	75	176–8°/8	114
δ-Bromovaleronitrile	—(CH$_2$)$_4$CN	Na powder in toluene, 18 hr	39	151–2°/0.5	115
o-Cyanobenzyl bromide	—CH$_2$C$_6$H$_4$CN	Na in toluene, 20 hr	62	m.p. 178–9°	116
o-Cyanophenethyl bromide	—(CH$_2$)$_2$C$_6$H$_4$CN	K in toluene, reflux 3 days	30	180–5°/2	115

Reagent	Structure	Conditions	Yield (%)	b.p. (°/mm)	Ref.
Diethylaminoethyl chloride	—(CH₂)₂N(C₂H₅)₂	Na-cpd in xylene at 0°, then 6 hr at 100°	43	149–51°/7	117
		NaH, benzene, 6 hr reflux	Mixt. of O and C-deriv.	—	118
Bromoacetone	—CH₂COCH₃	KOBu-t in t-BuOH, 3 hr, then r.t.,	50–70		121
		Na salt, heating in water (28%), alcohol (30%), butyl ether (44%), petroleum ether (55%), toluene (60%)		147–8°/9	
Chloroacetone	—CH₂COCH₃	Na powder in toluene, 6 hr	21	105–10°/15	122
Chloromethyl methyl sulfide	—CH₂SCH₃	K-cpd in benzene	Me ester 38	99–100°/0.01	119
		(also direct ring cleavage)	Et ester 28	155–7°/10	119
Chloromethyl ethyl sulfide	CH₂SC₂H₅	Na in benzene	Me ester	155–6°/11	119
Chloromethyl methyl ether	—CH₂OCH₃	K-cpd in benzene	Me ester	155–6°/11	119
		(also direct ring cleavage)	Et ester	135–6°/17	119
			Et ester	120°/9	119
1-Acetoxy-3-iodoacetone	—CH₂COCH₂OCOCH₃	t-Butyl ester under N₂ to NaNH₂ in benzene; after 8 hr add iodide and heat 5 hr longer	58	137–47°/0.04	13a
2-Chlorocyclohexanone	—C₆H₉O	Na salt in toluene, 2 hr, 80°	56 (also 0.5% O-alkylation m.p. 89–90)	126–8°/0.02	120
2-Chlorocyclohexanol	C-1 alkylation + lactone	130°	—	—	120
Phenacyl bromide	—CH₂COC₆H₅	Na salt in ether, 30 hr	41	m.p. 51° Me ester	121
		Na salt in toluene	76	191°/4	121

(continued)

TABLE 1 (*Continued*)

Halide	R	Procedure	Yield (%)	B.p. (°/mm)	Ref.
Methyl γ-bromobutyrate	—(CH₂)₃CO₂CH₃	NaOCH₃ in methanol, 3 hr	70	135-7°/3	123, 124
Ethyl bromoisobutyrate	Michael addition	K in xylene, 22 hr reflux	—	—	125
Ethyl γ-bromocrotonate	—CH₂CH=CHCO₂C₂H₅	Na in toluene	60	156-61°/2	122
Ethyl 4-bromo-2-pentenoate	—CHCH=CHCO₂C₂H₅ CH₃	Na in toluene	60 / 77	158-63°/2 / —	122, 126 / 127
Ethyl 4-bromo-3-methyl-2-butenoate	—CH₂C=CHCO₂C₂H₅ CH₃	—	64	162-8°/2	122
Ethyl 4-bromo-5-methyl-2-hexenoate	—CHCH=CHCO₂C₂H₅ CH(CH₃)₂	Na in toluene, 24 hr reflux	26	150-60°/1.5	122
1,3-Dibromopropane	—(CH₂)₃Br	K-cpd with KOH in excess dibromide 7 hr, 70-80°	50	135-8°/1-2	59a
1,5-Dibromopentane	—(CH₂)₅Br	K-cpd with KOH, 7 hr, 80-90° NaOC₂H₅	38	161-1.5°/2	59a
2-Methyl-3-piperidino-methylindole dimethyl sulfate	2-methylskatyl	Mannich base exchange reaction	—	—	128, 129
1,1-Dimethyl-4-oxopiperidinium iodide	—(CH₂)₂CO(CH₂)₂N(CH₃)₂	Direct condensation with 1,1-dimethyl-4-oxopiperidinium iodide	—	—	130
Thiacyclohexan-4-one methiodide	—(CH₂)₂CO(CH₂)₂SCH₃	—	—	—	131

[a] Note that a few entries are repeated because of recent revision of this table.

The condensation involving only one end of a dihalide and in which very reactive five-membered ring compounds are formed, is found to be of particular preparative interest (see Example 3 at the end of this chapter). Under special conditions the halide can condense at both ends to form esters of alkane bis(2-oxocyclopentanecarboxylic acid) (*16*). More recently ethylene bromide was condensed at both ends (*18a*), so that in this series the reaction product with methylene bromide is the only one unknown. These compounds have preparative significance because with acid cleavage, tetracarboxylic acids are formed, while ketone cleavage forms ω,ω'-(dicyclopentanonyl) alkane.

Although these condensations are simple preparations, ring opening can occur using improper conditions (use of moist solvents, excess alkali metal, alkoxides, or potassium hydroxide, or overheating), which may explain contradictory statements found in the literature. For example, numerous investigators have worked with haloacetate condensations in which a slight excess of metal leads to substituted adipic esters (Table 1).

Cleavage to Ketones and Acids

Cyclopentanone is formed by the hydrolysis of the esters of 2-cyclopentanonecarboxylic acid with acids or superheated water. Neunhoeffer and Paschke (*8*) were able to isolate the intermediate, the expected 2-cyclopentanonecarboxylic acid.

Alkali hydroxides hydrolyze the ester to adipic acid. This type of ketone and acid cleavage is only significant in the case of C-substituted derivatives of esters (Table 1), which were subjected to cleavage almost without exception.

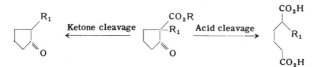

In ketone cleavage O-substituted cyclopentanones are formed which, because of the reactive ring carbonyl, can be important starting materials for the ortho ring closure on the five-membered ring (*58*). Preparatively important α-substituted adipic acids are formed through the acid cleavage reaction.

The ketone cleavage is usually brought about by heating with dilute or concentrated acids or hydrochloric acid–acetic acid (*109, 111*) (see Examples 4 and 5) and occurs satisfactorily with substituents containing up to 6 carbon atoms. Hückel and Kindler (*25*) used 20% perchloric acid with success. Also aqueous boric acid is suitable (*9*). Bromides are carefully treated with 40% hydrobromic acid, in which case the halogen is retained (*16*):

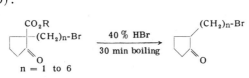

n = 1 to 6

The resulting bromoalkylcyclopentanone cyclizes under alkaline conditions with surprising ease to spirocycloalkanecyclopentanones (*59a*, *59b*), which may be rearranged to bicyclo [0.3.x] alkene (*59c, 59d*) after reduction to the alcohols.

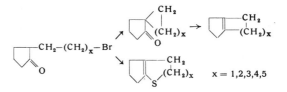

x = 1,2,3,4,5

Thiabicycloalkenes (*59e*) are formed from bromoalkylcyclopentanones with alkali metal acid sulfide and hydrogen sulfide.

The acid cleavage reaction in which hydrolysis is carried out with more or less concentrated alkali, goes almost quantitatively. Under cyclization conditions ketones, which are identical with those formed by ketone cleavage are formed from the α-substituted adipic acids.

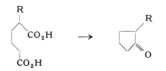

Thus, whenever a direct ketone cleavage fails, the desired ketone may be obtained through the acid cleavage reaction which is almost always successful. By the addition of a small amount of alkoxide the acid cleavage reaction goes directly to the esters of adipic acid through alcoholysis (yield: at least 80%, mostly 90–95%). According to Dieckmann (*60*) α,α'-dialkylcyclopentanones (*23*) may be obtained by cyclization followed by another alkylation:

Haworth and co-workers (*27*) utilized this possibility for syntheses in the steroid field, while Guha and Krishnamurthy (*30*) synthesized thujan:

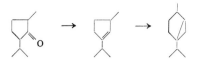

Further extension in the use of the cyclopentanones is merely noted here. Ruzicka and co-workers (*37*) have described a method in the cyclopentenonephenanthrene series:

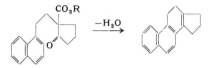

Tetrahydro-5-indanone resulted from the work of Prelog and Zimmermann (*55*). While Linstead and Meade (*43*) prepared bicyclo[0.3.3] octane from the cyclopentanone ester during the course of their pentalene work, Herz (*56*) described the syntheses of bicyclo[0.3.5]-decanones and their rearrangement to 1-, 1,5-, 2-, and 2,5-alkylazulenes. Aspinall and Baker (*51*) synthesized proazulene during their heptalene investigations; Nunn and Rapson (*38*) studied the synthesis of 4,5-benzazulene (*9*). According to Šorm (*45*) or Plattner (*44*) azulenes substituted in the 6-position may be obtained through the 1,2-cyclopentanediacetic acid (*43*):

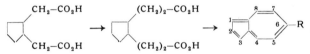

4,6-Dimethylazulenes are formed in a corresponding manner from α-bromopropionate esters and the cyclopentanone ester (*49*), while 5-substituted azulenes are obtained as follows (*50*):

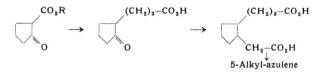

Ring-substituted (*16*) and isomeric (*62*) cyclopentanone esters need only be mentioned here. It is self-evident that all of the previously described syntheses are applicable to these. It is possible, for example, to prepare azulenes or steroids substituted in the five-membered ring.

Reduction

According to Mousseron and Jacquier (*63*) the reduction of the cyclopentanone esters with sodium amalgam gives the cyclopentanol ester

(*2,64*) and a dimer (b), both of which are readily converted to 1-cyclopentenecarboxylic acid (*65*).

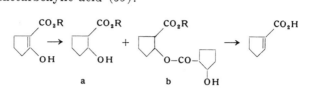

a   b

Moreover, sodium in absolute alcohol reduces the carboxyl group (*66*). According to our experiments, catalytic hydrogenation is the preparative method best suited for cyclopentanol esters (a). The method is advantageous in that the cyclopentanones arising from ketone cleavage may also be reduced (*66a*), and the splitting out of water (from the cyclic alcohol) is greatly reduced by a work-up using a high vacuum (see Example 6 at the end of this chapter).

The reduction of the carboxy group to the methylol group (*67*) may be carried out with lithium aluminum hydride, the ring-carbonyl group having been previously protected by acetalization with ethylene glycol (*68*):

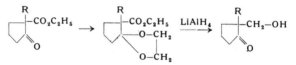

Otherwise there are formed, among others (*68a*):

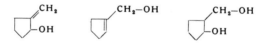

The reduction to *cis*- and *trans*-hydroxycyclopentanecarboxylic esters is said to go rather smoothly with sodium borohydride (*68b*).

The reduction of the ring carbonyl to a methylene group has not yet been carried out with derivatives of the type,

since even with careful reduction (*69*) cleavage products are also formed and consequently the synthesis of spirans is not possible. On the other hand spirans are directly accessible when the carbonyl group is protected (*70*). If the ester group is not desired in the final product, then the Clemmensen reduction with hydrochloric acid is used which, in one operation hydrolyzes, decarboxylates, and reduces:

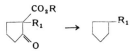

After the pharmacological activity of the chaulmoogra acid series became known, Bokil and Nargund (*52*) synthesized 11-cyclopentyl-undecanoic acid [$R_1 = (CH_2)_{10}COOH$)] in the above manner. Unfortunately some of the ω-halogenoalkanoic acids, necessary for the primary condensation, are difficult to obtain, so that up to now this method has become of preparative value only for certain members. An indirect method is possible using α-halogendicarboxylic acids, but the center carboxyl group can be decarboxylated only with difficulty (*53,54*).

In the electrolytic reduction of a cyclopentanone ester using a lead cathode, the cyclopentanol ester, cyclohexanol, the cyclopentane ester, and pinacol are formed (*71*). We could obtain pinacol readily using zinc and glacial acetic acid and thereby continue successfully in the azulene and tropolone series (*9*):

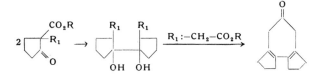

In the electrolysis of the sodium salt of the ethyl ester, diethyl 2,2'-dioxo[bicyclopentyl]-1,1'-dicarboxylate was obtained along with other products (*18a*). 1-(β-Diethylaminoethyl)-1-carbethoxy-2-cyclopentanol was formed in 65% yield by the reduction of the ketoester with aluminum isopropoxide in isopropyl alcohol (*117*). With respect to methylcyclopentanols, see reference (*102*).

Cyanohydrins

The activated carbonyl group of the cyclopentanone ester readily adds hydrocyanic acid (*72*) to give a distillable cyanohydrin, which serves as starting material for 1,2-dicarboxylic acids (*72a*). Similar reactions are successful with methyl derivatives (*72b*).

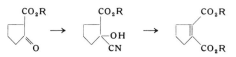

In contrast to the cycloheptanone derivatives which were investigated by Plattner (*73*), the equilibrium in the C-substituted cyclopentanone esters lies on the side of the cyanohydrins, which thus become suitable starting materials for *ortho*-ring closures in the cyclopentane system. A disadvantage is that with long chain substituents the compounds do not distill well and so are often difficult to purify. It is possible, however, in most instances to use the crude product (9). As an example:

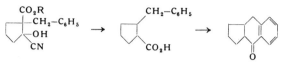

The Grignard and Reformatsky Reactions

Up to now the 2-cyclopentanonecarboxylates have been reacted unequivocally only at the active hydrogen of the enol (74a). A method for lengthening the chain of carboxylic acids by 5 carbon atoms from the MgBr salt of the enolic form of the ester depends on this reaction. On the other hand in carbon-substituted derivatives the carbonyl group reacts readily; thus a 60% yield is obtained in the action of β-phenylethylmagnesium bromide on 1-carbethoxy-1-methyl-2-cyclopentanone (74b). A benzazulene synthesis (74) should be pointed out as a preparative possibility (9):

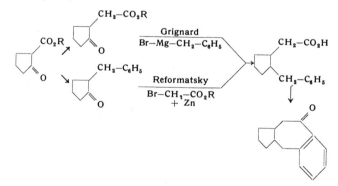

Besides this numerous 1,2-disubstituted 5-membered carbocyclics were obtained with the Grignard reaction (75) as test substances for physical measurements and made possible the further identification of petroleum-naphthene fractions. The combined yield, even with long-chain alkylenes, is mostly over 60% (74c).

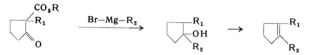

Enol Hydroxyl Exchange with Halogen

According to Rapson and Robinson (76) the enol hydroxyl group is replaced by chlorine using PCl₅, while with PBr₅ the reactive bromo compound is formed (9). Since the halide is readily reactive, the 2-substituted cyclopentanecarboxylic acids or their derivatives are conveniently obtained [for the formation of cycloalkanone derivatives see ref (77)]:

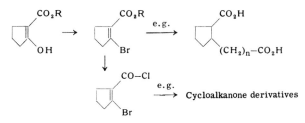

Replacement of the Carbonyl Oxygen by Sulfur

The thioesters (77a, 77b), obtained by the following reaction, have been investigated thoroughly in recent times (77b); it was discovered

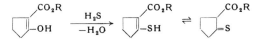

that, in contrast to the condensation of halides with 2-cyclopentanone-carboxylic esters, no carbon-substituted derivatives are obtained, but exclusively S-alkyl or S-acyl derivatives instead. Up to now (77b) methyl iodide, bromoacetate, β-bromopropionate, bromoacetone, and acetyl chloride (Examples 7 and 8) have been condensed. Carbon-substituted thioesters of the above type are not yet possible using the roundabout method of starting with a suitable cyclopentanone carboxylic ester.

The ring system of these thiocyclopentanone esters is surprisingly stable and it is not opened under the conditions for acid cleavage. Instead 2-thiocyclopentanonecarboxyl acids, present completely in the thio-enol form, are obtained; as also in the case of the ester, this may be oxidized quantitatively to the disulfide. By the addition of thioglycolic acid to the carbonyl group of ethyl 2-cyclopentanonecarboxylate and esterification with ethanol, the following compound is formed (77c):

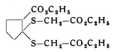

on distillation it is converted to the diethyl ester of 2-(carboxymethylthio)-1-cyclopentene-1-carboxylic acid, which may also be obtained by the direct condensation of bromoacetate with thiocyclopentanonecarboxylic ester (77b).

4,5-Cyclopenteno-1,2-dithiol-3-thione is isolated from the reaction of cyclopentanonecarboxylic esters with phosphorus pentasulfide (*77d*).

Condensation with Amines

Under 80° the amine adds primarily to the ring carbonyl and water splits out, so that both possible condensation products (a) and (b) are obtainable when ammonia is added (*2*):

Normally the exocyclic double bond is preferred on the basis of bond strain (*19, 20*). These Schiff bases can be converted to heterocyclic compounds through the reactive ester groups which are present on the ring.

In this manner aniline (*78*) or substituted anilines (*79*) reacted below 80° with the ring carbonyl, but cyclized to the 4-hydroxyquinoline derivative on distillation; e.g.,

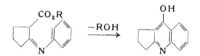

Schiff bases (see Example 9 at the end of this chapter) were also obtained with α-naphthylamine (*79a*), 5,6,7,8-tetrahydro-1-naphthyl-amine (*79a*), 1-amino-6-methoxynaphthalene (*79a*), 8-aminoquinoline (*79b*), and 5-aminoquinoline (*79b*). With dimethylamine (*79c*), ethyl 2-dimethylamino-1-cyclopentene-1-carboxylate was obtained.

In the reaction with benzylamine, investigated by us, the primary addition product is stable (*33*), splits out water at 70° and may close to a seven-membered ring:

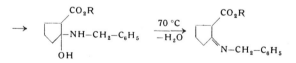

While practically no amides are formed below 80°, these are obtained in high yield by warming the reaction mixture. The numerous amides which have been prepared (Table 2) may be cyclized to 2-hydroxy-quinoline derivatives (*80*):

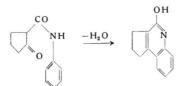

Amides have been obtained by other workers with 8-aminoisoquinoline (*79b*), *o*-toluidine (*79b*), aniline (*79d*), and α-naphthylamine (*79a*). These condensations with amines are simple preparations, although the purification and separation of the mixture are carried out with difficulty. Also to be considered here is the direct Dieckmann cyclization of N-alkyladipamates (*79e*) (Table 2, R-methyl, ethyl, *n*-propyl, *n*-butyl, *n*-hexyl, and phenyl).

TABLE 2
AMIDES

CO—NH—R

Amine	M.p. (°C)	Amine	M.p. (°C)
Aniline	104	*o*-Anisidine	155–6
p-Chloroaniline	115	2,5-Diethoxyaniline	95
p-Bromoaniline	132	α-Naphthylamine	162
o-Toluidine	95–6	β-Naphthylamine	172
m-Toluidine	98–9	Ethyl *p*-aminobenzoate	273–4
p-Toluidine	118–9	*o*-Phenylenediamine	158–9
2,5-Dichloroaniline	104	*m*-Phenylenediamine	217–8 (dec)
2,4-Dichloroaniline	156	*p*-Phenylenediamine	200 (dec)
Benzidine	270 (dec)	N,N-Diethyl-*p*-phenylenediamine	210–1
p-Anisidine	136–7		

In addition Barany and Pianka (*81*) applied the reactions to their photographic dyestuffs. Cook and co-workers (*82*) described the action of aminotriazole on the cyclopentanone ester. 5-Aminotetrazol (*82a*) affords on heating in alcohol solution a compound, $C_{10}H_{16}N_{10}O_2$. Other condensations were carried out with thiourea (*82b*), 2-aminobenzimidazole (*82c*), hydrazobenzene (*82d*), guanidine carbonate (*82d*), and glyoxalhydrazone hydrate (*82d*).

Diamine reacts simultaneously with the ring carbonyl and the carboxyl group. Thus, hydrazine (*2*) immediately forms the trimethylene-pyrazolone:

In all instances the nature of the reaction products is strongly dependent on condensation conditions: in alkaline media the 5-membered ring cleaves and the main product is adipic acid dihydrazide; in acetic acid solution 2 moles of 2-cyclopentanonecarboxylate ester reacts with one mole of hydrazine, the carbonyl group being involved (see Example 10).

Starting with phenylhydrazine, Mannich (*83*) obtained a highly active analog of antipyrin. During their work with antimalarials, Cliffe and co-workers (*84*) obtained cyclopentenopyrimidines by heating the ester with aryl biguanides. We effected condensation with urea and methylenediamines.

New preparative possibilities result from amino-condensation with the 2-substituted cyclopentanones obtained by ketone cleavage. For example, we were able to condense selectively the ring carbonyl group of the 2-cyclopentanoneacetate ester with aniline and cyclize to form 5- and 7-membered rings (*9*):

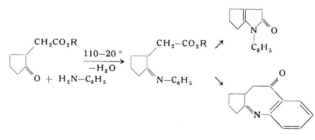

From this 5-7-6- ring compound with the nitrogen in the seven-membered ring heterocyclic azulenes and tropolone intermediates may be obtained.

Condensation with Phenols

In these reactions the carbonyl as well as the carboxyl group take part; with phosphorus pentoxide as condensing agent, chromones are formed (*5*). In this manner Hall and Plant (*85*) succeeded in obtaining 2,3-dihydropentachromone with phenol, while we prepared the corresponding thiochromone derivative with thiophenol (*86*).

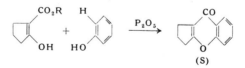

An extension of this reaction using *m*- or *p*-cresol, and β-naphthol is described by Ahmad and Desai (*87*). In the presence of strong acids chromones are not formed, but instead cumarins are obtained (*88*).

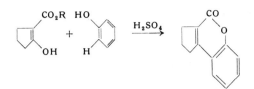

The following react in an analogous manner: *p*- and *m*-cresol, resorcinol, 4-ethylresorcinol, 4,6-diethylresorcinol (+POCl$_3$), orcinol, phloroglucinol, pyrogallol, and β-naphthol; also 1,8-dihydroxynaphthalene (*88a*), 1,4-, 1,5-, 1,6-, and 1,7-dihydroxynaphthalene (*88b*), as well as 1-hydroxy-5- or -8-methoxynaphthalene (*88b*) (see Example 11). Pillon (*89*) described the condensation with resorcinol without a condensing agent at 250°, obtaining at the same time chromones and coumarins, which could be separated through the differences in solubilities of their acyl or methoxy derivatives. Phenol, *p*-cresol, and 1,3,5-xylenol could not be condensed in this manner.

Direct Condensations

Direct condensations are typical of all β-keto esters, but in the case of the cyclopentanone ester are of preparative interest only because of the rearranged product. Gault and Daltroff (*90*) attempted repeatedly the reaction with formaldehyde, in which the resulting methylol derivative was to form *cis*-norcamphoric acid after acid cleavage. Owen and Peto (*90a*) were able to show the formation of α-methyleneadipic acid, which we obtained from the chloromethyl derivative (*16, 59b*).

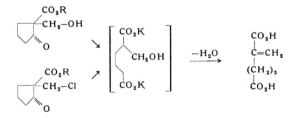

After 20 days' reaction of ethylene oxide in piperidine Pakendorf and Machus (*91*) could isolate the ester of ω-butyrolactonebutyric acid:

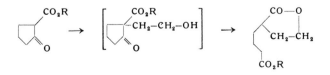

This transformation is only of theoretical interest, since condensation on one end with ethylene bromide leads to quicker and more certain results in this series (*16*).

Nitrous acid and the ester of 2-cyclopentanonecarboxylic acid react with ring cleavage to form the oxime of α-oxoadipic acid:

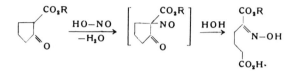

This reaction is suitable for the preparation of α-oxo- or α-amino-adipic acids. The latter was obtained by Kanao and Inagawa (*92*) from cyclopentanone ester and amyl nitrite followed by the reduction of the resulting esters of α-isonitrosoadipic acid (*92a*). Shaking the ester with sodium nitrite solution gave 1,2-cyclopentanedione monoxime (*92b*). An interesting parallel is found in the azo coupling reaction, in which the cyclopentanone ester couples with the aryldiazonium salt with simultaneous ring opening to form the arylhydrazone of the α-oxoadipic acid. From these compounds indoles may be synthesized using the Fischer procedure.

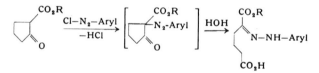

In this manner diazotized aniline (*93*), o-anisidine (*94*), p-toluidine (*95*), p-nitroaniline (*96*), m- and p-anisole (*97*), and 1-aminonaphthalene (*97a*) were reacted.

A direct condensation with 2-hexen-4-one, in which a new six-membered ring is formed, was effected by Coats and Cook (*97*), who started with an isopropylcyclopentanone ester so that finally 4,8-dimethyl-2-isopropylazulene was formed:

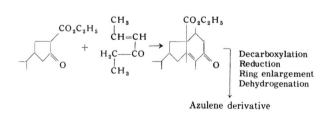

In the condensation of ethyl 2-cyclopentanonecarboxylate with ethyl cyanoacetate in the presence of piperidine a 50% yield of the diethylester of 2-carboxy-α-cyano-1-cyclopentene-1-acetic acid was obtained. Using the methyl ester a yield of 57% was obtained (*97b*). Other condensations have been made with diethyl maleate (*97c*), methyl methacrylate (*97d*), glyoxal (*97e*) and N,N'-bis(dimethylsulfamoyl)-p-benzoquinone diimine (*97f*).

In the presence of aluminum isopropoxide the cyclopentanone carboxylic ester was reacted with linalool (→geranylcyclopentanone), 2,3-dimethyl-1-penten-3-ol (→dimethylpentenylcyclopentanone), phenylvinylcarbinol (→cinnamylcyclopentanone) and cinnamyl alcohol (→phenylpropenylcyclopentanone) (*113*). With 3-methyl-7,8-dehydrolinalool a mixture of methylcitrylidenecyclopentanones was obtained (*97d*).

The reaction between oxalic ester and the cyclopentanone ester, examined by Komppa (*98*), deviated from the previously described course of reaction in that, surprisingly, a 90% yield of a 3- substituted derivative is formed, which could be transformed to norcamphor:

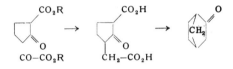

Reaction at Carbon-3

New synthetic possibilities arise, since aldehydes also condense in the 3-position (*99*) (see Example 12); e.g., with benzaldehyde the product is:

Since in the case of 3-monobenzalcyclopentanonecarboxylic esters, the ring carbonyl can still enolize, cyclizations are more readily possible than in the case of the monobenzalcyclopentanones (*100*).

An unforeseen reaction is the halogenation of the 2-cyclopentanone carboxylic ester in which substitution takes place in the 3-position among others (*101*).

Experimental Examples

Example 1

2-Carbethoxycyclopentanone (2-oxocyclopentane-carboxylic acid, ethyl ester) (see Pinkey in ref. (*7a*)). Dry sodium ethoxide (from 230 gm of sodium) is added to 2020 gm of diethyl adipate and about 2 liters of toluene and the solution is refluxed for 8 hr. The solution is acidified and the toluene layer separated. After distillation the yield is 1090 to 1208 gm (70–78%); b.p. 110–113°/22 mm; 109–111°/18 mm; 104–106°/14 mm; 102–103°/11 mm; 86–89°/2–3 mm; 80–81°/1–2 mm.

Example 2

Potassium salt of 2-carbethoxycyclopentanone (59a). A 112 gm portion of potassium hydroxide is dissolved in 30 ml of water and 550 ml of 96% alcohol and the solution is cooled to 5–10° with an ice-salt mixture. With stirring and outside cooling 312 gm of freshly distilled (!) 2-carbethoxycyclopentanone is added over a 3 min period and after 2 min 100 ml of ether is also added, care being taken that the reaction temperature does not exceed 20°. The pasty precipitate is suction filtered immediately, washed first with a small amount of ice cold 96% alcohol, then with ether. The solid is pressed on clay plates and is dried at 50–60° for 2 hr. Yield of crude product: 360 gm (93%). The product so obtained forms white, glistening, thick scales when recrystallized from alcohol. These do not deliquesce on standing in air, but with time acquire yellow color even in a closed amber bottle.

In most cases the crude product can be used for further reactions.

Example 3: Alkylation in the 1-Position

(a) *General procedure.* Molar quantities of the potassium salt of the ester (see Example 2) and the suitable alkyl halide in xylene or absolute alcohol are stirred and heated for several hours. The product is worked up in the usual manner and always purified by vacuum distillation. Yields are mostly greater than 50%.

(b) *1-(3-Bromopropyl)-1-carbethoxy-2-cyclopentanone (59a).* A 310 gm portion of the potassium salt of the ester (see Example 2) and 820 gm of 1,3-dibromopropane are stirred at 70–80° for 7 hr. The potassium bromide is suction filtered and the excess dibromopropane is distilled. The desired bromoester is obtained pure through two fractional vacuum distillations. Yield: 215 gm (50%); b.p. 135–138°/1–2 mm; $d_4^{20} =$ 1.3231; $n_D^{20} = 1.4898$.

Example 4: Ketone Cleavage

(a) *General procedure.* The ester to be cleaved is refluxed with stirring for 5–10 hr (occasionally 20–30 hr), with three times its volume of 25% hydrochloric acid or, if this acid cannot be used because of possible secondary reactions, with four times its volume of dilute sulfuric acid.

Normally a slow evolution of carbon dioxide begins after 30 min. The work-up depends upon the product, and may often involve a steam distillation.

(b) *1-(3-Bromopropyl)-2-cyclopentanone (59a).* A 240 gm portion of 1-(3-bromopropyl)-1-carbethoxy-2-cyclopentanone (Example 3b), 750 ml of 48% hydrobromic acid, and 15 gm of finely divided clay pieces are heated to vigorous boiling until the upper layer becomes a definite dark green (about 80 min); within a few minutes there is a definite evolution of carbon dioxide. After 1.2 liters of water have been added, the bromoketone is extracted with ether and purified by fractional distillation. Yield: 145 gm (80%); b.p. 98–105°/1–2 mm.

Example 5: Acid Cleavage

(a) *General procedure.* The ester to be cleaved is decomposed with an excess of dilute alkali hydroxide and refluxed for 4–20 hr. The ether extracts from the acidified reaction mixture are concentrated to encourage crystallization and the product is recrystallized from water, alcohol or a hydrocarbon. Purification through a difficultly soluble salt is usually not necessary.

(b) *α-Benzyladipic acid.* A 24.6 gm portion of 1-benzyl-1-carbethoxy-2-cyclopentanone is refluxed with 10% sodium hydroxide for 8 hr. The cooled solution is extracted with ether to remove any resins and acidified to precipitate α-benzyladipic acid as fine crystals. Yield: 90%; m.p. 116–117°.

Example 6

Ethyl 2-hydroxycyclopentanecarboxylate (66a). This compound is prepared by the reduction of ethyl 2-oxocyclopentanecarboxylate in an equal volume of ethanol using 10% platinum oxide and a pressure of 3–4 atm of hydrogen without warming. In the work-up a distillation at 0.1 mm is carried out. For derivatives and separation of isomers see ref. *(52)*; for cleavage with alcohol see ref. *(1)*.

Example 7

Ethyl 2-thiocyclopentanecarboxylate (77a, 77b). To 250 ml of absolute alcohol, first saturated with dry hydrogen chloride and then with hydrogen sulfide, is added 100 gm of ethyl 2-oxocyclopentanecarboxylate (Example 1). Then hydrogen sulfide is passed through the mixture for 11 hr. Purification is carried out in the usual manner through the lead salt. B. p. of ester (under nitrogen): 92–3°/3 mm. Yield: 75–80 gm (68–73%).

Example 8

Ethyl 2-carbethoxymethylthiolcyclopentanecarboxylate (77b). A 34.5 gm portion of the thio compound described in Example 7 is converted to its potassium salt in the manner used for its oxygen analog (Example 2), and condensed with 32 gm of ethyl bromoacetate in alcohol solution. B. p. 163–164°/2 mm. Yield: 26 gm (52%).

Example 9

Ethyl 2-Benzyliminocyclopentane-1-carboxylate (33). With shaking a cooled (0°) solution of 31.2 gm of ethyl 2-oxocyclopentanecarboxylate in 50 ml of benzene is treated slowly with 21.4 gm of precooled carbonate-free benzylamine in a carbon dioxide-free atmosphere. After the formation of a thick, white precipitate, the reaction mixture is warmed to 40° and suction filtered. The 2-benzylamino-1-carbethoxy-2-hydroxycyclopentane (colorless needles, m.p. 56–57°) is crystallized from the filtrate; the solid is dissolved in 50 ml of benzene and warmed to 70–71°. During the rapid splitting out of water, anhydrous sodium sulfate is added. The hot solution is filtered and the benzene distilled *in vacuo.* The pale yellow Schiff base crystallizes when kept in an ice-box. M. p. 26–27°. Yield: almost quantitative.

Example 10: Action of Hydrazine on Ethyl 2-Oxocyclopentanecarboxylate

(a) *Adipic acid dihydrazide.* A 30 gm portion of ethyl 2-oxocyclopentanecarboxylate is refluxed on the water bath for 5–6 hr with a threefold excess of an alcohol hydrazine hydrate solution. Then some of the alcohol is distilled off until the adipic acid dihydrazide crystallizes when the residue is cooled. Yield 27 gm (80%); m.p. 178° (from ethanol).

(b) *3,4-Trimethylene-2-pyrazolone.* A 10 gm portion of the ester is heated to boiling for 1–2 hours with a threefold excess of an aqueous 30% hydrazine hydrate solution. After about one hour the precipitation of fine crystals of 3,4-trimethylene-2-pyrazolone begins. After the solution has been cooled the insoluble pyrazolone is suction filtered and purified either from a large volume of alcohol or by vacuum sublimation at 200–220°. Yield: 6 gm (65%); m.p. 300–302° (in sealed capillary; slight decomposition at 250°).

(c) *bis(Carbethoxycyclopentylidene)hydrazine.* A 10 gm portion of the ester is refluxed for 8 hr with a threefold excess of 50% alcohol hydrazine hydrate solution, which is previously neutralized with glacial acetic acid and sodium acetate. After the solution is diluted with water and strongly cooled bis(carbethoxycyclopentylidene)hydrazine precipitates. M. p. 73–74° (from a very small amount of alcohol); yield 6 gm.

Example 11

2,3-Dihydropentachromone (*96*). A 40 gm portion of ethyl 2-oxocy-clopentanecarboxylate and 40 gm of phenol are treated with 80 gm of phosphorus pentoxide and after a few minutes the strong exothermic condensation is moderated with good external cooling. The reaction mixture is then heated at 100° for 3 hr, after which the excess phosphorus pentoxide is decomposed in the cold with ice water. From the alkaline solution the chromone is extracted with ether. Yield: 5 gm (11%); b.p. 185–195°/20 mm; m. p. 120–121° (from much water).

Example 12

Ethyl 3-benzal-2-oxocyclopentanecarboxylate (*99*). A 30.2 gm portion of ethyl 2-oxocyclopentanecarboxylate and 20.2 gm of benzaldehyde are dissolved in 100 ml of absolute methanol and 50 ml of 15% potassium hydroxide is added dropwise with stirring. The reaction mixture is kept in the cold for 2 hr, then diluted to 500 ml with water. After several hours colorless needles precipitate, which may be crystallized from methanol. M.p. 95°; yield: greater than 80%.

Prospect

The cyclopentanone ester can be used where reactive 1- and 1,2-cyclopentane derivatives are necessary for a series of syntheses. Furthermore the ester is suited for the synthesis of special 1,3-derivatives of cyclopentane, for they find particular use in the bicyclic series and further use in many condensation–cyclization reactions, which lead to carbo- and heterocyclic five-, six- and seven-membered rings. Our area of work is concerned with the problem of making adipic acids available for further syntheses through the cyclopentanone ester; of the latter bicyclic compounds, ring-closure reactions and direct condensations are being investigated.

REFERENCES

(1) W. Dieckmann, *Ber. deut. chem. Ges.* **27**, 965 (1894).
(2) W. Dieckmann, *Ann. Chem. Liebigs* **317**, 27–109 (1901).
(3) C. K. Ingold, "Structure and Mechanism in Organic Chemistry," p. 787 ff. Cornell Univ. Press, Ithaca, New York, 1953.
(4) R. I. Reed and M. B. Thornley, *J. Chem. Soc.* p. 2148 (1954).
(5) Cf. H. Henecka, "Chemie der Beta-Dicarbonyl-Verbindungen." Springer, Berlin, 1950.
(6) Methyl ester: M. N. Donin and co-workers, *J. Am. Chem. Soc.* **73**, 4286 (1951). Higher esters: H. Walther, Dissertation, Leipzig, 1954; also H. Walther, W. Treibs, and K. Michaelis, *Chem. Ber.* **89**, 60 (1956); V. G. Yashunskii and V. F. Vasil'eva, *Zhur. Obshcheĭ Khim.* **27**, 273 (1957); *Chem.*

Abstr. **51**, 12833 (1957); further especially references *6, 18, 19, 79, 89*. Polymethyl derivatives: J. C. Bardhan and R. N. Adhya, *J. Chem. Soc.* p. 2179 (1956). Cyclization of adiponitrile: Q. E. Thompson, *J. Am. Chem. Soc.* **80**, 5483 (1958).

(7) P. S. Pinkney, *Org. Syntheses* **17**, 30 (1937).

(7a) R. Mayer and U. Kubasch, *J. prakt. Chem.* [4], **9**, 43 (1959); cf. P. S. Pinkney, *Org. Syntheses* Coll. Vol. II, Wiley N.Y., 1943, p. 116; G. Komppa and A. Talvitie, Ann. Acad. Sci. Fennicae, Ser. **A57**, No. 15, 3 (1941); Chem. Abstr. **38**, 5496 (1944); also refs. 7 and 72.

(8) O. Neunhoeffer and P. Paschke, *Ber. deut. chem. Ges.* **72**, 919 (1939).

(9) R. Mayer, Inaugural dissertation, Leipzig, 1954.

(10) R. Mayer, *Chem. Ber.* **88**, 1861 (1955).

(10a) H. Orttmann, Private communication; cf. W. Treibs and H. Orttmann, *Naturwissenschaften* **45**, 85 (1958); *Chem. Ber.* **91**, 297 (1958).

(11) R. Mayer and W. Treibs, *Chem. Ber.* **87**, 349 (1954).

(12) W. Treibs and R. Mayer, *Chem. Ber.* **85**, 615 (1952).

(13) P. P. Patel and P. C. Guha, *J. Indian Inst. Sci.* **15A**, 125 (1932); *Chem. Abstr.* **27**, 3211 (1933).

(13a) C. R. Hauser and B. O. Linn, *J. Am. Chem. Soc.* **79**, 731 (1957); E. R. Clark and J. G. B. Howes, *J. Chem. Soc.* p. 1152 (1956).

(13b) J. C. Sauer, *J. Am. Chem. Soc.* **69**, 2444 (1947).

(14) P. G. Dayton, *Compt. rend. acad. sci.* **238**, 2316 (1954); cf. D. N. Shigorin, *Zhur. Fiz. Khim.* **24**, 924 (1950); *Chem. Abstr.* **45**, 1422 (1951).

(14a) D. N. Shigorin, *Izvest. Akad. Nauk S. S. S. R. Ser. Fiz.* **14**, 395 (1950); *Chem. Abstr.* **46**, 1868 (1952); N. J. Leonard, H. S. Gutowsky, W. J. Middleton, and E. M. Petersen, *J. Am. Chem. Soc.* **74**, 4070 (1952); P. G. Dayton, *Compt. rend. acad. sci.* **238**, 2316 (1954); E. S. Levin, *Bull. acad. sci. U.R.S.S. Sér. phys.* **11**, 413 (1947); *Chem. Abstr.* **42**, 3261 (1948).

(15) W. Dieckmann, *Ber. deut. chem. Ges.* **55**, 2470 (1921).

(15a) B. A. Arbuzov and V. S Vinogradova, *Doklady Akad. Nauk S.S.S.R.* **106**, 263 (1956); *Chem. Abstr.* **50**, 13787 (1956).

(15b) W. Strohmeier and I. Höhne, *Z. Naturforsch.* **8b**, 53 (1953); R. Schreck, *J. Am. Chem. Soc.* **71**, 1881 (1949).

(15c) F. Lacasa, J. Pascual, and L. V. del Arco, *Anales real soc. espān. fís. quím.* (*Madrid*) **52B**, 549 (1956); *Chem. Abstr.* **51**, 5711 (1957).

(16) R. Mayer and E. Alder, *Chem. Ber.* **88**, 1866 (1955).

(17) C. Weizmann, E. Bergmann, and M. Sulzbacher, *J. Org. Chem.* **15**, 918 (1950).

(18) R. T. Arnold, R. W. Amidon, and R. M. Dodson, *J. Am. Chem. Soc.* **72**, 2871 (1950).

(18a) A. M. Khaletskii and B. A. Zaputryaev, *Zhur. Obshchei Khim.* **26**, 3026 (1956); *Chem. Abstr.* **51**, 8019 (1957).

(19) M. v. Rysselberge, *Bull. sci. acad. roy. Belg.* [5], **12**, 171 (1926); *Chem. Abstr.* **21**, 375 (1927).

(20) F. H. Case and E. E. Reid, *J. Am. Chem. Soc.* **50**, 3062 (1928).

(21) R. Cornubert and C. Borrel, *Bull. soc. chim. France* [4], **47**, 301 (1930).

(22) G. Chiurdoglu, *Bull. soc. chim. Belges* **44**, 527 (1935).

(23) J. G. Hildebrandt and M. T. Bogert, *J. Am. Chem. Soc.* **58**, 650 (1936).

(24) A. Eschenmoser and A. Frey, *Helv. Chim. Acta* **35**, 1660 (1952).

(25) W. Hückel and H. Kindler, *Chem. Ber.* **80**, 202 (1947).

(26) M. E. Dobson, J. Ferns, and W. H. Perkin, *J. Chem. Soc.* **95**, 2010 (1909).

(27) R. D. Haworth, J. McKenna, and N. Singh, *J. Chem. Soc.* p. 831 (1949).
(28) M. M. Jamison, M. S. Lesslie, and E. E. Turner, *J. Inst. Petrol.* **35**, 590 (1949); *Chem. Abstr.* **44**, 3433 (1950).
(29) A. Kötz and P. Schüler, *Ann. Chem. Liebigs* **350**, 217 (1906).
(30) P. C. Guha and S. Krishnamurthy, *Ber. deut. chem. Ges.* **70**, 2112 (1937).
(31) B. Shive, W. W. Crouch, and H. L. Lochte, *J. Am. Chem. Soc.* **63**, 2979 (1941).
(32) W. S. Rapson and R. Robinson, *J. Chem. Soc.* p. 1533 (1935).
(33) W. Treibs, R. Mayer, and M. Madejski, *Chem. Ber.* **87**, 356 (1954).
(34) M. N. Donin, S. L. Burson, J. H. Müller, C. Chen, W. E. Behnke, and K. Hofmann, *J. Am. Chem. Soc.* **73**, 4286 (1951).
(35) J. R. Nunn and W. S. Rapson, *J. Chem. Soc.* p. 825 (1949).
(36) D. A. Duff and C. K. Ingold, *J. Chem. Soc.* p. 87 (1934).
(37) L. Ruzicka, L. Ehmann, M. W. Goldberg, and H. Hösli, *Helv. Chim. Acta* **16**, 833 (1933).
(38) J. R. Nunn and W. S. Rapson, *J. Chem. Soc.* p. 1051 (1949).
(39) H. Staudinger and L. Ruzicka, *Helv. Chim. Acta* **7**, 446 (1924).
(40) G. Komppa and A. Talvitie, *Ann. Acad. Sci. Fennicae Ser.* **A57**(15), 3 (1941); *Chem. Abstr.* **38**, 5496 (1944).
(41) A. Kötz, *Ann. Chem. Liebigs* **350**, 229 (1906).
(42) N. J. Leonard and W. J. Middleton, *J. Am. Chem. Soc.* **74**, 5114 (1952).
(43) R. P. Linstead and E. M. Meade, *J. Chem. Soc.* p. 935 (1934).
(44) P. A. Plattner and A. Studer, *Helv. Chim. Acta* **29**, 1432 (1946).
(45) F. Šorm and J. Fajkos, *Collection Czechoslov. Chem. Communs.* **12**, 81 (1947).
(46) Sukh Dev, *J. Indian Chem. Soc.* **30**, 815 (1953).
(47) See reference (*42*).
(48) Cf. N. N. Chatterjee, B. K. Das, and G. N. Barpujari, *J. Indian Chem. Soc.* **17**, 161 (1940).
(49) F. Šorm, Z. Šormová, and L. Šedivý, *Collection Czechoslov. Chem. Communs.* **12**, 554 (1947).
(50) F. Šorm, *Collection Czechoslov. Chem. Communs.* **12**, 251 (1947).
(51) G. O. Aspinall and W. Baker, *J. Chem. Soc.* p. 743 (1950).
(52) K. V. Bokil and K. S. Nargund, *J. Univ. Bombay* **6**, 93 (1937); *Chem. Abstr.* **32**, 3759 (1938).
(53) J. W. Baker, *J. Chem. Soc.* p. 1546 (1931).
(54) W. Treibs and R. Mayer, *Chem. Ber.* **85**, 615 (1952).
(55) V. Prelog and M. Zimmermann, *Helv. Chim. Acta* **32**, 2360 (1949).
(56) W. Herz, *J. Am. Chem. Soc.* **76**, 3349 (1954).
(57) N. D. Zelinsky and N. V. Elagina, *Izvest. Akad. Nauk S.S.S.R. Otdel. Khim. Nauk* p. 433 (1952). *Chem. Abstr.* **47**, 3803 (1953).
(58) o-Alkylsubstituted cyclopentanones are important in the perfume industry. Cf. S. M. Gupta and S. S. Deshapande, *J. Indian Chem. Soc.* **30**, 23 (1953).
(59a) R. Mayer, G. Wenschuh, and W. Töpelmann, *Chem. Ber.* **91**, 1616 (1958).
(59b) R. Mayer and H.-I. Schubert, *Chem. Ber.* **91**, 768 (1958).
(59c) R. Mayer and W. Töpelmann, *Chem. Ber.* **91**, 1764 (1958).
(59d) Cf. E. Vogel, *Chem. Ber.* **85**, 25 (1952).
(59e) R. Mayer and I. Liebster, *Angew. Chem.* **70**, 105 (1958).
(60) W. Dieckmann, *Ber. deut. chem. Ges.* **33**, 2672 (1900); **55**, 3344 (1922); cf. R. Cornubert and C. Borrel, *Bull. soc. chim. France* [4], **47**, 301 (1930).

(61) F. Šorm, V. Tomášek, and R. Vrba, *Collection Czechoslov. Chem. Communs.* **14**, 345 (1949); R. I. Reed and M. B. Thornley, *J. Chem. Soc.* p. 2148 (1954).

(62) D. K. Barnerjee and S. K. DasGupta, *J. Am. Chem. Soc.* **74**, 1318 (1952); P. C. Dutta, *J. Indian Chem. Soc.* **31**, 875 (1954); J. K. Roy, *J. Indian Chem. Soc.* **32**, 173 (1955).

(63) M. Mousseron and R. Jacquier, *Bull. soc. chim. France* [5], **17**, 648 (1950).

(64) J. Böeseken, G. Slooff, J. M. Hoeffelman, and H. E. Hirsch, *Rec. trav. chim.* **52**, 881 (1933).

(65) J. Pascual Vila and J. Castells, *Anales real soc. españ. fis. y. quím.* (*Madrid*) **46B**, 403 (1950); *Chem. Abstr.* **45**, 6589 (1951).

(66) N. D. Zelinsky and M. Ouschakoff, *Bull. soc. chim. France* [4], **35**, 484 (1924).

(66a) J. Pascual and J. Castells, *J. Am. Chem. Soc.* **74**, 2899 (1952); R. L. Kronenthal and E. I. Becker, *ibid.* **79**, 1095 (1957).

(67) See reference (*24*).

(68) Cf. L. Willimann and H. Schinz, *Helv. Chim. Acta* **32**, 2151 (1949).

(68a) A. S. Dreiding and J. A. Hartmann, *J. Am. Chem. Soc.* **75**, 939 (1953); E. Buchta and H. Bayer, *Ann. Chem. Liebigs* **573**, 227 (1951).

(68b) F. Lacasa and J. Pascual, *Anales real soc. españ. fis. y. quím.* (*Madrid*) **51B**, 551 (1955); *Chem. Abstr.* **50**, 11252 (1956).

(69) Cf. W. Steinkopf and A. Wolfram, *Ann. Chem. Liebigs* **430**, 113 (1923).

(70) Cf. S. C. S. Gupta and D. N. Chatterjee, *J. Indian Chem. Soc.* **31**, 911 (1954); **32**, 13 (1955).

(71) H. Stenzel, F. Fichter, and H. Arni, *Helv. Chim. Acta* **19**, 392 (1936).

(72) B. L. Nandi, *J. Indian Chem. Soc.* **11**, 213 (1934).

(72a) S. C. S. Gupta and N. N. Saha, *J. Indian Chem. Soc.* **29**, 331 (1952).

(72b) R. B. Bates, E. J. Eisenbraun, and S. M. McElvain, *J. Am. Chem. Soc.* **80**, 3413 (1958).

(73) P. A. Plattner, *Helv. Chim. Acta* **29**, 730 (1946).

(74) Cf. J. W. Cook, N. A. McGinnis, and S. Mitchell, *J. Chem. Soc.* p. 286 (1944); W. Keller, Dissertation, Zürich, 1952.

(74a) J. Plesek, *Chem. listy* **51**, 533 (1957); *Collection Czechoslov. Chem. Communs.* **22**, 1661 (1957); **21**, 1312 (1956).

(74b) E. Buchta and J. Kranz, *Ann. Chem. Liebigs* **601**, 170 (1956).

(74c) A. Deluzareche and A. Rudloff, *Compt. rend. acad. sci.* **240**, 2329 (1955).

(75) See reference (*28*).

(76) See reference (*32*).

(77) See reference (*63*).

(77a) K. Chandra, N. K. Chakrabarty, and S. K. Mitra, *J. Indian Chem. Soc.* **19**, 139 (1942).

(77b) R. Mayer and P. Barthel, *Chem. Ber.* **93**, 428 (1960).

(77c) H. Fiesselmann and F. Thoma, *Chem. Ber.* **89**, 1907 (1956).

(77d) N. Lozac'h and L. Legrand, *Compt. rend. acad. sci.* **234**, 1291 (1952); L. Legrand, Y. Mollier, and N. Lozac'h, *Bull. soc. chim. France* [5], **20**, 327 (1953).

(78) B. K. Blount, W. H. Perkin, Jr., and S. G. Plant, *J. Chem. Soc.* p. 1975 (1929).

(79) V. Petrow, *J. Chem. Soc.* p. 634 (1947).

(79a) G. R. Clemo and L. K. Mishra, *J. Chem. Soc.* p. 192 (1953).

(79b) D. G. Bew and G. R. Clemo, *J. Chem. Soc.* p. 1775 (1955).

(79c) J. Schmutz, *Helv. Chim. Acta* **38**, 1712 (1955).

(79d) B. Witkop, J. B. Patrick, and M. Rosenblum, *J. Am. Chem. Soc.* **73**, 2641 (1951).

(79e) D. H. Johnson, *J. Chem. Soc.* p. 1624 (1958).

(80) Cf. S. Z. Ahmad and R. D. Desai, *Proc. Indian Acad. Sci.* **A5**, 543 (1937); *Chem. Abstr.* **31**, 7875 (1937); D. Philpott and W. J. Jones, *J. Chem. Soc.* p. 337 (1938).

(81) H. C. Barany and M. Pianka, *J. Chem. Soc.* p. 1420 (1947).

(82) J. W. Cook, R. P. Gentles, and S. H. Tucker, *Rec. trav. chim.* **69**, 343 (1950).

(82a) J. W. Cook, R. P. Gentles, and S. H. Tucker, *Rec. trav. chim.* **69**, 1201 (1950).

(82b) M. Polonovski and D. Libermann, *Bull. soc. chim. France* [5], **14**, 1073 (1947).

(82c) A. de Cat and A. van Dormael, *Bull. soc. chim. Belges* **59**, 573 (1950); *Chem. Abstr.* **45**, 10247 (1951). Cf. French Patent 1,018,047 (1952).

(82d) G. Biglino, *Farmaco (Pavia) Ed. sci.* **12**, 72 (1957); *Chem. Abstr.* **53**, 20073 (1959).

(83) C. Mannich, *Ber. deut. pharm. Ges.* **267**, 699 (1929).

(84) W. H. Cliffe, F. H. S. Curd, F. L. Rose and M. Scott, *J. Chem. Soc.* p. 574 (1948).

(85) H. J. Hall and S. G. Plant, *J. Chem. Soc.* p. 232 (1933).

(86) R. Mayer. Unpublished result.

(87) S. Z. Ahmad and R. D. Desai, *Proc. Indian Acad. Sci.* **A6**, 6 (1937); *Chem. Abstr.* **32**, 559 (1938).

(88) S. Z. Ahmad and R. D. Desai, *Proc. Indian Acad. Sci.* **A5**, 277 (1937); *Chem. Abstr.* **31**, 5785 (1937).

(88a) N. P. Buu-Hoï and D. Lavit, *J. Chem. Soc.* p. 2412 (1956).

(88b) N. P. Buu-Hoï and D. Lavit, *J. Org. Chem.* **21**, 1022 (1956).

(89) D. Pillon, *Bull. soc. chim. France* [5], **19**, 324 (1952); cf. O. Dann and G. Mylius, *Ann. Chem. Liebigs* **587**, 1 (1954).

(90) H. Gault and L. Daltroff, *Compt. rend. acad. soc.* **209**, 997 (1939); cf. *Chem. Zentr.* I, 3377 (1941); *Ann. chim. (Paris)* [11], **14**, 207 (1940).

(90a) L. N. Owen and A. G. Peto, *J. Chem. Soc.* p. 1146 (1956).

(91) K. G. Pakendorf and F. F. Machus, *Doklady Akad. Nauk S.S.S.R.* **31**, 441 (1941); *Chem. Abstr.* **37**, 870 (1943).

(92) S. Kanao and S. Inagawa, *J. Pharm. Soc. Japan* **48**, 40 (1928); *Chem. Zentr.* II, 50 (1928); cf. *Chem. Abstr.* **22**, 2923 (1928).

(92a) Y. Inoue and S. Somo, *J. Agr. Chem. Soc. Japan* **23**, 396 (1950); M. Friedman and E. Boger, *J. Am. Chem. Soc.* **78**, 4659 (1956).

(92b) A. C. Cope, L. L. Estes, Jr., J. R. Emery, and A. C. Haven, Jr., *J. Am. Chem. Soc.* **73**, 1199 (1951).

(93) R. H. F. Manske and R. Robinson, *J. Chem. Soc.* p. 240 (1927).

(94) R. H. F. Manske, *Can. J. Research* **4**, 591 (1931).

(95) R. H. F. Manske and L. C. Leitch, *Can. J. Research* **B14**, 1 (1936).

(96) H. S. B. Barrett, W. H. Perkin, and R. Robinson, *J. Chem. Soc.* p. 2942 (1929).

(97) R. R. Coats and J. W. Cook, *J. Chem. Soc.* p. 559 (1942).

(97a) R. Justoni and R. Pessina, *Farmaco (Pavia) Ed. sci.* **10**, 356 (1955); *Chem. Abstr.* **49**, 13968 (1955); V. V. Feofilaktov, *Bull. Akad. Nauk S.S.S.R.* p. 521 (1941); *Chem. Abstr.* **37**, 2347 (1943).

(97b) M. Protiva, V. Mychajlyszyn, and J. O. Jilek, *Chem. listy* **49**, 1045 (1955); *Chem. Abstr.* **50**, 3476 (1956).

(97c) K. C. Ghosh, *J. Indian Chem. Soc.* **24**, 45 (1947).

(97d) Y.-R. Naves and P. Ardizio, *Bull. soc. chim. France* [5], p. 672 (1956).

(97e) J. Levisalles and P. Baranger, *Compt. rend. acad. sci.* **242**, 1336 (1956).

(97f) R. Adams and W. P. Samuels, Jr., *J. Am. Chem. Soc.* **77**, 5375 (1955).

(98) See reference (*40*).

(99) R. Mayer and B. Gebhardt, unpublished; cf. W. Treibs and W. Schroth, *Angew. Chem.* **71**, 71 (1959).

(100) Cf. R. Mayer, *Chem. Ber.* **88**, 1853 (1955).

(101) B. A. Zaputryaev and A. M. Khaletskii, *Zhur. Obshchei̇ Khim.* **27**, 2214 (1957); *Chem. Abstr.* **52**, 6207 (1958); R. P. Bell, R. D. Smith, and L. A. Woodward, *Proc. Roy. Soc.* **A192**, 479 (1948); R. P. Bell and J. C. Mc-Coubrey, *ibid.* **A234**, 192 (1956); R. P. Bell, J. A. Fendley, and J. R. Hulett, *ibid.* **A235**, 453 (1956). K. J. Pedersen, *Acta Chem. Scand.* **2**, 385 (1948).

(102) W. Hückel and H. D. Sauerland, *Chem. Ber.* **87**, 1003 (1954).

(103) I. N. Nazarov, L. D. Bergel'son, I. V. Torgov, and S. N. Ananchenko, *Izvest. Akad. Nauk. S.S.S.R. Otdel. Khim. Nauk* p. 889 (1953); *Chem. Abstr.* **49**, 1082 (1955).

(104) G. Eglinton, J. C. Nevenzel, A. I. Scott, and M. S. Newman, *J. Am. Chem. Soc.* **78**, 2331 (1956); cf. Y. I. Denisenko and A. D. Naber, *Bull. Acad. Sci. U. S. R. Div. Chem. Sci.* p. 35 (1945); *Chem. Abstr.* **40**, 2801 (1946).

(105) See reference (*24*).

(106) D. N. Chatterjee, *J. Am. Chem. Soc.* **77**, 414 (1955).

(107) D. N. Chatterjee, *J. Am. Chem. Soc.* **77**, 5131 (1955).

(108) R. Lukeš and J. Plesek, *Chem. listy* **49**, 1095 (1955); cf. *Collection Czechoslov. Chem. Communs.* **20**, 1253 (1955).

(109) A. Maillard, A. Deluzarche, and A. Rudloff, *Compt. rend. acad. sci.* **240**, 317 (1955).

(110) N. A. Milas, U. S. Patent 2,407,672; *Chem. Abstr.* **41**, 996 (1947).

(111) R. Cornubert, P. Aniani, and G. Morelle, *Bull. soc. chim. France* [5], **11**, 299 (1944).

(112) H. Adkins and G. F. Hager, *J. Am. Chem. Soc.* **71**, 2965 (1949).

(113) J. Dreux and J. Colonge, *Bull. soc. chim. France* [5], p. 1312 (1955).

(114) I. N. Nazarov, S I. Zav'yalov, and M. S. Burmistrova, *Izvest. Akad. Nauk S. S. S. R. Otdel. Khim. Nauk* p. 205 (1956); *Chem. Abstr.* **50**, 13762 (1956).

(115) W. Herz, *J. Org. Chem.* **22**, 630 (1957).

(116) W. Herz, *J. Am. Chem. Soc.* **78**, 1485, 2529 (1956).

(117) F. Winternitz, M. Mousseron, and M. Canet, *Bull. soc. chim. France* [5], **18**, 452 (1951).

(118) S. J. Rhoads, R. D. Reynolds, and R. Raulins, *J. Am. Chem. Soc.* **74**, 2889 (1952).

(119) H. Böhme and K. Kreitz, *Arch. Pharm.* **291**, 566 (1958).

(120) F. Winternitz and R. M. Thakker, *Bull. soc. chim. France* [5], **19**, 471 (1952).

(121) R. Fusco and R. Trave, *Gazz. chim. ital.* **80**, 496 (1950); O. Riobé, M. Lamant, L. Gouin, and R. Gigault, *Compt. rend. acad sci.* **246**, 1710 (1958).

(122) W. Herz, *J. Am. Chem. Soc.* **78**, 1485 (1956); *J. Org. Chem.* **22**, 585 (1957).

(123) J. F. Tinker, *J. Am. Chem. Soc.* **73**, 4493 (1951).

(124) Cf. J. Maillard, M. Benard, and R. Morin, *Bull. soc. chim. France* [5], p. 244 (1958).

(125) O. B. Talukdar and P. Bagchi, *J. Org. Chem.* **20,** 25 (1955).

(126) W. Herz, *J. Am. Chem. Soc.* **76,** 3349 (1954).

(127) D. K. Banerjee and T. R. Kasturi, *J. Am. Chem. Soc.* **79,** 926 (1957).

(128) H. Plieninger and T. Suehiro, *Chem. Ber.* **88,** 550 (1955).

(129) H. Plieninger, *Chem. Ber.* **86,** 404 (1953).

(130) H. M. E. Cardwell and F. J. McQuillin, *J. Chem. Soc.* p. 708 (1949).

(131) H. M. E. Cardwell, *J. Chem. Soc.* p. 715 (1949).

Ketene in Preparative Organic Chemistry

G. Quadbeck

*Max-Planck-Institut für Medizinische Forschung,
Institut für Chemie, Heidelberg*

Introduction

Ketene ($CH_2=C=O$), the inner anhydride of acetic acid, is distinguished among the acetylating agents, because theoretically no side products are formed in its addition reactions, as shown by the general equation,

$$XH + CH_2=C=O \longrightarrow X-CO-CH_3$$

It is the parent substance of a very reactive class of compounds, the ketenes (*1*).

In contrast to the disubstituted ketenes, e.g., diphenylketene or dimethylketene, ketene is not autoxidizable and is also significantly less reactive than these. Nevertheless, ketene reacts smoothly at room temperature with water, primary alcohols, and amines to form the corresponding acetyl derivatives. To its discoverers (*2*) it appeared to be a very useful acetylating agent. When this gaseous acetylating reagent, in spite of its obvious advantages, found only occasional use in the laboratory, the situation was primarily due to the fact that with ketene only a proportionally small number of reactions were possible, and these were already known to occur smoothly with other acetylating agents. J. van Alphen (*3, 4*) stated, because only a few acetylations had been successful in his hands, that ketene, while very convenient, was a less effective acetylating agent.

Ketene has become a very versatile reagent in preparative organic chemistry. This came about after the discovery that many acetylations occurred not only smoothly and with good yields, but also specifically, in the presence of proper catalysts (*5, 6, 7*). The same reactions without a catalyst went poorly or not at all.

General Properties

Very pure ketene [b. p. −41°, m.p. −134.6° (*8*)] is stable to some extent only at low temperatures (−80°) and so must be freshly prepared and used immediately. Ketene is used to a large extent in technical production of acetic anhydride (9).

$$H_3C-C\underset{OH}{\overset{O}{<}} \quad + \quad O=C=CH_2 \quad \rightarrow \quad \underset{CH_3-CO}{\overset{CH_3-CO}{>}}O$$

The compound is prepared either by the pyrolysis of acetic acid in the presence of the proper catalysts [e.g., triethyl phosphate (10, 11), or H_3PO_4 (12)],

$$H_3C-C\underset{OH}{\overset{O}{<}} \quad \xrightarrow[\text{catalyst}]{700\ °C} \quad CH_2=C=O + H_2O$$

or by the pyrolysis of acetone (2), which now can be economically obtained from propylene via 2-propanol. The unsaturated hydrocarbon is obtained from cracked gases. The pyrolysis of acetone occurs mostly without catalyst; however, in technical preparation a sulfur-containing compound is added to minimize carbonization (13, 14). The cracking process occurs according to the general equation

$$CH_3-CO-CH_3 \quad \xrightarrow{700-800\ °C} \quad CH_2=C=O + CH_4$$

The first pyrolysis reaction is not suited for laboratory use (15). The pyrolysis of acetone is the method of choice. Ketene may be obtained in the laboratory by the pyrolysis of acetic anhydride (2, 16) or of diketene (17), but these methods are seldom used. In most present laboratory ketene generators, pure acetone vapor is passed over an electrically heated (about 780°) chrome-nickel resistance wire (18, 19) and the ketene–methane gas mixture, freed from acetone and polyketene by passage through cold traps, is introduced directly into the reaction flask.

The pyrolysis of acetone is probably a free-radical chain reaction (20).

1.) $CH_3-CO-CH_3$ heat $\rightarrow 2\ CH_3{}^* + C=O$
2.) $2\ CH_3{}^* + 2\ CH_3-CO-CH_3 \rightarrow 2\ CH_4 + 2\ CH_3-CO-CH_2{}^*$
3.) $2\ CH_3-CO-CH_2{}^* \rightarrow 2\ CH_3{}^* + 2\ CH_2=C=O$

Neglecting the first reaction, one can see that there is one ketene molecule and one methane molecule formed for each acetone molecule. At higher temperature and also in light, ketene is split into methylene and carbon monoxide (21).

$$CH_2=C=O \xrightarrow{h\nu} CH_2 + CO$$

CH_2 is not a radical, but is very reactive nevertheless, so that it readily reacts with excess ketene.

$$CH_2 + CH_2=C=O \rightarrow H_2C=CH_2 + CO$$

Therefore ketene obtained by pyrolytic reactions is always contaminated with ethylene and carbon monoxide.

The carbonyl group of ketene is not reactive. No carbonyl reactions are known. Phenylhydrazine (22) and hydroxylamine (23) are N-acetylated. Practically all reactions take place at the carbon–carbon double bond. Compounds which are proton donors are acetylated.

Of the resonance structures which are important for the reaction behavior, structure I makes the main contribution to the ground state. For a reaction to take place it is necessary that a shift toward the mesomeric form II is induced through polarization. Hence, reactions proceed smoothly with ketene when the other reactant has a polar structure and is able to induce the necessary polarization of ketene (e.g., carboxylic acids, halogen acids, amines). Substances which do not bring about such a polarization generally react more slowly (secondary, tertiary or polyhydroxy alcohols). By addition of proper catalysts— for alcohols mostly strong acids—such compounds having little dipole character of their own can be polarized; they, in turn, can polarize ketene to the reactive form so that a quick and complete reaction takes place.

When working with ketene, it is well to remember that it is an extremely poisonous gas. Its toxicity approximates that of phosgene which it resembles clinically in its toxic symptoms (lung edema) (24, 25). Leaks in the ketene apparatus are easily recognized by the pungent, characteristic odor, reminiscent of acetic anhydride. Smokers are particularly sensitive to this unpleasant odor.

Reactions

Aliphatic or Aromatic Hydroxyl Group

$$R-OH + CH_2=C=O \rightarrow R-O-CO-CH_3$$

Ketene reacts smoothly with water (2, 22). In spite of this it is not practicable to destroy an excess of ketene by pouring the reaction mix-

ture into water, because the reaction proceeds too slowly. This fact makes
it possible to use water as a solvent for some acetylations. Addition of
acids, bases, or neutral salts increases the speed of the reaction between
ketene and water to form acetic acid.

Hydrogen peroxide reacts with ketene in the same fashion as water
(26). In this case it is difficult to obtain the primary reaction product,
peracetic acid, since ketene acetylates the latter very rapidly to form
diacetyl peroxide.

$$H-O-O-H + H_2C=C=O \rightarrow H-O-O-CO-CH_3$$
$$H_3C-CO-O-O-H + H_2C=C=O \rightarrow H_3C-CO-O-O-CO-CH_3$$

Diacetyl peroxide may be obtained in good yield by this method.

Methanol, ethanol, and 1-propanol are readily acetylated without a
catalyst at room temperature. The statement by J. P. Tsukervanik
(27) that catalysts with these alcohols lower the yield, probably is in
error. With the higher alcohols the acetylated product hinders further
reaction. 1-Butanol in a mixture of 75% butyl acetate is not further
acetylated with ketene (28). In the presence of water, sodium acetate,
or best, sulfuric acid, acetylation occurs almost completely. Tertiary
butyl alcohol, which does not react with ketene in the absence of a
catalyst, is esterified in good yield in the presence of 0.2–0.5% sulfuric
acid or p-toluenesulfonic acid (5). In the acetylation of alcohols acidic
catalysts are mostly used, although basic catalysts have been found
suitable (Table 1).

TABLE 1
CATALYSTS FOR THE ACETYLATION OF HYDROXYL GROUPS

Catalyst	Principal use	References
H_2SO_4	Alcohols, phenols	5, 24, 27, 28, 33
	Esters of hydroxy acids	34, 35, 36, 38, 39
	(Carbohydrates)	42, 43, 46
p-Toluenesulfonic acid	Alcohols, phenols	5, 35, 37, 38
Sodium acetate	Alcohols	29, 35, 39, 44
H_3PO_4, $HClO_4$	(Carbohydrates)	36, 37
$ZnCl_2$	(Carbohydrates)	33, 35, 37
Benzenesulfonic Acid	(Carbohydrates)	33, 36
Pyridine	(Carbohydrates), phenols	31, 39
Chlorosulfonic Acid	(Carbohydrates)	33
Water	Alcohols	28
$KHSO_4$	Alcohols	45
Urea	Furfuryl alcohol	45

Through the use of suitable catalysts other functional groups in the
molecule do not affect, in general, the acetylation of primary alcohols.

In contrast, the polyalcohols are often incompletely acetylated even in the presence of catalysts. Glycol can be completely acetylated in the presence of sodium acetate (29), while glycerine is only partially acetylated either without a catalyst (30) or with sulfuric acid (31). Attempts by J. van Alphen to acetylate glucose with ketene in the presence of pyridine failed (4). C. D. Hurd (31), using sulfuric acid with acetone as solvent, obtained only a partially acetylated sirup with glucose; it could not be further acetylated to pentaacetyl glucose with acetic anhydride. Glucose and ketene do not react in acetone or dioxane without a catalyst. However, glucose derivatives in which the hydroxyl group in the 1-position is blocked, react with ketene without a catalyst. Thus, methyl α-glucoside in dioxane is triacetylated, and α-methyl-6-tritylmethyl glucoside in acetone is converted to the 2,3,4-triacetyl derivative. In similar fashion glucose 1,2-dimethylketal can be acetylated to the 3,4,6-triacetyl derivative.

The preparation of acetyl cellulose is the most important commercial acetylation reaction. Cellulose is acetylated with acetic anhydride in the presence of strong acids and at higher temperature. It seemed natural to use ketene, a starting material for the commercial production of acetic anhydride. Rice and co-workers (8) could observe no reaction between ketene and cellulose. However, the patent literature reveals the smooth acetylation of cellulose and of starches with ketene. The following solvents are recommended: liquid SO_2 (32), glacial acetic acid (33, 34, 35), acetic anhydride, benzene, and benzine. Aside from SO_2 as solvent, acid catalysts such as H_2SO_4, chlorosulfonic acid, p-toluenesulfonic acid, HF, $ZnCl_2$, etc., are used.

By using glacial acetic acid, acetic anhydride or water-containing solvents, it is quite possible that ketene does not react directly with the carbohydrate, but reacts with the acetic acid either existing or formed in the solvent. The observed acetylations are then accounted for by the acetic anhydride which is formed (36, 37).

The reaction of ketene with phenols without a catalyst is uncertain and apparently dependent upon chance. Besides failures (4), conversions of 50% (38), 65–90% (27), and 80% (39) are recorded. By passing ketene through boiling phenol quantitative acetylation is obtained (8). Good yields are obtained regularly with H_2SO_4, p-toluenesulfonic acid or other acid catalysts (5, 38, 39). Phenol carboxylic acids, especially salicylic acid, react smoothly with ketene; in the case of salicylic acid either acetylsalicylic acid (4, 40) or the mixed anhydride (8, 41) is obtained, (see below) depending on reaction conditions. Among the polyphenols hydroquinone (8) and resorcinol (H_2SO_4) (39) are smoothly acetylated, while the reaction with phloroglucinol goes slowly and in poor yield even in the presence of H_2SO_4. As was the case with the alcohols the multiplicity of hydroxyl groups in phenols seems to reduce their activity towards ketene.

Because of the tendency for ketene to polymerize, impure products are often obtained in the acetylation of polyhydric alcohols. Often the acetylation is incomplete because the polymerization rate is greater than the reaction rate. R. E. Dunbar and L. L. Bolstadt (*41a*) could show that the rate of polymerization is strongly dependent on the solvent. At 0° ketene polymerizes in acetone 300 times more quickly than in carbon tetrachloride. In these solvents glucose, mannose, and sorbose are readily acetylated in good yields using H_2SO_4 as catalyst. Because of the insolubility of these carbohydrates, a suspension is used, the end of the reaction being detected by the disappearance of the suspended crystals.

Amines

$$R_1 \diagdown NH + CH_2{=}C{=}O \longrightarrow R_1 \diagdown N{-}CO{-}CH_3$$
$$R_2 \diagup \qquad\qquad\qquad R_2 \diagup$$

Ketene reacts quite readily with primary amines. Catalysts are not necessary in this reaction (*1, 2, 47*). In many cases the reaction proceeds in aqueous solution. In this manner M. Bergmann and F. Stern were able (*48, 49*) to N-acetylate glucosamine, aniline, and a large number of amino acids in good yields. Tyrosine was O,N-diacetylated in 87% yield in an aqueous alkaline solution. Amino acids may also be acetylated in weakly acid solutions. Under these conditions racemization occurs in some cases (e.g., tryptophan) (*50, 51*). Ketene acetylation is always used and is superior to other acetylations, when other functional groups (e.g., OH) in the molecule are not to be acetylated. It is possible to acetylate exclusively the nitrogen atom of amino alcohols or amino sugars in aqueous or methanol solutions.

The following are cited as examples: colamine (2-aminoethanol) (*29*), serine (*48*), p-aminophenol (*48*), glucosamine (*48*), and 3-0-methyl-1-glucosamine (*52*). Insulin is wholly inactivated by acetylation with acetic anhydride (*53, 54*). With ketene K. G. Stern and A. White (*55*) were able to acetylate exclusively the amino groups and in this manner were able to show these were not essential for the physiological activity of insulin, in contrast to the further acetylation of OH groups by other means which resulted in an inactive compound. Other proteins may be acetylated stepwise: pepsin (*56, 57*), tetanus toxin (*58*), hypophysin hormone (*59*), casein (*60*), and albumin (*61, 62*). Secondary amines react smoothly with ketene, if the nitrogen is still somewhat basic, but not in aqueous solution. The acetylation of N-methylaniline in dilute alcohol goes in 75% yield (48), while that of diphenylamine in ether at 0° gives only a 33% yield (63). Ethylenimine reacts readily with ketene, retaining the three-membered ring to give the very reactive N-acetylethylenimine (64).

$$\begin{array}{c} CH_2 \\ | \quad \diagdown \\ | \quad \diagup NH \\ CH_2 \end{array} + \begin{array}{c} O \\ \| \\ C=CH_2 \end{array} \qquad \begin{array}{c} CH_2 \\ | \quad \diagdown \\ | \quad \diagup N-CO-CH_3 \\ CH_2 \end{array}$$

Amides treated with an excess of ketene, and for a longer period of time, are further acetylated, especially in the presence of an acid catalyst such as sulfuric acid. By this means acetamide is converted to diacetamide (65) and triacetamide (66). Urea is monoacetylated in alcohol solution, but diacetylated in acetone or dioxane, using sulfuric acid as a catalyst. If an amide is reacted at a higher temperature, then a nitrile is obtained through the splitting out of water (8, 67).

$$R-CO-NH_2 + CH_2=C=O \rightarrow R-C\equiv N + CH_3-COOH$$

Ketene acetylates ammonia easily, but does not react with phosphine or arsine. With dimethylarsine, however, a good yield of acetyldimethylarsine is obtained (68).

$$\begin{array}{c} H_3C \\ \diagdown \\ \diagup As-H \\ H_3C \end{array} + CH_2=C=O \longrightarrow \begin{array}{c} H_3C \\ \diagdown \\ \diagup As-COCH_3 \\ H_3C \end{array}$$

Halogenated amines react according to the nature of the various substituents (69).

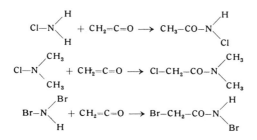

According to R. Kuhn and W. Kirschenlohr (69a) lactose oxime reacts with ketene in 70% methanol, picking up one acetyl group. On the basis of the IR spectrum it appears that N-acetylation has taken place.

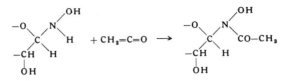

The acetylation of other amides with ketene was described by Dunbar and White (69b). Using sulfuric acid as catalyst they were able to obtain from formamide the hitherto undescribed diacetylformamide (m.p. 107°).

Thiol Compounds

$$RSH + CH_2=C=O \longrightarrow RS-CO-CH_3$$

Chick and Wilsmore were the first to react ketene with hydrogen sulfide (70). The liquid components were brought together to obtain thioacetic anhydride.

$$CH_2=C=O + H_2S \longrightarrow CH_3-CO-SH + CH_2=C=O \longrightarrow \begin{array}{c} CH_3-CO \\ CH_3-CO \end{array} S$$

Crouch (71) obtained thioacetic acid in good yield by passing the reactants in the vapor phase over an Al_2O_3-contact catalyst at 100°. Passing in ketene at 60° he obtained thioacetic anhydride.

Mercaptans react smoothly with ketene under proper conditions. Liquid ketene (72) may be used at low temperature or at normal temperatures, if the mercaptan is not too volatile (73, 74, 75). The use of strong acid catalysts is not advantageous according to prevailing experience (74). The thiol groups of amino acids (76, 77) or of proteins (61, 62) react smoothly with ketene in aqueous solution under neutral, weakly basic, or weakly acidic conditions. The thiol group is more easily acetylated with ketene than the hydroxyl group. This is ascribed to the stronger acid character of the thiol group.

Carboxylic Acids

$$R-COOH + CH_2=C=O \longrightarrow \begin{array}{c} R-CO \\ H_3C-CO \end{array} O$$

Carboxylic acids are readily acetylated by ketene, the reaction being autocatalyzed by the polar character of the acid. As previously indicated this reaction finds its use to a great extent in the preparation of acetic anhydride (78). Mixed anhydrides are formed with other acids using this reaction (79). These are converted spontaneously (better at higher temperature) to symmetrical anhydrides, especially when R is larger than CH_3.

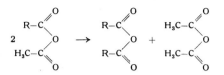

If the acid to be acetylated is a liquid, the reaction is carried out mostly without a solvent (*81, 85*). Solid acids are dissolved in ether (*79, 80, 82*), acetone (*82*) or benzene (*80, 84*). For these the reaction temperature does not appear to be important. Temperatures from 20° (*82*) to 90° (*84*), as well as ice-cooling (*81*), have been used. Addition of catalysts is not necessary. With hydroxy acids the hydroxyl group, in most instances, is acetylated first, followed by the carboxyl group. Also, amino acids can be converted to the N-acetylamino acid anhydride (*83*).

$$2\ H_2N-CH_2-COOH + 4\ CH_2{=}C{=}O \longrightarrow$$

$$\begin{matrix} H_3CCO-NH-CH_2-CO \\ H_3CCO-NH-CH_2-CO \end{matrix}\Big\rangle O + \begin{matrix} H_3CCO \\ H_3CCO \end{matrix}\Big\rangle O$$

The mixed anhydride with formic acid is stable and can be readily distilled (*5, 80, 84*). It reacts with amino groups, forming almost exclusively formyl derivatives, and so has proved to be a convenient and useful formylating agent. Sometimes it is possible to formylate by dissolving the amine in formic acid, then passing in the ketene. In most of the examples above, the acid component of the mixed acid anhydrides having the lower molecular weight reacts preferably as the acylating agent. The mixed acid anhydride of chloroacetic acid acetylates with one or the other of the acyl components depending upon the solvent. Thus the reaction with aniline in benzene gives 86% of the chloroacetyl derivative; with acetone–water as solvent 72% of acetanilide and only a small amount of the chloro-derivative is obtained (*85*).

Since the reaction between ketene and carboxylic acids runs smoothly and with good yields, this procedure is especially suitable for the preparation of acid anhydrides which are obtained with difficulty by other means.

Halogen Compounds

Compounds with active halogens react as if the ketone molecule inserts itself between the halogen and the rest of the molecule; the halogen usually attaches itself to the carbonyl group.

$$R \cdot Hal + CH_2=C=O \longrightarrow RCH_2-C {\overset{Hal}{\underset{O}{\diagdown}}}$$

Hydrogen halides react smoothly to form the corresponding acetyl halides (70). The reaction goes especially well in the gas phase over activated charcoal or silica gel at about 100° (86).

Bromine forms bromoacetyl bromide (22). While nitrosyl chloride forms exclusively chloroacetyl chloride (87), nitryl chloride gives chloroacetyl chloride and a small amount of nitroacetyl chloride (b.p. 68°/ 12 mm) (88).

$$2\ NO_2Cl + CH_2=CO \rightarrow ClCH_2-COCl + 2\ NO_2$$
$$NO_2Cl + CH_2=C=O \rightarrow NO_2-CH_2-COCl$$

Sulfur-bound halogen, reacting with ketene, attaches itself to the carbonyl atom.

$$SCl_2 + 2\ CH_2=C=O \rightarrow ClCO-CH_2-S-CH_2COCl$$
$$S_2Cl_2 + 2\ CH_2=C=O \rightarrow ClCO-CH_2-S-S-CH_2COCl$$

Both reactions can be carried out at −20° in carbon tetrachloride (89). Ketene reacts smoothly with 2-nitro-4-chlorophenylsulfenyl chloride to give a good yield of 2-nitro-4-chlorophenylmercaptoacetyl chloride (90).

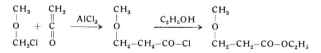

Ketene also reacts with carbon-bound halogens in the presence of AlCl₃ or other Friedel-Crafts type catalysts (91).

In general only those carbon-bound halogens react which are attached to a carbon atom carrying an ether group.

$$\bigcirc-{\overset{H}{\underset{O-CH_3}{\diagup}}}C-Cl\ + CH_2=C=O \xrightarrow{AlCl_3}\ \bigcirc-{\overset{H}{\underset{O-CH_3}{\diagup}}}C-CH_2-CO-Cl$$

Triphenylmethyl chloride reacts without a catalyst in nitrobenzene as a solvent (92).

$$(C_6H_5)_3C-Cl + CH_2=C=O \rightarrow (C_6H_5)_3C-CH_2-COCl$$

S-Acetylthioglycolyl chloride is obtained in good yield by passing ketene into a solution of acetyl sulfur chloride in methylene chloride (*92a*).

$$CH_3-CO-S-Cl + H_2C=C=O \rightarrow CH_3-CO-S-CH_2-CO-Cl$$

Mineral Acids

Acetylsulfoacetic acid is formed by passing ketene through water-free sulfuric acid (*93*).

$$H_2SO_4 + 2\ CH_2=C=O \rightarrow CH_3-CO-O-SO_2-CH_2-COOH$$

If SO_3 is passed into a vigorously stirred mixture of dioxane and ethylene chloride cooled to 15°C, and ketene is introduced simultaneously, sulfoacetic anhydride is obtained (*94*).

$$SO_3 + CH_2=C=O \longrightarrow \begin{array}{c} CH_2-CO \\ |\qquad| \\ SO_2-O \end{array}$$

Ketene reacts in the cold with fuming nitric acid in an anhydrous solvent (e.g., methylene chloride) to form acetyl nitrate (*95*).

$$HNO_3 + CH_2=C=O \rightarrow O_2NO-CO-CH_3$$

Tetranitromethane is obtained in good yield when ketene is passed into fuming nitric acid with ice-cooling and using no solvent (*96*).

$$CH_2=CO + HNO_3 \rightarrow NO_2-CH_2-COOH$$
$$NO_2-CH_2-COOH + 2\ HNO_3 \rightarrow (NO_2)_3\ C-COOH + 2\ H_2O$$
$$(NO_2)_3C-COOH \rightarrow (NO_2)_3CH + CO_2$$
$$(NO_2)_3CH + HNO_3 \rightarrow (NO_2)_4C + H_2O$$
$$|3|\ H_2O + 3\ CH_2=C=O \rightarrow 3\ CH_3COOH$$

$$\overline{|4\ CH_2=CO + 4\ HNO_3 \rightarrow C(NO_2)_4 + CO_2 + 3\ CH_3COOH}$$

In 1932 Hurd and Dull (*79*) had already observed that ketene was absorbed by phosphoric acid. Proceeding from this observation R. Bentley obtained, on passing ketene into an ice-cooled ether solution of 85% phosphoric acid, acetyl phosphate, which is prepared with greater difficulty by other procedures (*97*).

Hydrogen Cyanide

Soon after the initial preparation of ketene, Chick and Wilsmore (*70*) sought to react hydrocyanic acid with ketene. They observed a reaction, but could not obtain acetyl cyanide. Through the use of weakly basic catalysts (e.g., diethylamine), H. Vollmann and associates (*98*) succeeded in reacting ketene with hydrocyanic acid at low temperatures, whereby they obtained l-acetoxy-1,1-dicyanoethane along with α-acetoxyacrylonitrile.

$$H_2C=C=O + HCN \rightarrow H_3C-CO-CN \rightleftharpoons CH_2=COH-CN + \overset{\displaystyle CH_2=C=O}{\underset{\displaystyle CN}{|}} \longrightarrow$$

$$\underset{\displaystyle O-CO-CH_3}{\overset{\displaystyle H_2C=C-CN}{|}} \qquad 2\,H_3C-CO-CN \rightarrow \underset{\displaystyle CN}{\overset{\displaystyle CH_3-CO-O-\overset{|}{C}-CH_3}{|}}$$

If the reaction is run in acetic anhydride, only acetoxyacrylonitrile is obtained (*99*). It has been determined that sodium acetate is the best catalyst for this reaction, using ether or dioxane as solvent. In the absence of such a catalyst, diketene is chiefly obtained (*100*). Newer methods use temperature ranges of 300–400° for this reaction, obtaining either acetyl cyanide (*101*) or 1-acetoxy-1,1-dicyanoethane (*102, 103*), depending on the catalyst used.

Ether Compounds

Ketene reacts with especially active ether linkages in the presence of boron trifluoride. ε-Caprolactone can be obtained from tetrahydrofuran in this way (*104*).

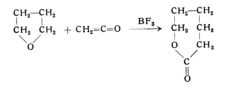

Ethyl orthoformate reacts by the insertion of the ketene molecule between an oxygen atom and the carbon atom of the acid group (*105*). Acetals react in an analogous manner (*106, 107*).

$$\underset{H}{\overset{C_2H_5-O}{\diagdown}}\!\!C_2H_5-O-C-O-C_2H_5 + CH_2=C=O \xrightarrow{BF_3} \underset{H}{\overset{C_2H_5O}{\diagdown}}\!\!C_2H_5O-C-CH_2-CO-OC_2H_5$$

$$\underset{H}{\overset{C_2H_5-O}{\diagdown}}\!\!C_2H_5-O-CH_2-C-O-C_2H_5 + CH_2=C=O \xrightarrow{BF_3} \underset{\cdot H}{\overset{C_2H_5-O}{\diagdown}}\!\!C_2H_5-OCH_2-C-CH_2-CO-OC_2H_5$$

Organometallic Compounds

Ketene reacts with Grignard reagents to form the corresponding ketones (*108, 109, 110*).

$$RMgBr + CH_2=C=O \longrightarrow R-\underset{\underset{O}{\|}}{C}-CH_3$$

In an analogous manner ketene reacts with halogenomercury (111, 112) and halogenocadmium compounds (113).

The yield in all of these reactions is usually not higher than 30%.

The use of ketene in the Friedel-Crafts reaction has not been fruitful to date. In most instances impure products have been obtained in poor yields (114–117). Since the Friedel-Crafts reaction gives purer products and better yields with acetic anhydride, the use of ketene in this reaction is as yet without preparative importance.

Diazomethane

Diazomethane forms cyclopropanone with ketene; it may be isolated as the hydrate if the reaction is carried out in the presence of water or as the hemiacetal if alcohol is present (118). By working in an anhydrous medium and using an excess of diazomethane, a ring enlargement takes place to form cyclobutanone (118–120) in good yield.

Enolizable Carbonyl Compounds

Carbonyl compounds having an enolizable carbonyl group react with ketene in the presence of acid catalysts to form chiefly enol acetates (100, 121–124).

Halogen sulfonic acids (125–127), sulfamic acids [NH_2SO_3H, $(CH_3)_2NSO_3H$] (125), alkylsulfonic acids, sulfocarboxylic acids (126), H_3PO_4 (127), and phosphorus oxychloride in addition to sulfuric acid, are useful as catalysts in these reactions. Especially high yields of isopropenyl acetate are obtained by the reaction of ketene with acetone at 60° in the presence of acetylsulfoacetic acid (93). Catalysts which are useful for the preparation of enolacetates (129) are obtained by sulfonation with concentrated H_2SO_4 of charred organic matter such as sawdust, coco fiber, spent sulfite liquors, etc.

These catalysts have the advantage that at the end of a reaction they can be filtered from the reaction mixture, whereas other acid catalysts must be destroyed with alkali.

Enol acetates may also be obtained from aldehydes. By this method a higher proportion of by-products of increasing chain length is obtained. Thus ketenization of butyraldehyde furnishes 7% of the expected 1-butenyl acetate against 51% of methyl pentenyl ketone (100, 130).

$$
H_3C-CH_2-CH_2-C\overset{\displaystyle O}{\underset{\displaystyle H}{\diagup}} + n\,CH_2=C=O + H_2SO_4 \left\{ \begin{array}{l} H_3C-CH_2-CH=CH-O-COCH_3 \quad 7\% \\ H_3C-CH_2-CH_2-CH=CH-CO-CH_3 \quad 51\% \end{array} \right.
$$

The same unsaturated ketones can be obtained without catalysts with ketene or in better yields with diketene. Thereby one can assume that when such unsaturated ketones are derived from aldehydes and ketene that diketene is formed first and then reacts with the aldehyde to form a β-lactone.

$$
H_3C-CO-CH=C=O + R-CH_2-C\overset{\displaystyle O}{\underset{\displaystyle H}{\diagup}} \longrightarrow \begin{array}{l} H_3C-CO-CH-CO \\ \quad\quad\quad | \quad\quad | \\ RCH_2-CH-O \end{array}
$$

Under the reaction conditions applied this β-lactone loses CO_2 and is converted to the unsaturated ketone.

$$
\begin{array}{l} CH_3-CO-CH-\!-CO \\ \quad\quad\quad | \quad\quad | \\ R-CH_2-CH-\!-O \end{array} \longrightarrow CH_3-CO-CH=CH-CH_2-R + CO_2
$$

To date no corresponding reaction has been observed with ketones. Diketones (100, 125, 131, 132) and esters of ketocarboxylic acids also form enol acetates (132).

$$
H_3C-CO-CH_2-COOC_2H_5 \xrightarrow[H_2SO_4]{+\,CH_2=C=O} \left\{ \begin{array}{l} CH_2=C-CH_2-COOC_2H_5 \\ \quad\quad | \\ \quad O-CO-CH_3 \\ CH_3-C=CH-COO-C_2H_5 \\ \quad\quad | \\ \quad O-CO-CH_3 \end{array} \right.
$$

Acetonylacetone reacts vigorously with ketene although no enol acetate is formed; instead dimethylfuran is formed through ring closure (132).

$$
\begin{array}{l} \quad\;\, CH_2-CH_2 \\ \quad\;\, | \quad\quad\; | \\ H_3C-C \quad\quad C-CH_3 \\ \quad\;\, \| \quad\quad\; \| \\ \quad\;\, O \quad\quad\; O \end{array} \xrightarrow[H_2SO_4]{+\,2\,CH_2=C=O} \begin{array}{l} \quad CH-\!\!-CH \\ \quad \| \quad\quad \| \\ H_3C-C \quad\quad C-CH_3 \\ \quad\;\; \diagdown\;\,\diagup \\ \quad\quad\;\; O \end{array} + 2\,CH_3COOH
$$

The preparation of greatest importance among the enol acetates is that of isopropenyl acetate, which is obtained from acetone in good yields. This compound may be viewed as a stabilized ketene since on warming in the presence of H_2SO_4, it decomposes into an equilibrium mixture with its two original components. Therefore it is a very convenient and versatile acetylating agent (*128*). To acetylate using isopropenyl acetate, the reactant is dissolved in the ester and, after adding a drop of H_2SO_4, the acetone which has formed is distilled.

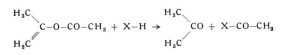

Ketene

Ketene reacts readily with itself through dimerization (*70*). Four different structures have been formulated for diketene:

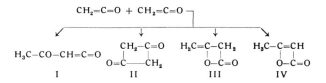

Arguments can be advanced for all four structures. However, on grounds of chemical and optical behavior one must conclude that structure III finds favorable support (*18, 133*).

In the laboratory diketene is best obtained by passage of ketene into very cold acetone. In the commercial procedures used mostly today, ketene is passed into diketene at 40–50° and the latter is driven off by the rising reaction temperature (*134*). In this manner diketene is obtained in yields of 90–95%. Diketene is quite a versatile reagent for acetoacetylation (*135*). Since diketene is formed readily from ketene in slow reactions, some diketene is always obtained as a by-product. Because the latter readily polymerizes to dehydroacetic acid, the acid can often be isolated in these slow reactions as beautiful crystals (m.p. 109°).

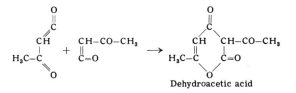
Dehydroacetic acid

Dehydroacetic acid can be readily detected by its intense sweet taste.

Addition to Carbonyl Groups

In the presence of suitable catalysts ketene forms β-lactones with carbonyl compounds.

$$\diagdown C=O + CH_2=C=O \longrightarrow \begin{array}{c} -\overset{|}{C}-CH_2 \\ | \quad | \\ O-C=O \end{array}$$

These β-lactones may be isolated as such and converted to β-substituted propionic acid derivatives, from which various products are obtained depending on reaction conditions; for example, the alcoholysis of a β-lactone:

$$
\begin{array}{c}
R_1-CH-CH_2 \\
| \quad\quad | \\
O \;—\; C=O
\end{array}
+ R_2OH
\begin{array}{l}
\xrightarrow{\text{basic}} R_1-CHOH-CH_2-COOR_2 \\[4pt]
\xrightarrow{\text{neutral}} \begin{array}{c} R_1-CH-CH_2-COOH \\ | \\ O-R_2 \end{array} \\[4pt]
\xrightarrow{\text{acidic}} R_1-CH=CH-COOR_2 + H_2O
\end{array}
$$

For further reactions of β-lactones see the work of T. L. Gresham and co-workers (136–139) and the review of H. E. Zaugg (140). In one process the β-lactones can be polymerized at high temperatures to polyesters which in turn, by heating with acid can be simultaneously saponified and dehydrated to unsaturated acids, hydrogenated to acids or decarboxylated and dehydrated to ethylene derivatives.

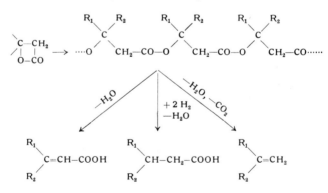

Many catalysts have been described for the preparation of β-lactones. In addition to catalysts of the Friedel-Crafts type, such as BF_3, $AlCl_3$, and $ZnCl_2$ (142–149), which are used as ether complexes, the following have been used: the chlorides of Fe, Sn, Ti, Hg (141, 142, 150), uranyl chloride, uranyl nitrate (151), zinc nitrate, zinc thiocyanate (152), boric acids and its esters (153, 154), oxides of aluminum, zirconium, thorium, and boron (*145*), perchlorate (*152*), acid-activated clays (*155*), Zn, Ni, Ba, Cu, and Hg salts of organic acids (*156, 157*), metal fluoroborates (*158*), difluorophosphates (*159*) and alkyl esters of ortho- and meta-phosphoric acids (*160*). In addition organic peroxides (*161*), alkali metal, and alkaline earth metal acetates (*162–164*) are suitable as catalysts. In the presence of basic catalysts the reaction probably proceeds to a small extent through the β-lactone, while the main Perkin-like reaction forms the unsaturated carboxylic acid directly (*162*).

The yields of β-lactones are influenced, aside from the catalysts, by the reaction conditions, such as solvent and temperature. Ketene can be converted by an aldehyde to a β-lactone, using ether or acetone as solvent, or, best, by using the aldehyde itself as a solvent (*145, 152*). The reaction of ketene with ketones to form β-lactones is best carried out without a solvent. The reaction temperature must be kept below 20–25°, otherwise the β-lactone which is formed polymerizes to the polyester.

If the β-lactone is not to be isolated in the pure state, the reaction can be carried out at higher temperature. Low molecular weight polyesters are then obtained, which are depolymerized more readily and with better yields. Depolymerization is carried out conveniently with 20–50% sulfuric acid or *p*-toluenesulfonic acid; if the ester is desired, the corresponding alkyl sulfate is used (*165*). Generally, β-lactones are formed with all carbonyl compounds, so that diketones and keto acids react in a similar manner. In most instances it is difficult to isolate the pure β-lactones. This has been done successfully only in the case of seven β-lactones (*136*). In most cases unsaturated acids are the end products. Thus, dicarboxylic acids are obtained from esters of keto acids, and either keto acids or dicarboxylic acids (by way of a dilactone) are formed from diketones (*144, 149*).

C-Acetylation

β-Diketones or keto acid esters are acetylated on the reactive carbon atom in the absence of any of the above catalysts (*166*). In this manner an 80% yield of triacetylmethane can be obtained from acetylacetone.

Sometimes catalysts are useful in these reactions. As such are used: SeO_2 (*166*), metals and their oxides of the first and second groups in the periodic table, and best of all magnesium (*167*) or organic peroxides (*168*).

If ketones are converted to Schiff bases with an amine, then the carbon atom adjacent to the ketimino group is acetylated by ketene. A catalyst is not necessary. Sometimes the reaction is accelerated by using $AlCl_3$, BF_3, or $ZnCl_2$ (*169, 170, 171*). The β-diketones are obtained by the hydrolysis of the ketimino group.

$$\begin{array}{c}CH_3\\|\\C=O\\|\\CH_3\end{array} + H_2N-R \rightarrow \begin{array}{c}CH_3\\|\\C=N-R\\|\\CH_3\end{array} + \begin{array}{c}CH_2\\||\\C\\||\\O\end{array} \xrightarrow{40-45°}$$

$$\begin{array}{c}CH_3\\|\\C=N-R\\|\\CH_2-CO-CH_3\end{array} \xrightarrow{HOH} \begin{array}{c}CH_3\\|\\C=O\\|\\CH_2\\|\\C=O\\|\\CH_3\end{array} + RNH_2$$

Ketene attaches itself probably to the C=C bond of the tautomeric form II.

$$\begin{array}{c}R-N\ \ H\\||\ \ |\\-C-C-\\|\ \ \ |\\I\end{array} \rightleftharpoons \begin{array}{c}R-N-H\\|\\-C=C-\\|\ \ \ |\\II\end{array}$$

This points to the fact that compounds with the —N=C—C-group only react with ketene when the —C=N— group does not belong to an aromatic system, in which case the above equilibrium is shifted to the left. Specific observations have shown that α-picoline (I), α-methylquinoline (II), and 2-methylthiazole (III) do not react with ketene, but reaction takes place with 2-methylthiazoline (IV) (*172*), 2-methyloxazoline (V) (*173*) (m.p. 120°) and especially with the so-called Fischer's base (VI) (*174*) in which the methylene group is fixed.

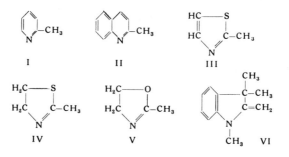

Addition to Double Bonds

Up to the present few addition reactions to double bonds (except $C=O$, discussed above) have been described. Brooks and Wilbert (*175*) obtained a bicyclic ketone by heating ketene with cyclopentadiene in an autoclave.

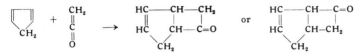

This reaction could be confirmed by Bloomquist and Kwiatek (*176*) and was found to go with cyclohexadiene also.

Some time ago H. Staudinger showed that at higher temperatures ketene could react with the $C=N$ bond of N-benzylideneaniline (*177*).

Recently, for the first time, G. O. Schenk and N. Engelhard were able to add ketene, at 15° and with irradiation, across the $N=N$ bond of *cis*-azobenzene, thereby adding this double bond system into the realm of ketene chemistry (*178*).

$$C_6H_5-N=N-C_6H_5 \quad \xrightarrow[CH_2=C=O]{hv} \quad C_6H_5-N\!-\!-\!-\!N-C_6H_5$$
$$\underset{CH_2-C=O}{|\qquad\qquad|}$$

In 1934 Wollenberg (*179*) already had obtained a crystalline product from the reaction of ketene with pyridine. This observation could be confirmed by Berson and Jones (*180*). One mole of pyridine reacts exothermically and with simultaneous splitting out of one molecule of water to form $C_{13}H_{11}NO_3$ (m.p. 208°). Two structures are possible for this compound.

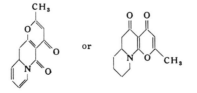

Ketene reacts quite smoothly with 3,4-dihydroisoquinoline. Thesing and Hofmann (*181*) showed that even at room temperature 2 moles of 3,4-dihydroisoquinoline and 1 mole of ketene unite to give a 4-oxohexahydropyrimidine in good yield.

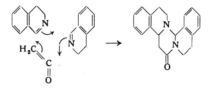

Examples of Experiments

The pictured and briefly described pieces of apparatus* were used in the following examples.

1. *Tert-Butyl acetate (5)*. Apparatus: The flask by which gas is introduced is shown in Fig. 1. Rate of addition: 0.65 mole ketene/hr. Following the addition of 0.5 ml concentrated H_2SO_4 to 74 gm of *tert*-butyl alcohol, the mixture is heated to 60° and ketene is passed in for 1.5 hr. The light brown reaction product is washed with 10 ml of $2N$ NaOH and finally with 20 ml of water. Both aqueous solutions are extracted with ether and the ether extracts added to the crude ester. After having been dried over K_2CO_3 the solution is distilled at atmospheric pressure. After a short forerun the *tert*-butyl acetate distills (b.p. 94–96°/750 mm; yield 83 gm).

2. *N-Acetylglucosamine*. Apparatus: as for example 1. Glucosamine (50 gm is added to 1 liter of boiling methanol contained in a 2 liter flask provided with a gas inlet tube. After the addition of 25 gm of triethylamine, ketene is introduced for 70 min. The methanol remains hot during this time because of the heat of reaction. In spite of this crystals may form at the lower end of the gas inlet tube, thereby blocking it. In such cases the reaction is interrupted and the crystals are removed. If toward the end of the reaction the contents become dark, the passage of gas is stopped. On refrigeration 24.6 gm of almost pure N-acetylglucosamine crystallizes. On addition of 2 liters of ether to the mother liquor 18 gm more is precipitated. The combined crystals are recrystallized from methanol. M. p. 202°. Yield of pure substance: 35.7 gm.

Note: acetylation in aqueous solution gives a higher yield, but a less pure product.

3. *S-Acetylthiophenol*. Apparatus: as in Fig. 1 (0.3 mole ketene/hr). For 30 min ketene is passed into 20 gm of thiophenol. The reaction product is fractionated *in vacuo*, b.p. 108°/12 mm. Yield: 24 gm.

4. *Formic acetic anhydride (5)*. Apparatus: Figure 2b, with water cooling in reaction vessel b; 0.65 mole ketene/hr. Anhydrous formic acid (46 gm) is added from the dropping funnel during 1 hr and simultaneously ketene is introduced into the reaction flask through tube a.

* Apparatus produced by L. Hormuth, owner N. Vetter, Heidelberg.

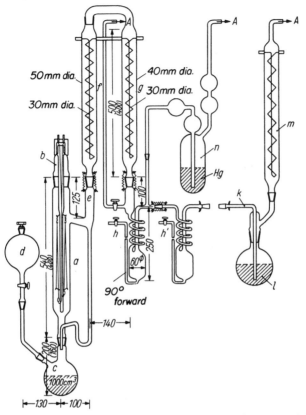

FIG. 1. Ketene apparatus with mercury safety valve, cooling trap, and collection flask. Acetone is heated to boiling in flask c. When acetone condenses in condenser f, the heating wire of insert b is brought to glowing by turning on the current. The cooling traps h and h′ are placed in Dewar flasks and cooled with an ice–salt mixture. Each cooling trap is equipped with a stopcock so that it is possible to empty the trap with a water aspirator without dismantling the apparatus. The cooling trap is equipped at the top with a stopcock so that when necessary it is possible to make a direct connection to the hood (e.g., if the apparatus becomes clogged). A mercury safety valve, n, is inserted between the two cooling traps in order to minimize any undesirable pressure increase. All openings through which ketene could escape are united in a collecting pipe which leads to a hood. At the end of a reaction the stopcock h is opened before the heating element in b is shut off. Only then is the collecting flask k disconnected at i from the rest of the apparatus.

Finally the contents of the reaction vessel, which are withdrawn through stopcock e, are allowed to circulate through the apparatus for 30 min. The almost colorless content of the reaction vessel is removed through e and fractionated at 20 mm. After a forerun of a few drops, 62 gm of formic acetic anhydride comes over at 33–35°.

Note: The reaction also occurs in aqueous formic acid. However, the consumption of ketene would be increased since 1 mole of water reacts with 2 moles of ketene.

5. *Isopropenyl acetate* (*100*). Apparatus: Fig. 2a. The column b, filled with Raschig rings, is heated with refluxing acetone from flask f

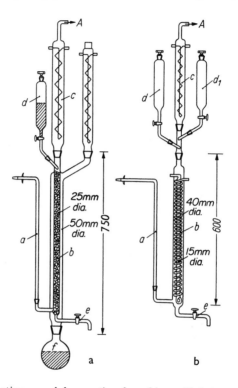

FIG. 2. (a) Reaction vessel for continual working with ketene with simultaneous application of heat; (b) with simultaneous cooling. The tube a is attached at i to the apparatus (Fig. 1). The ketene rises in column b (containing Raschig rings) counter to the flow of liquids released by the dropping funnel d and is lead to the connecting tube A through condenser c. Column b is heated by a suitable liquid in flask f, the heating temperature being regulated by the boiling point of the fluid used. In Fig. 2b the Rashig ring column is replaced by a condenser having a wide center tube. The winding around the center tube lies near the outer wall of the cooling tube so that liquids from the dropping funnels d and d' flowing down the winding come in contact with the rising ketene.

(0.65 mole ketene/hr). A 200 ml portion of acetone is placed in the dropping funnel d, and after addition of 1 ml of concentrated H_2SO_4, added dropwise to warmed column b at such a rate that a uniform amount of acetone is condensed in condenser c, which falls into column

b. At the same time ketene is admitted through tube a. The reaction product is continuously removed through stopcock e, care being taken to leave a 3 cm of liquid in the column. After about 3 hr all of the acetone is used up. The brown-colored reaction product is fractionated at atmospheric pressure, the major portion distills between 80 and 100°. The distillate is washed with 50 ml of saturated NaHCO₃ solution and dried over K_2CO_3. A second distillation gives 112 gm of product, b.p. 95—7°/752 mm.

6. *β-Butyrolactone (6)*. Apparatus: Figure 2b. The cooling coil in b is cooled with tap water, while the cooling coil in c is cooled by the passage of methanol, which has been cooled to —15° (0.65 mole ketene/hr).

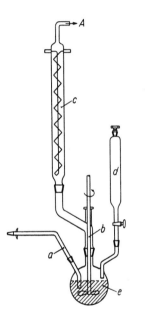

Fig. 3. The introduction of ketene into a solvent with simultaneous stirring: a) gas inlet tube: b) stirring attachment with centrifugal stirrer in KPG-stirrer ensemble; d) dropping funnel; c) reflux condenser; at A connection with tube leading to hood.

To dropping funnel d are added 50 ml of ether and 1 gm of $ZnCl_2$; to funnel d are added 44 gm of acetaldehyde and 150 ml of ether. During the passage of ketene through tube a, the contents of the two funnels are simultaneously added dropwise to the reaction vessel over a period of 2 hr. The reaction product is continuously withdrawn at e in such a manner that a liquid level of about 3 cm is maintained in the reaction vessel. At the end of the reaction the apparatus is rinsed with ether and the combined ether solution treated with 5 ml of concentrated NaOH. Finally it is washed with a small amount of cold water and dried over Na_2CO_3. The ether is removed *in vacuo* and the residue is distilled. There is obtained 50 gm of β-butyrolactone, b.p. 56–57°/11 mm.

Note: If β-butyrolactone is used as a solvent in place of ether, the yield is increased from 58 to 73%.

7. *Sorbic acid (148).* Apparatus: Figure 3 (0.65 mole ketene/hr). To the three-necked flask are added 250 ml of dry (over Na) ether and 1 ml of BF_3-saturated ether. Ketene is introduced through tube a with ice-cooling and vigorous stirring, while 50 gm of crotonaldehyde is added simultaneously over a period of 90 min. When the addition is completed, the passage of ketene is continued 10 min longer. After removal of the gas inlet tube and reflux condenser, the flask is heated on the steam bath for 3 hr, following the addition of 300 ml of 30% H_2SO_4. On cooling, pale brownish-yellow needles separate. These are filtered, dissolved in boiling water, and filtered hot through fluted filter paper. By this procedure the brown oil drops floating in the aqueous solution remain on the filter paper. On cooling sorbic acid is obtained as colorless crystals. M. p. 133–135°.

Yield: 72% of theory.

REFERENCES

(1) H. Staudinger, "Die Ketene," Enke, Stuttgart, 1912.
(2) N. T. M. Wilsmore and A. W. Stewart, *Nature* **75**, 510 (1907); *J. Chem. Soc.* **91**, 1938 (1907).
(3) J. van Alphen, *Rec. trav. chim.* **43**, 823 (1924).
(4) J. van Alphen, *Rec. trav. chim.* **44**, 838 (1925).
(5) C. D. Hurd and A. S. Roe, *J. Am. Chem. Soc.* **61**, 3355 (1939).
(6) F. E. King, U.S. Patent 2,356,459; *Chem. Abstr.* **39**, 88 (1945).
(7) B. H. Gwynn and E. F. Degering, *J. Am. Chem. Soc.* **64**, 2216 (1942).
(8) F. O. Rice, J. Greenberg, C. E. Waters, and R. E. Vollrath, *J. Am. Chem. Soc.* **56**, 1760 (1934).
(9) Ullmann's "Encyklopädie der technischen Chemie," 3rd ed., Vol. 6. Urban & Schwarzenberg, Munich, 1955.
(10) German Patent 408,715 (1922); P. Friedländer, "Fortschritte der Teerfarbenfabrikation und verwandter Industriezweige," Vol. 14, p. 259. Springer, Berlin, 1926; *Chem. Zentr.* I, 1528 (1925).
(11) I. G. Farbenindustrie A.-G. French Patent 878,651; *Chem. Zentr.* **II**, 953 (1943).
(12) L. Fallows and E. V. Mellers, U.S. Patent 2,295,644; *Chem. Abstr.* **37**, 1133 (1943).
(13) D. L. Tyler, German Patent 831,839 (1952); *Chem. Zentr.* p. 5649 (1952).
(14) G. M. Henderson, A. A. Moss, and G. A. Randal, British Patent 698,121; *Chem. Abstr.* **48**, 6109 (1954).
(15) C. D. Hurd and K. A. Martin, *J. Am. Chem. Soc.* **51**, 3614 (1929).
(16) G. F. Fisher, A. F. McLean, and A. W. Schnizer, *J. Org. Chem.* **18**, 1055 (1933).
(17) A. B. Boese, Jr., U.S. Patent 2,218,066; *Chem. Abstr.* **35**, 1072 (1941).

(18) W. E. Hanford and J. C. Sauer, "Organic Reactions," Vol. 3. J. Wiley, New York, 1946.
(19) G. Quadbeck, *Chem. Ing. Tech.* **24**, 210 (1952); *Chem. Abstr.* **46**, 5893 (1952).
(20) F. O. Rice and W.|D. Walters, *J. Am. Chem. Soc.* **63**, 1700 (1941).
(21) T. G. Pearson, R. H. Purcell, and G. S. Saigh, *J. Chem. Soc.* p. 409 (1938).
(22) H. Staudinger and H. W. Klever, *Ber. deut. chem. Ges.* **41**, 594 (1908).
(23) C. D. Hurd and P. B. Cochran, *J. Am. Chem. Soc.* **45**, 515 (1923).
(24) A. A. Wooster, C. C. Lushbaugh, and C. E. Redeman, *J. Am. Chem. Soc.* **68**, 2743 (1946).
(25) J. F. Treon, H. E. Sigmon, K. V. Kitzmiller, F. F. Heyroth, W. J. Younker, and J. Cholak, *J. Ind. Hyg. Toxicol.* **31**, 209 (1949).
(26) J d'Ans and W. Frey, *Ber. deut. chem. Ges.* **45**, 1845 (1912).
(27) J. P. Tsukervanik and J. A. Ermolenko, *Bull. univ. état Asie centrale* **22**, 215 (1938); *Chem. Abstr.* **34**, 4727 (1940).
(28) G. H. Morey, *Ind. Eng. Chem.* **31**, 1129 (1939).
(29) A. A. Ponomarev and Y. B. Isaev, *Zhur. Obshcheĭ Khim.* **20**, 1079 (1950); *Chem. Abstr.* **44**, 9349 (1950).
(30) U.S. Patent 2,018,759; *Chem. Abstr.* **30**, 107 (1936).
(31) C. D. Hurd, S. M. Cantor, and A. S. Roe, *J. Am. Chem. Soc.* **61**, 426 (1939).
(32) British Patent 378,044 (1932); *Chem Abstr.* **27**, 4077 (1933).
(33) D. A. Nightingal, British Patent 237,591 (1925); *Chem. Abstr.* **20**, 1522 (1926).
(34) E. B. Middleton, U.S. Patent 1,685,220; *Chem. Abstr.* **22**, 4536 (1928).
(35) C. A. Burkhard and E. F. Degering, *Rayon Textile Monthly* **23**, 340 (1942); *Chem. Abstr.* **37**, 5612 (1943).
(36) C. Hamalainen and J. D. Reid, *Ind. Eng. Chem.* **41**, 1018 (1949).
(37) E. A. Talley and L. T. Smith, *J. Org. Chem.* **10**, 101 (1945).
(38) G. De Witt Graves, U. S. Patent 2,007,968; *Chem. Abstr.* **29**, 5857 (1935).
(39) R. Nodzu and T. Isoshima, *Bull. Inst. Chem. Research Kyoto Univ.* **32**, 139 (1954); *Chem. Abstr.* **49**, 8174 (1955).
(40) D. A. Nightingal, British Patent 237,574 (1925); *Chem. Zentr.* I, 232 (1926).
(41) Russian Patent 66,328; *Chem. Abstr.* **41**, 2441 (1947).
(41a) R. E. Dunbar and L. L. Bolstadt, *J. Org. Chem.* **21**, 1041 (1956).
(42) G. De Witt Graves, U.S. Patent 1,990,483; *Chem. Abstr.* **29**, 1983 (1935).
(43) H. V. Claborn and L. T. Smith, *J. Am. Chem. Soc.* **61**, 2727 (1939).
(44) A. A. Ponomarev and Y. B. Isaev, *Zhur. Obshcheĭ Khim.* **22**, 652 (1952); *Chem. Abstr.* **47**, 2695 (1953).
(45) A. A. Ponomarev and Y. B. Isaev, *Zhur. Obshcheĭ Khim.* **21**, 1045 (1951); *Chem. Abstr.* **46**, 1440 (1952).
(46) C. D. Hurd and W. D. McPhee, *J. Am. Chem. Soc.* **71**, 398 (1949).
(47) J. Schmidlin and M. Bergmann, *Ber. deut. chem. Ges.* **43**, 2821 (1910).
(48) M. Bergmann and F. Stern, German Patent 453,577; P. Friedländer, "Fortschritte der Teerfarbenfabrikation und verwandter Industriezweige," Vol. 16, p. 237. Springer, Berlin, 1927.
(49) M. Bergmann and F. Stern, *Ber. deut. chem. Ges.* **63**, 437 (1930).
(50) R. W. Jackson and W. M. Cahill, *J. Biol. Chem.* **126**, 37 (1938).
(51) W. M. Cahill and J. F. Burton, *J. Biol. Chem.* **132**, 161 (1940).
(52) R. Kuhn, A. Gauhe, and H. H. Baer, *Chem. Ber.* **87**, 1138 (1954).
(53) K. Freudenberg, W. Dirscherl, *Z. physiol. Chem. Hoppe-Seyler's* **175** (1928).

(54) K. Freudenberg, W. Dirscherl, and H. Eyer, *Z. physiol. Chem. Hoppe-Seyler's* **187**, 89 (1930).

(55) K. G. Stern and A. White, *J. Biol. Chem.* **122**, 371 (1938).

(56) R. M. Herriot and J. H. Northrop, *J. Gen. Physiol.* **18**, 35 (1934).

(57) R. M. Herriot, *J. Gen. Physiol.* **19**, 283 (1936).

(58) H. Goldie and G. Sandor, *Compt. rend. soc. biol.* **130**, 1530 (1939).

(59) C. Li and A. Kalman, *J. Am. Chem. Soc.* **68**, 285 (1946).

(60) A. Schöberl and H. Wolff, *Chemie, Die* **55**, 64 (1942).

(61) M. P. Desnuelle and N. Rowery, *Compt. rend. acad. sci.* **224**, 235 (1947); *Biochim. et Biophys. Acta* **1**, 497 (1947).

(62) H. Fraenkel-Conrat, *J. Biol. Chem.* **152**, 385 (1944).

(63) C. D. Hurd, *J. Am. Chem. Soc.* **48**, 291 (1926).

(64) H. Bestian, *Ann. Chem. Liebigs* **566**, 218 (1949); German Patent 735,008 (1940); *Chem. Abstr.* **38**, 1251 (1943).

(65) D. M. Padgham and J. B. Poya, *Australian J. Sci.* **13**, 113 (1951); *Chem. Abstr.* **45**, 7006 (1951).

(66) M. V. Smirnova, A. P. Skoldinov, and K. A. Kocheshkov, *Doklady Akad. Nauk S.S.S.R.* **84**, 737 (1952); *Chem. Abstr.* **47**, 3233 (1953).

(67) H. J. Hagemeyer, Jr., U.S. Patent 2,458,373; *Chem. Abstr.* **43**, 3836 (1949).

(68) H. Albers, W. Künzel, and W. Schuler, *Chem. Ber.* **85**, 239 (1952).

(69) G. H. Coleman, R. L. Peterson, and G. E. Goheen, *J. Am. Chem. Soc.* **58**, 1874 (1936).

(69a) R. Kuhn and W. Kirschenlohr, *Ann. Chem. Liebigs* **600**, 135 (1956).

(69b) R. E. Dunbar and G. C. White, *J. Org. Chem.* **23**, 915 (1958).

(70) F. Chick and N. T. M. Wilsmore, *Proc. Chem. Soc.* **24**, 77 (1908).

(71) W. W. Crouch, U.S. Patent 2,639,293; *Chem. Abstr.* **48**, 3387 (1954).

(72) C. D Hurd and J. W. Williams, *J. Am. Chem. Soc.* **58**, 962 (1936).

(73) W. W. Crouch, U.S. Patent 2,509,483; *Chem. Abstr.* **44**, 10730 (1950).

(74) R. E. Dunbar and A. N. Bolstad, *J. Am. Chem. Soc.* **77**, 4672 (1955).

(75) R. Kuhn and G. Quadbeck, *Chem. Ber.* **84**, 844 (1951).

(76) A. Neuberger, *Biochem. J.* **32**, 1452 (1938).

(77) J. J. Perez and G. Sandor, *Bull. soc. chim. biol.* **33**, 149 (1940).

(78) D. A. Nightingal, British Patent 237,573 (1925); *Chem. Abstr.* **20**, 1415 (1926).

(79) C. D. Hurd and M. F. Dull, *J. Am. Chem. Soc.* **54**, 3427 (1932).

(80) R. E. Dunbar and F. C. Garven, *Proc. N. Dakota Acad. Sci.* **3**, 24 (1949); *Chem Abstr.* **44**, 5313 (1950).

(81) J. W. Williams and J. A. Krynitsky, *Org. Syntheses* **21**, 13 (1941).

(82) A. H. Gleason, U.S. Patent 2,178, 752; *Chem. Abstr.* **34**, 1336 (1940).

(83) P. J. Gaylor, U.S. Patent 2,236,125; *Chem. Abstr.* **35**, 4042 (1941).

(84) G. DeWitt Graves, U.S. Patent 2,135,709; *Chem. Abstr.* **33**, 1347 (1939).

(85) A. R. Emery and V. Gold, *J. Chem. Soc.* p. 1443 (1950).

(86) W. Eschenbach, German Patent 638,441; *Chem. Abstr.* **31**, 1042 (1937).

(87) S. Deakin and N. T. M. Wilsmore, *J. Chem. Soc.* **97**, 1977 (1910).

(88) W. Steinkopf and M. Kühnel, *Ber. deut. chem. Ges.* **75**, 1323 (1942).

(89) D. Harmann and C. W. Smith, British Patent 670,130; *Chem. Abstr.* **47**, 5430 (1953).

(90) A. Roe and J. W. McGeehee, *J. Am. Chem. Soc.* **70**, 1662 (1948).

(91) H. P. Staudinger and K. H. W. Türck, British Patent 539,163; *Chem. Abstr.* **36**, 3509 (1942).

(92) A. T. Bloomquist R. W. Holley, and O. J. Sweeting, *J. Am. Chem. Soc.* **69**, 2356 (1947).

(92a) H. Böhme, H. Bezzenberger, and H. D. Stachel, *Ann. Chem. Liebigs* **602**, 1 (1957).

(93) T. F. Doumani and J. F. Cuneo, U.S. Patent 2,411,823; *Chem. Abstr.* **41**, 1234 (1947).

(94) C. W. Smith, U.S. Patent 2,566,810; *Chem. Abstr.* **46**, 2576 (1952).

(95) M. Reuter, German Patent 849,405; *Chem. Abstr.* **47**, 4899 (1953).

(96) G. Darzens and G. Lévy, *Compt. rend. acad. sci.* **229**, 1081 (1949).

(97) R. Bentley, *J. Am. Chem. Soc.* **70**, 2183 (1948).

(98) H. Vollmann, F. Schloffer, and W. Ostrowski, German Patent 736,504; *Chem. Abstr.* **38**, 2970 (1944).

(99) F. Johnston and L. W. Newton, U.S. Patent 2,395,930; *Chem. Abstr.* **40**, 4078 (1946).

(100) H. J. Hagemeyer, Jr., *Ind. Eng. Chem.* **41**, 765 (1949).

(101) G. C. Ray, U.S. Patent 2,396,201; *Chem. Abstr.* **40**, 4078 (1946).

(102) A. E. Ardis and F. D. Stewart, German Patent 849,549; *Chem. Zentr.* 918, 1953; U.S. Patent 2,574,234; *Chem. Abstr.* **46**, 6143 (1952).

(103) F. D. Stewart, U.S. Patent 2,596,826; *Chem. Abstr.* **47**, 1732 (1953).

(104) W. E. Grigsby, U.S. Patent 2,443,451; *Chem. Abstr.* **42**, 7324 (1948).

(105) W. F. Gresham, U.S. Patent 2,449, 471; *Chem. Abstr.* **43**, 1055 (1949).

(106) R. B. Brooks, U.S. Patent 2,449,447; *Chem. Abstr.* **43**, 1055 (1949).

(107) W. F. Gresham, U.S. Patent 2,504,407; *Chem. Abstr.* **44**, 5902 (1950).

(108) C. D. Hurd, A. D. Sweet, and C. L. Thomas, *J. Am. Chem. Soc.* **55**, 335 (1933).

(109) B. N. Dashkevich, *Zhur. Obshchei Khim.* **8**, 779 (1938); *Chem. Abstr.* **33**, 1293 (1939).

(110) B. N. Dashkevich, *Zhur. Obshchei Khim.* **18**, 205 (1948); *Chem. Abstr.* **42**, 7244 (1948).

(111) H. Gilman, B. L. Wooley, and G. F. Wright, *J. Am. Chem. Soc.* **55**, 2609 (1933).

(112) W. J. Chute, W. M. Orchard, and G. F. Wright, *J. Org. Chem.* **6**, 157 (1941).

(113) H. Gilman and J. F. Nelson, *Rec. trav. chim.* **55**, 518 (1936).

(114) C. D. Hurd, *J. Am. Chem. Soc.* **47**, 2777 (1925).

(115) K. Packendorff, N. D. Zelinsky, and L. Leder-Packendorff, *Ber. deut. chem. Ges.* **66**, 1069 (1933).

(116) J. W. Williams and J. M. Osburn, *J. Am. Chem. Soc.* **61**, 3438 (1939).

(117) B. N. Dashkevich, *Zhur. Obshchei Khim.* **16**, 739 (1946); *Chem. Abstr.* **41**, 1217 (1947).

(118) P. Lipp, J. Buchkremer, and H. Seeles, *Ann. Chem. Liebigs* **499**, 1 (1932).

(119) P. Lipp and R. Köster, *Ber. deut. chem. Ges.* **64**, 2823 (1931).

(120) S. Kaarsemaker and J. Coops, *Rec. trav. chim.* **70**, 1033 (1951).

(121) B. H. Gwynn and E. F. Degering, U.S. Patent 2,383,965; *Chem. Abstr.* **40**, 346 (1946).

(122) B. H. Gwynn, Canadian Patent 465,721; *Chem. Zentr.* I, 250 (1951).

(123) B. H. Gwynn and E. F. Degering, U.S. Patent 2,418,708; *Chem. Abstr.* **41**, 4507 (1947).

(124) J. A. Spence and E. F. Degering, *J. Am. Chem. Soc.* **66**, 1624 (1944).

(125) J. A. Spence and E. F. Degering, U.S. Patent 2,407,301; *Chem. Abstr.* **41**, 478 (1947); E. F. Degering, U.S. Patent 2,446,655; *Chem. Abstr.* **43**, 7505 (1949).

(126) F. G. Young, U.S. Patent 2,461,016; *Chem. Abstr.* **43**, 3838 (1949).

(127) A. W. Agett, U.S. Patent 2,421,976; *Chem. Abstr.* **41**, 6279 (1947).

(128) H. J. Hagemeyer, Jr. and D. C. Hull, *Ind. Eng. Chem.* **41**, 2920 (1949).

(129) F. G. Young, U.S. Patent 2,511,423; *Chem. Abstr.* **44**, 9980 (1950).

(130) D. C. Hull and A. H. Agett, U.S. Patent 2,422,679; *Chem. Abstr.* **41**, 6895 (1947).

(131) British Patent 605,471; *Chem. Abstr.* **43**, 1436 (1949).

(132) C. D. Hurd, O. E. Edwards, and I. R. Roach, *J. Am. Chem. Soc.* **66**, 2013 (1944).

(133) A. T. Blomquist and F. H. Baldwin, *J. Am. Chem. Soc.* **70**, 29 (1948).

(134) M. Mugdan and J. Sixt, British Patent 498,280; *Chem. Abstr.* **33**, 3820 (1939).

(135) A. B. Boese, Jr., *Ind. Eng. Chem.* **32**, 16 (1940).

(136) T. L. Gresham, J. E. Jansen, and F. W. Shaver, *J. Am. Chem. Soc.* **70**, 998 (1948).

(137) T. L. Gresham, J. E. Jansen, F. W. Shaver and J. T. Gregory, *J. Am. Chem. Soc.* **70**, 999 (1948).

(138) T. L. Gresham, J. E. Jansen, F. W. Shaver, R. A. Bankert, W. L. Beears, and M. G. Prendergast, *J. Am. Chem. Soc.* **71**, 661 (1949).

(139) T. L. Gresham, J. E. Jansen, F. W. Shaver, and R. A. Bankert, *J. Am. Chem. Soc.* **71**, 2807 (1949).

(140) H. E. Zaugg, *Org. Reactions* **8**, 365 (1954).

(141) A. B. Boese, Jr., U.S. Patent 2,382,464; *Chem. Abstr.* **40**, 1867 (1946).

(142) T. R. Steadman, U.S. Patent 2,424,589; *Chem. Abstr.* **41**, 7413 (1947).

(143) H. J. Hagemeyer, Jr., U.S. Patent 2,250,132; *Chem. Abstr.* **43**, 1056 (1949).

(144) H. J. Hagemeyer, Jr., U.S. Patent 2,456,503; *Chem. Abstr.* **43**, 2635 (1949).

(145) J. R. Caldwell and H. J. Hagemeyer, Jr., U.S. Patent 2,462,357; *Chem. Abstr.* **43**, 3840 (1949).

(146) H. J. Hagemeyer, Jr., U.S. Patent 2,478,388; *Chem. Abstr.* **44**, 1133 (1950).

(147) H. J. Hagemeyer, Jr., U.S. Patent 2,481,742; *Chem. Abstr.* **44**, 4504 (1950).

(148) A. B. Boese, Jr., U.S. Patent 2,484,067; *Chem. Abstr.* **44**, 1529 (1950).

(149) H. J. Hagemeyer, Jr., U.S. Patent 2,496,791; *Chem. Abstr.* **44**, 4026 (1950).

(150) H. J. Hagemeyer, Jr., U.S. Patent 2,450,134; *Chem. Abstr.* **43**, 1056 (1949).

(151) J. R. Caldwell, U.S. Patent 2,585,223; *Chem. Abstr.* **46**, 8672 (1952).

(152) J. R. Caldwell, U.S. Patent 2,450,116; *Chem. Abstr.* **43**, 1055 (1949).

(153) H. J. Hagemeyer, Jr., U.S. Patent 2,469,110; *Chem. Abstr.* **43**, 5414 (1949).

(154) H. J. Hagemeyer, Jr. and D. C. Cooper, U.S. Patent 2,469,690; *Chem. Abstr.* **43**, 5794 (1949).

(155) F. G. Young and J. T. Fitzpatrick, U.S. Patent 2,580,714; *Chem. Abstr.* **46**, 8147 (1952).

(156) J. R. Caldwell, U.S. Patent Appl. 252,194; *Chem. Abstr.* **48**, 12,169 (1954).

(157) H. J. Hagemeyer, Jr., U.S. Patent 2,466,420; *Chem. Abstr.* **43**, 5037 (1949).

(158) H. J. Hagemeyer, Jr., U.S. Patent 2,450,133; *Chem. Abstr.* **43**, 1056 (1949).

(159) J. R. Caldwell, U.S. Patent 2,518,662; *Chem. Abstr.* **44**, 10,732 (1950).

(160) H. J. Hagemeyer, Jr., U.S. Patent 2,450, 131; *Chem. Abstr.* **43**, 1056 (1949).

(161) B. Barnett, U.S. Patent 2,513,615; *Chem. Abstr.* **44**, 9475 (1950).

(162) C. D. Hurd and C. L. Thomas, *J. Am. Chem. Soc.* **55**, 275 (1933).

(163) British Patent 668,569 (1949); *Chem. Abstr.* **46**, 7114 (1952).

(164) B. P. Geyer and S. A. Ballard, German Patent 828,245; *Chem. Zentr.* p. 6605 (1952).

(165) T. L. Gresham and F. W. Shaver, U.S. Patent 2,449,995; *Chem. Abstr.* **46,** 155 (1949).

(166) J. A. Spence and E. F. Degering, U.S. Patent 2,417,381; *Chem. Abstr.* **41,** 4169 (1947).

(167) A. B. Boese, Jr., U.S. Patent 2,432,499; *Chem. Abstr.* **42,** 2615 (1948).

(168) D. S. Melstron and R. T. Holm, U.S. Patent 2,569,132; *Chem. Abstr.* **46,** 5078 (1952).

(169) V. E. Haury, L. Cerrito, and S. A. Ballard, U.S. Patent 2,418,173; *Chem. Abstr.* **41,** 4510 (1947).

(170) British Patent 638,091; *Chem. Abstr.* **44,** 9476 (1950).

(171) V. E. Haury and S. A. Ballard, French Patent 951,655; *Chem. Zentr.* II, 1876 (1950).

(172) R. Kuhn, G. Quadbeck and E. Röhm, *Chem. Ber.* **86,** 468 (1953).

(173) G. Quadbeck and E. Röhm, unpublished results.

(174) M. Koenen, *Chem. Ber.* **80,** 546 (1947).

(175) T. Brooks and G. Wilbert, *J. Am. Chem. Soc.* **63,** 870 (1941).

(176) A. T. Bloomquist and J. Kwiatek, *J. Am. Chem. Soc.* **73,** 2098 (1951).

(177) H. Staudinger, *Chem. Ber.* **50,** 1035 (1917).

(178) G. O. Schenk and N. Engelhard, *Angew. Chem.* **68,** 71 (1956).

(179) O. Wollenberg, *Ber. deut. chem. Ges.* **67,** 1675 (1934).

(180) J. A. Berson and W. M. Jones, *J. Am. Chem. Soc.* **78,** 1625 (1956).

(181) J. Thesing and K. Hofmann, *Chem. Ber.* **90,** 229 (1957).

Preparative and Analytical Importance of Phosphines and Related Compounds

L. Horner and H. Hoffmann

Organisch-Chemisches Institut der Universität Mainz

Preparation of Quaternary Compounds

Relation between Polarity and Reactivity

The high polarity of the phosphines is in keeping with their strong nucleophilic character. Table 1 shows the dipole moments of the triaryl derivatives of the group 5 elements (*1*).

TABLE 1
Dipole Moments

$(C_6H_5)_3N$	0.26 D
$(C_6H_5)_3P$	1.45 D
$(C_6H_5)_3As$	1.07 D
$(C_6H_5)_3Sb$	0.57 D
$(C_6H_5)_3Bi$	0 D

The ability to react with methyl iodide runs parallel to the dipole moment: whereas triphenylamine, triphenylstibine, and triphenylbismuthine do not react with methyl iodide, and triphenylarsine reacts only at higher temperatures, triphenylphosphine strongly reacts exothermically (*2*).

The rate of quaternization has been investigated by Davies and Lewis with aryldialkylphosphines and the amines. In all cases the phosphines were more active. Electron acceptors in the *para* position of the aromatic ring slowed down, while electron-donating groups accelerated, the reaction. However, the influence of substituents in the phosphines is distinctly less than for the corresponding amines.

The larger radius of the central atom in phosphine, in contrast to that of the amines, makes it possible for a fourth ligand to approach without steric hindrance. As the existence of (1-naphthyl)-triphenylphosphonium salts shows, very bulky ligands can be accommodated (*3*).

Addition of Tertiary Phosphines to Systems Having a Polarized or Polarizable Double Bond

Reaction Scheme

The tendency of phosphines to quaternize becomes especially evident in the forming of adducts, having the character of inner phosphonium

163

salts, with a series of compounds which possess polar or readily polarizable double bonds.

$$X = Y + |PR_3 \rightarrow \overset{\ominus}{X} - Y - \overset{\oplus}{PR_3}$$

The reaction is accompanied generally by a deepening of color. The adducts possess a salt-like solubility behavior and add to polar reagents:

$$\overset{\ominus}{X} - Y - \overset{\oplus}{PR_3} + HCl \rightarrow [HX - Y - \overset{\oplus}{PR_3}]Cl^{\ominus}$$

$$+ H_2O \rightarrow [HX - Y - \overset{\oplus}{PR_3}]OH^{\ominus}$$

$$+ CH_3I \rightarrow [H_3C - X - Y - \overset{\oplus}{PR_3}]I^{\ominus}$$

With hydrochloric acid normal phosphonium chlorides are formed; with water or alkali phosphonium hydroxides are formed which can decompose to phosphine oxide and the hydrated form of the starting materials. Alkyl halides also are added on in several instances.

ADDITION TO C=S AND C=O BONDS

The red adducts of aliphatic phosphines with carbon disulfide have been known the longest (4–7).

A Cahours and A. W. Hofmann formulate the compounds as thioesters (I). Armstrong (8) assumes bimolecular ring compounds. Hantzsch and Hibbert (9) determined the molecular weight, which indicated a monomolecular species, and proposed formula II. They attributed the strong light absorption to the three-membered ring structure. The cyclic chromophore is said to be broken down through the opening of the ring by the action of acids, by means of which the colorless hydrochloride, III, is produced. In the case of the addition of methyl iodide the ring sulfur atom is thought to act as the coordination center, the three-ring system being retained (the red color is retained) (IV) (10).

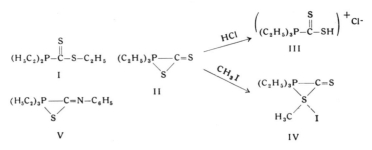

For the yellow adduct from triethylphosphine and phenyl isothiocyanate to which Hofmann (11) assigned a urea-like structure, Hantzsch (9) proposed formula V.

According to our present-day knowledge the results are interpreted best by formulas IIa–Va. (*12*).

$$(C_2H_5)_3\overset{\oplus}{P}-C=S \xrightarrow{\text{HCl}} \left[(C_2H_5)_3\overset{\oplus}{P}-C=S\right] Cl^{\ominus} \quad \text{III a}$$
$$\underset{S^{\ominus}}{|} \qquad\qquad\qquad \underset{SH}{|}$$

IIa

$$\xrightarrow{\text{CH}_3\text{I}} \left[(C_2H_5)_3\overset{\oplus}{P}-C=S\right] I^{\ominus} \quad \text{IVa}$$
$$\underset{SCH_3}{|}$$

$$(C_2H_5)_3\overset{\oplus}{P}-C=N-C_6H_5 \qquad \left[(C_2H_5)_3\overset{\oplus}{P}-C=N-C_6H_5\right] I^{\ominus} \quad \text{VI}$$
$$\underset{S^{\ominus}\quad \text{Va}}{|} \qquad\qquad\qquad \underset{S-CH_3}{|}$$

Structure VI may be assigned to the addition product (still yellow) obtained by the action of methyl iodide on V.

In this manner the thermal decomposition of Va to phenyl isonitrile and triethylphosphine sulfide may be explained (*13*).

$$\text{Va} \rightarrow (C_2H_5)_3 \text{ PS} + C=N-C_6H_5$$

The structurally analogous oxygen compounds behave differently from carbon disulfide and phenyl isothiocyanate. Carbon oxysulfide and carbon dioxide show no tendency to add the triethylphosphine. In contrast, as Hofmann (*13*) recognized, the isocyanates react with traces of triethylphosphine to trimerize to isomers of esters of cyanuric acid, whose structures were elucidated by Slotta and Tschesche (*14*). They found that at low temperature the asymmetric trimer VII is formed via non-isolable red intermediary products, whereas in the presence of and incorporation of carbon dioxide, VIII is formed. VII is transformed into VIII by hydrogen chloride.

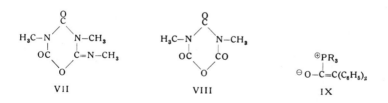

VII   VIII   IX

In order to obtain organic derivatives of pentavalent phosphorus, Staudinger and Meyer (*15*) reacted ketenes with triethylphosphine. With diphenylketene they obtained a very labile adduct in a ratio of 1:1, which at present is assigned formula IX.

R_3P reacts with diphenylcarbodiimide to form first a yellow color, then to form phenylisonitrile and pentaphenyl bisguanide (*16*).

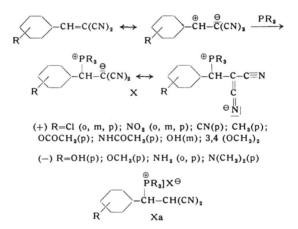

$$C_6H_5-N=C=N-C_6H_5 \xrightarrow{PR_3 \ (+ \ H_2O)}$$
$$C_6H_5N=C + C_6H_5NH_2 + OPR_3$$

ADDITION TO COMPOUNDS CONTAINING POLARIZED CARBON–CARBON DOUBLE BONDS

The character of the alkene double bond is determined by the nature of the attached substituents. We found that alkenes with electrophilic substituents could undergo nucleophilic addition of tertiary phosphines. Methylene malononitrile, benzal malononitrile, substituted benzal cyano-acetic ester, and substituted benzal malonic ester add triethylphosphine with decreasing ease (16).

(+) R=Cl (o, m, p); NO₂ (o, m, p); CN(p); CH₃(p); OCOCH₃(p); NHCOCH₃(p); OH(m); 3,4 (OCH₃)₂

(−) R=OH(p); OCH₃(p); NH₂ (o, p); N(CH₃)₂(p)

The inner phosphonium salts dissolve in dilute, aqueous acids with retention of the C–P bond as salt Xa and may be precipitated unchanged by the addition of sodium acetate. The nature and position of the substituent R in the aromatic ring have great influence on the formation of the adduct itself, and the stability of the adduct. Electrophilic substituents (+) promote the formation of adducts, while electron-donating substituents (−) hinder the formation. The cause of inhibition is the involvement of the lone electron doublet of the para-substituted key atom in the resonance of the total system. The UV absorption also substantiates the point that the electronic configuration of a compound with R (−) has shifted largely in the direction of the resonance structure XI which, however, no longer possesses a polarized double bond.

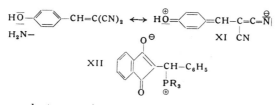

If the lone electron pair of the *para*-substituted central atom is furnished a resonating partner, e.g. through acylation, then the double bond system remains intact and reactive towards tertiary phosphines.

The adduct from 2-benzal-1,3-diketohydrindene and triethylphosphine is noteworthy for its relatively great stability. The reason for this is the optimal, favorable, planar attachment of the two carbonyl groups needed for resonance. Compound XII has indicator properties. Other adducts are formed with triethylphosphine by: furfural malononitrile; α-thienylmethylenemalononitrile, the low melting *cis*-α-nitrostilbene, dibenzal fulgid (dibenzalsuccinonitrile), 2-oxo-Δ³,α-indolinemalononitrile, (labile), and 1-methyl-2-oxo-Δ³,α-indolinemalononitrile.

No adducts are formed by: α,β-unsaturated sulfones (e.g., β-tolyl-ω-styrylsulfone), esters of cinnamic acid, cinnamyl nitrile, chalcone, benzal-hydantoin and α-benzal-γ-phenylcrotolactone, dibenzalcyclopentanone and dibenzalpentenone, monobenzalsuccinic anhydride (play of colors), succinic anhydride, and 2,3-dimethylmaleic anhydride.

Adduct Formation with Aromatization

With Azlactones (16)

The carbon–carbon double bond in azlactones and benzalbarbituric acids behaves anomalously and is not susceptible to catalytic hydrogenation, for example. The reason for this is the polarity of the alkene double bond, which is evident also in the adduct formation with triethylphosphine.

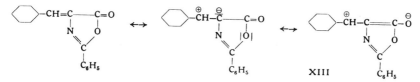

With a polar reactant, such as a tertiary phosphine or an aliphatic Grignard reagent (17) the azlactone reacts as if in the resonance structure XIII and adds on the tertiary phosphine or the carbanion of the Grignard reagent at the cationic carbon atom. Thus the polarity of the carbon–carbon double bond in azlactones may be indicated and localized with triethylphosphine. The polarity of the double bond depends on the tendency towards aromatization on the part of the oxazolidone ring. It already possesses two electron doublets and requires a third electron pair. The latter is borrowed from the alkene double bond to form a quasi-aromatic state. On the same basis the double bond in benzalbarbituric acid derivatives (XIV) is polarized and capable of adding triethylphosphine.

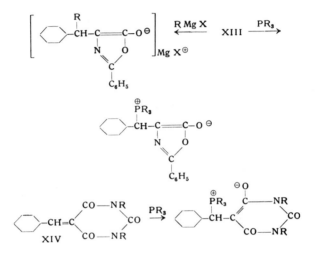

The situation in the case of tertiary phosphines was the reason for the examination of the addition of the Grignard reagents, whose aliphatic representatives act in a corresponding manner. Aromatic Grignard reagents, on the other hand, react with the carbonyl group (17, 18).

Adducts with Quinones and Quinone Derivatives

The examples show that the tertiary phosphines are strong "ansolvobases" and are able to attach themselves because of sufficient polarizability to a double bond system functioning as an acid.

Therefore it was not surprising that not only para, but also ortho-quinones and also other α,β-unsaturated carbonyl compounds can function as addition partners. As Davies and Walters (12) discovered, an unstable 1:1 adduct is obtained from p-quinone and triethylphosphine; they assigned structure XV to the adduct. Schönberg and Michaelis (19, 20) later described the yellow and stable adduct from p-quinone and triphenylphosphine. A similar compound is formed from p-naphthoquinone and triphenylphosphine. Also p-quinone derivatives having a sufficient redox potential are able to form adducts; for example, N,N′-bis(phenylsulfonyl)p-quinone diimine (16) and benzoquinone azine (21). All compounds of this type are easily hydrolyzable; the Schönberg adduct decomposes, e.g., into hydroquinone and triphenylphosphine oxide, by heating with alkali.

$$C_6H_5-SO_2-N=\langle\!\!\!\bigcirc\!\!\!\rangle=N-SO_2C_6H_5;\ O=\langle\!\!\!\bigcirc\!\!\!\rangle=N-N=\langle\!\!\!\bigcirc\!\!\!\rangle=O$$

Different possibilities for the constitution of these compounds have been discussed; in the case of the p-benzoquinonetriphenylphosphine adduct (Schönberg adduct) they can be expressed by the formulas XV, XVa, and XVI:

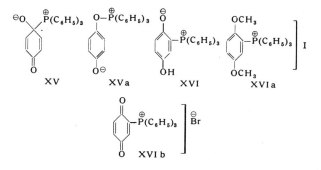

Through synthesis formula XVI could be linked to the Schönberg adduct (21); a phosphonium salt of formula XVIa is obtained with the "cobalt chloride method" (21a) from triphenylphosphine and the dimethyl ether of bromohydroquinone. This compound, through dealkylation and the splitting out of HBr, can be transposed to a compound identical with the Schönberg adduct. Formula XVI is also supported in that the Schönberg adduct can be mono- and dialkylated (in the latter case XVIa or analogous products are formed), and it can be oxidized to quinone derivatives (XVIb).

The phosphine adduct of tetrachloro-p-quinone, investigated by Ramirez (22), has another structure, for which the formula XVII can be stated with certainty:

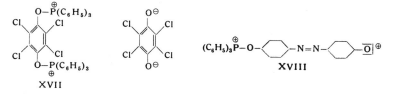

Since o-quinones easily form quinhydrone-like adducts with suitable tertiary amines (23), they were readily expected with tertiary phosphines. o-Benzoquinone and some substitution products such as tetrachloro-o-quinone and 6,7-dichlorobenzotriazol-o-quinone give colorless to light yellow adducts of the ratio 1:1, which also decompose with water to form pyrocatechol derivatives and phosphine oxide (16).

In summary it may be said that p- and o-quinones form betaines with tertiary phosphines, which may account energy-wise for the return to the aromatic state.

Adducts with Vinylogous Dicarbonyl Compounds (16)

The electronic alteration of the total system after the incorporation of the tertiary phosphines can be simply demonstrated: *cis-* and *trans-*dibenzylethylene have in common with p-quinone two carbonyl groups, which are joined by one or two double bonds. The same adduct, XIX, with triethylphosphine is obtained from the *cis* as well as from the *trans* compound; the structure of the adduct is expressed by the cyclic mesomeric forms XIXa and XIXb.

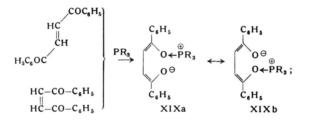

Through the formation of the adduct the configuration responsible for the geometric isomerism is changed in such a manner that free rotation is restored.

In further analogy to p-quinone, XIX adds 1 mole of methyl iodide (XX) and decomposes in the presence of moisture via an isolable hydrate into dibenzoylethylene and triphenylphosphine oxide. XX rearranges on alkaline hydrolysis to 2,5-diphenylfuran, XXI (16, 21).

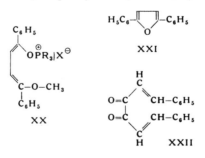

Corresponding models for o-quinone may also be found. In the 1,6-diphenyl-1,5-hexadiene-3,4-dione (XXII) of Schlenk (24) the carbonyl and double bond hold positions analogous to the o-quinone. A

change in the model substance XXII is recognized by the strong formation of red color with triethylphosphine; however, a definite adduct can
not be isolated (16).

With respect to maleic anhydride and p-benzoquinone (and its
derivatives), Schönberg and Ismail (20) make the statement, that
monosubstituted—but not disubstituted—maleic anhydride derivatives
also react at higher dilution with the formation of a red-orange color.
The color reaction is thought to be specific for the structure A:

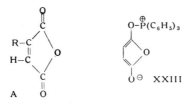

A crystalline, pale yellow-colored adduct (1:1) is said to possess the
formula XXIII, analogous to the adduct from p-benzoquinone and triphenylphosphine (XVa). The reaction products responsible for the color
reaction are not explained.

Adducts with 1,2-Dicarbonylacetylene Compounds (21, 22)

Tertiary phosphines react with suitably substituted acetylene compounds in essentially the same manner as with alkene components except
that the reaction is more complicated. Dimethyl acetylenedicarboxylate
yields with triphenylphosphine an adduct (1:1) for which we propose
formula XXIVa, and with triethylphosphine an adduct (2:1) with the
suggested formula XXIVb. Dibenzoyldiacetylene with two moles of triphenylphosphine yields a yellow adduct, for which we present formula
XXV for discussion (22, 24a):

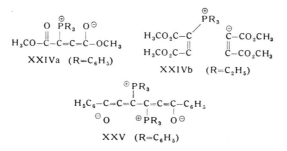

Structure XXIV is based on the analysis as well as the analogy to the
addition of the acetylenedicarboxylic ester to pyridine, according to
Diels and Alder (25). XXIII and XXIV decompose in the presence of
water to dimethyl fumarate and phosphine oxide to the extent of 80%

under proper conditions *(21)*. Suitably substituted double- and triple-bond compounds can be reduced by means of tertiary phosphines.

The Anionic Polymerization with Alkenes *(26)*

With one end of the ethylene molecule linked with electrophilic substituents ($R=CN$, $COCH_3$, CHO, CO_2R) an adduct in the ratio of 1:1 is formed first; however it is not sufficiently stabilized intramolecularly, but instead adds on additional alkene molecules because of previous polarization. Chain termination takes place by the saturation of the polar end with polar substances capable of splitting, such as water. This, as well as the insensitivity of the polymerization towards oxygen and the still vigorous reaction at $-70°$, exclude a radical reaction mechanism. Polyacrylonitrile, prepared carefully and with exclusion of polar agents, contains on the average one phosphorus atom per chain. The following reaction scheme agrees well with this result:

Chain initiation:

$$H_2C=CH-R \longleftrightarrow \underset{\oplus \quad \ominus}{H_2C-CH-R} \xrightarrow{PR_3'} \overset{\oplus}{R_3'P}-CH_2-\overset{\ominus}{CH}-R$$

(A)

Chain propagation:

$$A + nCH_2=CH-R \longrightarrow \overset{\oplus}{R_3'P}-(CH_2-CH-R)_n-CH_2-\underset{\ominus}{CH}-R$$

(B)

Chain termination:

$$(B) + HY \longrightarrow Y[\overset{\oplus}{R_3'P}-(CH_2-CHR)_n-CH_2-CH_2-R]$$

(C)

ω-Nitrostyrene and derivatives also yield short-chain polymers with triethylphosphine.

Adducts with Triphenylmethane Dyes *(27)*

According to Weitz *(28)* the strong light absorption of the triphenyl-methane dyes may be attributed to "distributed heteropolarity."

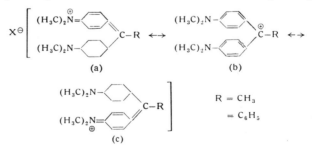

(a)   (b)

(c)

$R = CH_3$

$= C_6H_5$

Tertiary phosphines, as strong nucleophilic reactants, are said to be able to form adducts with the mesomeric form (b). With the use of BF_3-etherate as an anion-former, the cationic site in (b) may be blocked by triethylphosphine with the loss of color. This reaction goes especially well with the unsymmetrical bis(p-dimethylaminophenyl)ethylene (R = CH_3) which is less sterically hindered than Malachite Green:

$$R = CH_3$$
$$R' = C_2H_5$$

Phosphines as Selective Reducing Agents

Direct Addition of Oxygen, Sulfur, Selenium, and the Halogens

Aliphatic phosphines react even at room temperature with the oxygen in the air, while pure aromatic phosphines are not autoxidizable. Within the aliphatic series the larger alkyl groups reduce the tendency towards oxidation, whereas methyl and benzyl increase it.

Sulfur and selenium add in a manner similar to oxygen to form the corresponding phosphine sulfides and selenides; aromatic phosphines react readily.

The addition products of the halogens and pseudohalogens are very readily formed (29). These have been used recently in preparative work because of their high reactivity (30).

Cleavage of Phosphonium Hydroxides and Reductive Dehalogenation

The tendency to form a phosphorus–oxygen double bond as the reaction-determining step is clearly demonstrated in the so-called Michaelis-Arbuzov reaction (31), namely, the reaction of alkyl or aryl halides with compounds which contain an alkoxy or phenoxy group attached directly to the trivalent phosphorus atom:

XXVI

The oxygen-bound group, R_3, in the phosphonium-salt–like intermediate (XXVI) detaches itself as a cation and unites with the anion.

A very elegant application of the Arbuzov rearrangement for the preparation of alkyl halides was discovered by Landauer and Rydon (31a). These authors used the observation that triphenylphosphite forms with methyl iodide, benzyl bromide or benzyl chloride, phosphonium-salt–like adducts, which are stable and do not decompose into esters of phosphonic acid and aryl halides according to the scheme of the Arbuzov reaction. If the adduct is treated with an alcohol, transesterification occurs to form an intermediate which decomposes immediately to form alkyl halides:

$$(C_6H_5O)_3P + RX$$
$$\downarrow$$
$$[(C_6H_5O)_3PR]X \xrightarrow{R'OH} [(C_6H_5O)_2P-R]X + C_6H_5OH$$
$$\underset{OR'}{|}$$
$$\downarrow$$
$$\overset{O}{\underset{\|}{}}$$
$$(C_6H_5O)_2\overset{\|}{P}-R + R'X$$

The procedure also produces exceptional results in difficult cases, e.g., neopentyl iodide (*31b*).

The Michaelis-Arbuzov reaction closely resembles the thermal decomposition of phosphonium hydroxides, which characteristically proceeds quite differently than decomposition of the corresponding ammonium hydroxides (*32*).

$$\begin{bmatrix} R & R \\ & P \\ R & R \end{bmatrix} OH \leftrightarrow \begin{bmatrix} R & R \\ R-P \\ R & O\,H \end{bmatrix} \rightarrow \begin{array}{c} R \\ R \end{array} P=O + RH$$

$$(C_6H_5)_2CH-CH_2-PR_3]OH \rightarrow (C_6H_5)_2C=CH_2 + R_3P + H_2O$$

Decomposition into phosphine, alkene and water, analogous to the Hofmann degradation, takes place only with strong activation in the β-position. Otherwise phosphine oxide and hydrocarbons are formed exclusively (*32*). According to Ingold an intermediate with pentavalent phosphorus is formed, from which the strongest anionic group is removed along with the proton of the hydroxyl group. If there are different groups attached to the phosphorus atom, then these split off in the following order (*32*):

$$C_6H_5CH_2 > C_6H_5 > CH_3 > C_6H_5-CH_2-CH_2 > C_2H_5 > \text{Higher alkyl groups}$$

The result of hydrolysis of different substituted arylphosphonium salts is in agreement with this. It becomes evident that relative to the unsubstituted phenyl group, substituents with acceptor properties facilitate cleavages, whereas donor groups make it more difficult (*32a*).

o-, *m*-, *p*-Nitrophenyl-, *p*-chlorophenyl-, *p*-carbethoxyphenyl-, *p*-biphenylyl-, and α- and β-naphthyl groups are split off more easily while *p*- and *m*-aminophenyl-, *p*- and *m*-tolyl-, *p*- and *m*-methoxyphenyl-, and *p*- and *m*-hydroxyphenyl groups with greater difficulty than the unsubstituted phenyl groups. The difference is so pronounced, that the cleavage proceeds consistently as, for example:

$$\left[(C_6H_5)_3P-\!\!\left\langle\!\!=\!\!\right\rangle\!\!-NH_2 \right] I \xrightarrow{\text{NaOH}} (C_6H_5)_2\overset{\overset{O}{\|}}{P}-\!\!\left\langle\!\!=\!\!\right\rangle\!\!-NH_2 + C_6H_6$$

$$\left[(C_6H_5)_3P-\!\!\left\langle\!\!=\!\!\right\rangle\!\!-NO_2 \right] I \xrightarrow{\text{NaOH}} (C_6H_5)_3P\!=\!O + C_6H_5NO_2$$

The investigation of the cleavage rate also leads to a confirmation of the Ingold postulation that the anionic stability of the leaving group is the controlling factor for the ease of cleavage. The cleavage rates of benzyltriphenylphosphonium hydroxides, in which the benzyl group is variously substituted, obey Hammett's equation (32b).

In consideration of the often very easy formation of phosphonium salts, it is possible therefore by attention to the above directions, to carry out a planned synthesis of the desired phosphine oxides or to dehalogenate aromatic and aliphatic halogen compounds.

Reduction of Organic Peroxides and Disulfides

Derivatives of hydrogen peroxide can be reduced with tertiary phosphines according to the scheme (33):

$$R_1-O-O-R_2 + PR_3{'} \rightarrow R_1-O-R_2 + OPR_3$$

One may obtain in this manner from:

Hydrogen peroxide → water (in ether)
Alkyl hydroperoxides → alcohols
Unsaturated hydroperoxides → unsaturated alcohols
Hydroxyalkyl hydroperoxides → aldehydes
Dihydroxyalkyl hydroperoxides → ketones
Peroxy acids → acids
Peroxy acid esters → esters
Diacyl peroxides → acid anhydrides
endo-Peroxides → oxide compounds
Ozonides → ketones (or aldehydes)

Almost all peroxide representatives react at room temperature. Only the open-chain and cyclic dialkyl peroxides react more slowly, the rate depending upon the effective radius of R_1 and R_2, and require the application of heat.

Alkyl-, Alkenyl, and Hydroxyalkyl Hydroperoxides

At room temperature the following react to form the corresponding alcohols: cumene hydroperoxide (88% yield), butyl hydroperoxide (90%), tetralin hydroperoxide (99%), tetrahydrofuran hydroperoxide (90%), diethylether hydroperoxide, triphenylmethyl hydroperoxide

(98%), cyclohexane hydroperoxide (71%), and α-hydroxyalkyl hydroperoxide (100%).

Solvents, for example ether, can be made peroxide-free by simple distillation from a sufficiently large amount of triphenyl phosphine. The alkene double bonds are not touched by the tertiary phosphines.

DIALKYL PEROXIDES AND *endo*-PEROXIDES

Ethyl peroxide yields ethyl ether with triethylphosphine at 80°, and *t*-butyl peroxide gives the *t*-butyl ether with triphenylphosphine at 110–120°; on the other hand triphenylmethyl peroxide, as well as 3,3,5,5-tetramethyl-1,2-dioxacyclopentane and 3,3,6,6-tetramethyl-1,2-dioxacyclohexane are resistant towards triethyl phosphine as well as triphenylphosphine.*

Because of the fact that dialkyl peroxides react with tertiary phosphines more slowly in order of magnitude than the alkyl hydroperoxides, it is possible to distinguish them qualitatively and in certain cases determine both quantitatively.

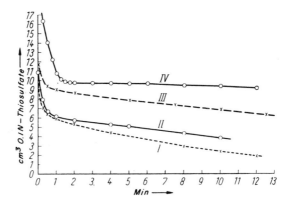

FIG. 1. (*33*). I, cumene hydroperoxide + triphenylphosphine; II, tetrahydrofuran peroxide + triphenylphosphine; III, benzoyl peroxide + triphenylphosphine; IV, cyclohexanone peroxide + triphenyl phosphine. All components 0.01 mole in ether.

As Fig. 1 shows, two differently bound peroxide groups can be determined quantitatively by titration:

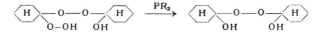

It should be possible to elucidate autoxidation processes preparatively with the aid of tertiary phosphines. Ascaridol, also a representative of

* R. Criegee, private communication.

the *endo*-peroxides, behaves as a dialkyl peroxide and is transformed at 100° to the endoxide XXVIII.

XXVIII

OZONIDES

Ozonides, according to the structure concept of Staudinger and Criegee and co-workers (*34*), are also readily reduced to dicarboxyl systems with tertiary phosphines (*35*).

$$\overset{\backslash}{/}C\overset{O-O}{\underset{O}{\diagup\diagdown}}C\overset{\diagup}{\backslash} \xrightarrow{PR_3} \overset{\backslash}{/}C=O + O=C\overset{\diagup}{\backslash} + OPR_3$$

The ozonides of the following compounds are reduced specifically at the ozonide group (*36*): dimethylbutadiene sulfone (89% yield), cyclohexane (70%), 4,5-dimethyl-*cis*-tetrahydrophthalic anhydride (65%), 1,2-dimethyl-1-cyclopentene (92%), and 1,4-dibenzoyl-1-butyne (45%), and others.

DIACYL PEROXIDES

Well-purified diacyl peroxides (*37, 34*) react quickly with tertiary phosphines to give acid anhydrides and phosphine oxide in good yield and high purity. The following diacyl peroxides were converted to the corresponding acid anhydrides: dibenzoyl peroxide (80% yield), di-*p*-chlorobenzoyl peroxide (80–90%), benzoyl anisoyl peroxide (60%), benzoyl hydrocinnamoyl peroxide (70%), benzoyl *p*-nitrobenzoyl peroxide (90%), benzoyl phenacetyl peroxide (98%), methyl terephthaloyl peroxide (54%), N-benzoyl-ε-aminocaproyl peroxide (40%), and phthalic acid peroxide.

MECHANISM OF REACTION

Diacyl peroxides in general decompose thermally, photolytically, or by action of suitable electron donors, according to a radical mechanism. According to Leffler (*38*) the insertion of an acetyl or nitro group into the 4,4′-position of dibenzoyl peroxide induces so strong a polarity in the peroxide bridge, that a rearrangement takes place via krypto-ions. Still more pronounced is the peroxide bridge in the esters of peroxyacids, examined by Criegee and Kaspar, which polarize according to the polarity of the reaction medium (*39*).

For the explanation of the reaction, (a) a strong polarizing tertiary phosphine and (b) its strong affinity for oxygen, are essential.

$$R_1\text{--}O\text{--}O\text{--}R_2 + PR_3' \rightarrow [R_1\text{--}O\text{--}O\text{--}R_2] \rightarrow [R_1\text{--}\overline{\underset{}{O}}{}^{\ominus}\,|\overline{\underset{}{O}}\text{--}R_2]$$
$$\underset{XXVIIa}{\overset{}{PR_3'}} \qquad \underset{XXVIIb}{\overset{\oplus}{PR_3'}}$$

$$\begin{array}{c} R_1\text{--}O\text{--}R_2 \\ O\!=\!PR_3' \end{array} \leftarrow \begin{bmatrix} R_1\text{--}\overline{\underset{}{O}}{}^{\ominus} & \overset{\oplus}{R_2} \\ O\!=\!PR_3' & \end{bmatrix}$$
$$\text{XXVIIc}$$

In the intermediate complex, XXVIIa, both of these factors finally bring about polar cleavage, by way of XXVIIb (*40*) and XXVIIc, with the phosphine oxide and the oxygen-poorer R_1—O—R_2. No experimental evidence (initiation of polymerization and sensitiveness towards oxygen) for a radical reaction mechanism could be found.

The observations set forth concerning the polar mechanism of the reaction of peroxides with teriary phosphines were confirmed by the work of Greenbaum and associates (*40a*). The authors caused carbonyl-O^{18}-dibenzoyl peroxide to react and arrived at the following conclusions based on the distribution of O^{18}:

1. The primary step consists of a nucleophilic attachment of the phosphine to the oxygen of the peroxide group*:

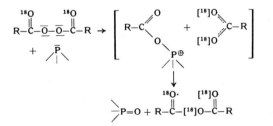

2. In unsymmetrical peroxides that oxygen atom is attacked preferentially which has the lower electron density. With heterolytic cleavage of the peroxide compound an ion pair is formed which breaks down into phosphine oxide and carboxylic acid anhýdride.

DISULFIDES

The disulfides, analogous to the peroxides, behave in quite a similar fashion (*42,43*). Here, also, the affinity of the tertiary phosphine for sulfur becomes the reaction-determining factor.

* The symbol [^{18}]O means that half of the isotope contents of the original carbonyl oxygen is found in this position of the molecule.

$$R_1-S-S-R_2 \xrightarrow{PR_3'} R_1-S-R_2 + SPR_3'$$

$$R_1 = R_2 = COC_6H_5$$
$$= \alpha\, COC_{10}H_7$$
$$= CH_2-CH=CH_2$$
$$= \langle \rangle - N(CH_3)_2$$
$$= C=SN(CH_3)_2$$

Dibenzyl disulfides, p,p'-dinitrodiphenyl disulfide, dibenzyhydryl disulfide, and diethyl disulfide are stable with triphenylphosphine in boiling benzene (42). On the other hand tertiary phosphines remove the sulfur from ethylene sulfide and its derivatives (44). Cystine is converted to lanthionine, having been converted first to dibenzoylcystine, which is sufficiently soluble in decalin (45).

Even if the disulfides can decompose thermally or photolytically into radicals, we prefer the polar mechanism in contrast to the views of Schönberg. (Compare the scheme for the reaction with peroxides) (42). For example, the half-life time of the radicals from dibenzoyl disulfide, which is about 3000 years, argues against a primary decomposition into radicals (46).

Reduction of Systems Containing N–O, I–O, and C–O Bonds

The tendency of tertiary phosphines to change over to the pentavalent phosphine oxide state is used advantageously in removing loosely bound oxygen atoms in other substrate molecules.

NITROGEN OXIDES

Dinitrogen oxide is reduced to nitrogen with triethylphosphine at 127°, according to Staudinger and Hauser (47). Nitrogen dioxide is converted quantitatively to nitrogen oxide and triphenylphosphine at room temperature (33).

AMINE OXIDES (36)

Trimethylamine oxide releases its oxygen practically quantitatively to triphenylphosphine in boiling glacial acetic acid.

$$(H_3C)_3N{\rightarrow}O + PR_3 \rightarrow (H_3C)_3N + OPR_3$$

In contrast, the N-oxides of the aromatic, tertiary amines, such as pyridine N-oxide and quinoline N-oxide turn out to be quite stable towards triethyl- or triphenylphosphine (47a). The tendency to transfer the semipolar bonded oxygen to the tertiary phosphine apparently decreases with the dipole moment of the amine oxide (trimethylamine oxide, 5.04 D; pyridine N-oxide, 4.24 D).

ALDONITRONES

Aldonitrones (*36*), which contain oxygen with a semipolar bond, are also susceptible to reduction by tertiary phosphines. The corresponding Schiff bases are formed in about 90% yields.

$$R_1-\overset{\overset{O}{\uparrow}}{N}=CH-R_2 + PR_3' \rightarrow R_1N=CH-R_2 + OPR_3'$$

AZOXY COMPOUNDS

The difference in reactivity between triphenylphosphine and triethylphosphine becomes fully apparent with the azoxy compounds. Only with triethylphosphine may azoxybenzene be converted practically quantitatively at 150° to azobenzene.

Aromatic nitro compounds, which also contain a polarly bound oxygen, and therefore should react with tertiary phosphines, show only strong deepening of color with tertiary phosphines. Nitrobenzene forms neither an isolable adduct nor is it reduced. 2,4,6-Trinitroanisole with triphenylphosphine forms solely methyltriphenylphosphonium picrate (*36*). In contrast, *m*-dinitrophenol with triphenylphosphine in benzene is converted at 70° into a resin of unknown structure.

NITROSO COMPOUNDS

Aromatic nitroso compounds (*36*) substituted in the *para* position are converted to azoxy compounds with triphenylphosphine in about 50% yields.

$$2\ R-\!\!\!\left\langle\bigcirc\right\rangle\!\!\!-NO + PR_3' \rightarrow R-\!\!\!\left\langle\bigcirc\right\rangle\!\!\!-\overset{\overset{O}{\uparrow}}{N}=N-\!\!\!\left\langle\bigcirc\right\rangle\!\!\!-R + OPR_3'$$

$$R = Cl,\ CH_3,\ N(CH_3)_2.$$

An amorphous, phosphorus-containing, brown substance is formed below −10° from nitrosobenzene. N-Nitroso compounds are also indifferent toward triethylphosphine.

IODOSO COMPOUNDS (*48, 36*)

Iodosobenzene releases its oxygen spontaneously and quantitatively to triphenylphosphine.

ETHYLENE OXIDES

Ethylene oxides are surprisingly stable towards tertiary phosphines and, according to Wittig and Haag (*41*), are reduced at 150° to alkenes. The following interpretation of the reaction course is advanced:

$$R_1-CH—CH-R_2 + PR_3' \rightarrow \left[\begin{array}{c} R_1-CH-CH-R_2 \\ | \quad\quad | \\ R_3'P \quad |\underline{O}| \\ \oplus \quad\ominus \end{array} \right] \quad \begin{array}{c} R_1-CH=CH-R_2 \\ \rightarrow \quad R_3'P=O \end{array}$$

Up to now styrene oxide and phenylglycidic esters have not been transformed in this way.

Alkene sulfides react with triphenylphosphine much more readily than alkene oxides. Thus the splitting out of sulfur from cyclohexene sulfide and propylene sulfide with triphenylphosphine occurs at room temperature (*48a, 48b*):

$$\left(H\right)S + (C_6H_5)_3P \rightarrow \left(\quad\right) + (C_6H_5)_3PS$$

Triethylphosphine reacts in a similar manner.

REDUCTION OF *o*-NITROBENZALDEHYDE TO *o,o'*-DINITROHYDROBENZOIN (*16, 21*)

o-Nitrobenzaldehyde combines with triethylphosphine in moist ether to form a colorless, crystalline adduct (1:1) which on warming in methanol is transformed, on addition of a small amount of glacial acetic acid, into the *o,o'*-dinitrohydrobenzoin, which had not been obtained up to now. The compound reverts to *o*-nitrobenzaldehyde on treatment with lead tetraacetate. *o*-Dinitrobenzene also forms an adduct (1:1); on the other hand *o*-phthaldehyde and *o*-nitrobenzonitrile do not.

Reduction of Systems Containing S–O Bonds (*49*)

AROMATIC SULFONYL HALIDES (*49*)

Benzenesulfonyl chloride at about 0° is very rapidly reduced by tri-phenyl- or triethylphosphine to thiophenol (about 50%) and diphenyl disulfide (about 35%).

$$ArSO_2Cl \xrightarrow{PR_3} ArSO_2H \xrightarrow{PR_3} ArSH + Ar-S-S-Ar$$

In this case also a labile, very hygroscopic adduct is formed, which may be isolated in petroleum ether as the solvent.

With careful working conditions the sulfinic acid, which is formed as an intermediate, may be isolated.

PHENYL BENZENETHIOSULFINATE

This is readily reduced to diphenyl disulfide with triphenyl- or triethylphosphine (*36*).

$$Ar-SO_2-S-Ar \xrightarrow{2\ PR_3} Ar-S-S-Ar + 2\ OPR_3$$

PHENYL DISULFONE

Phenyl disulfone is quite stable towards triphenylphosphine. On the other hand with triethylphosphine in boiling ether an 80–90% yield of diphenyl disulfide (36) is obtained.

ARYLSULFINIC ACIDS

Benzenesulfinic acid is transformed by triphenylphosphine into thiophenol at room temperature in almost quantitative yields (49).

SULFOXIDES AND SULFONES

The diphenyl derivatives are stable against triphenyl- and triethylphosphine (36).

The Action of Triphenylphosphine on Diazonium Salts (50, 51)

Three reactions may occur between triphenylphosphine and diazonium salts, depending on reaction conditions.

REDUCTIVE REPLACEMENT OF THE DIAZONIUM GROUP BY HYDROGEN WITH
THE RATIO OF REACTANTS 1:1

Triphenylphosphine reacts with diazonium salts in methanol in a 1:1 ratio with intensive red coloration and release of nitrogen. Phosphine oxide, the hydrocarbon (yields to 50%), and acid are formed.

$$ArN_2Cl + (C_6H_5)_3P \rightarrow [ArN=N-P(C_6H_5)_3]Cl \xrightarrow{H_2O}$$
$$ArH + (C_6H_5)_3PO + HCl$$

REDUCTION TO ARYLHYDRAZINE WITH THE RATIO OF REACTANTS 2:1

Using excess triphenylphosphine, alcohol solutions of diazonium salts are extensively reduced with a transient red color formation. Along with triphenylphosphine oxide triphenylhydrazinophosphonium salts (XXVIII) are formed which are readily cleaved quantitatively to arylhydrazines:

$$[ArN=N-P(C_6H_5)_3]Cl + P(C_6H_5)_3 + H_2O \rightarrow$$
$$[ArNH-NH-P(C_6H_5)_3]Cl + OP(C_6H_5)_3$$
$$XXVIII$$

$$XXVIII + H_2O \xrightarrow{HCl} ArNH-NH_2 + OPR_3$$

The red, unusually unstable azophosphonium salts can not be isolated as such, but only as the deep red impure mercuric chloride double salt. Their existance as an intermediate seems to be verified by the fact that it is possible to proceed to the arylhydrazines from the red intermediate with stannous chloride.

According to Suckfüll and Haubrich (51a) an excellent synthesis of arylhydrazines exists in the action of the readily available phosphonic acid esters on diazonium salts. An arylazophosphonic ester is first formed, from which the arylhydrazine is obtained by reduction and hydrolysis:

$$(ArN_2)X + H\overset{\overset{\displaystyle O}{\|}}{P}(OCH_3)_2 \rightarrow Ar\!-\!N\!=\!N\!-\!\overset{\overset{\displaystyle O}{\|}}{P}(OCH_3)_2$$

$$\rightarrow ArNH\!-\!NH\!-\!\overset{\overset{\displaystyle O}{\|}}{P}(OCH_3)_2 \rightarrow Ar\!-\!NH\!-\!NH_2 + HO\!-\!\overset{\overset{\displaystyle O}{\|}}{P}(OCH_3)_2$$

With this method sensitive hydrazines are accessible.

ARYLPHOSPHONIUM SALT FORMATION IN A BUFFERED TWO-PHASE SYSTEM

If an acetate-buffered aqueous solution of diazonium salt is stirred with a solution of triphenylphosphine in ethyl acetate, all of the nitrogen is quickly released and an aryltriphenylphosphonium salt is formed (yields of 40–80%).

$$\underset{R}{\langle \rangle}\!-\!N_2Cl + P(C_6H_5)_3 \rightarrow \left[\underset{R}{\langle \rangle}\!-\!P(C_6H_5)_3 \right]Cl + N_2$$

R=H; o-, m-, and p-NO$_2$; p-C$_2$H$_5$OOC; o-, m-, and p- Cl

At the same time a reductive deamination takes place to a small extent. Presumably the phosphonium salt formation presupposes the conversion of the diazonium salt into covalent compounds, diazoacetate or -hydroxide. In support of this is the fact that phosphonium salts are also formed from triphenylphosphine and N-nitrosoarylacylamines, though in poor yields (51).

The classical method for the preparation of tetraarylphosphonium salts is the so-called Dodonow Reaction (51c) in which oxygen is permitted to act upon triphenylphosphine in the presence of a Grignard reagent. The mechanism of this reaction is still uncertain. Recently we were also able to obtain tetraarylphosphonium salts from Grignard reagents, triphenylphosphine, and aryl halides in the presence of catalytic amounts of cobalt chloride (51b). We assume that radicals play a role not only in the latter reaction but also in the formation of phosphonium salts from covalent diazo compounds.

PHOSPHAZINES

Closely allied with the 1:1 reaction of triphenylphosphine and diazonium salts (see above) is the reaction of diazoalkanes with triphenyl- or triethylphosphine (52).

Here also an adduct which can be isolated is formed, a phosphazine, which is hydrolyzed in the presence of large amounts of water to a hydrazone and phosphine oxide.

$$R_3'P + N_2\overset{R_1}{C}R_2 \rightarrow R_3'P{=}N{-}N{=}\overset{R_1}{C}R_2 \overset{H_2O}{\longrightarrow}$$

$$H_2N{-}N{=}\overset{R_1}{C}R_2 + OPR_3'$$

$$R'{=}C_2H_5;\ C_6H_5.\ \ R_1{=}H;\ R_2{=}CO_2C_2H_5.\ \ R_1{=}C_6H_5;$$

$$R_2{=}COC_6H_5.\ \ R_1{=}CO_2C_6H_5;\ R_2{=}\underset{C_6H_5}{\overset{|}{CO}}$$

With small amounts of water tetrazine derivatives are formed in an unexplained manner:

$$(B)\ \ 2\ (H_5C_2)_3P{=}N{-}N{=}C(C_6H_5)_2 + H_2O \longrightarrow$$

$$(H_5C_6)_2C\overset{\overset{\displaystyle N{=}N}{\diagup\ \ \diagdown}}{\underset{\underset{\displaystyle NH{-}NH}{\diagdown\ \ \diagup}}{}}C(C_6H_5)_2 + OP(C_2H_5)_3$$

The strongly polar phosphazines can take up 2 moles of hydrogen chloride and 1 mole of methyl iodide. It is interesting that phosphazines may be converted thermally into phosphinemethylene derivatives (53, 54, 55):

$$(C_6H_5)_3P{=}N{-}N{=}CR_2 \rightarrow N_2 + (C_6H_5)_3P{=}CR_2$$

Derivatives of Tertiary Phosphines of Apparent Higher Valence

According to Raman spectroscopic investigations as well as electron diffraction, the electronic configuration of the phosphorus–oxygen double bond is assumed to be mixed, that is the overlapping of a semipolar bond with a true double bond:

$$\underset{(a)}{R_3P{=}O} \longleftrightarrow \underset{(b)}{R_3\overset{\oplus}{P}{\rightarrow}\overset{\ominus}{O}|}$$

This is based on the assumption that phosphorus, in contrast to nitrogen, is able to expand its electron octet, which is demonstrated by pentaphenylphosphorus, prepared by Wittig and Rieber (56). The compound was formed by the action of phenyllithium on tetraphenylphosphonium iodide and is very reactive, as expected.

The contributions of the polar and nonpolar mesomeric forms determine not only the physical properties of the phosphine oxides, but also their reaction behavior; in agreement with the nonpolar mesomeric form (a) alkali metals add to form colored metal ketyl-like compounds according to Hein (57), while, in harmony with the semipolar mesomeric form (b), polar reagents such as water and hydrogen halides are added.

The strong participation of the semipolar mesomeric form in the phosphorus–oxygen double bond makes it understandable that the methyl and methylene groups attached to phosphorus in phosphine oxides, phosphinic, and phosphonic acid esters are activated considerably (57a); in treatment with metallic agents, such as alkali alkoxides, sodamide, and phenyllithium, the hydrogen is exchanged for the metal. The resulting organometallic compounds may be converted with carbon dioxide to carboxylic acids; β-ketophosphine oxides are formed from esters of carboxylic acids. With aldehydes and ketones the intermediate β-hydroxyphosphine oxides (O-metalated) are formed; these are isolable only under certain conditions, for they decompose readily into alkenes and salts of phosphinic acid.

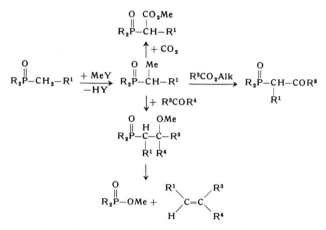

The conversion of α-metalated phosphine oxides and related compounds with aldehydes and ketones is analogous to the Wittig preparation of alkenes with phosphorus-"ylides." As shown in Table 2, various types of aldehydes and ketones are used. Dienes are obtained with diketones and dialdehydes; these may also be obtained with bisphosphine oxides. The position of the resulting carbon–carbon double bond is always the one expected according to the above scheme. No displacements have been observed as yet.

Nitroso compounds react basically in the same manner as carbonyl compounds, resulting in the formation of Schiff bases. Reference may also be made to the considerable autoxidizability of the α-metalated phosphine oxides, which are decomposed with oxygen to phosphinic acids. Moreover, depending on conditions, aldehydes or degradation products are formed (70).

The capacity for polar addition is more pronounced in the case of phosphine imides and phosphinomethylenes, whose simplest representatives are isosteric to phosphine oxides:

$$R_3\overset{\oplus}{P}{\to}\overset{\ominus}{\underline{N}}R \leftrightarrow R_3P{=}N{-}R; \quad R_3\overset{\oplus}{P}{\to}C(\overset{\ominus}{R_1})R_2 \leftrightarrow R_3P{=}C(R_1)R_2$$

TABLE 2

REACTION OF PHOSPHINE OXIDES WITH ALDEHYDES AND KETONES

Phosphine oxide	Carbonyl cpd.	Solvent	Bath temp. (°C)	Reaction time (hr)	Crude yield of phosphinic acid (%)	M.p. (°C)	Olefin	Yield, pure (%)	(M.p.) or b.p./mm
$(C_6H_5)_2P(O)CH_2C_6H_5$	$(C_6H_5)_2CO$	Benzene	100	9	83	189–190	$(C_6H_5)_2C=CHC_6H_5$	70	(67–68)
$(C_6H_5)_2P(O)CH_3$	$(C_6H_5)_2CO$	Toluene	130	3	83	187–189	$(C_6H_5)_2C=CH_2$	61	140–1/14 (6)
$(C_6H_5)_2P(O)C_2H_5$	$(C_6H_5)_2CO$	Toluene	130	9	64	188–189	$(C_6H_5)_2C=CHCH_3$	51	(50–51)
$(C_6H_5)_2P(O)C_4H_9$	$(C_6H_5)_2CO$	Toluene	130	10	55	187–190	$(C_6H_5)_2C=CHC_3H_7$	43	170/13
$(C_6H_5)_2P(O)CH_2C_6H_5$	$C_6H_5COCH_3$	Benzene	100	14	80	188–190	$(C_6H_5)(CH_3)C=CHC_6H_5$	60	(81–82)
$(C_6H_5)_2P(O)CH_2C_6H_5$	C_6H_5CHO	Benzene	100	9	70	188–190	$C_6H_5CH=CHC_6H_5$	70	(123–124)
$(C_6H_5)_2P(O)CH_2C_6H_5$	cyclohexanone ($=O$)	Benzene	100	9	70	190–191	cyclohexylidene $=CHC_6H_5$	47	125–6/14 n_D^{20} 1.5606
$(C_6H_5)_2P(O)CH_2C_6H_5$	$C_6H_5CH=CHCHO$	Benzene	100	14	56	187–190	$C_6H_5CH=CHCH=CHC_6H_5$	46	(151–2)
$(C_6H_5)_2P(O)CH_2C_6H_5$	fluorenone ($C=O$)	Benzene	100	9	55	184–186	fluorenylidene $C=CHC_6H_5$	43	(75–6)
$(C_6H_5)_2P(O)CH_2C_6H_5$	$C_2H_5COCH_3$	Benzene	100	10	92	186–189	$C_6H_5CH=C(CH_3)(C_4H_9)$	54	198–200/760
$(C_6H_5)_2P(O)CH_2C_6H_5$	$C_6H_5COCOC_6H_5$	Toluene	130	7	78	187–189	$C_6H_5CH=CH$ CHC_6H_5	50	(182–3)
$(C_6H_5)_2P(O)CH_2C_6H_5$	OHC–C_6H_4–O–C_6H_4–CHO	Toluene	130	12	87	184–186	bis($CH=CHC_6H_5$) diphenyl ether	57	(255–6)
$(C_6H_5)_2P(O)CH_2C_6H_5$	pyridine–CHO	Toluene	130	12	74	184–188	pyridine–$CH=CHC_6H_5$	58	(80–81)
$(C_6H_5)_2P(O)CH_2C_6H_5$	pyridine–CHO	Toluene	130	12	57	187–191	pyridine–$CH=CHC_6H_5$	47	(126–8)
$(C_6H_5O)_2P(O)CH_2C_6H_5$	$(C_6H_5)_2CO$	Toluene	130	12	—	—	$(C_6H_5)_2C=CHC_6H_5$	70	(65–9)
$(C_6H_5O)P(O)CH_2CH=$	C_6H_5CHO	Toluene	130	10	—	—	$C_6H_5CH=CHCH=CHCOOH$ after alkaline saponification	52	(165–6)

The capacity for addition and the tendency for phosphine oxide formation enables the phosphine imides and the phosphinomethylenes to undergo a large number of important reactions.

Phosphine Imides

This class of substances was discovered in 1919 by H. Staudinger and J. Meyer (53) and studied thoroughly (58). They are obtained from azides and tertiary phosphines in excellent yields. The triphenylphosphine imides crystallize especially well.

$$R_3'P + N_3R \rightarrow [R_3'\overset{\oplus}{P} \rightarrow N = N - \overset{\ominus}{N} - R] \rightarrow R_3'P = N - R + N_2$$

In general the primary adduct decomposes at room temperature to nitrogen and phosphine imide. An exception is the o-azidobenzoic acid which forms a crystalline primary adduct which is stable at room temperature and decomposes only upon warming (59).

Phosphine dibromides with primary amides furnish phosphine imides in a smooth reaction (30):

$$R_3'PBr_2 + H_2N-R \xrightarrow{\text{Triethylamine}} [R_3'\overset{\oplus}{P}-NH-R]Br^{\ominus} \xrightarrow{\text{NaOH}} R_3'P=N-R'$$

This second procedure is simpler and quicker with primary aromatic amines than the azide procedure. In this manner it is possible to introduce two phosphine imide groups into the aromatic ring; strongly activating groups such as the nitro group do not interfere.

Surprisingly the salts of phosphine imides are also formed by the reaction of o- or p- bromo (or iodo) arylamines with tertiary phosphines, e.g.,

$$(C_6H_5)_3P + Br-\langle\rangle-NH_2 \rightarrow \left[\langle\rangle-NH-P(C_6H_5)_3\right] Br$$

The reaction, which may take place in the molten state as well as by heating in toluene or benzene, is catalyzed by acids, and inhibited by strong bases. In all probability a facile electrophilic substitution of the halogen by a proton takes place primarily owing to the presence of the phosphine. In this manner then there is formed in the reaction system on the one hand the dehalogenated amine, on the other hand the phosphine dihalogenide, which reacts to form the phosphine imide.

$$R_3P + HBr + Br-\langle\rangle-NH_2 \rightarrow \left[R_3PBr_2 + \langle\rangle-NH_2\right] \rightarrow \left[R_3P-NH-\langle\rangle\right] Br$$

An analogous reaction takes place with o- or p-halogenated phenols. The resulting intermediates XXIX or XXX are extraordinarily susceptible to hydrolysis, so that as final products only the dehalogenated phenol and phosphine oxide are obtained (Table 3).

$$(C_6H_5)_3P + Br-\langle\!=\!\rangle-OH \rightarrow \left[(C_6H_5)_3P-OC_6H_5\right] Br$$
$$\downarrow + H_2O$$
$$(C_6H_5)_3PO + C_6H_5OH + HBr$$

The strongly polar phosphorus–nitrogen bond readily adds on alkyl halides. Final hydrolysis leads in part to good yields of the secondary

TABLE 3
REACTION OF TERTIARY PHOSPHINES WITH ARYL AMINES AND ALCOHOLS

Starting material	Temp.	Reaction product	Yield (%)
o-Bromophenol	200	} Phenol	90
p-Bromophenol	200		90
α-Bromo-β-naphthol	90	β-Naphthol	97
2,6-Diiodo-p-cresol	150	2-Iodo-p-cresol	80
2,6-Diiodo-p-hydroxybenzoic acid	150	2-Iodo-p-hydroxybenzoic acid	80
o-Bromoaniline	200	{ Tetraphenylphosphine imine	75
p-Bromoaniline	200		77

amine and phosphine oxide via the isolable disubstituted aminophos-phonium salt (60):

$$(C_6H_5)_3P{=}N{-}R + R'Br \rightarrow [(C_6H_5)_3\overset{\oplus}{P}{-}NR] \; Br^{\ominus} \xrightarrow{\text{NaOH}} (C_6H_5)_3PO + HN{-}R$$
$$R' \qquad\qquad\qquad R'$$

In this manner primary amines may be converted to secondary amines.

Staudinger and Hauser (58) already have observed that phosphine imides decompose on hydrolysis into primary amines and phosphine oxides. This also represents a reductive process based on the azides which, however, is quicker and more selective than all other methods for the conversion of azide groups into primary amino groups .This method may be used with good results for the preparation of α-amino acids (59):

$$R{-}CH_2{-}CO_2H \xrightarrow{Br_2} R{-}CHBr{-}CO_2H \xrightarrow{\text{NaN}_3} R{-}CH(N_3){-}CO_2H$$
$$\downarrow + R_3P({-}N_2)$$
$$OPR_3 + R{-}CH(NH_2){-}CO_2H \xleftarrow[\text{HBr}]{H_2O} R{-}CH{-}CO_2H$$
$$N{=}PR_3$$

The following amino acids were prepared (as hydrobromides) in this manner: glycine (92% yield), α-aminoisobutyric acid (88%), β-alanine

(88%), ε-benzoyllysine (68%), p-nitrophenylalanine (77%), phenyl-alanine (75%), and glutamic acid (65%).

Hydroxy groups, after tosylation, may be replaced by triazo groups in good yield; the latter then are converted to primary amino groups via the phosphine imide step. The last-named reaction may be set out as a "one reaction vessel" synthesis (59).

Acid azides also yield (with tertiary phosphines) definite acylated phosphine imides which were thermally decomposed into benzonitrile and phosphine oxide, as discovered by Staudinger and Hauser (58).

$$C_6H_5CON_3 \xrightarrow{PR_3} C_6H_5CON=PR_3 \rightarrow C_6H_5CN + OPR_3$$

Thiobenzoic acid azide is subject to the same conversion. The thio-benzoylphosphine imide cannot be isolated. However, triphenylphosphine benzenesulfonimide is not convertible (61).

Phosphine imides react abnormally with compounds containing twin double bonds such as carbon dioxide, carbon disulfide, sulfur dioxide, isocyanates, isothiocyanates, ketenes, and also ketones. Phosphine oxide or phosphine sulfide splits out as the reaction-determining step via inter-mediates probably containing a four-membered ring structure which cannot be isolated. The remaining portions of the molecule automatically combine (52):

$$\begin{array}{c} R_3P=N-R' \\ O=C=O \end{array} \rightarrow \left[\begin{array}{c} R_3P\cdots N-R' \\ \vdots \quad \vdots \\ O\cdots C=O \end{array} \right] \rightarrow \begin{array}{c} R_3P \\ \| \\ O \end{array} + \begin{array}{c} N-R' \\ \| \\ C=O \end{array}$$

With carbon dioxide, isocyanates are formed; with carbon disulfide, isothiocyanates; with sulfur dioxide, thionyl amines; with isocyanates and isothiocyanates, carbodiimides; and with benzophenones, anils.

$$RN = PR'_3 \begin{cases} + \text{ OCO} & \rightarrow RN=C=O + OPR'_3 \\ + \text{ S=C=S} & \rightarrow RN=C=S + SPR'_3 \\ + \text{ O=S=O} & \rightarrow R-N=S=O + OPR'_3 \\ + \text{ R''}-N=C=O & \rightarrow R-N=C=N-R'' + OPR'_3 \\ + \text{ R''}-N=C=S & \rightarrow R-N=C=N-R'' + SPR'_3 \\ + \text{ OC(C}_6\text{H}_5)_2 & \rightarrow R-N=C(C_6H_5)_2 + OPR'_3 \\ + \text{ OC=C Ph}_2 & \rightarrow Ph_2=C=C=N-R + OPR'_3 \end{cases}$$

These reactions strongly call to mind the behavior of diphenylketene with double bond systems, in which four-membered ring structures are obtained (a) or are intermediates, as in the case of the p-quinones (b) (62).

a)
$$\begin{array}{c} \diagdown C=C \diagup \\ R_2C=C=O \end{array} \rightarrow \begin{array}{c} -\overset{|}{C}-\overset{|}{C}- \\ R_2\overset{|}{C}-\overset{|}{C}=O \end{array} \qquad R=C_6H_5$$

b)

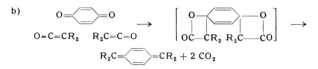

$$R_2C=\langle\;\rangle=CR_2 + 2\;CO_2$$

Tetrafluoroethylene also shows an unexpected tendency toward four-membered ring formation as the dimerization to octafluorocyclobutane (*63*) and the addition to styrene show (*64*).

Phosphinomethylenes (Phospho-ylide-ylene)

The oldest method of preparation is the thermal decomposition of phosphazines (*53*):

$$(C_6H_5)_3P=N-N=CR_2 \rightarrow N_2 + (C_6H_5)_3P=CR_2$$

The phosphorus-ylides were first accessible in relatively good yields by the method of Wittig and co-workers (*65*), in which HX is split out of phosphonium salts by means of phenyllithium:

$$[(C_6H_5)_3PCH_2-R]X + C_6H_5Li \rightarrow (C_6H_5)_3P=CHR + LiX + C_6H_6$$

The polar ylide-formula makes it conceivable that the phosphinomethylenes readily convert to phosphonium salts by polar addition in reverse manner to their mode of formation:

$$R_3\overset{\oplus}{P}-\overset{\ominus}{C}R_2 + HX \rightarrow [R_3\overset{\oplus}{P}-CHR_2]\;X^{\ominus}$$

The ability to react with polar oxygen and sulfur compounds, characteristic of phosphine imides, is also found here.

Staudinger described the reactions with phenyl isocyanate, carbon disulfide, and sulfur (*53*):

$$R_3P=CR_2 + C_6H_5N=C=O \rightarrow R_3PO + C_6H_5N=C=CR_2$$
$$+ CS_2 \rightarrow R_3PS + S=C=CR_2$$
$$+ S_n \rightarrow R_3PS + S=CR_2$$

The important Wittig reaction, in which a carbonyl oxygen is exchanged for a methyl group is in accord with this reaction scheme (*65*).

$$\begin{array}{c} R_3\overset{\oplus}{P}-\overset{\ominus}{C}R_2 \\ \overset{\ominus}{|\underline{O}}-CR_2' \\ \overset{\oplus}{} \end{array} \rightarrow \begin{bmatrix} R-P\cdots CR_2 \\ O\cdots CR_2' \end{bmatrix} \rightarrow \begin{array}{c} R_3PO + CR_2 \\ \parallel \\ CR_2' \end{array}$$

Phosphine Dihalides

Phosphine dihalides are formed from tertiary phosphines and elemental halogens with exceptional ease. They are also formed along with phosphorus oxychloride by heating phosphine oxides with phosphorus pentachloride. (The adducts from tertiary phosphines and cyanogen bromide react analogously to the dihalides.)

The phosphine dihalides possess a high rate of reactivity, in many respects remindful of the phosphorus pentahalides. Therefore they must be prepared and reacted with strict exclusion of moisture, as they hydrolyze very readily to phosphine oxides. In a corresponding manner phosphine sulfides are formed with carbon disulfide (65a):

$$R_3PX_2 + H_2O(S) \rightarrow R_3PO(S) + 2HX$$

Alkyl halides are formed by reaction with alcohols. In this reaction a Walden rearrangement takes place, as was shown, for example, in the conversion of (−)-menthol to (+)-neomenthyl chloride (65a):

$$R_3PX_2 + R'OH \rightarrow R'Cl + R_3PO + HX$$
$$R = C_6H_5, C_6H_5O; R' = Alkyl$$

For the preparative formation of alkyl halides the triphenylphosphite dihalides used by Coe et al. (65b) are preferred because of the better availability of the starting materials. With these compounds phenolic hydroxyl groups can be replaced by halogen (65c). From triphenylphosphine dihalides and phenol there is formed, dependent on reaction procedures, the extraordinarily hydrolysis-sensitive substances XXIX and XXX (65a):

$$(C_6H_5)_3P \Big\langle \begin{matrix} OC_6H_5 \\ Br \end{matrix} \qquad (C_6H_5)_3P(OC_6H_5)_2$$

$$\text{XXIX} \qquad\qquad \text{XXX}$$

The phosphine dihalides resemble the phosphorus pentahalides in their behavior toward carbonyl compounds. From carboxylic acids, acid chlorides are obtained; from aldehydes and ketones, gem-dihalogen compounds (65a):

$$(C_6H_5)_3PX_2 + R-CO_2H \rightarrow (C_6H_5)_3P{=}O + R-C\underset{X}{\overset{O}{\big\langle}} + HX$$

$$(C_6H_5)_3PX_2 + \underset{R'}{\overset{R}{\big\rangle}}C{=}O \rightarrow (C_6H_5)_3P{=}O + \underset{R'}{\overset{R}{\big\rangle}}CX_2$$

Carboxamides, under the reaction conditions, do not react to form the expected stable acylphosphine imides, but go directly to the nitriles and phosphine oxides (65a):

$$(C_6H_5)_3PX_2 + R-C\underset{NH_2}{\overset{O}{\diagdown}} \nearrow (C_6H_5)_3PO + R-CN + 2HX$$

$$\searrow (C_6H_5)_3P=N-\overset{O}{\overset{\|}{C}}-R + 2HX$$

The triphenylphosphine dihalides also react with compounds containing an active methylene group in an unexpected manner (65d). Thus phospho-ylides are formed in the presence of triethyl amine:

$$(C_6H_5)_3PX_2 + H_2C\overset{R}{\underset{R}{\diagup}} + 2(C_2H_5)_3N \rightarrow (C_6H_5)_3P=C\overset{R}{\underset{R}{\diagup}}$$

$$+ 2(C_2H_5)_3N \cdot HX$$

R = CN, CO$_2$R, >C=O

Just as unexpected is the reaction with alkyl halides, which leads to the formation of phosphonium perhalides (65e):

$$(C_6H_5)_3PX_2 + RX \rightarrow [(C_6H_5)_3PR]X \cdot X_2$$

Supplement: Adducts with Aldehydes

Tertiary phosphines also very easily form phosphonium-salt–like adducts with aldehydes in the presence of acids. For example, an easily soluble triphenylhydroxymethylphosphonium salt is formed by warming triphenylphosphine with formalin and hydrochloric acid:

$$(C_6H_5)_3P + H_2CO \underset{+ NaOH}{\overset{+ HCl}{\rightleftarrows}} [(C_6H_5)_3P-CH_2OH] Cl$$

This compound is stable in acid or neutral solution, so that the hydroxyl group can be acetylated or replaced by halogen. In alkaline solution the hydroxy compound decomposes quantitatively to the starting materials. In nonpolar solvents analogous adducts can be obtained with aromatic aldehydes. The ease of formation and decomposition of the α-hydroxyphosphonium salt is suitable for the isolation of aldehydes on the one hand and of the tertiary phosphines on the other.

The Reactivity of Tertiary Arsines (also Stibine and Bismuthine)*

It is obvious to react tertiary arsines, stilbines, and bismuthines with all such substrates which react with tertiary phosphines. H. Staudinger and co-workers have already experimentally investigated this question at one time or another. Other systematic investigations concerning this problem are not known to us.

* Together with E. Jürgens, H. Schaefer, and H. G. Wippel.

The comparison of the dipole moments of the tertiary organic compounds of the elements in group 5 (see Table 1) shows that arsine stands nearest to phosphine. Yet the decreased reactivity of the tertiary arsines is plainly evident, paralleling the lower dipole moment.

According to Staudinger and Meyer triphenylarsine and triphenylstibine react neither with diazo compounds nor with azides (53). We could confirm this, but discovered that it is possible to bring about a reaction between aliphatic tertiary arsines, such as triethylarsine, and azides, depending upon the nature of the reaction medium. On the other hand arsines do not react with carbon disulfide or phenyl isothiocyanate, or with compounds of the benzal malononitrile type; only the extremely reactive vinylidenedinitrile shows a reaction. The reduction reaction is still possible with tertiary arsines, although weaker than in the case of the tertiary phosphines.

Thus dibenzoyl peroxide is converted to arsine oxide and benzoic acid via an adduct (1:1) which can be isolated. Tetralin hydrogen peroxide is converted quantitatively to tetralol. In analogous fashion ozonides are selectively deoxygenated to carbonyl functions by tertiary arsines.

Benzenesulfonyl chloride is deoxygenated to diphenyl disulfide only through the reactive triethylarsine—not with triphenylarsine. The desulfuration action of triethylarsine is still retained. Thus, phenyl disulfide is desulfurized to diphenyl sulfide.

Concerning the mode of reaction of tertiary stilbines and bismuthines no knowledge is available, with the exception of a short note by Staudinger and Hauser (58).

Preparation of Phosphines (31, 66)

Substitution Reactions

The modification of aromatic phosphines by electrophilic addition of substituents leads mostly to derivatives of pentavalent phosphorus. In this manner the corresponding phosphine dihalides (29) are obtained from tertiary phosphines with halogens and with nitric acid the nitrated phosphine oxides (67). On sulfonation of triphenylphosphine with concentrated sulfuric acid the formation of phosphine oxide does not take place, and meta-sulfonated triphenylphosphine (68) is formed.

The metalation of triphenylphosphine in the meta-position with phenyllithium, first observed by Gilman and Brown (69), seems quite capable of extension to aromatic substituted tertiary phosphines.

The Grignard reagents from halogenated aromatic phosphines have general preparative importance. They can be utilized in the usual manner for syntheses (70).

TABLE 4

REDUCTION OF PHOSPHORUS AND ORGANOPHOSPHORUS COMPOUNDS TO PRIMARY, SECONDARY, AND TERTIARY PHOSPHINES

Phosphine: $R_1R_2R_3P$	Starting material	Reducing Agent	Solvent	B.p./mm (M.p.)	Yield (%)	Lit. ref.
$R_1 = R_2 = R_3 = H$	PCl_3	Na	Toluene	−87.8	70	75
	PBr_3, PCl_3	K, Na	Naphthalene/THF	−87.8	70	9
	PCl_5	$LiBH_4$	Ether	−87.8	70	76a
		$LiAlH_4$				
$(PH)_x$	PBr_3	$LiAlH_4$	Ether	—	100	76b
$R_1 = CH_3$; $R_2 = R_3 = H$	Dichloromethylphosphine	$LiAlH_4$	—	−14	—	113
$R_1 = C_2H_5$; $R_2 = R_3 = H$	Dichloroethylphosphine	$LiAlH_4$	—	25	—	113
$R_1 = C_6H_{11}$; $R_2 = R_3 = H$	Cyclohexylphosphonyl chloride	$LiAlH_4$	Ether	146	47.5	73
		Na	Toluene	146	65	75
$R_1 = C_6H_5CH_2$; $R_2 = R_3 = H$	Diethyl benzylphosphonite	$LiAlH_4$	Ether	180	48	73
$R_1 = C_6H_5$; $R_2 = R_3 = H$	Dichlorophenylphosphine	$LiAlH_4$	Ether	160	59	70
		LiH	THF	160	59	70
		Na	Toluene	160	71.5	75
	Phenylphosphonyl chloride	$LiAlH_4$	Ether	160	55	76c
		$LiBH_4$	THF	160	—	76c
	Phenylphosphonic acid	$LiAlH_4$	Ether	160	13	76d
$R_1 = R_2 = C_6H_5$; $R_3 = H$	Diphenyldithiophosphinic acid	Na	THF/Naphthalene	280	85	75
	Diphenyltrichlorophosphorane	$LiAlH_4$	Ether	130/15	30	73
	Diphenylphosphinyl chloride	$LiAlH_4$	Ether	130/15	93	73
		Na	Toluene	—	13	75
	Diphenylphosphinic acid	$LiAlH_4$	Dioxane	185–190/14	40–50	74
	Chlorodiphenylphosphine	Na	Toluene	155/16	85.5	75
$R_1 = CH_3$; $R_2 = C_6H_5$; $R_3 = H$	Ethyl methylphenylphosphinate	$LiAlH_4$	Ether	63/11	53	73
$R_1 = R_2 = C_2H_5$; $R_3 = H$	Diethylphosphinic chloride	$LiAlH_4$	Ether	85	20	73
	Tetraethyldiphosphine disulfide	$LiAlH_4$	Ether	85	70	106
	Triethylphosphine oxide	Na	—	85	—	75
$R_1 = R_2 = n\text{-}C_4H_7$; $R_4 = H$	Dibutylphosphinous acid	$LiAlH_4$	Ether	71/17	52	73
	Dibutyl-N-diethylaminophosphine	Na	Toluene	186	53	70
	Tetrabutyldiphosphine disulfide	Na	Toluene	186	69	70
		$LiAlH_4$	Ether	184–6	86	106
	Tributylphosphine oxide	Na	—	186	48	75
	Trioctylphosphine oxide	Na	—	—	—	75

R groups	Compound	Reducing agent	Solvent	b.p./m.p.	Yield (%)	Ref
$R_1 = R_2 = R_3 = C_2H_5$	Triethylphosphine oxide	$LiAlH_4$	Dioxane	127	90	74
	Triethylphosphine sulfide	$Ca(AlH_4)_2$	Dioxane	127	51.5	74
		$LiAlH_4$	Dioxane	127	80	74
		Na	—	—	—	75e
$R_1 = R_2 = R_3 = n\text{-}C_4H_7$	Tributylphosphine oxide	$LiAlH_6$	Dioxane	240	71	74
		$Ca(AlH_4)_2$	Dioxane	240	42.5	74
$R_1 = R_2 = R_3 = C_6H_{11}$	Tricyclohexylphosphine oxide	$LiAlH_4$	Dioxane	?	70	74
		$Ca(AlH_4)_2$	Dioxane	?	45	74
$R_1 = C_2H_4; R_2 = p\text{-}(CH_3)_2NC_6H_4; R_3 = H$	p-Dimethylaminophenyl-ethylphosphine oxide	$LiAlH_4$	Diisopropyl ether/benzene	45–8	68	73
$R_1 = CH_3; R_2 = C_6H_5; R_3 = p\text{-}CH_3OC_6H_4$	p-Methoxyphenylmethylphenylphosphine oxide	$LiAlH_4$	Dibutyl ether	153–6/0.8	65	73
$R_1 = R_2 = R_3 = C_6H_5C_6H_4$	Trixenylphosphine oxide	$LiAlH_4$	Dioxane	—	20	74
$R_1 = R_2 = R_3 = C_6H_5$	Triphenylphosphine oxide	$LiAlH_4$	Dibutylether/benzene	(80)	60	73
	Triphenylphosphine sulfide	$LiAlH_4$	Dioxane	(80)	38	73
		NaH	—	(80)	80	73
		Na	Toluene	(80)	50	70
			THF/Naphthalene	(80)	90	70
	Triphenylphosphorus dichloride	Raney-Ni	Methanol	(80)	29	73
		$LiAlH_4$	Ether	(80)	50	73
		Na	Toluene	(80)	54	73
	Benzyl-triphenylphosphonium chloride	PNa_3	Toluene	(80)	—	70
	Tetraphenylphosphonium iodide	Na	Naphthalene/THF	(80)	63.5	75
		Na	Toluene	(80)	54	75
	β-Hydroxyethyl-triphenylphosphonium chloride	Electrolysis	Water	(80)	81.5	70
	Benzyl-triphenylphosphonium chloride	Electrolysis	Water	(80)	89	70
	t-Butyl-triphenylphosphonium chloride	Na	Toluene	(80)	70	70
	Methyl-triphenylphosphonium bromide	Electrolysis	Water	(80)	5.5	70
	Ethyl-triphenylphosphonium bromide	Electrolysis	Water	(80)	35	70
	n-Butyl-triphenylphosphonium bromide	Electrolysis	Water	(80)	46	70
	i-Propyl-triphenylphosphonium bromide	Electrolysis	Water	(80)	52	70
	Methyl-triphenylphosphonium bromide	$LiAlH_4$	THF	—	85	75f
		Na	$NH_3(l)$	—	29	75f
			Ethanol	—	64	75f
			Benzene	—	77	75f
$R_1 = C_2H_5; R_2 = R_3 = C_6H_5CH_2$	Ethyl-tribenzylphosphonium bromide	Electrolysis	Water	320–30	90	70
$R_1 = R_3 = CH_3; R_2 = C_6H_5CH_2$	Dibenzyl-dimethylphosphonium bromide	$LiAlH_4$	THF	93–6/12	81	75f
$R_1 = R_2 = R_3 = CH_3$	Benzyl-trimethylphosphonium bromide	$LiAlH_4$	THF	37.8	67	75f

(continued)

TABLE 4 (*Continued*)

Phosphine: $R_1R_2R_3P$	Starting material	Reducing Agent	Solvent	B.p./mm (M.p.)	Yield (%)	Lit. ref.
$R_1 = CH_3$; $R_2 = R_3 = C_6H_5$	Methyl-triphenylphosphonium bromide	Electrolysis	Water	37.8	47	70
	Methyl-triphenylphosphonium iodide	Na	Toluene	284	60	75
	Diphenyl-ethyl-methylphosphonium bromide	Electrolysis	Water	284	66.5	70
	Methyl-triphenylphosphonium bromide	Electrolysis	Water	284	83	70
	Dimethyl-diphenylphosphonium bromide	Electrolysis	Water	284	26	70
$R_1 = C_2H_5$; $R_2 = R_3 = C_6H_5$	Ethyl-triphenylphosphonium iodide	Na	Toluene	293	52	75
	Ethyl-triphenylphosphonium bromide	Electrolysis	Water	293	59	70
$R_1 = R_2 = C_6H_5$; $R_3 = C_6H_5CH_2$	Benzyl-triphenylphosphonium chloride	Na	Toluene	205–8/1.5	53	75
$R_1 = n\text{-}C_4H_9$; $R_2 = R_3 = C_6H_5$	n-Butyl-triphenylphosphonium bromide	Electrolysis	Toluene	172–4/13	50	70
$R_1 = i\text{-}C_3H_7$; $R_2 = R_3 = C_6H_5$	i-Propyl-triphenylphosphonium bromide	Electrolysis	Water	165/13	25	70
$R_1 = CH_2CH=CH_2$; $R_2 = R_3 = C_6H_5$	Allyl-triphenylphosphonium bromide	Na	Toluene	194–200/15	52	75
$R_1 = R_2 = CH_3$; $R_3 = C_6H_5$	Dimethyl-diphenylphosphonium iodide	Na	Toluene	192	48.7	70
	Dimethyl-diphenylphosphonium bromide	Electrolysis	Water	85–6/13	69	70
	Phenyl-trimethylphosphonium iodide	Na	Toluene	192	48.7	70
	Phenyl-trimethylphosphonium bromide	Electrolysis	Water	192	40	70
	Ethyl-dimethyl-phenylphosphonium iodide	Na	Toluene	192	50	70
$R_1 = R_2 = C_2H_5$; $R_3 = C_6H_5$	Diethyl-diphenylphosphonium iodide	Na	Toluene	222	53	70
	Phenyl-triethylphosphonium iodide	Na	Toluene	222	45.3	70
$R_1 = C_6H_5$; $R_2 = R_3 = C_6H_5CH_2$	Phenyl-tribenzylphosphonium chloride	Na	Toluene	170/10	49.5	70
$R_1 = CH_3$; $R_2 = C_2H_5$; $R_3 = C_6H_5$	Diphenyl-ethyl-methylphosphonium iodide	Na	Toluene	96–7/15	51.5	70
	Diphenyl-ethyl-methylphosphonium bromide	Electrolysis	Water	96–7/15	33	70
$R_1 = R_2 = R_3 = C_6H_5CH_2$	Tetrabenzylphosphonium chloride	Na	Toluene	(92–5)	—	70
		PNa_3	Xylene	(92–5)	—	75g
$R_1 = CH_3$; $R_2 = C_6H_5$; $R_3 = C_6H_5CH_2$	Dibenzyl-methyl-phenylphosphonium bromide	Electrolysis	Water	156–8/12	86	70
$R_1 = C_2H_5$; $R_2 = C_6H_5$; $R_3 = C_6H_5CH_2$	Dibenzyl-ethyl-phenylphosphonium bromide	Electrolysis	Water	168/12	91	70
$R_1 = n\text{-}C_3H_7$; $R_2 = C_6H_5$; $R_3 = C_6H_5CH_2$	Dibenzyl-phenyl-n-propylphosphonium bromide	Electrolysis	Water	173–4/12	82	70
$R_1 = C_4H_9$; $R_2 = C_6H_5$; $R_3 = C_6H_5CH_2$	Butyl-dibenzyl-phenylphosphonium bromide	Electrolysis	Water	151–2/3	81	70
$R_1 = HOCH_2CH_2$; $R_2 = C_6H_5$; $R_3 = C_6H_5CH_2$	Dibenzyl-β-hydroxyethyl-phenyl-phosphonium bromide	Electrolysis	Water	—	—	70
$R_1 = CH_3$; $R_2 = C_2H_5$; $R_3 = C_6H_5$	Benzyl-ethyl-methylphenylphosphonium bromide	Electrolysis	Water	96–7/15	77	70
$R_1 = C_2H_5$; $R_2 = CH_2CH=CH_2$; $R_3 = C_6H_5$	Allyl-benzyl-ethyl-phenylphosphonium bromide	Electrolysis	Water	113–5/15	71.5	70
$R_1 = C_2H_5$; $R_2 = C_6H_5$; $R_3 = C_6H_5CH_2$	Butyl-dibenzyl-ethylphosphonium bromide	Electrolysis	Water	137–9/16	86	70
$R_1 = C_2H_5$; $R_2 = n\text{-}C_4H_9$; $R_3 = C_{12}H_{25}$	Benzyl-n-butyl-dodecyl-ethylphosphonium bromide	Electrolysis	Water	188–191/13	83	70
$R_1 = C_2H_5$; $R_2 = R_3 = CH_2CH_2CN$	Ethyl-tri-β-cyanoethylphosphonium bromide	Electrolysis	Water	—	71	70
$R_1 = CH_3$; $R_2 = C_6H_5$; $R_3 = (CH_3)C_6H_5PCH_2CH_2$	Ethylene-bis(benzyl-methyl-phenylphosphonium bromide)	Electrolysis	Water	—	82	70
$R_1 = CH_3$; $R_2 = C_6H_5$; $R_3 = (CH_3)C_6H_5P(CH_2)_4$	Tetramethylene-bis(benzyl-methyl-phenylphosphonium bromide)	Electrolysis	Water	178–180/1	80	70

$$(C_6H_5)_2P\text{-}\langle\!\!=\!\!\rangle\text{-}Cl + Mg \rightarrow (C_6H_5)_2P\text{-}\langle\!\!=\!\!\rangle\text{-}MgCl$$

Reduction with Hydrides and Metals

The reduction of the readily accessible pentavalent phosphorus derivatives to trivalent phosphorus compounds has acquired great preparative importance. The first experiments with classical reducing agents were unsuccessful (71). Halides, oxides, sulfides, acids, and esters of phosphorus and organophosphorus compounds were reduced (73) for the first time with lithium aluminum hydride (72). However, the high cost of lithium aluminum hydride, as well as the degradation occasionally observed, militates against a wider use (74).

Far more economical are the metals such as lithium, sodium, potassium, magnesium, and zinc, which are suitable for the reduction of phosphorus halo and phosphorus sulfur compounds, less suitable for oxyhalo compounds (75). Since phosphorus–oxygen compounds can be readily converted to phosphosulfur or phosphohalo compounds (75) practically every organophosphorus compound with a phosphorus–oxygen bond is capable of being reduced with metals according to the following reaction scheme:

$$R_3PO \xrightarrow[P_2S_5]{PCl_5} \begin{array}{c} R_3PCl_2 \\ R_3PS \end{array} \xrightarrow{Me} R_3P$$

$$R_2PO_2H \xrightarrow{PCl_5} R_2PCl_3 \xrightarrow[(H_2O)]{Me} R_2PH$$

The above-named metals are superior to the hydrides in the cleavage of P–P, P–N, and P–C bonds (70).

Table 4 shows a survey of the phosphines obtained by reductive methods.

From the numerous examples in Table 4 it may be seen that primary and secondary phosphines can be quite easily and elegantly prepared with the reductive procedure. The use of older procedures is recommended only in the unusual cases. Tertiary phosphines having the same groups may be prepared from phosphorus halides with organometallic compounds in good yields; tertiary aromatic phosphines may also be prepared from phosphohalo compounds and aromatic halides with metallic sodium according to Wurtz. For the preparation of tertiary phosphines with unlike groups (not aromatic) cathodic reduction or alkali cleavage of phosphonium salts are preferred. In electrolytic cleavage the strength of the ligand bond is dependent upon the choice of the cathode material.

Phosphonium salts containing benzyl or β-cyano (or hydroxy) ethyl groups will preferably lose these groups. With the correct choice of starting materials tertiary phosphines with three or, after quaternization, phosphonium salts with four different ligands can be prepared simply and in good yields according to these methods.

With the cleavage of phosphonium salts with alkali metals another series of bond strengths is encountered. The phenyl group is split out under suitable conditions from triphenylphosphonium salts (an exception: t-butyltriphenylphosphonium salt). The preferred splitting of aromatic ligands with sodium is also applicable to benzyltriphenylphosphonium salts. The benzyl group is removed by sodium phosphide. Sodium preferentially splits off an alkyl group (ethyl > methyl) from those trialkylphenylphosphonium salts which have been investigated up to now.

With lithium aluminum hydride the benzyl group is eliminated first in all cases investigated. Tetraphenylphosphonium salts are inert to this reagent.

Syntheses

EXCHANGE OF PHOSPHORUS-BOUND HALOGEN

With organometallic compounds the phosphorus-bound halogen is exchanged for alkyl or aryl groups:

$$PCl_3 + 3\,RMe \rightarrow R_3P + 3\,MeCl$$

In general Grignard reagents (76, 77) are used, although in some cases organolithium compounds have also been successful (78, 79).

The reaction of phosphohalo compounds with halogenated aromatics and sodium analogous to the Wurtz Reaction also furnishes good results (29, 80).

$$3\,ArX + 6\,Na + PCl_3 \rightarrow Ar_3P + 3\,NaCl + 3\,NaX \quad \text{(a)}$$
$$RPCl_2 + R'MgX \rightarrow RPR'_2 + 2\,MgXCl \;\Big\}$$
$$R_2PCl + R'MgX \rightarrow R_2PR' + MgXCl \;\Big\} \text{ (b)}$$

Symmetrical tertiary phosphines may be obtained starting with phosphorus trihalides (a) or tertiary phosphines with unlike ligands from organophosphorous halides (b) (32).

The dihalophosphines can be prepared readily from aromatic hydrocarbons and phosphorous trihalides using the Friedel-Crafts reaction (81, 82).

$$ArH + PCl_3 \xrightarrow{\;AlCl_3\;} ArPCl_2 + HCl$$

The corresponding aliphatic compounds are formed to some extent in good yields, (a) from alkyl halides and phosphorus (83); (b) from alkyl halides, phosphorus trichloride, and aluminum chloride with subsequent reduction (84); and (c) by thermal decomposition of dialkyltrichlorophosphoranes (85).

$$R_2PCl_3 \rightarrow RPCl_2 + RCl$$

The monohalophosphines are accessible through the thermal splitting of trialkylphosphine dichlorides (85) or through disproportionation of aromatic dichlorophosphines (70).

A general, practical way to the halophosphines occurs through the exchange of halogen by secondary amino groups (a), reaction with Grignard reagents (b), and the cleavage with hydrogen chloride in which a halogen atom attaches itself to the phosphorus atom (c) (70).

(a) $PX_3 + 2R_2NH \rightarrow X_2PNR_2 + R_2NH \cdot HX$
(b) $X_2PNR_2 + 2R'MgX \rightarrow R_2'PNR_2 + 2MgX_2$
(c) $R_2'PNR_2 + 2HCl \rightarrow R_2'PCl + R_2NH \cdot HCl$

This method, which in principle goes back to A. Michaelis (89a), was used in our group for the preparation of arylphenylchlorophosphines starting from phenyldiethylaminochlorophosphines (89b). Burg (86) and Issleib (112) prepared dialkylchlorophosphines from dialkylamino-dichlorophosphines in analogous manner. Through the use of dimethylamino groups the phosphorus–nitrogen bond can be cleaved partially (86). The classical methods with dialkylmercury, dialkylcadmium or tetraethyllead and phosphorus trichloride are cumbersome and generally not very productive (87). With diethylmercury a stepwise substitution is also possible (81).

EXCHANGE OF HYDROGEN AND METALS

The hydrogen in the para-position may be exchanged for alkyl if phosphonium iodide is heated with alkyl halides and zinc oxide. A mixture of primary, secondary, and tertiary phosphines and some phosphonium salt is obtained (88, 89). Alkylated phosphines, however, can also be obtained directly from phosphines with alkyl halides by working up the reaction mixture with alkali (90).

$$RPH_2 \xrightarrow{R'X} \left[RR'PH_2\right] X \xrightarrow{H_2O} RR'PH + HX$$

The reaction of organic halogen compounds goes unequivocally with metal phosphides which are obtainable from phosphines with organometallic compounds (91) or with metals, or from phosphohalogen compounds by reaction with metals (*75*). The degree of substitution is determined by the number of phosphorus–metal bonds (*91, 92*).

$$MePH_2 + RX \rightarrow RPH_2 + MeX$$

With very reactive alkyl halides the reaction can go to the phosphonium salt (*75*). Even aryl halides may be used in certain cases (*93*).

Especially advantageous is the use of metallic phosphides for the reaction with such compounds which, because of the presence of other functional groups, cannot form the Grignard reagent, such as aldehydes, ketones, acid chlorides, esters, and alkylene dihalides (*70*). In this manner phosphines with reactive groups are obtained; with dihalides diphosphines may also be made.

Addition Reactions

The addition of phosphine compounds to carbon–carbon double bonds is becoming next in importance to the reduction reactions. No catalyst is necessary with alkenes whose double bond is activated by electrophilic substituents, such as acrylonitrile or acrylate esters (*94*).

$$R_2PH + CH_2=CH-CN \rightarrow R_2P-CH_2-CH_2-CN$$

In other cases activation may take place with methylsulfonic acid (*95*), with ultraviolet light (*96*), or di-tertiary butyl peroxide (*97*). Phosphines may also be obtained directly by heating phosphorus, hydrogen, and the alkene under pressure (*98*). Still simpler is the preparation of the trifluoromethyl iodide type from phosphorus and alkyl halides (*99*). By heating trifluoromethyl iodide with phosphorus the following equilibrium is set up:

$$P + CF_3I \rightleftarrows CF_3PI_2 \rightleftarrows (CF_3)_2PI \rightleftarrows P(CF_3)_3$$

The addition of aldehydes to phosphine leads to α-hydroxyphosphines (*100*).

$$3CH_2O + PH_3 \rightarrow P(CH_2OH)_3$$

Decomposition

Phosphonium halides decompose with heating into tertiary phosphines and alkyl or aryl halides (*101*).

$$[PR_4]X \rightarrow R_3P + RX$$

When the substituents are alike the yield is good. With different ligands on the phosphorus atom the selectivity of splitting off is more weakly defined than in the case of alkali cleavage, so that mixtures are often obtained (*102*).

A better chance for obtaining tertiary phosphines with different ligands, is the reductive cleavage of phosphonium salts with sodium or potassium (75). The electrolysis of phosphonium halides has proved to be the best (70). Also, in special cases, many phosphonium hydroxides decompose into the corresponding phosphines (103, 104).

$$[(ClCH_2)_4P]Cl + 2\,NaOH \rightarrow (ClCH_2)_3P + CH_2O + 2\,NaCl + H_2O$$

$$[RP(CH_2-CH_2-CN)_3]X + NaOR \rightarrow RP(CH_2-CH_2CN)_2 \\ + ROCH_2-CH_2-CN$$

Usually, however, phosphonium hydroxides cleave to phosphine oxide and completely hydrogenated ligands (32).

$$[R_4P]X + NaOH \rightarrow R_3PO + RH + NaX$$

Primary and secondary phosphines can be obtained in some cases by the disproportionation of phosphonous and phosphinous acids. The latter mostly react at room temperature (105).

$$2\,R_2POH \rightarrow R_2PH + R_2PO_2H$$

$$3\,RP(OH)_2 \rightarrow RPH_2 + 2\,R\overset{O}{\overset{\|}{-P}}(OH)_2$$

These procedures no longer have any significance today. Secondary phosphines are obtained quite simply when dialkylamino-dialkylphosphines are cleaved with sodium (70).

$$R_2PNR_2' + 2\,Na \rightarrow R_2PNa + R_2'NNa$$

Likewise diphosphines may be transformed with lithium aluminum hydride (106) or with alkali metals (70, 93, 106).

$$R_2P-PR_2 + 2\,Na \rightarrow 2\,R_2PNa$$

Diphosphinedisulfides are also susceptible to this reaction with lithium aluminum hydride (107) and sodium (70).

$$\overset{S\ \ S}{R_2P-PR_2} \xrightarrow{\ 6\,Na\ } 2\,R_2PNa + 2\,Na_2S$$

Also, in some cases, tertiary phosphines may be cleaved with the help of alkali metals to secondary metal phosphides and arylmetal compounds (70, 108, 109).

$$Ar_3P \xrightarrow{\ 2\,Na\ (\ or\ Li\ or\ K)\ } Ar_2PNa + ArNa$$

$$Ar_2RP \xrightarrow{\ 2\,K\ } ArRPK + ArK$$

Primary phosphines are formed by the reduction of the so-called quasi-phosphonium salts with sodium (75). The latter may be readily formed, for example, from triphenyl phosphite or tri-N-piperidylphosphine and alkyl halides (75).

$$[(C_6H_5O)_3PR]X + 6Na \rightarrow RPNa_2 + 3C_6H_5ONa + NaX$$
$$[(R_2N)_3PR']X + 6Na \rightarrow R'PNa_2 + 3R_2NNa + NaX$$

Preparation of Diphosphines

Diphosphines are formed by the reaction of primary or secondary phosphines with chlorophosphines or from chlorophosphines with metal phosphides (93, 110, 111).

A one-step procedure, which leads to symmetrical diphosphines only, makes use of the reduction of phosphine halides with lithium aluminum hydride in diethyl ether (70), lithium hydride in tetrahydrofuran (73), or magnesium in tetrahydrofuran (70). Diphosphines are formed when phosphine halides are treated with less than the equivalent amount of sodium in an inert solvent (106, 112). Lithium aluminum hydride cleaves the P–P bond in tetrahydrofuran (106). The diphosphine disulfides resulting from the action of Grignard reagents on thiophosphoryl chloride may be reduced to the corresponding diphosphines with zinc or tertiary phosphines (113, 114).

On the other hand reduction with lithium aluminum hydride (107) or with sodium (70) furnishes secondary phosphines. From alkylated phosphinothioic halides unsymmetrical diphosphine disulfides are obtained, which can be reduced to unsymmetrical diphosphines (114).

Procedures

REDUCTION OF PEROXIDES (33)

The organic peroxide is dissolved in ether, petroleum ether, or benzene and decomposed with the solution of phosphine. Difficultly soluble peroxides can be reacted as suspensions. Using triethylphosphine the experiment must be carried out with the exclusion of air. As a rule the reaction goes quickly and exothermically, only dialkylperoxides requiring vigorous conditions (20–30 hr at 80–100°). The resulting triethylphosphine oxide is extracted with water. Triphenylphosphine oxide is quite difficultly soluble in ether and petroleum ether in the cold and is largely removed through filtration. Unreacted triethylphosphine is readily converted to the oxide by passing through a stream of dry air. Excess triphenylphosphine is advantageously separated as the difficultly soluble mercuric chloride double salt. Further work up is dictated by the properties of the expected reaction product.

1,2,3,4-Tetrahydro-1-naphthol (33). A 675 mg (4 millimole) portion of crystalline tetralin hydroperoxide is allowed to react with 472 mg (4 millimole) of triethylphosphine in ether as described. After evaporation of the solvent 585 mg of 1,2,3,4-tetrahydro-1-naphthol remains (99% yield); it is purified by distillation (b.p. 138°/16 mm). $n_D = 1.5689$.

REDUCTION OF OZONIDES (33, 36)

Ozonides can be prepared according to usual procedures. Ethyl chloride has proven especially useful as a solvent (36). It is not necessary to isolate the ozonides. Excess ozone is removed by the passage of oxygen at −70° Afterwards the still cold solution of ozonide is added to the correct amount of triphenylphosphine in ether solution.*

The reaction takes place immediately and with evolution of heat. Then the ethyl chloride is distilled. The remaining ether solution is cooled and after standing for some time the precipitated phosphine oxide is filtered off. The separation can be accelerated by the addition of petroleum ether. The reduced product is found in the filtrate.

Dimethylcyclopentene ozonide (36). A 3.7 gm (25.5 millimole) portion of dimethylcyclopentene ozonide is dissolved in 10 ml of ether and a solution of 6.7 gm of triphenylphosphine in 20 ml of ether is added dropwise with cooling. A little warming takes place. The resulting phosphine oxide is filtered and the filtrate fractionated. The fraction boiling at 98–100°/14 mm (3.0 gm; 23.5 millimole) crystallizes on cooling (m.p. 32–34°). Yield of 2,6-heptanedione is 91%.

PREPARATION OF ARYLHYDRAZINES (50)

The calculated amount of triphenylphosphine (2.5 equivalents) is dissolved or suspended in methanol or ethanol with the addition of some ether. The alcoholic diazonium salt solution, prepared in the usual manner, is added in portions at room temperature and vigorously shaken from time to time, until the red coloration disappears or at least is lightened considerably. Then the clear, almost colorless solution is allowed to stand for 2 hr, the alcohol is distilled off almost completely, and the last traces are removed by steam distillation. An oil which sometimes crystallizes immediately separates in the flask. It consists of phosphonium salts, phosphine oxide, and excess triphenylphosphine. After cooling the supernatant is decanted and the residue digested with benzene, in which triphenylphosphine and triphenylphosphine oxide are dissolved, and the undissolved phosphonium salt remains. The latter is taken up in a small amount of chloroform and crystallization induced by the addition of ether. The phosphonium salts may be recrystallized from

---

* In place of triphenylphosphine or triethylphosphine the cheaper esters of phosphorous acid can be used.

a chloroform–ether mixture. The tendency of triphenylarylhydrazylphosphonium salts to crystallize is good with the exception of the p-alkoxy derivatives; they are difficultly soluble in cold water. For conversion into arylhydrazines the phosphonium salt is allowed to react in five times its weight in alcohol with an equal volume of $5\,N$ hydrochloric acid and heated for 5 hr on the water bath. On addition of water the triphenylphosphine oxide precipitates. The hydrazine derivative remains in the aqueous phase and can be obtained in pure form as the hydrochloride by concentrating the solution *in vacuo*.

PREPARATION OF ARYLTRIPHENYLPHOSPHONIUM SALTS (*51*)

The experiment is carried out expediently in a three-necked flask which is equipped with a stirrer or vibrating mixer, gas inlet tube, and dropping funnel with pressure equalizer, and set in an ice bath. In order to be able to follow the course of the reaction, the resulting nitrogen is measured. The aqueous diazonium salt solution is prepared in the usual manner and filtered into the three-necked flask; a concentration of about 0.2 mole/liter has proven to be suitable. To the diazo solution is added 30–50 gm of anhydrous sodium acetate per liter; in case the solution is strongly acid, this is partially neutralized beforehand with sodium hydroxide. The flask is closed and an ethyl acetate solution (concentration 1 mole/liter) of triphenylphosphine (equivalent to the diazonium salt) is added in portions from the dropping funnel, the addition being governed by the rate of gas evolution. The reaction is finished when, after the addition of the requisite amount of triphenylphosphine, no further evolution of gas takes place. As a rule the trapped gas volume amounts to 80–100% of the nitrogen contained in the diazo compound. The aqueous layer is separated from the ethyl acetate and extracted several times with ether, whereupon a portion of the colored impurities is removed. Further work up and purification are determined according to the different anion employed.

Chloride. To isolate the chloride the aqueous phase is treated with excess hydrochloric acid, concentrated somewhat and extracted with chloroform in a liquid-liquid extractor. After evaporation of the chloroform the phosphonium chloride remains as residue.

Bromide. Tetraphenylphosphonium bromide is only moderately soluble in cold water and therefore already precipitates during its formation.

Iodide. The phosphonium iodides are difficultly soluble in cold water, moderately soluble in hot water. On addition of sodium iodide to the aqueous phase the iodides largely precipitate. They are recrystallized from water or aqueous alcohol with the addition of decolorizing charcoal.

Perchlorate. The perchlorates are also difficultly soluble in water and precipitate almost quantitatively on addition of perchloric acid to the final aqueous solution. They are purified by recrystallization from alcohol. These salts must be handled carefully as they EXPLODE ON HEATING.

The yields of phosphonium salts using the described reaction conditions lie in the range of 40–80% of theory.

PREPARATION OF TETRAARYLPHOSPHONIUM SALTS BY THE
OXYGEN METHOD (*51c*)

In a three-necked flask equipped with stirrer, reflux condenser and gas inlet tube, a nearly 1 *N* solution of triphenylphosphine is mixed with a fourfold excess of a 2 *N* ether solution of arylmagnesium bromide; dry oxygen is passed over the mixture with ice-cooling and vigorous stirring. Soon a separation takes place. After 2 hr of reaction time, the reaction is finished. Gradually 2 *N* hydrochloric acid is added, until two clear layers have formed. The aqueous layer is separated and the tetraarylphosphonium iodide is precipitated by addition of excess sodium iodide. If the generally more readily soluble bromide is to be isolated then the iodide is decomposed with only a small amount of 15% hydrobromic acid, the reaction allowed to take place over a period of time and then the crystalline precipitate filtered off. In the filtrate the aqueous layer is separated from the ether layer, and the filtered residue is dissolved in the aqueous phase with heating. On cooling the tetraarylphosphonium bromide precipitates.

PREPARATION OF PHOSPHONIUM SALTS BY THE COBALT CHLORIDE METHOD

In a solution of 0.05 mole of tertiary phosphine (aromatic-aliphatic phosphines can be used also) and 0.1 mole of aryl halide in 75 ml of ether, 5 millimoles of anhydrous cobalt chloride [prepared according to Hecht (*115*)] is suspended and a 2 *N* ether solution of phenylmagnesium bromide (0.05) mole) is added dropwise under nitrogen.* The reaction is permitted to go for ½ hr with vigorous stirring and finally heated for 3 hr to boiling. For work-up about 100 ml of 2 *N* hydrochloric acid is added, then the solution filtered and the very small residue extracted on the filter with hot water. The aqueous layer of the filtrate is separated and the phosphonium salt is precipitated by the addition of sodium iodide. This is recrystallized from alcohol–water or from water alone. Yields are about 50% based on the phosphine.

---

* It is not the aryl group of the Grignard compound which enters the phosphonium salt, but that of the aryl halide.

PREPARATION OF AROMATIC PHOSPHINE IMIDES (*30*)

A 2.62 gm portion of triphenylphosphine is dissolved in 20 ml of anhydrous carbon tetrachloride or benzene and 1.59 gm of bromine dissolved in 15 ml of the same solvent is added dropwise with stirring and the exclusion of moisture. With slight warming the pale yellow-colored triphenylphosphine–bromine adduct precipitates. To the suspension of the adduct is added 0.03 mole of anhydrous triethylamine in 10 ml of solvent and then a solution of 0.01 mole of the aromatic amine is added dropwise. If necessary the finely powdered amine can be added little by little. When the addition is complete, the mixture is heated for 10–15 min to boiling, allowed to cool, and filtered from the precipitate. As a rule this consists only of the amine hydrochloride. Some phosphine imides (2,4-dinitroaniline, picramide), which are difficultly soluble in the solvents used, also precipitate at this point and can be freed from the amine hydrochloride by washing with a small amount of methanol. Normally the phosphine imide is found in the filtered solution and remains as a residue on evaporation of the solvent. It is best purified by chromatography using basic aluminum oxide.

INTRODUCTION OF PRIMARY AMINO GROUPS (*59*)

The azides can be prepared by heating for a long time the halogen compound, dissolved in absolute methanol, with activated sodium azide. If the aliphatic-bound halogen is not active enough, then it is advantageous to proceed from the toluenesulfonic esters of the alcohols, which react smoothly with the sodium azide in acetone-water mixture. To prepare the phosphine imide, the azide is treated with triphenylphosphine in benzene until the evolution of nitrogen stops. The phosphine imide, remaining as a residue after the distillation of the benzene, is saponified to the amino compound and triphenylphosphine oxide with a mixture (1:1) of glacial acetic acid and 40% hydrobromic acid.

PHENYLALANINE

A 44 gm portion of diethyl benzylbromomalonate is heated with 15 gm of activated sodium azide in 100 ml of absolute ethanol for 15 hr. Finally the solvent is distilled, the residue treated with water, and the ester extracted with ether. After drying over anhydrous sodium sulfate, the benzyltriazomalonic ester is obtained as an orange-colored oil, which contains only traces of halogen. Yield: 38.2 gm (100%). A 29.1 gm portion of this ester in benzene is allowed to react with 30 gm of triphenylphosphine. Thereupon the remainder of the existing bromo ester precipitates as the quarternary phosphonium salt and can be separated (about 0.25 gm). When the evolution of gas stops, the benzene is distilled and the residue is treated with petroleum ether until it crystallizes. After standing for awhile, the mixture is filtered with suction and washed with ether. The triphenylphosphineiminobenzylmalonic ester is recrystallized twice from a benzene–ligroin mixture (m.p. 118°). The yield of colorless substance is 31 gm (59%).

Saponification takes place in a mixture (1:1) of glacial acetic acid and 40% hydrobromic acid. Heating is continued until a specimen on dilution with water and shaking with benzene dissolves clearly in both phases; this is attained after 3–5 hr of heating. A 95% yield of phenylalanine hydrobromide is obtained.

REDUCTION WITH LITHIUM ALUMINUM HYDRIDE

To a suspension of one mole (37.5 gm) of lithium aluminum hydride in 250 ml of ether there is added dropwise over a period of 2 hr a solution of one mole (236.5 gm) of diphenylphosphinyl chloride in 250 ml of ether. After the reaction has ceased the mixture is heated to boiling for 2 hr and finally 400 ml of concentrated hydrochloric acid is added in the cold, heated for a short time and then 400 ml of water is added. The ether layer is separated, dried with sodium sulfate and the phosphine purified by distillation. Yield: 173 gm (93%) of diphenylphosphine; b.p. 130°/15 mm.

REDUCTION WITH SODIUM

A 30.4 gm (1.32 gram-atom) portion of sodium is suspended in 450 ml of toluene at 100° with the help of a high-speed agitator. To this suspension a solution of 53.6 gm (0.3 mole) of phenyldichlorophosphine in 50 ml of toluene is added dropwise at such a rate that the toluene refluxes moderately. After this the mixture is stirred for 9 hr at 90°, and then decomposed in the cold by dropwise addition of 200 ml of water. The layers are separated the toluene layer dried, and the toluene–phosphine mixture fractionated using a short column. Yield: 23.6 gm (71.5%) of phenylphosphine; b.p. 160°.

REDUCTION WITH SODIUM IN NAPHTHALENE–TETRAHYDROFURAN

To a solution of 0.5 gm (0.022 gram-atom) of sodium and 2.6 gm (0.02 mole) of naphthalene in 50 ml of tetrahydrofuran [according to Scott (116)] is added 4.7 gm (0.01 mole) of tetraphenylphosphonium iodide. The reaction continues with slight warming and is finished in 4 hr. Residual naphthalene is removed with steam and the remaining triphenylphosphine is recrystallized from methanol. Yield: 1.6 gm (61%); m.p. 79°.

REDUCTION WITH MAGNESIUM

To 7.2 gm (0.3 gram-atom) of magnesium in 100 ml of tetrahydrofuran is added 13.7 gm (0.1 mole) of phosphorous trichloride.

The greenish-brown-colored suspension of a magnesium phosphide is formed with an exothermic reaction. Finally the mixture is heated to boiling for 1 hr. On addition of 38 gm (0.3 mole) of benzyl chloride and finally oxidation with hydrogen peroxide, 11.8 gm (37%) of tribenzylphosphine oxide (m.p. 212°) is obtained, as well as 3.1 gm (12%) of dibenzylphosphinic acid (m.p. 192°).

REACTION OF PHOSPHINE OXIDES WITH ALDEHYDES AND KETONES

Equimolar quantities of phosphine oxide (or phosphonous esters) and of the carbonyl compound are dissolved in anhydrous toluene or benzene and reacted with an excess of potassium tert-butoxide. With a 0.01 molar charge 2 gm of potassium tert-butoxide and 75 ml of solvent are used. After heating for 6 to 12 hr, the reaction mixture is cooled and treated with water. The alkaline aqueous layer gives the corresponding phosphinic acid on acidification; the alkene is formed in the organic phase and is purified, after removal of the solvent, by distillation or recrystallization.

REFERENCES

(1) E. Bergmann and W. Schütz, Z. physik. Chem. (Leipzig) B19, 401 (1932).
(2) W. C. Davies and W. P. G. Lewis, J. Chem. Soc. p. 1599 (1934).
(3) H. V. Medoks, Zhur. Obshchei Khim. 8, 298 (1938); Chem. Abstr. 32, 5394 (1938).
(4) A. Cahours and A. W. Hofmann, Ann. Chem. Pharm. 104, 1 (1857).
(5) First observation may be traced to P. Thénard, Compt. rend. acad. sci. 21, 144 (1845); 25, 892 (1847).
(6) Mono-, di-, tri-, and tetrahalogen hydrocarbons react spontaneously with triethylphosphine, with carbon tetrachloride explosively.
(7) A. W. Hofmann, Proc. Roy. Soc. 10, 186, 616 (1860); 11, 291 (1862); Ber. deut. chem. Ges. 6, 292 (1873); A. Hantzsch and H. Hibbert, ibid. 40, 1508 (1907).
(8) H. E. Armstrong, J. Chem. Soc., Trans. 69, 637 (1896); especially p. 673 ff.
(9) A. Hantzsch and H. Hibbert, Ber. deut. chem. Ges. 40, 1508 (1907).
(10) Some investigations show that in these instances the polarizability of the anion plays a part (unpublished results).
(11) A. W. Hofmann, Ann. Chem. Pharm. Suppl. 1, 1 (1861).
(12) W. C. Davies and W. P. Walters, J. Chem. Soc. p. 1786 (1935); W. C. Davies and C. I. O. R. Morris, Bull. soc. chim. France [4] 53, 980 (1933).
(13) A. W. Hofmann, Ber. deut. chem. Ges. 3, 765 (1870).
(14) K. H. Slotta and R. Tschesche, Ber. deut. chem. Ges. 60, 295 (1927).
(15) H. Staudinger and J. Meyer, Helv. Chim. Acta 2, 612 (1919).
(16) L. Horner and K. Klüpfel, Ann. Chem. Liebigs 591, 69 (1955).
(17) L. Horner and H. Schwahn, Ann. Chem. Liebigs 591, 99 (1955); cf. H. Beck, Dissertation, Univ. Mainz, 1956.

(18) H. Schwahn, Diplomarbeit (thesis), Frankfurt (am Main) 1954; R. Gompper and J. Ruf, *Angew. Chem.* **67**, 653 (1955).

(19) A. Schönberg and A. Michaelis, *Ber. deut. chem. Ges.* **69**, 1080 (1936).

(20) A. Schönberg and A. F. A. Ismail, *J. Chem. Soc.* p. 1374 (1940).

(21) H. Hoffmann, L. Horner, and G. Hassel, *Chem. Ber.* **91**, 58 (1958).

(21a) L. Horner and H. Hoffmann, *Chem. Ber.* **91**, 50 (1958).

(22) F. Ramirez and S. Dershowitz, *J. Am. Chem. Soc.* **78**, 5614 (1956).

(23) L. Horner and W. Spietschka, *Ann. Chem. Liebigs* **591**, 1 (1955).

(24) H. Schlenk, *Chem. Ber.* **85**, 901 (1952).

(24a) See also A. W. Johnson and J. C. Tebby, *J. Chem. Soc.* p. 2126 (1961) (added by translator).

(25) O. Diels and K. Alder, *Ann. Chem. Liebigs* **498**, 16 (1932).

(26) L. Horner, W. Jurgeleit, and K. Klüpfel, *Ann. Chem. Liebigs* **591**, 108 (1955).

(27) A series of other tertiary oxonium salts also forms stable adducts with triethylphosphine. B. Nippe, Dissertation, Univ. Mainz, 1956 (unpublished).

(28) E. Weitz, *Angew. Chem.* **66**, 658 (1954).

(29) A. Michaelis, *Ann. Chem. Liebigs* **315**, 43 (1901).

(30) H. Oediger, Diplomarbeit, Univ. Mainz, 1956 (unpublished).

(31) G. M. Kosolapoff, "Organophosphorus Compounds." Wiley, New York, 1950.

(31a) S. R. Landauer and H. N. Rydon, *J. Chem. Soc.* p. 2224 (1953).

(31b) N. Kornblum and D. C. Iffland, *J. Am. Chem. Soc.* **77**, 6653 (1955).

(32) J. Meisenheimer, J. Casper, M. Höring, W. Lauter, L. Lichtenstadt, and W. Samuel, *Ann. Chem. Liebigs* **449**, 213 (1926); G. F. Fenton and C. K. Ingold, *J. Chem. Soc.* p. 2342 (1929).

(32a) L. Horner, H. Hoffmann, H. G. Wippel, and G. Hassel, *Chem. Ber.* **91**, 52 (1958).

(32b) H. Hoffmann, *Ann. Chem. Liebigs* **634**, 1 (1960).

(33) L. Horner and W. Jurgeleit, *Ann. Chem. Liebigs* **591**, 138 (1955).

(34) R. Criegee, *Ann. Chem. Liebigs* **583**, 1 (1953).

(35) Also esters of phosphorus acid, tertiary arsines, and thioethers can be used (*36*).

(36) H. Schaefer, Diplomarbeit, Univ. Mainz, 1955 (unpublished).

(37) F. Challenger and V. K. Wilson, *J. Chem. Soc.* p. 213 (1927).

(38) J. L. Leffler, *J. Am. Chem. Soc.* **72**, 67 (1950).

(39) R. Criegee and R. Kaspar, *Ann. Chem. Liebigs* **560**, 127 (1948).

(40) Dibenzoyl peroxide combines with triphenylstibene and -bismuthine to form isolatable dibenzoates (*37*) analogous to XXVIIb.

(40a) M. A. Greenbaum, D. B. Denney, and A. K. Hoffmann, *J. Am. Chem. Soc.* **78**, 2563 (1956); **79**, 979 (1957).

(41) G. Wittig and W. Haag, *Chem. Ber.* **88**, 1659 (1956).

(42) A. Schönberg, *Ber. deut. chem. Ges.* **68**, 163 (1935); A. Schönberg and M. Z. Barakat, *J. Chem. Soc.* p. 892 (1949).

(43) F. Challenger and D. Greenwood, *J. Chem. Soc.* p. 26 (1950).

(44) C. C. J. Culvenor, W. Davies, and N. S. Heath, *J. Chem. Soc.* p. 282 (1949).

(45) W. Jurgeleit, Dissertation, Frankfurt (am Main), 1954 (unpublished).

(46) J. W. Breitenbach, *Monatsh. Chem.* **84**, 820 (1953).

(47) H. Staudinger and E. Hauser, *Helv. Chim. Acta* **4**, 861 (1921).

(47a) cf. E. Howard, Jr. and W. F. Olszewski, *J. Am. Chem. Soc.* **81**, 1483 (1959).

(48) K. Klüpfel, Dissertation, Univ. Mainz, 1954 (unpublished).

(48a) R. E. Davis, *J. Org. Chem.* **23**, 1767 (1958).

(48b) R. D. Schuetz and R. L. Jacobs, *J. Org. Chem.* **23**, 1799 (1958).

(49) L. Horner and H. Nickel, *Ann. Chem. Liebigs* **597**, 20 (1955).

(50) L. Horner and H. Nickel, *Chem. Ber.* **86**, 1066 (1953).

(51) H. Hoffmann, Diplomarbeit, Frankfurt (am Main), 1955; L. Horner and H. Hoffmann, *Chem. Ber.* **91**, 45 (1958).

(51a) F. Suckfüll and H. Haubrich, *Angew. Chem.* **70**, 238 (1958).

(51b) M. S. Kharasch, S. C. Kleiger, J. A. Martin, and F. R. Mayo, *J. Am. Chem. Soc.* **63**, 2305 (1941); M. S. Kharasch and M. Kleiman **65**, 491 (1943).

(51c) J. Dodonow and H. Medox, *Ber. deut. chem. Ges.* **61**, 907 (1928).

(52) H. Staudinger and J. Meyer, *Helv. Chim. Acta* **2**, 619 (1919); H. Staudinger and G. Lüscher **5**, 75 (1922).

(53) H. Staudinger and J. Meyer, *Helv. Chim. Acta* **2**, 635 (1919).

(54) L. A. Pinck, *J. Am. Chem. Soc.* **69**, 723 (1947).

(55) L. Horner and E. Lengnau, *Ann. Chem. Liebigs* **591**, 135 (1955).

(56) cf. G. Wittig, *Angew. Chem.* **68**, 505 (1956); G. Wittig and M. Rieber, *Ann. Chem. Liebigs* **562**, 187 (1949).

(57) F. Hein, *Z. anorg. u. allgem. Chem.* **272**, 25 (1953).

(57a) L. Horner, H. Hoffmann, and H. G. Wippel, *Chem. Ber.* **91**, 61 (1958); L. Horner, H. Hoffmann, H. G. Wippel, and G. Klahre, *ibid.* **92**, 2499 (1959).

(58) H. Staudinger and E. Hauser, *Helv. Chim. Acta* **4**, 861 (1921).

(59) L. Horner and A. Gross, *Ann. Chem. Liebigs* **591**, 117 (1955).

(60) Together with D. Schlüter (unpublished).

(61) A. Gross, Dissertation, Frankfurt (am Main) 1953 (unpublished).

(62) H. Staudinger, "Die Ketene," Enke, Stuttgart, 1912.

(63) Summary: E. Vogel, *Fortschr. chem. Forsch.* **3**, 456 (1955).

(64) E. J. Smutny and J. D. Roberts, *J. Am. Chem. Soc.* **77**, 3420 (1955).

(65) Comprehensive summary by G. Wittig, *Experientia* **12**, 41 (1956).

(65a) L. Horner, H. Oediger, and H. Hoffmann, *Ann. Chem. Liebigs* **626**, 26 (1959).

(65b) D. G. Coe, S. R. Landauer, and H. N. Rydon, *J. Chem. Soc.* p. 228 (1954).

(65c) D. G. Coe, H. N. Rydon, and B. L. Tonge, *J. Chem. Soc.* p. 323 (1957).

(65d) L. Horner and H. Oediger, *Chem. Ber.* **91**, 437 (1958).

(65e) R. Grünewald, Dissertation, Univ. Mainz, 1960.

(66) This section was rewritten by Dr. P. Beck.

(67) A. Michaelis and H. V. Soden, *Ber. deut. chem. Ges.* **17**, 921 (1884).

(68) S. Ahrland, J. Chatt, N. R. Davies, and A. A. Williams, *J. Chem. Soc.* p. 276 (1958).

(69) H. Gilman and G. E. Brown, *J. Am. Chem. Soc.* **67**, 284 (1945).

(70) Unpublished.

(71) A. Michaelis, *Ber. deut. chem. Ges.* **7**, 6 (1874).

(72) R. J. Horvat and A. Furst, *J. Am. Chem. Soc.* **74**, 562 (1952).

(73) L. Horner, H. Hoffmann, and P. Beck, *Chem. Ber.* **91**, 1583 (1958).

(74) F. Hein, K. Issleib, and H. Rabold, *Z. anorg. u. allgem. Chem.* **287**, 208 (1956).

(75) L. Horner, P. Beck, and H. Hoffmann, *Chem. Ber.* **92**, 2086 (1959).

(75a) E. Wiberg and K. Mödritzer, *Z. Naturforsch.* **11b**, 747 (1956).

(75b) E. Wiberg and G. Müller-Schiedmayer, *Chem. Ber.* **92**, 2372 (1959).

(75c) L. D. Freedman and G. O. Doak, *J. Am. Chem. Soc.* **74**, 3414 (1952).

(75d) T. Weil, B. Prijs, and H. Erlinmeyer, *Helv. Chim. Acta* **36**, 142 (1953).

(75e) A. W. Hofmann, *Ann. Chem. Pharm. Suppl.* **1**, 26 (1861).

(75f) W. J. Bailey and S. A. Buckler, *J. Am. Chem. Soc.* **79**, 3567 (1957) .

(75g) E. A. Letts and W. Collie, *Trans. Roy. Soc. Edinburgh* **30**, 181 (1883).

(76) H. Hibbert, *Ber. deut. chem. Ges.* **32**, 160 (1906).

(77) W. C. Davies, P. L. Pearse, and W. J. Jones, *J. Chem. Soc.* p. 1262 (1929).

(78) H. Gilman and C. G. Stuckwisch, *J. Am. Chem. Soc.* **63**, 2849 (1941).
(79) B. M. Mikhailov and N. F. Kucherova, *Doklady Akad. Nauk S.S.S.R.* **74**, 501 (1950); *Chem. Abstr.* **45**, 3343 (1951); *Zuhr. Obshchei Khim.* **22**, 792 (1952); *Chem. Abstr.* **47**, 5388 (1953).
(80) A. Michaelis and A. Reese, *Ber. deut. chem. Ges.* **15**, 1610 (1882).
(81) A. Michaelis, *Ann. Chem. Liebigs* **315**, 43 (1901).
(81a) G. M. Kosolapoff, *Org. Reactions* **6**, 292 (1951).
(82) B. Buchner and L. B. Lockhart, *J. Am. Chem. Soc.* **73**, 755 (1951).
(83) L. Maier, *Angew. Chem.* **71**, 574 (1959).
(84) I. P. Komkov, K. V. Karavanov, and S. Z. Ivin, *Zhur. Obshchei Khim.* **28**, 2963 (1958); *Chem. Abstr.* **53**, 9035 (1959).
(85) G. M. Kosolapoff, *Org. Reactions* **6**, 319 (1951).
(86) A. B. Burg and P. J. Slota, Jr., *J. Am. Chem. Soc.* **80**, 1107 (1958).
(87) R. B. Fox, *J. Am. Chem. Soc.* **72**, 4147 (1950).
(88) A. W. Hofmann, *Ber. deut. chem. Ges.* **4**, 430, 605 (1871).
(89) N. Davidson and H. C. Brown, *J. Am. Chem. Soc.* **64**, 718 (1942).
(89a) A. Michaelis and F. W. Wegner, *Ber. deut. chem. Ges.* **48**, 316 (1915).
(89b) H. Hoffmann, Dissertation, Univ. Mainz, 1956 and unpublished work.
(90) A. W. Hofmann, *Ber. deut. chem. Ges.* **6**, 292 (1873).
(91) H. Albers and W. Schuler, *Ber. deut. chem. Ges.* **76**, 23 (1943); N. Kreutzkamp, *Chem. Ber.* **87**, 919 (1954); A. Job and G. Dusollier, *Compt. rend. acad. sci.* **184**, 1454 (1927).
(92) A. Joannis, *Ann. chim. et phys.* [8] **7**, 105 (1906); C. Walling, U.S. Patent 2,437,795–6–7; *Chem. Abstr.* **42**, 4198, 4199 (1948).
(93) P. R. Bloomfield and K. Parvin, *Chem. & Ind. (London)* p. 541 (1959).
(94) F. G. Mann and J. T. Miller, *J. Chem. Soc.* p. 4453 (1952); H. Hoffmann, Dissertation, Univ. Mainz, 1956.
(95) H. C. Brown, U.S. Patent 2,584,113 (1952); *Chem. Abstr.* **46**, 9580 (1952).
(96) A. R. Stiles, F. F. Rust, and W. E. Vaughan, *J. Am. Chem. Soc.* **74**, 3282 (1952).
(97) N. V. de Bataafsche Petroleum Maatschappij, British Patent 673,451 (1952); *Chem. Abstr.* **47**, 5426 (1953).
(98) A. L. Oppegard, U.S. Patent 2,687,437 (1954); *Chem. Abstr.* **49**, 11000 (1955).
(99) F. W. Bennett, H. J. Emeleus, and R. N. Haszeldine, *J. Chem. Soc.* p. 1565 (1953).
(100) M. Reuter and L. Arthner, German Patent 1,035,135; *Chem. Abstr.* **54**, 14125 (1960).
(101) N. Collie, *Trans. Chem. Soc.* **53**, 636 (1888).
(102) G. F. Fenton, L. Hey, and C. K. Ingold, *J. Chem. Soc.* p. 989 (1933).
(103) A. Hoffman, *J. Am. Chem. Soc.* **52**, 2995 (1930).
(104) M. Grayson, P. T. Keough, and G. A. Johnson, *J. Am. Chem. Soc.* **81**, 4803 (1959).
(105) A. Michaelis, *Ann. Chem. Liebigs* **293**, 193 (1896).
(106) F. Pass and M. Schindlbauer, *Monatsh. Chem.* **90**, 148 (1959).
(107) K. Issleib and A. Tzschach, *Chem. Ber.* **92**, 704 (1959).
(108) D. Wittenberg and H. Gilman, *J. Org. Chem.* **23**, 1063 (1958).
(109) K. Issleib and H. O. Fröhlich, *Z. Naturforsch.* **14b**, 349 (1959).
(110) C. Dörken, *Ber. deut. chem. Ges.* **21**, 1505 (1888).
(111) H. Köhler and A. Michaelis, *Ber. deut. chem. Ges.* **10**, 807 (1877).
(112) K. Issleib and W. Seidel, *Chem. Ber.* **92**, 2681 (1959).
(113) W. Kuchen and H. Buchwald, *Angew. Chem.* **71**, 162 (1959).
(114) L. Maier, *Angew. Chem.* **71**, 575 (1959).

(115) H. Hecht, *Z. anorg. Chem.* **259**, 51 (1947).
(116) N. G. Scott, J. F. Walker, and V. L. Hansley, *J. Am. Chem. Soc.* **58**, 2442
       (1936); U.S. Patent 2,019,832; *Chem. Abstr.* **30**, 490 (1936).

Reduction of Carbonyl Compounds with Complex Hydrides

DR. HELMUT HÖRMANN

Max-Planck Institut für Eiweiss- und Lederforschung, Regensburg

Since the discovery of lithium aluminum hydride by Finholt and associates (1), the importance of metal hydrides as reducing agents in organic chemistry has increased significantly. The exceptional developments which these substances initiated lay in the possibility in making available a group of clean-cut reductions, which previously could be brought about only through the use of more strenuous conditions. The carboxyl group and its derivatives, such as esters, halides, anhydrides, amides, and even the carboxylate ion are to be considered primarily in this chapter.

Up to now metal hydrides with the highest reductive power were desired. Only seldom was a weaker reducing agent desired, to react specifically with a definite class of substances. However, the need to differentiate among the individual carbonyl compounds mentioned above, to reduce selectively definite groups, and to allow others to remain completely intact, has become ever more evident in recent investigations.

$LiAlH_4$, $LiBH_4$ (2), $NaBH_4$, and KBH_4 (3) are already well established and are commercially available. In addition, $Mg(AlH_4)_2$ (4), $NaAlH_4$ (5), AlH_3 (6), $Al(BH_4)_3$ (7), $Ca(BH_4)_2$ (8,9), and $NaHB(OCH_3)_3$ (10) have been investigated recently for their reducing activity on organic carbonyl compounds (11).

Theoretical Interpretation

The reducing power of the compounds listed at the top of Table 1 decreases from left to right. A rule for expressing reducing power may be stated in the following axiom: the more salt-like the structure of the hydride, the less is its reducing power.

The symmetry of the complex hydride anions, which chiefly determine reduction, increases with increasing salt character, which causes reactivity to decrease. In contrast as the anion becomes more reactive, the more strongly is it polarized to the cationic partner through covalent binding, or the more assymetric it becomes. So, for example, the compounds of the more readily polarizable AlH_4-anion are stronger reducing agents than the significantly more heteropolar boron hydrides. The

TABLE 1

SUMMARY OF THE REDUCTION OF DIFFERENT CARBONYL COMPOUNDS
WITH COMPLEX HYDRIDES

	LiAlH₄ Mg(AlH₄)₂ (14) NaAlH₄	AlH₃	Al(BH₄)₂	Ca(BH₄)₂ Sr(BH₄)₂ Ba(BH₄)₂	LiBH₄	NaHB(OCH₃)₃	KB⟩ NaB
$-C{\overset{O}{\underset{Cl}{}}}$	+ (13)	+ (6)	+	+	+	+ (10)	+ (2
$-C{\overset{O}{\underset{H}{}}}$, $-C{\overset{O}{\underset{CH_3}{}}}$	+ (13)	+ (6)	+ (7)	+ (8)	+ (18)	+ (10)	+ (2.
$-C{\overset{O}{\underset{OCH_3}{}}}$	+ (5)	+ (6)	+ (7)	+ (8)	+ (18)	± (10)	− (2.
$-C{\overset{O}{\underset{OH}{}}}$. $-C{\equiv}N$	+ (13)	+ (6)	+ (7)	± (7, 9)	−[b]	—	−[b]
$-C{\overset{O}{\underset{NR_2}{}}}$	+ (16)	± (17)	?	—	− (19)	—	—
$-C{\overset{O}{\underset{O^{\ominus}}{}}}$	+ (15)	?	—	—	—	—	− (2.

[a] As in text, italic numbers in parentheses are reference numbers.
[b] Carboxylic acids are attacked to a small extent, nitrile groups remain intact [LiBH₄ (18, 19, 2 NaBH₄ (21)].

sodium salt of the unsymmetrical trimethoxy boron hydride reduces more powerfully than the symmetrical BH₄-ions.

The different reducing power of the hydrides may be compared with the reducibility of the carbonyl compounds. This may be clarified by a consideration of the reaction scheme of reduction with lithium aluminum hydride, as an example.

The complex hydride anion furnishes to the polarized form of the carbonyl group a hydrogen anion, which attaches itself to the positive carbon atom, while the central atom, in the present example aluminum, migrates to the negative oxygen (6, 12). This reaction is possible four times on the AlH₄ anion. The complex, I, is then decomposed with water, and the alcohol, II, and aluminum hydroxide are formed.

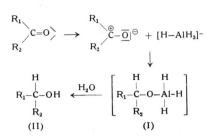

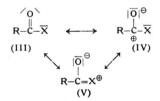

This reaction path is analogous to the reaction of organometallic compounds (e.g., Grignard reagents) with carbonyl groups, in which case a carbanion is transferred instead of the hydrogen anion.

The attachment of the hydrogen anion can be hindered, if the positive excess charge of the carbonyl carbon is weakened. This can be achieved through basic substituents, which are in the position to furnish electrons to the carbonyl group and in this manner form a mesomeric form V. This is the case, with increasing effectiveness, for esters, free carboxylic acids, amides, and the carboxylate ion. This results in a series of carbonyl compounds having decreasing reductibility, as presented in the first column of Table 1. Nitriles can be placed in about the same position as the free carboxylic acids.

The fraction of the mesomeric form, V, present has been investigated accurately in the case of the carboxylate ion (22) and with acid amides (23) and amounts to about 50% in both cases. With carboxylic acids and their esters this effect decreases. At the same time, owing to the greater negativity of the substituents, an inductive effect becomes

evident, which counteracts the mesomeric effect. The resonance energy of the carboxyl group nevertheless always amounts to 28 kcal (24) and that of the ester group to 24 kcal (24), attributable in large part to structure V.

It is more difficult to classify the acid chlorides in this scheme. According to molecular refraction measurements (25) and infrared absorption (26), the inductive effect, that is the acquisition of positive charge of the carbonyl-carbon, outweighs the mesomeric effect. It was indeed questionable whether this effect, which is opposed by a definite resonance energy, is adequate to make the carbonyl group more active than that in aldehydes or ketones. The discovery of Brown and Mead (10) that sodium trimethoxyborohydride at −80° still reacts completely with benzoyl chloride with considerable formation of benzyl alcohol, whereas aldehydes are barely attacked, seems to answer this question in the affirmative. In Table 1, therefore, the acid halides are listed before the aldehydes.

Furthermore, the fact that in the reduction of carboxylic acids their proton reacts primarily with a portion of the hydride with the evolution of hydrogen must be taken into account. If the resulting compound

$$4 \text{ R}-\text{COOH} + \text{LiAlH}_4 \longrightarrow \text{Li}^+ + \text{Al}^{3+} + 4 \text{ R}-\text{COO}^- + 2 \text{ H}_2$$
$$4 \text{ R}-\text{COOH} + \text{LiBH}_4 \longrightarrow \text{Li}^+ + [\text{B}(\text{CH}_3\text{COO})]^- + 2 \text{ H}_2$$

formed is of a heteropolar nature, which is largely the case with the aluminum salts, then the excess negative charge of the carboxylate ion is made available for the formation of the mesomeric structure V. The reducing ability then corresponds to that of other carboxyl anions. If, on the other hand, boric acid–acyl compounds are formed, with practically a covalent bond between both moieties, there is made available for the formation of the mesomeric form V only a slightly larger percentage charge than for esters. Therefore the grouping between esters and amides seem to be justifiable. Because of the greater selectivity of the borohydrides the last case is more important.

As follows from Table 1, lithium aluminum hydride as an especially strong reducing agent is able to reduce all listed carbonyl compounds. Thus, aldehydes, ketones, acid halides, anhydrides esters, and carboxylic acids are reduced to alcohols, nitriles and acid amides to amines (the latter also to alcohols in special cases). Carbon double and triple bond compounds react only above 100° (27), provided they are polarized, as for example, the α,β-unsaturated carbonyl compounds (28).

$$\text{R}-\text{CH}=\text{CH}-\text{CH}=\text{O} \xrightarrow{\text{LiAlH}_4} \text{R}-\text{CH}_2-\text{CH}_2-\text{CH}_2\text{OH}$$

Sodium aluminum hydride (5) and magnesium aluminum hydride (4) possess a similar strong reducing capacity, and they have also been recommended as cheaper substitutes for lithium aluminum hydride. The reductive capacity of aluminum hydride itself is somewhat less, for it does not reduce acid amides completely (17).

The analogous lithium borohydride is a weaker reducing agent than lithium aluminum hydride. It is no longer able to reduce amide bonds (19). Also carbon–nitrogen double and triple bonds are not touched, at least at room temperature (20, 29). Only the oximes, which are converted to amines, are an exception.

Examples

Protection of Carbonyl Groups

The fact that carbon–nitrogen double bonds are reduced by lithium borohydride only with difficulty may be used to advantage in the protection of certain keto groups adjacent to others which are to be reduced. Thus Wendler and co-workers (20) have reduced with lithium borohydride specifically the 11-keto group in 20-cyano-17-pregnene-21-ol-3,11-dione, after they had formed the semicarbazone with the 3-keto group, whose carbon–nitrogen double bond resisted reduction. The nitrile group in position 20 also remained untouched.

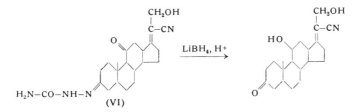

To protect carbonyl groups against attack from hydrides, they may also be acetalated. Acetals are also not reduced by lithium aluminum hydride (29a). On the other hand ortho esters are converted to acetals (29b).

Protection of Amino Groups

In the reduction of various carbonyl compounds with free amino groups it is often necessary to protect the amino groups in order to eliminate troublesome side reactions. This can be done with acetylation only if lithium borohydride or another mild reducing agent is used, which does not attack amide bonds. The reduction of diethyl glutamate to glutaminediol [2-amino-1,5-pentanediol] may be given as an example; without protection of the amino group, a definite side reaction consisting of cyclization to prolinol [2-hydroxymethylpyrrolidine] (30) occurs. On the other hand if the amino group is acetylated and the ester group is selectively reduced with lithium borohydride, glutaminediol is obtained in very good yield on saponification of the acetyl group (19). In the reduction of serine and threonine esters the protection of the amino group has also proved its value (19).

Reduction of Peptides

The carboxyl group of peptides can be determined since it may be reductively changed to a primary hydroxyl group and identified as an aminoalcohol after hydrolysis of the end group. In order that the reduced peptide can still be hydrolyzed, the peptide linkages must remain intact during the reduction, and this occurs only with lithium borohydride and not with lithium aluminum hydride (31). With the latter the peptides are partially reduced to secondary amines which can no longer be hydrolyzed (17, 32).

Numerous authors have described the reduction of esters (18, 33) or anhydrides (34) containing nitro groups with lithium borohydride. However, nitro groups are not resistant to lithium borohydride in all cases (18), therefore caution is necessary in these reductions.

The alkaline earth borohydrides investigated by Kollonitsch and co-workers (8, 9) possess a somewhat stronger reducing power than lithium borohydride. More powerful still is aluminum borohydride, by means of which nitriles can be completely reduced to amines. The same reduction occurs only incompletely with calcium borohydride (7).

In contrast potassium and sodium borohydrides react significantly less. With these only aldehydes and ketones can be reduced to alcohols (21). The hydrogenation of pyruvic acid to lactic acid (35) and of 5-ketogluconic to gluconic acid and its diastereoisomer, idonic acid (36) are examples of selective reduction. Significantly more important may be the reduction of keto groups in the presence of aliphatic halogens and of nitro groups, carried out with good yields in the case of ω-bromoacetophenone and m-nitrobenzaldehyde (21, 37). Potassium and sodium borohydride gain further consideration in that they readily form lithium borohydride in the reaction medium in the presence of lithium halides and are thus available for the reduction of esters (33, 38).

In the borohydride series the increase of reducing power of the alkali compounds over that of lithium, which is related to the alkaline earth metals, and the increase from the alkaline earth metals up to aluminum go hand in hand with the increase of the covalent character of the compounds. The initial members are sluggish and decidedly salt-like compounds. Sodium borohydride remains stable up to 400°, where it decomposes gradually (3). The reactive lithium borohydride melts at 279° (2). By contrast the decidedly covalent aluminum borohydride, which shows the most powerful reducing power, boils at 44° at atmospheric pressure (7).

Reaction Conditions

After a critical inspection of Table 1, consideration is to be given to the fact that variations in reaction conditions, such as increase in temperature or cooling, can alter the reducing power. Thus many reactions succeed even at higher temperature, while in the cold a greater selectivity is attained. In some cases the influence of solvents has been observed (*38*). Furthermore the reducibility of some carbonyl groups can be increased by the addition of aluminum or magnesium chloride to the reaction medium. With this aid it was possible, for example, to reduce esters with sodium borohydride to alcohols in good yields (*38, 39*). The action of the catalyst is probably due to an attachment to the carbonyl oxygen, where the carbon–oxygen double bond is extended and the positive excess charge on the carbonyl carbon is increased.

$$\overset{\text{X}}{\underset{\oplus}{\text{R}-\text{C}}}-\overset{\ominus}{\text{O}} \rightarrow \text{AlCl}_3$$

Influence of Structure

Along with these external influences, however, structural peculiarities can alter the reducibility of some carbonyl groups considerably. Groups which increase the positive charge on the carbonyl carbon facilitate reduction, while, conversely, electron leakage to the carbonyl group impedes the reaction.

We have already become familiar with the substitution of the carbonyl group by basic groups as an example of the latter type of hindrance of reducibility, and in this manner have explained the various degrees of ease of reduction of the individual acid derivatives. Further, benzophenone (*6*), benzoyl chloride (*21*), and esters of benzoic acid (*8*) exhibit less reducibility than the corresponding aliphatic compounds; this is also explained by an electron-leakage effect of the benzene ring to the carbonyl group with resultant development of mesomeric structures.

Conversely, however, the sluggishness of reaction of the various acid derivatives can be strongly repressed, if the free electron pair on the hetero element, which leads to the formation of the reaction-inhibiting structure (V), is claimed by other substituents. As such, the acyl or sulfonyl groups, among others, come into consideration. Thus, for example, acid anhydrides are reduced with sodium trimethoxyborohydride substantially more smoothly than the esters (*10*). N-Tosylated acid amides are reduced with lithium borohydride, which otherwise does not attack the amide linkage. As example of this one may refer to the specific reduction of the lactam group of pyrrolidonecarboxamide with lithium borohydride after tosylation of the lactam nitrogen. The second amide group remained untouched. This reaction is a critical step in the synthesis of proline from glutamic acid (*40*).

A similar case of a reactive amide group exists, when the amide nitrogen is built into a resonance system and its electron pair is available for mesomerism. This is true, for example, for the N-acyl derivatives of indole and carbazole, which are reduced with lithium borohydride (*41*).

Increased reactivity of ester groups is also found sometimes in compounds rich in hydroxyl groups, for example, aldonic acid lactones, which can be reduced with sodium borohydride (*42*). A correct explanation of these exceptions, which is related possibly to the complex formation tendency of carbohydrates with boric acid, is still lacking.

Furthermore reference must be made especially to the behavior of acid amides on reduction with lithium aluminum hydride. Unsubstituted and N-monoalkylated amides are reduced almost exclusively to amines, in the course of which the carbon-nitrogen bond is split only to a very small degree (*16*). It is different with N-disubstituted amides. In this instance alcohols are frequently formed, exclusively in the case of the reduction of N,N-dimethylbenzamide (*16*). The difference in behavior can probably be explained by the fact that amides which still carry a hydrogen on the nitrogen, after reduction to the ketone-step (complex Ia) can split off to an aldimine, which then is reduced further to the amine. With N,N-dialkylated amides a somewhat different reaction mechanism is involved (*43*).

$$R-C\overset{O}{\underset{NHR'}{\diagdown}} \xrightarrow{AlH_4^{\ominus}} \left[R-\overset{H}{\underset{NHR'}{\overset{|}{C}}}-O-AlH_3 \right]^{-} \xrightarrow{-[HO-AlH_3]^{\ominus}}$$

$$\longrightarrow R-CH=NR' \xrightarrow[\text{(Ia)}]{AlH_4^{\ominus}} R-CH_2-NHR'$$

Reduction to Aldehyde

In some cases the reduction of carboxylic acid derivatives is successfully interrupted at the aldehyde stage. For example, the nitrogen of acid amides may be substituted with groups capable of resonance, which stabilize the complex I ($R_2 = NR'_2$) at the aldehyde step. Moreover, N,N-disubstituted compounds must be involved, so that at the aldehyde step no aldimine can be formed (see above). The following have been reduced to the aldehyde stage: the N-methylanilides of carboxylic acids, by Weygand and co-workers (*43*); N-cinnamoylcarbazole, by Wittig and Hornberger (*41*); and N-benzoylbenztriazole, by Gaylord (*44*). It is possible to hinder the further reduction of the amide linkage of dialkylated amides by incorporating the linkage in a 5- or 6-membered ring system. Monoalkylated amides can give rise to aldimine formation and therefore are unsuited. Examples of such a reduction are the formation of ω-methylaminobutyraldehyde and -valeraldehyde from N-methyl-pyrrolidone and -piperidone (*45*). Furthermore, it appears that the alde-hyde step may also be stabilized when the aluminum atom in complex I is bound in chelate fashion to several groups in the same molecule. The reduction of dimethyl oxalate to glyoxal (*43*) and of dimethyl asparagi-nate to aminosuccinaldehyde (*19*) are noted as examples. In both cases the chelate complexes are the intermediates of the expected aluminum compounds. Thus the aldehyde step seems to be the more stabilized, the more groups of the same molecule surround the central atom. Finally, steric hindrances are yet to be mentioned; they may probably be decisive in the reduction of the bisdimethylamide or piperidide of phthalic acid to phthalaldehyde (*46*).

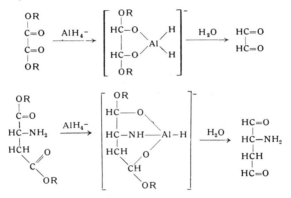

Supplement

The data cited concerning the mode of reaction of complex hydrides with carbonyl compounds show qualitatively a gradation of the reducing power of the hydrides. In order to obtain a quantitative measurement, Schmidt and Nordwig (*47*) allowed an equimolecular mixture of two double hydrides [double hydride: $LiXH_4$ type] to react in excess with a carbonyl compound (cyclopentanone), separated the precipitated com-plex and determined the composition of the unused hydrides in the supernatant liquid. They determined thus the ratio in which the two hydrides had taken part in the reaction and thereby arrived at a relative measurement of the reducing power. In the series $LiAlH_4$, $LiBH_4$, and $LiGaH_4$ the activity decreased $100:34:17$, respectively. At the same time they ascertained that $LiAlH_4$ alone reacts quantitatively with cyclopentanone in the ratio of $1:4$, whereas after reduction with $LiBH_4$ unreacted hydride always was detected.

The investigation was extended further to the development of new hydrides with improvement of the reduction of carboxylic acid derivatives to aldehydes as the special goal. The nitriles, with which the formation of aldehydes along with amines has been frequently observed during lithium aluminum hydride reduction ($5, 48$), seemed to be the most suitable as acid derivatives. Further, in their reduction, dimerization was demonstrated repeatedly, which is explained by the condensation of intermediary aldimine structures (48). With $NaHAl(OC_2H_5)_3$ and aromatic aldehydes Hesse and Schrödel (49) obtained an exceptionally resonance-stabilized complex at the aldehyde step, which was not further reduced even at $65°$. Aliphatic nitriles give only poor yields of aldehydes.

Earlier, aldehydes were obtained in poor yields from acid chlorides with sodium trimethoxyborohydride at low temperature (10). The reduction succeeds much more smoothly with lithium tri-*tert*-butoxy-aluminum hydride, $LiHAl(O—C_4H_9-tert)_3$ in dimethyldiethyleneglycol or tetrahydrofuran at $-75°$ (50). This reagent also has the advantage of being prepared more readily, since up to three hydrogen atoms in the AlH_4^- anion can be substituted by the *tert*-butoxy group (51). Esters and nitriles are not reduced, but aldehydes and ketones reduce well (51). Brown and Tsukamoto (52) reduced aliphatic N-dimethylamides to aldehydes with $LiH_2Al(OC_2H_5)_2$ at $0°$ in ether.

The complex hydrides of aluminum partly lose their reducing action with the substitution of a hydrogen by an alkoxy group, while in contrast the reducing power of the borohydrides increases.

$$LiAlH_4 > LiH_2Al(OC_2H_5)_2 > LiHAl(OC_2H_5)_3 > LiHAl(O-tert.-C_4H_9)_3$$
$$LiBH_4 < LiHB(OCH_3)_3$$

In the case of the aluminum hydrides the strong electronegativity of the alkoxy groups undoubtedly hinders the release of the hydride ion. This effect is also present in the borohydrides; it is, however, over-shadowed by the possibility of the formation of mesomeric structures, in which the lone electron pair of the oxygen atoms fills out the electron deficiency which resulted from the expulsion of a hydride ion from the complex. This possibility for resonance stabilization of the intermediate is possessed only by boron, for aluminum, as an element of the second row, is inclined less readily to the formation of double bonds (51).

$$\left[H—Al \begin{matrix} OR \\ OR \\ OR \end{matrix} \right]^- ; \left[H—B \begin{matrix} OR \\ OR \\ OR \end{matrix} \right]^- \rightleftarrows H^- + RO—B \begin{matrix} OR \\ OR \end{matrix}$$

$$\updownarrow$$

$$RO^\oplus{=}B^\ominus \begin{matrix} OR \\ OR \end{matrix}$$

The cyano group works quite differently from the alkoxy groups. Through its strong electronegativity it impedes the release of the hydride ion. Lithium monocyanoborohydride (53) has the power to reduce only aldehydes and α-hydroxyketones. Even ketones and carboxylic acid derivatives remain untouched. Thus an important reagent is furnished to reduce specific aldehyde groups in the presence of ketones.

Other hydrides which are experimentally suited for the exclusive reduction of the aldehydes and ketones, are $Ca[HB(OCH_3)_3]_2$ (54) and $(C_6H_5)_2SnH_2$ (55). In the reduction of α,β-unsaturated carbonyl compounds with these compounds, as well as with $NaHAl(OC_2H_5)_3$ (49), predominantly α,β-unsaturated alcohols are formed. Under the same conditions with LiAlH₄ the double bond is also reduced (28). LiInH₄ reduces only quinone (56).

A further aim of research has been the reduction of carbonyl compounds to hydrocarbons. The reduction succeeds with LiAlH₄ only when the compound to be reduced can dissociate at the alcohol stage to a resonance-stabilized carbonium ion, which then can react once again with LiAlH₄ (57). This is the case, for example, with aromatic carbonyl compounds containing o- or p-methoxy, or dimethylamino groups (57,58) with α,β-unsaturated carbonyl compounds (59), or diaryl ketones (60). The requisite dissociation proceeds especially favorably with the aid of a catalyst, e.g., AlCl₃; the assistance, however, does not appear to be necessary in all cases (58). At least two moles of catalyst are required, for one mole reacts beforehand with LiAlH₄ with the formation of LiCl and AlH₂Cl or AlHCl₂, which then release the necessary reducing agent (61). Examples of this type of reduction are: p-methoxybenzaldehyde → p-methoxytoluene (57), cholest-4-en-3-one → cholest-4-ene (59), and benzophenone → diphenylmethane (60).

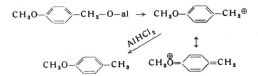

In the reduction of 1,3-dicarbonyl compounds a hydrogenolysis of carbonyl groups to the hydrocarbon is also observed frequently (62). However, the reactions in general do not proceed uniformly (63). The mixture LiAlH₄-AlCl₃ appears in other respects to be advantageous: nitriles are reduced to amines in good yields without side reactions (see above) (64). Even the often observed evolution of hydrogen, which is traced back to activated α-hydrogen atoms, is absent. Of significance appears to be the selective reduction of acid chlorides or esters in the presence of aliphatic halogen (65), reductions which do not proceed with LiAlH₄ alone.

While C=N compounds with tertiary nitrogen (semicarbazones, phenylhydrazones) are not reduced with $LiBH_4$ (66), C=N compounds with quaternary nitrogen are hydrogenated with the substantially weaker reducing agent $NaBH_4$ (67). This reaction has attained a definite importance in alkaloid research (68). Of interest also is the reduction of urethanes (69), isocyanates, and isothiocyanates (70) with lithium aluminum hydride, as it leads, in a very smooth reaction, to N-methyl-amines which often are obtained only in a laborious manner.

Comprehensive summaries of all compounds reduced with complex metal hydrides have been published by Mićović and Mihailović (71), and by Gaylord (72), as well as by Rudinger and Ferles (73).

REFERENCES

(1) A. E. Finholt, A. C. Bond, Jr., and H. I. Schlesinger, *J. Am. Chem. Soc.* **69,** 1199 (1947).

(2) H. I. Schlesinger and H. C. Brown, *J. Am. Chem. Soc.* **62,** 3429 (1940); G. Wittig and P. Hornberger, *Z. Naturforsch.* **6b,** 225 (1951).

(3) H. I. Schlesinger, H. C. Brown, B. Abraham, A. C. Bond, N. Davidson, A. E. Finholt, J. R. Gilbreath, H. Hoekstra, L. Horvitz, E. K. Hyde, J. J. Katz, J. Knight, R. A. Lad, D. L. Mayfield, L. Rapp, D. M. Ritter, A. M. Schwartz, I. Sheft, L. D. Tuck, and A. O. Walker, *J. Am. Chem. Soc.* **75,** 186 (1953); H. I. Schlesinger, H. C. Brown, H. R. Hoekstra, and L. R. Rapp, *J. Am. Chem. Soc.* **75,** 199 (1953).

(4) E. Wiberg and R. Bauer, *Z. Naturforsch.* **5b,** 397 (1950); **7b,** 131 (1952).

(5) A. E. Finholt, E. C. Jacobson, A. E. Ogard, and P. Thompson, *J. Am. Chem. Soc.* **77,** 4163 (1955).

(6) E. Wiberg and A. Jahn, *Z. Naturforsch.* **7b,** 581 (1952).

(7) J. Kollonitsch and O. Fuchs, *Nature* **176,** 1081 (1955); see also H. I. Schlesinger, R. T. Sanderson, and A. B. Burg, *J. Am. Chem. Soc.* **62,** 3421 (1940).

(8) J. Kollonitsch, O. Fuchs, and V. Gabor, *Nature* **175,** 346 (1955).

(9) J. Kollonitsch, O. Fuchs, and V. Gabor, *Nature* **173,** 125 (1954).

(10) H. C. Brown and E. J. Mead, *J. Am. Chem. Soc.* **75,** 6263 (1953).

(11) E. Wiberg has described a large number of additional hydrides in a comprehensive summary, *Angew. Chem.* **65,** 16 (1953); compare also E. Wiberg, Hydride. *In* "Ullmann's Encyklopädie der technischen Chemie," 3rd ed., Vol. 8, p. 714. Urban & Schwarzenberg, Munich, 1957). As yet nothing is known concerning their reducing power towards carbonyl compounds.

(12) L. W. Trevory and W. G. Brown, *J. Am. Chem. Soc.* **71,** 1675 (1949); G. W. Kenner and M. A. Murray, *J. Chem. Soc.* p. 406 (1950).

(13) R. F. Nystrom and W. G. Brown, *J. Am. Chem. Soc.* **69,** 1197 (1947).

(14) E. Wiberg and R. Bauer, *Z. Naturforsch.* **7b,** 131 (1952).

(15) R. F. Nystrom and W. G. Brown, *J. Am. Chem. Soc.* **69,** 2548 (1947).

(16) R. F. Nystrom and W. G. Brown, *J. Am. Chem. Soc.* **70,** 3738 (1948); A. Uffer and E. Schlittler, *Helv. Chim. Acta* **31,** 1397 (1948).

(17) J. L. Bailey, *Biochem. J.* **60,** 170 (1955).

(18) R. F. Nystrom, S. W. Chaikin, and W. G. Brown, *J. Am. Chem. Soc.* **71,** 3245 (1949).

(19) W. Grassmann, H. Hörmann, and H. Endres, *Chem. Ber.* **88,** 102 (1955).

(20) N. L. Wendler and R. P. Greber, *J. Am. Chem. Soc.* **72**, 5793 (1950); N. L. Wendler, Huang-Minlon, and M. Tischler, *ibid.* **73**, 3818 (1951).

(21) S. W. Chaikin and W. G. Brown, *J. Am. Chem. Soc.* **71**, 122 (1949).

(22) L. Pauling, "The Nature of the Chemical Bond," p. 202. Cornell Univ. Press, Ithaca, New York, 1948.

(23) R. B. Corey and J. Donohue, *J. Am. Chem. Soc.* **72**, 2899 (1950); L. Pauling, R. B. Corey, and H. R. Branson, *Proc. Natl. Acad. Sci. U.S.* **37**, 205 (1951), see this for additional literature.

(24) L. Pauling, "The Nature of the Chemical Bond," p. 138. Cornell Univ. Press, Ithaca, New York, 1948.

(25) C. K. Ingold, "Structure and Mechanism in Organic Chemistry," p. 129. Cornell Univ. Press, Ithaca, New York, 1953.

(26) L. J. Bellamy, *J. Chem. Soc.* p. 4221 (1955).

(27) K. Ziegler, *Angew. Chem.* **64**, 323, 330 (1952); K. Ziegler, H. G. Gellert, H. Martin, K. Nagel, and J. Schneider, *Ann. Chem. Liebigs* **589**, 91 (1954).

(28) F. A. Hochstein and W. G. Brown, *J. Am. Chem. Soc.* **70**, 3484 (1948); A. Dornow, G. Winter, and W. Vissering, *Chem. Ber.* **87**, 629 (1954).

(29) See also Huang-Minlon and R. H. Pettebone, *J. Am. Chem. Soc.* **74**, 1562 (1952).

(29a) L. A. Cohen and B. Witkop, *J. Am. Chem. Soc.* **77**, 6595 (1955).

(29b) C. J. Claus and J. L. Morgenthau, *J. Am. Chem. Soc.* **73**, 5005 (1951).

(30) P. Karrer and P. Portmann, *Helv. Chim. Acta* **31**, 2088 (1948).

(31) W. Grassmann, H. Hörmann, and H. Endres, *Chem. Ber.* **86**, 1477 (1953); see also reference (*17*).

(32) P. Karrer and B. J. R. Nicolaus, *Helv. Chim. Acta* **35**, 1581 (1952); M. Justisz, D. M. Meyer, and L. Penasse, *Bull. soc. chim. France* [5], **21**, 1087 (1954).

(33) P. Raymond and N. Joseph, *Bull. soc. chim. France* [5], 550 (1955).

(34) K. Heyns and K. Stange, *Z. Naturforsch.* **10b**, 252 (1955).

(35) E. B. Reid and J. R. Siegel, *J. Chem. Soc.* p. 520 (1954).

(36) J. K. Hamilton and F. Smith, *J. Am. Chem. Soc.* **76**, 3543 (1954).

(37) H. Shechter, D. E. Ley, and L. Zeldin, *J. Am. Chem. Soc.* **74**, 3664 (1952).

(38) H. C. Brown, E. J. Mead, and B. C. Subba Rao, *J. Am. Chem. Soc.* **77**, 6209 (1955).

(39) H. C. Brown and B. C. Subba Rao, *J. Am. Chem. Soc.* **77**, 3164 (1955).

(40) Z. Pravda and J. Rudinger, *Chem. listy* **48**, 1663 (1954); *Collection Czechoslov. Chem. Communs.* **20**, 1 (1955).

(41) G. Wittig and P. Hornberger, *Ann. Chem. Liebigs* **577**, 18 (1952).

(42) M. L. Wolfrom and H. B. Woody, *J. Am. Chem. Soc.* **73**, 2933 (1951); M. L. Wolfrom and K. Anno, *ibid.* **74**, 5583 (1952); H. L. Frush and H. S. Isbell, *ibid.* **78**, 2844 (1956). Concerning the mechanism of the reduction of carbohydrates by lithium aluminum hydride see H. Endres and M. Oppelt, *Chem. Ber.* **91**, 478 (1958).

(43) F. Weygand, G. Eberhardt, H. Linden, F. Schäfer, and J. Eigen, *Angew. Chem.* **65**, 525 (1933).

(44) N. G. Gaylord, *Experientia* **10**, 423 (1954).

(45) F. Gallinowsky .and R. Weiser, *Experientia* **6**, 377 (1951); F. Gallinowsky, A. Wagner, and R. Weiser, *Monatsh. Chem.* **82**, 551 (1951).

(46) F. Weygand and D. Tietjen, *Chem. Ber.* **84**, 625 (1951).

(47) M. Schmidt and A. Nordwig, *Chem. Ber.* **91**, 506 (1958).

(48) L. M. Soffer and M. Katz, *J. Am. Chem. Soc.* **78**, 1705 (1956); see also A. L. Henne, R. L. Pelley, and R. L. Alm, *ibid.* **72**, 3370 (1950).

(49) G. Hesse and R. Schrödel, *Ann. Chem. Liebigs* **607**, 24 (1957); *Angew. Chem.* **69**, 743 (1957).

(50) H. C. Brown and R. F. MacFarlin, *J. Am. Chem. Soc.* **78**, 252 (1956); H. C. Brown and B. C. Subba Rao, *ibid.* **80**, 5377 (1958).

(51) H. C. Brown and R. F. MacFarlin, *J. Am. Chem. Soc.* **80**, 5372 (1958).

(52) H. C. Brown and A. Tsukamoto, *J. Am. Chem. Soc.* **81**, 502 (1959).

(53) G. Drefahl and E. Keil, *J. prakt. Chem.* [4], **6**, 80 (1958); *Chem. Abstr.* **53**, 2147 (1959).

(54) G. Hesse and H. Jäger, *Chem. Ber.* **92**, 2022 (1959); G. Hesse, *Angew. Chem.* **71**, 525 (1959).

(55) H. G. Kuivila and O. F. Beumel, Jr., *J. Am. Chem. Soc.* **80**, 3798 (1958).

(56) E. Wiberg and M. Schmidt, *Z. Naturforsch.* **12b**, 54 (1957).

(57) B. R. Brown and A. M. S. White, *J. Chem. Soc.* p. 3755 (1957).

(58) L. H. Conover and D. S. Tarbell, *J. Am. Chem. Soc.* **72**, 3586 (1950); N. G. Gaylord, *Experientia* **10**, 166 (1954); A. Treibs and H. Derra-Scherer, *Ann. Chem. Liebigs* **589**, 188 (1954).

(59) J. Broome and B. R. Brown, *Chem. & Ind.* (*London*) p. 1307 (1956).

(60) R. F. Nystrom and C. R. A. Berger, *J. Am. Chem. Soc.* **80**, 2896 (1958).

(61) E. Wiberg and M. Schmidt, *Z. Naturforsch.* **6b**, 460 (1951).

(62) H. Jäger and W. Färber, *Chem. Ber.* **92**, 2492 (1959).

(63) A. S. Dreiding and J. A. Hartmann, *J. Am. Chem. Soc.* **75**, 939, 3723 (1953); A. Dornow and K. J. Fust, *Chem. Ber.* **87**, 985 (1954); V. M. Mićović and M. L. Mihailović, *Bull. soc. chim. Belgrade* **19**, 329 (1954).

(64) R. F. Nystrom, *J. Am. Chem. Soc.* **77**, 2544 (1955).

(65) R. F. Nystrom, *J. Am. Chem. Soc.* **81**, 610 (1959).

(66) Compare in contrast the reduction of N-benzylidene-aniline with $NaBH_4$; J. H. Billmann and A. C. Diesing, *J. Org. Chem.* **22**, 1068 (1957).

(67) B. Witkop and J. B. Patrick, *J. Am. Chem. Soc.* **75**, 4474 (1953).

(68) J. J. Panouse, *Compt. rend. acad. sci.* **233**, 260 (1951); B. Witkop, *J. Am. Chem. Soc.* **75**, 3361 (1953); A. P. Gray, E. E. Spinner, and C. J. Cavallito, *ibid.* **76**, 2792 (1954).

(69) J. Knabe, *Arch. Pharm.* **288**, 469 (1955); R. L. Dannley, M. Lukin, and J. Shapiro, *J. Org. Chem.* **20**, 92 (1955).

(70) W. Ried and F. Müller, *Chem. Ber.* **85**, 470 (1952); A. E. Finholt, C. D. Anderson, and C. L. Agre, *J. Org. Chem.* **18**, 1338 (1953).

(71) V. M. Mićović and M. L. Mihailović, "Lithium Aluminum Hydride in Organic Chemistry." Izdavaćko Preduzeće, Belgrade, 1955.

(72) N. G. Gaylord, "Reduction with Complex Hydrides." Interscience, New York, 1956.

(73) J. Rudinger and M. Ferles, "Hydride Lithno-Hlinity a přibuznà čindia v organické chemii." Ceskoslovenská Akademie ved, Prague, 1956 (in Czechoslovakian).

Alkylation of Aromatic Amines

R. STROH,* J. EBERSBERGER, H. HABERLAND, AND W. HAHN

Farbenfabriken Bayer A. G., Leverkusen

Ring Alkylation of Aromatic Amines

Essential Reaction and Catalyst

Aluminum in the form of dust (bronze), powder, or shavings, dissolves in aniline (1) on warming with the evolution of hydrogen and the formation of aluminum anilide. Ethylene is taken up rapidly when forced into a solution of aluminum anilide in excess aniline and the temperature is increased to 330°. The reaction comes to a standstill after 2 moles of ethylene are consumed per mole of aniline. The distillative work-up gives as a main product a primary amine boiling at 240°/760 mm. According to analytical results the compound is a diethylaniline. The determination of the structure (see below) showed that the compound was 2,6-diethylaniline.

This fundamental reaction was the starting point for further work in which the reaction of alkenes with aromatic amines, phenols, and hydrocarbons was investigated on a broader scale. The alkylation of aromatic amines with alkenes is reported below.

The effective catalyst in the ethylation of aniline is the aluminum anilide. To obtain quick solution of the aluminum, the latter can be activated with some mercuric chloride. On distilling off the aniline containing the dissolved aluminum trianilide, the latter is obtained as a gray-green, compact substance which, when powdered, sometimes bursts into flame on contact with air and reacts vigorously with water or alcohols with decomposition.

Isolation of the aluminum anilide for the alkylation reaction is never required. In general 1–3% aluminum, based on the weight of the amine, is used.

A 300 gm portion of aniline, 6 gm of aluminum in the form of

---

* The present description of ring alkylation of aromatic amines using aluminum as a catalyst was first communicated by one of us (St.) on April 26, 1956 on the occasion of the chemical meeting in Salzburg [*Angew. Chem.* **68**, 387 (1956)]. In the June issue of the *Journal of Organic Chemistry* [**21**, 711 (1956)] there appeared a communication from the research laboratory of the Ethyl Corporation stating that the same reaction had been discovered independently. The method is the subject of several patent applications of the Farbenfabriken Bayer A. G., Leverkusen.

granules, powder, or shavings, and 0.1–0.2 gm of mercuric chloride are heated to 330–340° in a high-pressure autoclave. The aluminum anilide formation takes place with hydrogen evolution during the heating period. The resulting hydrogen can remain in the autoclave so that when the reaction temperature is reached ethylene can be introduced immediately under a pressure of 200 atm. The reaction goes immediately with a decrease in pressure. From time to time ethylene is introduced under pressure. The reaction is completed as soon as two moles of ethylene per mole of aniline are used up. Usually this is the case after 2–2½ hr.

The reaction mixture is decomposed with sodium hydroxide solution, the aqueous layer is separated, and the nonaqueous is distilled. The main fraction, 2,6-diethylaniline, boils at 110°/10 mm and is obtained in a yield of 85–88%. As by-products there are small amounts of hydrocarbons as well as lower and higher boiling amines.

Proof that the unexpected bis *ortho* substitution takes place was furnished in the following manner:

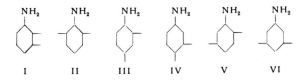

Of the six possible isomers the 2,4- and 2,5-diethylaniline (III and V) are described in the literature (2) and are not identical with the product found. Deamination by boiling the diazonium compound with formaldehyde or stannous chloride leads to a diethylbenzene, which gave isophthalic acid on oxidation with permanganate, identified in the form of the dimethyl ester. Thus 2,3- and 3,4-diethylanilines (I and IV) are eliminated. Only the isomers, 2,6- and 3,5-diethylaniline (II and VI) remain for consideration. The instability of the diazonium compound as well as the fact that the acetyl compound is hydrolyzed only with difficulty by boiling with concentrated hydrochloric acid or sodium hydroxide supported formula II. Finally definite evidence for the 2,6-positions of the ethyl groups was the identification of the known 2,6-diethylphenol (m.p. 38°) obtained from the diazonium compound. The phenol is also formed by the ethylation of phenol in the presence of aluminum phenolate (3). On oxidation with chromic acid the known 3,3′,5,5′-tetraethyldiphenoquinone (4) is obtained.

The lower boiling base (213°/760 mm), obtained in small yield in the ethylation of aniline, was identified as being o-ethylaniline, which was identical with the base obtained by v. Braun and co-workers (5) in the reductive cleavage of indole.

From the higher boiling fraction an oil (b.p. 126–127°/10 mm) was separated whose analysis indicated a "triethylaniline." The substance takes up 1 mole of bromine on titration with alkaline bromine solution and is not identical with the 2,4,6-triethylaniline described in the literature (6).

The oxidation of the hydrocarbon obtained by deamination gave isophthalic acid. The ultraviolet spectrum of the amine as well as of the hydrocarbon points to two *meta* alkyl groups. No tertiary butyl group could be found. These results and the fact that the same product is obtained by the butylation of *o*-ethylaniline with butylene (see below) support the presence of 6-*sec*-butyl-2-ethylaniline. In this instance, contrary to all expectation, an *ortho* ethyl group is further ethylated; the *para* position in the aniline molecule remains open.

VII

Since *o*-ethylaniline is observed in the ethylation of aniline, one can assume that significant amounts of *o*-ethylaniline can be obtained by interrupting the reaction after 1 mole of ethylene has reacted. However, this is not the case. On the contrary, an investigation of the reaction kinetics shows that both steps occur with the same rate so that the calculated amounts of mono- and diethylaniline are always obtained for this reaction (see Fig. 1).

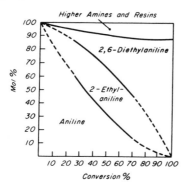

FIG. 1. Composition of an ethylation mixture as a function of conversion.

As can be seen from Fig. 1, higher alkylated amines and resins are obtained up to 15%. By further development of the catalyst it is possible to lower the reaction temperature and shorten the reaction time, in which case the formation of by-products is suppressed extensively at the same time. It became evident that the addition of aluminum chloride and other Friedel-Crafts catalysts such as stannic chloride, titanium tetrachloride, silicon tetrachloride, boron trifluoride, or zinc chloride to aluminum anilide definitely activates the reaction. The favorable influence of these additions is surprising since aniline forms very stable complexes with Friedel-Crafts catalysts, which generally are not considered to have catalytic action (7).

While aromatic hydrocarbons and phenols are known to alkylate readily with Friedel-Crafts catalysts and alkenes, the opinion exists that only tertiary or N-acylated primary and secondary anilines are open to alkyl substitution. In these instances substitution takes place *para* to the amino group (8).

The ethylation of aniline with $AlCl_3$ alone gives with low conversions a poor yield of 2-ethylaniline. Mainly residues of a resinous character and hydrocarbons are formed. This changes immediately on using aluminum anilide and aluminum chloride as catalyst. An optimum conversion and yield is obtained using the molar ratio of aluminum to aluminum chloride as 2:1. In this way 2,6-diethylaniline in yields of 96% is easily attained.

Moreover, it is surprising that ring alkylation is also possible with alkali metals and aluminum chloride, while alkali metals alone—as described on page 246 —lead only to alkylation on the nitrogen. Also, the addition of iodine and iodine compounds such as nickel iodide, phosphorus triiodide, and others, activate ring alkylation with aluminum anilide as catalyst.

PREPARATION OF 2,6-DIETHYLANILINE (ACTIVATION WITH ALUMINUM CHLORIDE)

18 gm of aluminum chloride is dissolved in 300 gm of aniline and the solution, together with 6 gm of aluminum, is placed in a high-pressure autoclave. The formation of aluminum anilide usually proceeds during the warm-up period, but can also be activated by the addition of small amounts of mercuric chloride. As soon as the temperature reaches 300°, ethylene is introduced to a pressure of 200 atm. As the ethylene is consumed, more ethylene is forced into the reaction mixture. The reaction is finished in about 40–50 min. The consumption of ethylene amounts to 2 moles of ethylene per mole of aniline.

PREPARATION OF o-ETHYLANILINE

2-Ethylaniline can be prepared by interrupting the ethylation prematurely. By the use of 1.2 moles of ethylene, for example, there is obtained an amine mixture which consists of 23.3% of aniline, 37.5%

of 2-ethylaniline, and 37.0% of 2,6-diethylaniline and which can be easily separated by fractional distillation. Based upon recovered aniline the yields are 48.8% 2-ethylaniline and 48.3% 2,6-diethylaniline.

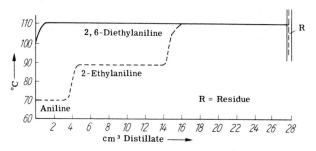

FIG. 2. Distillation curves for 2-ethyl- and 2,6-diethylaniline. Boiling points at 10 mm.

The composition of the reaction mixture is illustrated by the distillation curves in Fig. 2.

Ethylation of Primary Aromatic Amines

The extension of the alkylation process to toluidine, xylidine, and others, confirmed the observations with aniline.

In the ethylation of o-toluidine only 1 mole of ethylene is taken up to form 6-ethyl-2-methylaniline. With p-toluidine 2 moles of ethylene are taken up, and 2,6-diethyl-4-methylaniline is formed in excellent yield. The m-toluidine gives 2,6-diethyl-3-methylaniline. The substitution of xylidines also occurs in an analogous manner. Thus, 2,6-diethyl-3,5-dimethylaniline is prepared from sym-m-xylidine; with asym-m-xylidine, since one ortho position is already taken, only one ethyl group can be introduced to form 2,4-dimethyl-6-ethylaniline.

The only example up to now in which para substitution was observed was that of vic-m-xylidine. The absorption of ethylene corresponds to the introduction of one ethyl group.

The following structures could be formed:

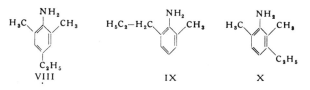

One of the first indications for the existence of VIII was furnished by bromine titration, which established that no free para position was present. Thereupon the amine, after careful diazotization, was deami-

TABLE 1

RING ALKYLATED PRIMARY MONOAMINES

Starting amine	Ethylated product	Yield %	B.p. °C/mm	Derivatives[a] solidifying point, °C
Aniline	2,6-Diethylaniline	96	111/10	Ac 137–138 Bz 232–233
Aniline	2-Ethylaniline	49	89/10	Bz 153–154
Aniline	6-sec-Butyl-2-ethylaniline	—	126–127/10	Bz 198–200
o-Toluidine	6-Ethyl-2-methylaniline	87	101/10	Ac 126–127 Bz 196–198
o-Toluidine	2-Ethyl-6-n-propylaniline	—	121/10	Bz 187–188
o-Toluidine	6-sec-Butyl-2-methylaniline	—	118–121/10	Bz 200–201
m-Toluidine	2,6-Diethyl-3-methylaniline	93	125/10	Ac 153–154 Bz 208–210
p-Toluidine	2,6-Diethyl-4-methylaniline	95	121/10	Ac 165 Bz 215–217
p-Toluidine	2-Ethyl-4-methylaniline	—	106/10	Ac 131–132 Bz 175–176
p-Toluidine	6-sec-Butyl-2-ethyl-4-methylaniline	—	132–136/10	Bz 197–198
vic-m-Xylidine	2,6-Dimethyl-4-ethylaniline	80	95/5	Ac 150–151
asym-m-Xylidine	2,4-Dimethyl-6-ethylaniline	85	102–104/3.5	Ac 156
sym-m-Xylidine	2,6-Diethyl-3,5-dimethylaniline	79	102–103/0.65 M.p. 46.4	Ac 205–206
o-Propylaniline	2-Ethyl-6-propylaniline	75	124/10	Bz 190
o-Chloroaniline	2-Chloro-6-ethylaniline	85	108–110/10	Ac 115–116
m-Chloroaniline	3-Chloro-2,6-diethylaniline	94	137–139/10	Ac 154–155
m-Chloroaniline	3-Chloro-2-ethylaniline	—	114–116/10	Ac 165–166
m-Chloroaniline	5-Chloro-2-ethylaniline	—	121–124/10	Ac 141–142
α-Naphthylamine	1-Amino-2-ethylnaphthalene	90	157–158/5	Ac 160.5–161 Bz 200.5–201
β-Naphthylamine	2-Amino-1-ethylnaphthalene	—	M.p. 24–26 157/5	Ac 188.7–189.5 Bz 182–184.5
3-Benzylaniline	3-Benzyl-2,6-diethylaniline	85	M.p. 44.5–46 189–190/5	Ac 139–140 Bz 133–135
4-Benzylaniline	4-Benzyl-2,6-diethylaniline	85	186–187/5	Ac 136–138 Bz 196.5–198

nated with alkaline stannous chloride solution and the resulting hydrocarbon oxidized. The permanganate oxidation unequivocally furnished
trimesinic acid which was identified as the methyl ester. Thus it was
shown that the ethyl group entered *vic-m*-xylidine *para* to the amino
group.

Different experiments showed that 6-ethyl-2-methylaniline may be
ethylated further. Under various conditions 2 moles of ethylene were
absorbed by 1 mole of *o*-toluidine. A bromine titration showed that the
para position was not occupied. The work-up showed rather that not
only 2-ethyl-6-*n*-propylaniline but also 6-*sec*-butyl-2-methylaniline was
formed.

Of the chloroanilines the *o*-chloroaniline is converted to the 2-chloro-
6-ethylaniline and the *m*-chloroaniline to 3-chloro-2,6-diethylaniline.
Benzylaniline and naphthylamine may be ethylated also.

Ethlylation of Diamines

The alkylation of aromatic *m*-diamines is also possible. In order to
obtain good conversions the preformed aluminum anilide is added to the
diamine. The reaction goes most favorably with about 1.5–2% aluminum in the form of aluminum anilide. The amount of excess aniline has
no decided influence upon the course of the reaction. The greater portion
is recovered unreacted during the work-up of the mixture. *m*-Phenylene-
diamine in the presence of aluminum anilide takes up ethylene briskly
at 280°. The ethylated mixture gives three fractions using a spinning
band column. The analysis of the first fraction indicates a monoethylated
phenylenediamine; the second fraction is also mainly a monoethyl
derivative with a small amount of a diethyl product; the third fraction
conforms to the theoretical value for a diethylated *m*-phenylenediamine.

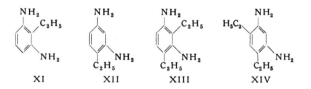

| XI | XII | XIII | XIV |

The lowest boiling compound is 1,3-diamino-2-ethylbenzene (XI),
fraction 2 is 1,3-diamino-4-ethylbenzene (XII) (*9*), fraction 3 is 1,3-
diamino-4,6-diethylbenzene (XIV). The proportionate yields, after distillation of the monoamine, are: 40% of the reaction product is fraction
1, 33% is fraction 2, and 20% is fraction 3. Of course these results may
be varied by the length of the reaction time.

In the presence of aluminum anilide as catalyst the ethylation of toluene-2,4-diamine goes still easier and more uniform to form 1,3-diamino-2,6-diethyl-4-methylbenzene in about 90% yield.

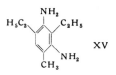

XV

The ethylation of toluene-2,6-diamine proceeds in a completely analogous manner and also with excellent yield. There is obtained 1,3-diamino-4,6-diethyl-2-methylbenzene (XVI). As was to be expected 1,3-diamino-4,6-dimethylbenzene picks up only 1 mole of ethylene, the ethyl group entering between the two amino groups. 1,3-Diamino-4,6-dimethyl-2-ethylbenzene (XVII) is formed.

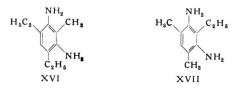

XVI   XVII

The ring alkylation of phenylenediamines may also be activated by the addition of aluminum chloride. The reaction velocity is increased almost 50% with 2–4% aluminum chloride, based on the diamine, and a content of 2% aluminum in the form of aluminum anilide. For example, 1,3-diamino-2,6-diethyl-4-methylbenzene is obtained with this catalyst from toluene-2,4-diamine in 95% yield. At 280° under these conditions the aniline in the mixture is also ethylated. It reacts, however, substantially slower than the diamine and is converted to the 2-ethylaniline. 2,6-Diethylaniline is present only in traces.

PREPARATION OF 1,3-DIAMINO-2,6-DIETHYL-4-METHYLBENZENE

A 200 gm portion of toluene-2,4-diamine with 8 gm of anhydrous aluminum chloride and 150 gm of a solution of aluminum anilide in aniline (content: 3 gm aluminum) are heated in a stirred autoclave at 280°, and 200 atm of ethylene is introduced. The reaction begins to take up ethylene immediately. If the pressure falls to 100–150 atm it is brought again to 200 atm with ethylene. After about 100 gm of ethylene has been taken up during the course of 2–2½ hr, the reaction becomes significantly slower. The reaction mixture is allowed to cool, the autoclave is vented, and the crude product is shaken with dilute sodium hydroxide solution to remove the catalyst. By fractional distillation of the amine mixture there is recovered about 70% of the unchanged aniline; the remainder is converted to 2-ethylaniline. Except for a

TABLE 2
ETHYLATED DIAMINES

Starting amine	Alkylated product	Yield %	B.p. °C/mm	Derivatives[a] m.p. °C
m-Phenylenediamine	1,3-Diamino-2-ethylbenzene	To 40	140/5 151/10	DiAc 333–335
m-Phenylenediamine	1,3-Diamino-4-ethylbenzene	To 30	145/5 159/10	DiAc 229–230
m-Phenylenediamine	1,3-Diamino-2,4-diethylbenzene	To 20	160/10	DiAc 305–307
m-Phenylenediamine	1,3-Diamino-4,6-diethylbenzene	To 20	150/5 167/10	DiAc 272–274
m-Phenylenediamine	1,3-Diamino-2,4,6-triethylbenzene	90	157/5 169/10	DiAc 318–320
Toluene-2,4-diamine	1,3-Diamino-2,6-diethyl-4-methylbenzene	95	150/5 164/10	DiAc 311–312
Toluene-2,6-diamine	1,3-Diamino-4,6-diethyl-2-methylbenzene	96	154/5 M.p. 75–77	DiAc 324–326
1,3-Diamino-4,6-dimethylbenzene	1,3-Diamino-4,6-dimethyl-2-ethylbenzene	85	154/7	DiAc 325–327
Benzidine	3,3',5,5'-Tetraethylbenzidine	~80	~250/7	DiAc 346–348 2 HCl 229–231
1,5-Diaminonaphthalene	1,5-Diamino-2,6-diethylnaphthalene	80	M.p. 137–138	DiAc 365–368 (dec)

[a] DiAc = Diacetyl compound; 2HCl = Dihydrochloride.

small forerun the diamine portion distills constantly at 164°/10 mm. 1,3-Diamino-2,6-diethyl-4-methylbenzene is obtained in 95% yield. The product is a light yellow, viscous liquid, furnishing a diacetyl derivative (m.p. 310–312°).

The ethylation of toluene-2,6-diamine goes even more quickly in the presence of aluminum anilide and aluminum chloride. It goes quantitatively to 1,3-diamino-4,6-diethyl-2-methylbenzene. In this case the ethylation of aniline is not hindered so strongly, so that it is converted to 2,6-diethylaniline during a sufficiently long period of reaction.

The activation of aluminum anilide with aluminum chloride allows the introduction of a third ethyl group into m-phenylenediamine resulting in the formation of 1,3-diamino-2,4,6-triethylbenzene. Also, 1,3-diamino-2,4-diethylbenzene (XIII) can be isolated following this procedure.

In the naphthalene series the ethylation of 1,5-diaminonaphthalene in the presence of aluminum anilide as catalyst leads to 1,5-diamino-2,6-diethylnaphthalene.

The proportions in the alkylation of benzidine are similar to those used with the described diamines. Amide formation obviously does not occur or occurs only in small amounts on heating benzidine with aluminum, so that under normal conditions an uptake of ethylene (300–340°) does not take place. If preformed aluminum anilide is used, ethylene is taken up, at first slowly, later more quickly. Along with 2-ethyl- and 2,6-diethylaniline a substance is isolated via the acetyl derivatives which crystallizes from dimethylformamide in colorless leaflets. The analysis indicates a diacetyl derivative of a tetraethylbenzidine. The base itself is a highly viscous oil and forms a difficultly soluble dihydrochloride. Analogous to the previously observed regularity of substitution and judging from the behavior of the tetraethylbenzidine the assumption is made that the ethyl groups are in positions *ortho* to the amino groups. The ethylation of benzidine may be accelerated with concomitant lowering of the reaction temperature to 280° by the addition of aluminum chloride.

ETHYLATION OF BENZIDINE (TETRAETHYLBENZIDINE)

A mixture of 200 gm of benzidine, 9 gm of anhydrous aluminum chloride and 150 gm of a solution of aluminum anilide (3 gm aluminum) in aniline is heated in a stirred autoclave at 280–300° with ethylene at 200 atm. After overcoming a somewhat sluggish initial step, the reaction proceeds comparatively quickly and is finished in 3–3½ hr. The ethylene uptake amounts to 180–200 gm. The mixture is worked up by extracting with dilute sodium hydroxide solution and the monoamine fractionally distilled. There is obtained 20% of 2-ethylaniline and 80% of 2,6-diethylaniline based on the aniline used. The benzidine portion is a very viscous mass, which may be distilled at about 250°/7 mm with slight decomposition. The crude product contains about 80% tetraethylbenzidine and also some less ethylated benzidines. The tetraethylbenzidine may be obtained pure in the form of a diacetyl compound (m.p. 346–348°) or as the dihydrochloride (m.p. 229–231°).

Ring Alkylation of Secondary Amines

Aluminum also reacts with diphenylamine to form an amide; but substantially longer reaction times are needed than with aniline. The uptake of ethylene then proceeds very rapidly to form diethyldiphenylamine, an *ortho* disubstituted product. The same substance is obtained when the reaction is carried out in the presence of an aluminum anilide solution.

PREPARATION OF 2,2′-DIETHYLDIPHENYLAMINE

In a high-pressure autoclave ethylene is allowed to react with 200 gm of diphenylamine and 150 ml of a solution of aluminum anilide in aniline (containing 3 gm of aluminum) at 310–320°. In 3 hr about 150 gm of ethylene is used up. The reaction comes to a standstill. The absorption corresponds to a conversion of 2 moles of ethylene per mole of amine (aniline + diphenylamine). The amine mixture, after removal of the catalyst with sodium hydroxide solution, is fractionally distilled in vacuum. It is composed almost entirely of 2,6-diethylaniline and a diethylated diphenylamine; b.p. 173°/10 mm; yield: 95%.

The ethylation in the position *ortho* to the nitrogen was determined as follows: since the acetyl and benzoyl derivatives of the amine were obtained as oils, the crystalline nitrosoamine was prepared, which was readily formed from the hydrochloride in alcohol and aqueous nitrite solution. Since *ortho* substitution was to be considered, the following structures were up for discussion:

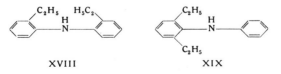

XVIII   XIX

The structure determination was conducted *via* the *p*-nitroso compound which was obtained by the rearrangement of the N-nitrosoamine. On alkaline hydrolysis of this *p*-nitroso compound there must be obtained as cleavage products *o*-ethylaniline (in the case of XVIII) or aniline and 2,6-diethylaniline (if XIX) along with the corresponding nitrosophenols. Only *o*-ethylaniline was found on cleavage. The hydro-lytic cleavage product, ethyl-*p*-nitrosophenol could not be isolated in the pure form. Furthermore infrared spectrum of the amine contained curves which indicated only a substituent *ortho* to nitrogen. With this the structure was established as being 2,2′-diethyldiphenylamine (XVIII).

If the ethylation is carried out with only 1 mole of ethylene per mole of diphenylamine, a monoethyldiphenylamine may be isolated. It is surprising that even when ethylation is prematurely interrupted, practi-cally all of the aniline which was added is converted to diethylaniline. Here the proportions are the reverse of those found in the aniline/*m*-phenylenediamine/aluminum anilide system. In the latter the diamine is the first to be ethylated and then the aniline.

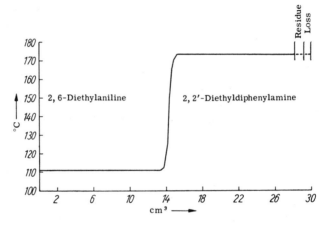

Fɪɢ. 3. Distillation curve of an ethylation of diphenylamine. Boiling points at 10 mm.

The addition of aluminum chloride also considerably activates the ethylation of diphenylamine. The reaction takes place at 280° with such velocity that the heating must be stopped at 250° because of the excessive rise in temperature. The course of reaction in a 2 liter autoclave clearly goes in two reaction steps: after the slow step (ethylation of aniline) is overcome, the rapid ethylation of diphenylamine begins. After the uptake of 2 moles of ethylene for each mole of amine the reaction comes to a standstill. The yield of 2,6-diethylaniline and of 2,2′-diethyldi-phenylamine is almost quantitative.

When aluminum anilide is not used, amide formation can be then accelerated when aluminum or sodium are used together with aluminum chloride as catalyst. In this case amide formation even begins during the warming-up period and as rapidly as with aniline. The ethylation of this solution goes so rapidly that the formation of diethyldiphenylamine is finished at 250° in 8–10 min, at 200° in 30–40 min, or at 180° in 1 hr.

PREPARATION OF 2,2′-DIETHYLDIPHENYLAMINE WITH ALUMINUM CHLORIDE AND SODIUM

A mixture of 300 gm of diphenylamine, 18 gm of aluminum chloride, and 6 gm of sodium is heated at 200° in a high pressure autoclave. The ethylene added at 50 atm is taken up very quickly and supplemented at the rate of its consumption. After 30–40 min the reaction becomes significantly slower. The work-up gives 2,2′-diethyldiphenylamine as the only product in 95% yield.

The alkylation of α- and β-phenylaminoaphthalene goes in an analogous manner.

The ring ethylation of secondary alkylanilines such as N-methyl- or N-ethylaniline is also possible. As is known from the literature, in these cases a migration of the N-alkyl group into the ring takes place readily (10). Aluminum or aluminum anilide does not bring about a rearrangement of N-alkylanilines. In contrast, N-ethylaniline can be completely rearranged at 250° with aluminum chloride. This rearrangement is checked or hindered by the addition of aluminum or aluminum anilide.

Good yields and complete conversion of ring ethylated N-ethylaniline are obtained, for example, by the use of aluminum, aluminum chloride, and aniline. The optimum temperature of the reaction is 250°. N,2-Diethylaniline is obtained from N-ethylaniline as the only reaction product. Thus only 1 mole of ethylene enters the ring of the secondary amine. In addition 2,6-diethylaniline is formed from the aniline which was added. The most favorable molar ratio for the catalyst is aluminum: aluminum chloride: aniline = 2:1:6.

PREPARATION OF N,2-DIETHYLANILINE

A 200 gm portion of N-ethylaniline, 42 gm of aniline, 4 gm of aluminum granules, and 10 gm of aluminum chloride are ethylated at 240–250° with ethylene at 200 atm pressure. For each mole of aniline 1–1.1 mole of ethylene is consumed in 1 hr. The work-up furnishes N,2-diethylaniline in 85% yield, based on N-ethylaniline, in addition to the 2,6-diethylaniline which is formed from the aniline.

The identification of N,2-diethylaniline is substantiated by the urea prepared with α-naphthyl isocyanate in cyclohexane.

The same compound could be prepared from a secondary diethylaniline which had been prepared from 2-ethylaniline and ethyl bromide or from 2-ethylaniline and ethylene in the presence of sodium.

TABLE 3
ALKYLATED SECONDARY AMINES

Starting amine	Alkylated product	Yield %	B.p. °C/mm	Derivatives[a] m.p. °C
Diphenylamine	2-Ethyldiphenylamine	25	149/5	—
Diphenylamine	2,2'-Diethyldiphenylamine	95	159/5 173/10	Nitrosoamine 65
Diphenylamine	2-Isopropyldiphenylamine	57	152/5	—
Diphenylamine	2,2'-Diisopropyldiphenylamine	20	162/5	Nitrosoamine 101–103
Diphenylamine	2-sec-Butyldiphenylamine	85	176–177/10	—
Diphenylamine	2,2'-Di-sec-butyldiphenylamine	75	194–195/10	—
N-Methylaniline	2-Ethyl-N-methylaniline	85	96–97/10	H. 88–92
N-Ethylaniline	N,2-Diethylaniline	85	101–102/10	H. 101–102

[a] H. = Urea deriv. with α-naphthyl isocyanate.

Propylation and Butylation of Aromatic Amines

If the alkylation of aromatic amines is carried out with propylene or butylene in the presence of aluminum or the aluminum compound of the amine, then o-alkyl substituted products are also formed. However, the activity decreases from ethylene to propylene, to butylene. The alkylation goes with good yields if a mixture of aluminum or aluminum anilide and aluminum chloride is used as catalyst. The most favorable reaction temperature is 300° or less. The procedure is carried out in such a manner that the liquid alkene is pumped into the preheated mixture of amine and catalyst.

Propylene always enters the aromatic ring as an isopropyl group.

PREPARATION OF 2,6-DIISOPROPYLANILINE AND 2-ISOPROPYLANILINE

A mixture of 300 gm of aniline, 18 gm of aluminum chloride and 6 gm of aluminum (granules or powder) is heated to 290° in a high-pressure autoclave. With the use of a liquid pump propylene is forced in up to a pressure of 250 atm. A reaction takes place which is made evident by the drop in pressure. From time to time propylene is added under pressure. After about 8 hr the pressure drop becomes noticeably slower. The experiment is stopped and the product worked up by extraction with dilute sodium hydroxide solution. Distillation gives 78% of 2,6-diisopropylaniline besides 15% of 2-isopropylaniline and small amounts of higher boiling constituents (2,4,6-triisopropylaniline). If the reaction is interrupted prematurely, the yield of 2-isopropylaniline can be increased.

2-Isopropylaniline gives an acetyl compound [m.p. 73–75° (11)]

TABLE 4

RING PROPYLATED AND BUTYLATED AMINES

Starting amine	Alkylated product	Yield %	B.p. °C/10 mm	Derivatives[b] m.p. °C
Aniline	2-Isopropylaniline	15[a]	95–96	Ac 73–75 Bz 148–148.5
Aniline	2,6-Diisopropylaniline	78	120–122	Ac 184.5–187 Bz 254–256
Aniline	2,4,6-Triisopropylaniline	—	139–141	Ac 176–178
Aniline	2-sec-Butylaniline	50	106–108	Bz 124–125.5
Aniline	2,6-Di-sec-Butylaniline	25	140–141	Bz 224.5–226
Aniline	2-tert-Butylaniline	63	105–106	Ac 160–161 Bz 192–194
Aniline	4-tert-Butylaniline	85	110	Ac 170–172 Bz 143.5–145
o-Toluidine	6-Isopropyl-2-methylaniline	75	108–110	Bz 240–241
o-Toluidine	6-sec-Butyl-2-methylaniline	54	118–121	Bz 200–201
o-Toluidine	4-tert-Butyl-2-methylaniline	85	120	Ac 164–166 Bz 172–173
p-Toluidine	2-Isopropyl-4-methylaniline	32	108–112	Bz 130–131
p-Toluidine	2,6-Diisopropyl-4-methylaniline	42	132–134	Bz 233–235
2-Ethylaniline	2-Ethyl-6-isopropylaniline	85	118–120	Bz 246–247
2-Ethylaniline	2-sec-Butyl-2-ethylaniline	53	126–129	Bz 198–200
2-Ethyl-4-methylaniline	6-sec-Butyl-2-ethyl-4-methylaniline	51	132–136	Bz 197–198

[a] The yield is somewhat larger when smaller amounts are used.
[b] Ac = Acetyl compound; Bz = Benzoyl compound.

TABLE 5

ALKYLATED HETEROCYCLES

Starting compound	Alkylated product	Yield %	B.p. °C/mm	M.p. °C	Derivatives[a] m.p. °C
Carbazole	1-Ethylcarbazole	90	—	76–78	P. 161–163
Carbazole	1-Isopropylcarbazole	40	—	62–63	P. 151–152
2-Methylindole	7-Ethyl-2-methylindole	92	145/10	33	P. 143–145
2,3-Dimethylindole	2,3-Dimethyl-7-ethylindole	87	155/10	—	P. 130–131
2,3,5-Trimethylindole	7-Ethyl-2,3,5-trimethylindole	63	162/10	112–114	P. 168–169
2-Phenylindole	7-Ethyl-2-phenylindole	82	202/5	58.5–60	P. 136–137
			218/10		
Phenothiazine	1-Ethylphenothiazine	86	—	124–126	Ac 108–109
1,2,3,4-Tetrahydroquinoline	8-Ethyl-1,2,3,4-tetrahydroquinoline	95	132–10	—	Bz 97–99

[a] P. = Picrate; Ac = Acetyl compound; Bz = Benzoyl compound.

with acetic anhydride and a benzoyl derivative (m.p. 148–148.5°) with benzoyl chloride. For structure determination the amine can be converted via the diazonium compound to the corresponding phenol, whose phenylurethane melts at 106–107° and gives no melting point depression with the product obtained in another manner.

The acetyl derivative of 2,6-diisopropylaniline melts at 184.5–187°, the benzoyl derivative at 254–256°.

The last melting point does not agree with that given in the literature (12). Therefore, for purposes of structure clarification, the amine was diazotized and converted to the phenol. The phenylurethane of this phenol (m.p. 150–151°) is identical with a comparative product prepared in another way. Likewise, the diphenoquinone (m.p. 198–199°) obtained from the phenol by chromic acid oxidation gave no melting point depression with 3,3′,5,5′-tetraisopropyldiphenoquinone, whose structure was verified.

The acetyl derivative of 2,4,6-triisopropylaniline melts at 176–178°. Similar results are obtained with butylene which enters the *ortho* position of the aromatic amine as a *sec*-butyl group.

The alkylation of aromatic amines with isobutylene occurs with greater difficulty. This reaction proceeds with aluminum or aluminum anilide but very slowly and incompletely. On addition of aluminum chloride or other Friedel-Crafts catalysts the reaction is accelerated. The reaction succeeds, however, at 200–250° also with aluminum chloride, or fuller's earth (Montmorillonite), or boron trifluoride without the addition of aluminum. Mostly mixtures of *o*- and *p-tert*-butylanilines are obtained, since the *tert*-butyl group readily migrates from the *ortho* position to the *para* position under the reaction conditions. With fuller's earth *p-tert*-butylaniline is formed in good yield as the only product.

It is noteworthy that according to the literature the Friedel-Crafts reaction had never been used for the alkylation of aromatic amines with these alkenes. The consensus of opinion prevailed that the Friedel-Crafts catalysts formed so stable a complex with the amines that they could no longer work in catalytic fashion (see above). Thomas (13) stated, moreover, that aluminum chloride was seldom used for the alkylation of N-compounds. He mentioned only some examples with tertiary amines or acylated primary amines, but no free primary amines and no alkenes.

Alkylation of Nitrogen Heterocycles (13a)

Some nitrogen heterocyclic compounds are alkylated successfully with alkenes under the conditions of ring alkylation of aromatic amines. In principle, those compounds are suitable for this reaction which still possess on the nitrogen a hydrogen atom replaceable by metal. Such heterocycles as carbazole, indole, and others generally react not at all or only very sluggishly with metallic aluminum with metal amide formation. This difficulty may be overcome by working in the presence of aluminum compounds of aromatic amines, such as aluminum anilide, in which the aromatic amine can be present in excess. Under these conditions the amine involved is also alkylated in the *ortho* position along with the heterocyclic compound.

The procedure is demonstrated using the ethylation of carbazole as an example.

An aluminum anilide solution, prepared from 3 gm of aluminum granules and 150 gm of aniline, together with 200 gm of carbazole is allowed to react at 280° with ethylene at 200 atm pressure in a stirred autoclave. After 1 hr the uptake of ethylene (135 gm) is ended. The cooled reaction mixture is poured into dilute sulfuric acid, in which case the 2,6-diethylaniline, which is formed, goes into solution and the solid ethylcarbazole remains. The latter crystallizes from ligroin in colorless crystals, m.p. 76–78°. The yield amounts to 90%.

The ethylated product is identical with the 1-ethylcarbazole (XX) described in the literature (*13b*).

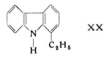

XX

By using propylene the 1-isopropylcarbazole is formed according to the same procedures.

While no uniform alkylation products of unsubstituted indole could be obtained, the ethylation of alkyl substituted indole can be carried out very smoothly. In this procedure the alkyl group goes into the 7-position of the indole ring.

The compound 2-methylindole reacts with ethylene at 280–300° in the presence of aluminum anilide in aniline to furnish as the main product (87%), 7-ethyl-2-methylindole (XXIa). In addition there is formed in smaller amounts a diethylated methylindole, which probably is the 3,7-diethyl-2-methylindole. The constitution of XXIa could be demonstrated by its identity with a comparison preparation, which was synthesized not only from *o*-ethylphenylhydrazine and acetone according to E. Fischer's method, but also from *o*-ethylaniline and chloroacetone (*13c*).

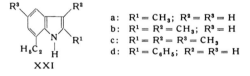

a: $R^1 = CH_3$; $R^2 = R^3 = H$
b: $R^1 = R^2 = CH_3$; $R^3 = H$
c: $R^1 = R^2 = R^3 = CH_3$
d: $R^1 = C_6H_5$; $R^2 = R^3 = H$

XXI

Under the same conditions 2,3-dimethylindole may be alkylated to 2,3-dimethyl-7-ethylindole (XXIb), 2,3,5-trimethylindole to 7-ethyl-2,3,5-trimethylindole (XXIc), and 2-phenylindole to 7-ethyl-2-phenylindole (XXId). The ethylation of 2,3-dihydro-2-methylindole occurs with simultaneous dehydration and also furnishes 7-ethyl-2-methylindole. N-Alkylindoles, as expected, are not susceptible to this reaction.

In the series of six-membered heterocycles the 1,2,3,4-tetrahydroquinoline may be alkylated in the 8-position in the presence of aluminum anilide solution (e.g. XXII).

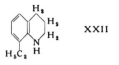

In addition to nitrogen still other heteroatoms may be present in the compound to be alkylated. Thus, phenothiazine reacts with the absorption of 1 mole of alkene, which enters the position *ortho* to the nitrogen. The resulting 1-alkylphenothiazines (XXIII) may be synthesized by

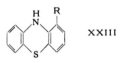

the ring closure of 2-alkyldiphenylamines with sulfur, which proves their structure. The addition of Friedel-Crafts catalysts successfully employed in the alkylation of amines may likewise be used in the case of the heterocycles with concomitant increase in reaction velocity. In the indole series, however, it produces poorer conversions and resinification. In some cases the aluminum arylamide catalyst may be replaced with advantage by a mixture of metallic sodium and aluminum chloride, e.g. in the ethylation of tetrahydroquinoline.

PREPARATION OF 8-ETHYL-1,2,3,4-TETRAHYDROQUINOLINE (XXII)

A 300 gm portion of tetrahydroquinoline is mixed with 6 gm of sodium and 18 gm of anhydrous aluminum chloride and is allowed to react with ethylene under 200 atm in a stirred autoclave. After 3 hr the uptake of alkene is practically finished. The catalyst is decomposed with dilute sodium hydroxide solution and the ethyl compound (XXII) is obtained by the fractional distillation of the reaction product in better than 95% yield.

N-Alkylation of Aromatic Amines

Catalysts

After the surprising action of aluminum in the ring alkylation of aromatic amines was observed, the behavior of other metals was also examined. It was shown that the ability to ring-alkylate aromatic amines belongs only to aluminum. Herein N-alkylation was never observed. Nor was it possible, with aluminum or the aluminum compounds of amines, to rearrange N-alkylated amines into ring alkylated compounds.

Surprising, therefore, was the behavior of alkali or alkaline earth metal compounds of aromatic amines. Sodium dissolves in an excess of aniline with the formation of sodium anilide, which is known (14). This anilide formation may be activated by the addition of metals or metallic oxides according to a patent of the Deutschen Gold- und Silberscheide-anstalt (15). If ethylene under pressure at 250–330° is allowed to react on such a solution, the alkene is taken up quickly. The work-up gives, surprisingly, a mixture of N-ethylaniline and N,N-diethylaniline in over 90% yield without the slightest ring alkylation.

Lithium and potassium as catalysts are also very effective. While with 0.33% of sodium, conversions of 80% are attained, only 0.1% of lithium is necessary. On the other hand with potassium at least 0.6% is necessary. A comparison of the atomic weight and the smallest amount of alkali metal necessary for the beginning of the reaction, points to a definite relationship:

	Li	Na	K
Atomic weight	6.9	23	39
Minimum amount in weight %	0.1	0.33	0.66
Minimum amount in mole %	1.35	1.35	1.41

The minimum amount of alkali calculated on a mole % basis is a constant. Magnesium and calcium are also suitable as catalysts for N-alkylation of aromatic amines. The conversions proceed slower than with the alkali metals; nevertheless good yields are also obtained.

In addition, investigations with the hydrides and amides of the alkali and alkaline earth metals (e.g., sodamide) were carried out, which also furnished the corresponding metal derivatives with amines and which catalyzed N-alkylation.

If preformed sodium anilide is used as an ethylation catalyst, then the N-ethylation proceeds practically in the same yield and with the same reaction as if sodium metal and aniline are used.

The alkylation of ammonia and amines with alkenes in the presence of alkali metals and alkali metal hydrides is described in a patent of the du Pont Company (16). This patent is concerned chiefly with the alkylation of ammonia and aliphatic amines. The ethylation of aniline is also mentioned however; only 33% N-ethylaniline and 11% N,N-diethylaniline were obtained. Since only a small amount of aniline was recovered, one must assume that a large quantity of by-products was formed.

In an American publication (17) this reaction was described in more detail. It is stated there that the sodium used as a catalyst was quantitatively recovered as metal in all the reactions of alkenes with amines (an exception with ammonia) and that no conversion to alkylated sodium amides or sodium hydrides took place. According to our observations there occurs a complete solution of the sodium metal at 150° —especially if the amide formation is activated by additions according to the patent of Degussa (15)—so that a direct recovery of the metal is precluded. The observation that the alkali metal compounds of aromatic amines make excellent catalysts for the N-alkylation of aromatic amines was therefore not known previously.

N-Ethylation of Aromatic Amines

For the N-ethylation of aniline the following procedure is given.

PREPARATION OF N-ETHYLANILINE AND N,N-DIETHYLANILINE

A mixture of 300 gm of aniline, 1 gm of sodium, and 0.1–0.2 gm of copper oxide is heated to 290–310° in an autoclave. The sodium goes into solution during the initial heating with the evolution of hydrogen and the formation of anilide. Then ethylene is introduced up to 200 atm pressure and the pressure is restored from time to time. The reaction is completed after 4–5 hr. The absorption of ethylene amounts to about 1–1.2 mole. For work-up the reaction mixture is decomposed with water, separated, and distilled. There is obtained 86% of N-ethylaniline and 9% N,N-diethylaniline. With somewhat smaller amounts N-ethylaniline is obtained as the sole reaction product.

If ethylation takes place at higher temperatures (350–400°), the yield of definable products becomes increasingly smaller, the higher the temperature selected, although a vigorous absorption of ethylene takes place. Also the use of larger amounts of catalyst worked out unfavorably. For example, with 8% sodium considerable amounts of higher boiling products were obtained in addition to the two ethylanilines, without the aniline being completely converted. A higher boiling amine (b.p. 110°/ 10 mm was detected as a by-product, which was formed by the absorption of 2 moles of ethylene, and which gave the reactions of a secondary amine. This product could be definitely identified as N-*n*-butylaniline. This is quite remarkable, since with ring ethylation of aniline a higher boiling amine can also be isolated, which, however, was identified as being 2-sec-butylaniline. Other N-alkylamines prepared by the sodium method are presented in Table 6. The toluidines, *m*-phenylenediamine, as well as the naphthylamines may also be alkylated on the nitrogen atom.

In place of sodium, technical calcium hydride may also be used. The necessary amount of catalyst for a good reaction comes to about 5 gm for 300 gm of aniline. In 4 hr about 1 mole of ethylene is consumed. The yield of N-ethylaniline amounts to 75%, calculated on the aniline, of which about 5% is recovered unchanged.

N-Propylation and N-Butylation of Aromatic Amines

If propylene is allowed to react with aniline in the presence of alkali metals, then alkylation takes place exclusively on the nitrogen. The reaction proceeds more sluggishly than with ethylene. Larger amounts of catalyst are necessary and in general monoalkylation is not exceeded. In addition small amounts of hydrocarbons are formed. The propylene always enters on the nitrogen as an isopropyl group.

Preparation of N-Isopropylaniline

A mixture of 300 gm of aniline, 6 gm of sodium, and 0.1 gm of copper oxide is heated to 300° in an autoclave. Then propylene is introduced under pressure. On distillation N-isopropylaniline is obtained as the sole reaction product along with unchanged aniline. The yield is 48% based on the aniline.

The butylation of aniline in the presence of sodium proceeds still more slowly. With butylene the polymerization of the alkene is made evident quite strongly. Theoretically the following amines are to be expected in the N-butylation of aniline: N-*n*-butylaniline and N-*sec*-butylaniline, which were also confirmed.

Isobutylene is even less suitable for N-alkylation of aniline than butylene. The formation of hydrocarbons predominates. Only traces of higher boiling amines are obtained, which have not been identified.

Reaction Mechanisms

In attempting to explain the catalytic ring alkylation by means of aluminum compounds of aromatic amines, one must start from the fact that the electron gap of aluminum in aluminum trianilide takes part in this peculiar reaction. If the electron gap of aluminum is saturated by

TABLE 6

N-Alkylated Products of Some Aromatic Amines

Starting amine	Alkylated product	Yield %	B.p. °C/10 mm	Derivatives[a] m.p. °C
Aniline	N-Ethylaniline	90	84–85	P. 137–138 Ac 54–55
Aniline	N,N-Diethylaniline	—	90–91	P. 138–139.5
Aniline	N-Isopropylaniline	30–45	83–84	Bz 62–66
Aniline	N-n-Butylaniline	—	110–113	H. 100–102
Aniline	N-sec-Butylaniline	—	96–98	H. 91–92
o-Toluidine	N-Ethyl-o-toluidine	68	90–93	H. 85–87
m-Toluidine	N-Ethyl-m-toluidine	69	94–96	H. 96–97
p-Toluidine	N-Ethyl-p-toluidine	85	95–98	H. 101–103
2-Ethylaniline	N,2-Diethylaniline	49	101–102	H. 101–102
2,6-Diethylaniline	N,2,6-Triethylaniline	—	126	—
asym-m-Xylidine	2,4-Dimethyl-N-ethylaniline	70	102	—
α-Naphthylamine	N-Ethyl-α-naphthylamine	70	159.5–160.5	Ac 68–70 Bz 108–109 H. 164–165

[a] P. = Picrate; Ac = Acetyl compound; Bz = Benzoyl compound; H. = Urea from amine and α-naphthyl isocyanate.

complex formation from another source, then its catalytic effect must disappear. This is actually the case. If 1 mole of lithium or sodium is added to 1 mole of aluminum in the anilide solution, then neither ring- nor N-alkylation takes place. Also lithium aluminum hydride, which goes instantly into solution in aniline with hydrogen evolution, is completely inactive. We assume therefore that an alkali metal-aluminumtetra- anilide, $Me^I[Al(NHC_6H_5)_4]$ is formed from aluminum- and alkali metal anilide with complex formation, in which the electron gap of aluminum is filled up by a fourth aniline group.

The catalytic activity of aluminum anilide may be explained in the following manner:

Under the reaction conditions ethylene may be expressed by its polar hybrid structures:

$$H_2C=CH_2 \longleftrightarrow H_2\overset{\ominus}{C}-\overset{\oplus}{C}H_2 \longleftrightarrow H_2\overset{\oplus}{C}-\overset{\ominus}{C}H_2$$

The π-electron pair now interacts with the electron gap of aluminum anilide. An orientation of the positive ethylene carbon atom toward the weakly negative *ortho* carbon atom of aniline (mesomerism) under formation of a ring appears plausible.

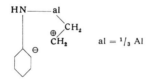

$al = {}^1/_3\ Al$

Finally a true bond is formed with the splitting off of the proton, which attaches itself to the ethylene, whose bond with aluminum is broken.

Similar ideas were expressed in the earlier paper from the Ethyl Corporation (see footnote*, page 227).

In fact the resultant heat of reaction of 34.2 kcal mole for the entry of one ethyl group, or 63.3 kcal/mole for two ethyl groups (calculated from the heat of combustion of 2-ethylaniline and 2,6-diethylaniline) is of the same order of magnitude as the heat of hydrogenation of an aliphatic double bond.

These results are in agreement with the data of investigations by reaction kinetics. Reference has been made already to the same speed of formation of the mono- and diethyl stages (Fig. 1). Moreover, the reaction rate is practically independent of the concentration of the starting amine. From this it is evident that the reaction proceeds *via* an inter- mediate step, perhaps the addition product of ethylene with aluminum anilide. A direct combination of ethylene with aniline to form the ethylanilines is excluded in any case.

The N-ethylation in the presence of alkali metals proceeds differently. Just as the ring alkylation may be blocked by the addition of sodium, so is N-alkylation prevented by the addition of molar (based on sodium) amounts of aluminum. It follows, therefore, that in both cases the reactive centers of the catalysts become inactive by the formation of complexes as mentioned above.

With aluminum we assume that the electron gap is the active center; with sodium anilide the lone electron pair of the nitrogen is responsible. The assumption suggests that here the positive end of ethylene in its polar form interacts with the lone electron pair. It is of no consequence here, whether a more or less ionized form of sodium anilide is assumed. In the second stage a proton transfer from a second aniline molecule to the ethylene addition product takes place. Simultaneously a new molecule of sodium anilide is formed. The kinetics of N-alkylation are also different from those in ring alkylation, since the reaction rate is dependent upon the concentration of aniline.

Summary

The aluminum compounds of aromatic amines act as catalysts in the reaction of alkenes with aromatic amines. The alkene enters the aromatic ring as an alkyl group, principally in the position *ortho* to the amino group, if this is not already occupied. This holds also for the diamines and secondary amines as well as for some nitrogen heterocycles, which possess a nitrogen-hydrogen bond.

The reactivity of the alkenes decreases in the following order: ethylene > propylene > butylene, isobutylene. The catalytic action of the aluminum compounds may be increased considerably by the addition of aluminum chloride and other Friedel-Crafts catalysts.

In contrast to aluminum, the alkali and alkaline earth compounds of aromatic amines bring about an addition of the alkene onto the nitrogen with the formation of N-alkylamines. Here also the reactivity of the alkenes decreases with increasing number of carbon atoms.

Since complex compounds of the type $Me^IAl(NHC_6H_5)_4$ no longer show any catalytic activity, it is assumed that in the case of aluminum the electron gap is responsible for the catalytic activity, while N-alkylation with alkali metals follows a different reaction mechanism.

A large number of *o*-alkyl substituted aromatic amines have been made conveniently possible by the method of ring alkylation with aluminum.

The chemical behavior—especially in the case of *ortho* disubstituted amines—frequently differs from that of the starting materials. The new compounds may present a stimulus to theory and practical applications, based on their interesting properties.

Phenols may be alkylated with alkenes in the presence of aluminum phenolates in a similar manner. Here the alkene also enters the aromatic ring with the formation of predominantly *ortho* substituted alkylphenols (*3*). These reactions are discussed in a later chapter (p. 337).

REFERENCES

(1) German Patent 287,601 (1914) Badische Anilin- und Sodafabrik; P. Friedländer, Fortschritte der Teerfarbenfabrikation und verwandter Industriezweige," Vol. 12, p. 123. Springer, Berlin, 1914–1916; **12**, 123 (1914–1916) ; *Chem. Abstr.* **10**, 1913 (1916).

(2) J. E. Copenhaver and E. E. Reid, *J. Am. Chem. Soc.* **49**, 3161 (1927) ; A. Voswinkel, *Ber. deut. chem. Ges.* **22**, 316 (1889) ; K. v. Auwers, M. Lachner, and H. Bundesmann, *ibid.* **58**, 48 (1925).

(3) R. Stroh and R. Seydel, Farbenfabriken Bayer A. G., German Patent 944,014 (1956) ; *Chem. Abstr.* **53**, 321 (1959).

(4) K. v. Auwers and G. Wittig, *Ber. deut. chem. Ges.* **57**, 1275 (1924).

(5) J. v. Braun, O. Bayer, and G. Blessing, *Ber. deut. chem. Ges.* **57**, 398 (1924).

(6) W. B. Dillingham and E. E. Reid, *J. Am. Chem. Soc.* **60**, 2606 (1938).

(7) J. Houben, T. Weyl, and E. Müller, "Methoden der organischen Chemie," 4th ed., Vol. IV, Pt. 2, p. 89. G. Thieme, Stuttgart, 1955; D. Kästner, *Angew. Chem.* **54**, 281 (1941).

(8) See, for example, F. Klages, "Lehrbuch der organischen Chemie," Vol. 1/2, p. 932. W. de Grutyer & Co., Berlin, 1953.

(9) Cf. G. Weisweiller, *Monatsh. Chem.* **21**, 41 (1900).

(10) e.g. W. J. Hickinbottom, *J. Chem. Soc.* p. 1700 (1934).

(11) J. v. Braun, O. Bayer, and G. Blessing, *Ber. deut. chem. Ges.* **57**, 397 (1924) ; E. J. Constam and H. Goldschmidt, *ibid.* **21**, 1162 (1888).

(12) A. Newton, *J. Am. Chem. Soc.* **65**, 2434 (1943).

(13) C. A. Thomas, "Anhydrous Aluminum Chloride in Organic Chemistry," p. 193. Reinhold, New York, 1941.

(13a) For details see R. Stroh and W. Hahn, *Ann. Chem. Liebigs* **623**, 176 (1959).

(13b) K. H. Pausacker, *J. Chem. Soc.* p. 621 (1950).

(13c) R. Möhlau, *Ber. deut. chem. Ges.* **15**, 2466 (1882); A. Bischler, *ibid.* **25**, 2860 (1892).

(14) "Beilsteins Handbuch der Organischen Chemie" 4th ed., Hauptwerk, Vol. 12, p. 115, Erganz. II, Vol. 12, p. 67. Springer, Berlin, 1929, 1950.

(15) German Patent 215,339; P. Friedländer, "Fortschritte der Teerfarbenfabrikation und verwandter Industriezweige," Vol. 9, p. 123. Springer, Berlin, 1908–1910.

(16) G. M. Whitman, U.S. Patent 2,501,556 (1950) ; *Chem. Abstr.* **44**, 5379 (1950).

(17) B. W. Howk, E. L. Little, S. L. Scott, and G. M. Whitman, *J. Am. Chem. Soc.* **76**, 1899 (1954).

Chemical Synthesis of Intermediates of Carbohydrate Metabolism

HERMANN O. L. FISCHER*

Department of Biochemistry, University of California in Berkeley

Lactic acid formation in animal tissues and alcohol fermentation, both being modifications of the same reaction sequence, today belong to the best known biochemical reactions, owing to the work of Harden and Young, Neuberg, Embden, Meyerhof, Warburg, and others.

The important role of phosphoric acid in carbohydrate degradation was discovered by Harden and Young. Without phosphate neither fermentation nor lactic acid formation (glycolysis) takes place. Carbohydrate is available for degradation only when it is esterified with phosphoric acid.

Our present knowledge of these reactions is reflected in the well-known Embden-Meyerhof scheme of fermentation and glycolysis. A significant aid to the development of this scheme came from organic chemistry: in the laboratory of Hermann O. L. Fischer in Berlin, Basel, Toronto, and Berkeley a total of seven phosphate-containing intermediates of the scheme were synthesized. Co-workers in this field were Erich Baer, H. A. Lardy, C. E. Ballou, and D. L. MacDonald.

The availability of these substances fulfills, so to speak, a dream of the enzyme chemists, who are now able to place their highly purified, in many cases crystalline, enzymes in contact with chemically pure, well-defined substrates, in order to study the enzymatic activity qualitatively and quantitatively. To isolate these same substances from a fermentation mixture or muscle brei is most difficult, if not impossible, since the intermediates exist only for a moment in minute amounts and are very unstable.

The seven intermediates of the Embden-Meyerhof scheme mentioned previously are characterized in Scheme 1 by having their names underlined: glucose-6-phosphate, D-glyceraldehyde-3-phosphate, dihydroxyacetone phosphate, L(−)α-glycerophosphate, D-glyceric acid-3-phosphate, D-glyceric acid-2-phosphate, and phosphoenol pyruvic acid. Their chemical synthesis will be discussed in the same order. The success achieved in synthetic carbohydrate chemistry depends on suitable use of protective groups and upon the empirical rule that phosphorylation

* Deceased.

253

succeeds best when all the hydroxyl groups are blocked except the one which is to carry the phosphoric acid group.

Scheme 1: alcohol fermentation and glycolysis (Embden-Meyerhof-Scheme).

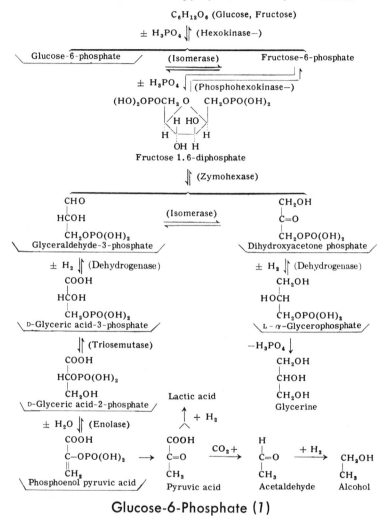

Glucose-6-Phosphate (1)

As starting material we used 1,2,3,4-tetracetyl-D-glucopyranose (I), which was prepared, according to Helferich and Klein (2), from 6-trityl-1,2,3,4-tetraacetyl-D-glucose by detritylation with hydrogen bromide in glacial acetic acid. Diphenylphosphoryl chloride, $(C_6H_5O)_2POCl$ (3), (diphenylphosphorochloridate) proved effective as a phosphorylating agent; it reacted with the free hydroxyl group of the carbohydrate derivative (I) in good yield and produced a beautifully crystalline coupled product (II). Now only the protective groups of the phosphoric acid group had to be removed with hydrogen and platinum oxide (Adams' catalyst) and the acetyl groups removed with potassium methoxide. Thus beautifully crystalline dipotassium glucose-6-phosphate, a very good starting material for enzyme research was obtained in good purity and yield. Further methods for the preparation of glucose-6-phosphate have been described by Seegmiller and Horecker (*3a*) as well as by Viscontini and Olivier (*3b*).

The synthetic preparation of the two triose phosphates, glyceraldehyde-3-phosphate, and dihydroxyacetone phosphate was important for the elucidation of the fermentation scheme. The preparation of racemic glyceraldehyde phosphate occurred at a time when the fermentation

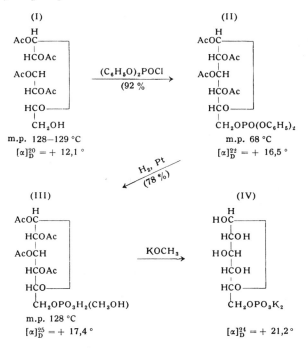

theory of Carl Neuberg was universally accepted. In this theory methylglyoxal (pyruvaldehyde), although non-fermentable itself, was the central substance of carbohydrate decomposition and phosphoric acid derivatives were not implicated. Today we know that the methylglyoxal is formed by the ready decomposition of triose phosphate in acid solution. In Neuberg's experiments it was isolated in abundant quantities in the form of its bis(2,4-dinitrophenylhydrazone) from a fermentation broth, interrupted by iodine-acetic acid. In 1932 Fischer and Baer achieved the first synthesis of racemic glyceraldehyde-3-phosphate (4) and in 1933 Smythe and Gerischer (5) from Otto Warburg's Institute described the first experiments demonstrating the biological importance of the substance. Since then, the synthetic material has been widely used and proved useful in the biochemical study of systems in which D-glyceraldehyde-3-phosphate occurs (6). For example, abundant use of the synthetic compound has been made in the elucidation of the Embden-Meyerhof schemes for alcoholic fermentation and glycolysis. A fine summary of the central role of D-glyceraldehyde-phosphate in fermentation and glycolysis comes from the pen of B. L. Horecker (7).

D-Glyceraldehyde-3-Phosphate

In the meantime the synthesis of the racemic or D,L-glyceraldehyde-3-phosphate has lost its importance, since Ballou and Fischer succeeded in preparing chemically pure natural or D-component (8). Naturally, because of the steric specificity of biological systems, this was greatly desired. Resolution of the racemic substance into its optical antipodes was naturally hopeless in view of the great instability of the triose phosphates. Therefore Ballou and Fischer proceeded from D-mannitol, which was readily obtainable, and utilized the asymmetry of carbon atoms 2 and 5 of the mannitol for their synthesis. The same principle, applying the isopropylidene protecting group, had already been used successfully in 1937 by Fischer and Baer for the preparation of natural L(—)α-glycerophosphate (9).

The effective key substance for the synthesis is 2-benzyl-D-glyceraldehyde (V). In order to obtain this substance, the authors had to proceed from the readily accessible 1,3,4,6-di-O-methylene D-mannitol (10). The protective methylene group is quite easily introduced, but can only be split off under relatively drastic conditions. It was therefore a particularly fortunate observation of Ballou that a 2,5-dibenzylated derivative of dimethylene D-mannitol (III) (11) could be freed from the methylene groups with retention of the benzyl groups in about 27% yield under acetolysis conditions. If one proceeds from 2,5-di-O-benzyl D-mannitol (IV), obtainable from inexpensive materials, the yields of the successive steps are quite acceptable. IV is cleaved with sodium metaperiodate into two molecules of 2-O-benzyl-D-glyceraldehyde (V) which is converted via the mercaptal (VI) into its dimethyl acetal (VII). VII, which contains only one free hydroxyl group, can be phosphorylated with diphenylphosphoryl chloride to form VIII, and then there only remains the question of removing a benzyl and two phenyl groups by the mildest hydrogenation possible. First the benzyl group in position 2 is cleaved by hydrogenolysis with palladium and hydrogen and then the two phenyl groups are removed from the phosphoric acid moiety with platinum oxide and hydrogen. If an attempt is made to remove all three protective groups in one reaction with platinum oxide and hydrogen, then the benzyl residue, because of the more active catalyst, is hydrogenated to cyclohexylmethyl and is then no longer susceptible to cleavage (*12*). The catalytic removal of the three protective groups leads to the dimethyl acetal of D-glyceraldehyde-3-phosphate (IX), which is obtained in the form of its crystalline dicyclohexylamine salt. The triosephosphate can be stored in this form and is marketed by the California Foundation for Biochemical Research, Los Angeles, California. If it is desired to obtain free D-glyceraldehyde-3-phosphate from the salt for enzyme research, for example, then an aqueous solution of the salt is shaken for a few minutes with Dowex 50 (H^+) to remove the amine and the filtered solution of the free acid allowed to stand at 38° for 72 hr in order to hydrolyze the acetal group. After this time the solution shows a constant rotation of $[\alpha]_D = +14.5°$ (in $0.1 N$ HCl), is free from inorganic phosphate, and gives the same hydrolysis curve as the synthetic DL-compound and the natural substance.

Thus, through synthesis, a stable derivative of D-glyceraldehyde-3-phosphate from which optically pure, free triose phosphate can be readily obtained is available to the biochemist in any desired amount. The new chemical procedure is far superior to the enzymatic one and eliminates all of the uncertainties of the latter. The chemical and optical purity of the synthetic product makes it easy to follow analytically by polarimetry any reactions in which the substance takes part.

The synthetic path is described in the following scheme.

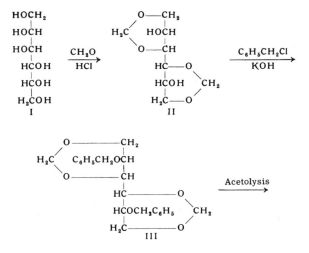

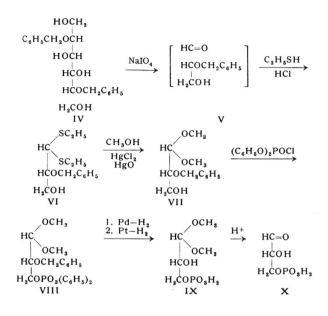

Dihydroxyacetone Phosphate (14a)

The isomer, dihydroxyacetone phosphate (13), which contains no asymmetric carbon atom, was obtained comparatively easily in our laboratories (14) by the same methods and by utilizing older processes. 2,3-Isopropylidene chlorohydrin (I) (15) was distilled with powdered potassium hydroxide and the isopropylidene 2-propen-1,2-diol (II) formed oxidized with lead tetraacetate. With dilute acid the product, III, gave monoacetyl dihydroxyacetone (IV) the effective key substance of the synthesis. IV may be acetalated with methyl orthoformate and ammonium chloride to give V. In V a free hydroxyl group can be phosphorylated by means of diphenylphosphoryl chloride and pyridine to form VI in good yield.

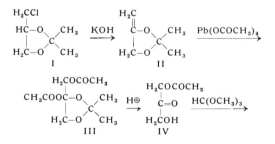

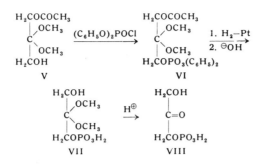

The protective phenyl groups are hydrogenated off with platinum oxide and hydrogen, and the acetyl group removed with barium hydroxide. The beautifully crystalline dicyclohexylamine salt of the ketalated dihydroxyacetone phosphate (VII) may then be obtained from the solution. In this form the triose phosphate is stable and commercially available. If the free dihydroxyacetone phosphate is desired in solution, the cyclohexylamine is removed by shaking with Dowex 50 (H⁺). In aqueous solution the acid substance soon loses its acetal groups and is then ready for enzymatic investigations.

The new synthesis makes ample dihydroxyacetone phosphate available in pure, stable form and has obvious advantages over the enzymatic preparation from D-fructose-1,6-diphosphate (16) and the direct phosphorylation of dihydroxyacetone (17).

METHODS OF PREPARATION

One gram of ammonium chloride is dissolved in 50 ml of dry boiling methanol, the solution cooled to room temperature and mixed with 50 ml of freshly distilled trimethyl orthoformate; 20 gm of acetyl dihydroxyacetone is added and the mixture allowed to stand for 7 days at room temperature.

The pale yellow solution is treated with 200 ml of ether and 75 ml of 0.2 N NH₄OH, shaken in a separatory funnel, and the ether layer separated. The aqueous phase is extracted twice more with 100 ml portions of ether and the combined ether extracts dried over sodium sulfate (17a). The solution is concentrated in a vacuum (water pump) to a thin sirup and distilled in a high vacuum. Yield: 25–29 gm of acetyl dihydroxyacetone dimethyl ketal (V). B.p. 65–73°/0.1–0.2 mm. After redistillation: 23–25 gm. B.p. 70–2°/0.1 mm.

A 3.0 gm portion of V is dissolved in 10 ml of dry pyridine, cooled with ice water, and 6.0 gm of diphenylphosphoryl chloride added dropwise during 5 min. The mixture (stoppered) is allowed to stand at 5° overnight. Excess phosphorylating agent is destroyed with a few drops of water and the pyridine removed at the water pump. The sirupy residue is taken up in 75 ml of benzene and washed successively with 50-ml portions of water, cold 1 N HCl, cold 1 M NaHCO$_3$ solution, and water. The benzene layer is dried over sodium sulfate and concentrated to a sirup (VI). Yield: 6.7 gm (theory: 6.9 gm).

The crude product is taken up in 250 ml of absolute ethanol, 1.0 gm of platinum oxide added and the material hydrogenated at atmospheric pressure. Hydrogen uptake: 3050 ml in 30 min (theory: 2930 ml). The catalyst is removed by centrifugation and the supernatant treated with 7.5 gm of barium hydroxide in 100 ml of hot water. The solution is concentrated to about 50 ml. The strongly basic concentrate is allowed to stand for 1 hr and treated with a solution of 7.15 gm of cyclohexylamine sulfate (17b) in 25 ml of water. The mixture is heated to 80° and filtered through Filter-Cel on hardened filter paper. The filtrate is concentrated to dryness in vacuo. The residue is extracted with 25 ml of warm, absolute ethanol. A small amount of insoluble inorganic phosphate is removed by filtration, and the filtrate concentrated to dryness leaving a white, crystalline mass. This is suspended in 50 ml of acetone, filtered, and the residue washed further with acetone. Yield: 5.5 gm of air-dried material. This is taken up in 15 ml of water, and 25 ml of acetone added. The solution is filtered and acetone (about 40 ml) added to the filtrate until cloudy. After standing at 5° for 18 hr, the crystalline needles formed are filtered off, washed on the funnel with acetone and dried in air. Yield: 4.5 gm of the cyclohexylamine salt of VII. An additional 0.5 gm precipitates on addition of acetone to the concentrated mother liquor. M. p. 183–5° (dec.).

A 100 mg portion of the cyclohexylamine salt is dissolved in 5.0 ml of water; stirred for 30 sec with 2 ml of Dowex 50 (H$^+$), filtered, and the filtrate allowed to stand for 4 hr at 40° to complete hydrolysis of the ketal. The acid solution is adjusted to pH 4.5 with calcium bicarbonate solution and stored in the frozen state. After hydrolysis the resulting methanol may be removed in vacuo.

Hydroxypyruvic Acid Phosphate

Once in possession of the cyclohexylamine salt of ketalated dihydroxyacetone phosphate, Ballou and Hesse (18) converted it into the potassium salt and were able to oxidize it with KMnO$_4$ in weakly alkaline solution to a derivative of the phosphorylated hydroxypyruvic acid (II). The free hydroxypyruvic acid phosphate (III) was obtained from II in a manner analogous to the isolation of dihydroxyacetone phosphate. The substance is not present in the Embden-Meyerhof scheme, but has nevertheless biological significance, as I. Ichihara and D. M. Greenberg were able to demonstrate with the preparation of Ballou and Hesse; it furnishes serine (19) in good yields through an enzyme from rat liver and transamination with glutamic acid.

METHOD OF PREPARATION

One gram of the cyclohexylamine salt of ketalated dihydroxyacetone phosphate is dissolved in 25 ml of 1 N KOH, treated with 50 ml of water and concentrated at 35° to a sirup at the water pump. The concentrate is dissolved in 25 ml of water, cooled in ice water, and treated with 0.75 gm of $KMnO_4$. The mixture is allowed to warm to room temperature, whereupon the permanganate goes into solution. The stoppered flask is allowed to stand for 36 hr at room temperature. The excess oxidizing agent is destroyed by careful dropwise addition of 30% H_2O_2 (about 100 drops), the mixture filtered through Celite, the clear filtrate percolated through a column of about 30 ml of Dowex 50 (H^+) and eluted with water until the pH of the eluate reaches 5–6. The solution is brought immediately to pH 8 by addition of cyclohexylamine and concentrated to dryness at 40–45° with the water pump. The residue is extracted with 25 ml of warm (40–45°) absolute ethanol, the extract freed from inorganic phosphate by addition of about 60 ml of ether, filtered, and the filtrate concentrated to dryness with the water pump. The dry, crystalline residue is dissolved in 1 ml of water, a few drops of cyclohexylamine added, and the solution treated with acetone to cloudiness. The solution is allowed to stand at room temperature until crystallization begins, then stoppered and kept at 5° overnight. The crystals are filtered off and washed with acetone. Yield: 1.1 gm of air-dried material (87%). M.p. 183–5° (slight browning at 180°).

A 100 mg portion of the dimethyl ketal (II) prepared thus is dissolved in 10 ml of water, stirred for 1 min with about 2 ml of Dowex 50 (H^+), filtered, and the filtrate allowed to stand for 4 days at 40° to hydrolyze the ketal. At the beginning of the hydrolysis only the ketal ($R_f = 0.52$) is found on descending chromatograms (butanol: acetic acid: water, 35:10:25; Whatman No. 1 acid washed paper). After 24 hr about 50% of the ketal is hydrolyzed and the chromatogram shows a new organophosphorus compound at $R_f = 0.32$. After standing for 4 days the solution is neutralized. An attempt to obtain a barium salt (addition of 70 mg of barium acetate to the acid solution, precipitation of the salt with ethanol) gave only amorphous material with a poor analysis.

L(—)α-Glycerophosphate

After this digression we return to the Embden-Meyerhof scheme: L(—)α-glycerophosphate is formed by enzymatic reduction of dihydroxyacetone phosphate. Proof was furnished by demonstrating (through configuration determination) that natural α-glycerophosphate from fermentation and glycolysis belongs to the L series, since it could not be obtained from D-glyceraldehyde phosphate without inversion. This synthesis was already carried out in Basel by Fischer and Baer and is illustrated by the following formulas (20).

D-Mannitol (I) is acetonated under special conditions in the 1,2- and 5,6-positions to a di-O-isopropylidene-mannitol (II) in which only the 3- and 4-hydroxyl groups are free. II may be cleaved into two molecules of isopropylidene-D-glyceraldehyde (III) with lead tetraacetate in benzene. III is reduced with Raney nickel and hydrogen to D(+)-isopropylidene-glycerol which becomes the parent substance not only for L(—)α-glycerophosphate, but also for the L-series of optically active α-monoglycerides (21). D(+)isopropylidene-glycerol (IV) is phosphorylated with phosphorus oxychloride in quinoline to form V.

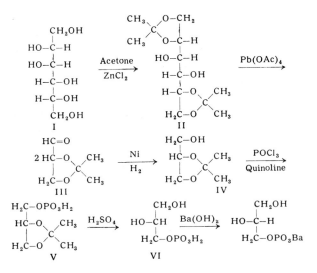

After acid hydrolysis of the protective isopropylidene group, V furnishes natural L(—)α-glycerophosphate (VI), which in contrast to its optical antipodes (21a) is completely destroyed by muscle enzymes.

The principle of using the optical activity of sugar alcohols (mannitol) for the synthesis of smaller molecules having only one asymmetric carbon atom, was first used in the case of the synthesis of L(—)α-glycerophosphate and then in the aforementioned synthesis of D-glyceraldehyde-3-phosphate and then again in the synthesis of D-glyceric acid-3-phosphate and D-glyceric acid-2-phosphate.

Both phosphates of D-glyceric acid appear in the Embden-Meyerhof scheme; the latter acid will be discussed next.

D-Glyceric Acid-2-Phosphate (2-Phosphoglyceric Acid) (22)

The preparation of this substance was attained by phosphorylation of methyl 3-O-benzyl-D-glycerate (VIII) with diphenylphosphoryl chloride, followed by removal of the protecting groups. VIII was obtained from D-galactose (I) following a series of conventional reactions (see scheme).

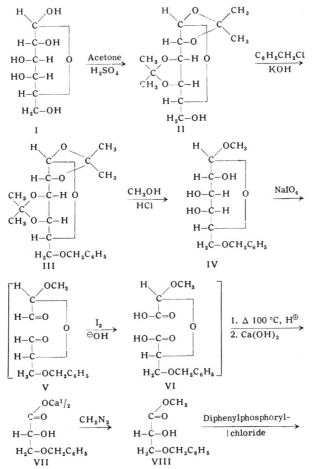

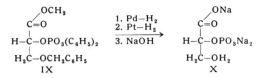

D-Galactose is acetonated to 1,2:3,4-di-O-isopropylidene-D-galacto-pyranose (II). In II the sole remaining free hydroxyl group in position 6 is benzylated to give III. On treatment with methanolic hydrogen chloride, III is transformed to methyl 6-O-benzyl-α-D-galactopyranoside (IV). With sodium metaperiodate IV furnishes the dialdehyde (V), which is oxidized further to the corresponding dicarboxylic acid (VI) with iodine. VI is hydrolyzed without isolation to glyoxylic acid and 3-O-benzyl-D-glyceric acid and the latter isolated as its calcium salt (VII). The methyl ester (VIII) is formed from VII with the aid of diazomethane and, as already mentioned above, is phosphorylated to IX. The protective benzyl group in the 3-position in IX is hydrogenated off with palladium and hydrogen and then both phenyl groups of the phosphoric acid moiety are removed with platinum oxide and hydrogen.

After hydrolysis of the methyl ester the D-glyceric acid-2-phosphate is isolated as its beautifully crystalline trisodium salt (X). Our D-glyceric acid-2-phosphate shows a rotation of $[\alpha]_D = +13°$ (in $1\,N$ HCl). This value does not agree with earlier observations. We will attempt to explain this discrepancy in a further publication.

METHOD OF PREPARATION

A 40 gm portion of sodium metaperiodate is dissolved in 300 ml of water, cooled, and 20 gm of methyl 6-O-benzyl-α-D-galactopyranoside is added. The solution is allowed to stand over night at room temperature, extracted four times with 400-ml portions of ether, and the combined ether extracts, without previous drying (22a), poured into a 2-liter flask containing 100 ml of water, and the ether vaporized at 35°. The aqueous solution of the dialdehyde ($[\alpha]_D = +82.5°$) contains 64.4 oxidation equivalents (theory: 63.0).

The solution is diluted with water to about 400 ml. A solution of 56 gm of iodine and 70 gm of potassium iodide in 50 ml of water is added, followed immediately by a buffer solution of 65 gm K_2CO_3 and 48 gm of $KHCO_3$ in 500 ml of water. The mixture is stirred well and allowed to stand in the dark for 2 hr at room temperature. A sirup separates, which later goes back into solution (occasional shaking). After completion of the oxidation the flask is placed in a large dish, in order to minimize any loss from foaming, and 142 ml of $10\,N$ H_2SO_4 added carefully (gas evolution). The excess iodide is reduced with solid

$Na_2S_2O_3$ (40–50 gm), and the clear solution is filtered through a cotton cloth to separate a small amount of dark oil. The filtrate is extracted four times with 1000-ml portions of ether (*22b*). The ether extract is mixed with 100 ml of water, and the ether vaporized in a vacuum at 50°. The rotation of the aqueous solution is $[\alpha]_D = +14.6°$.

The solution is heated on a steam bath for 2 hr. During this time the optical rotation falls off to 0° (hydrolysis of the acetal). The cooled solution is extracted four times with 100-ml portions of ether, the extracts dried over sodium sulfate and concentrated to a sirup at 50° *in vacuo*. The residue is dissolved in 50 ml of water, and the solution again concentrated to remove small amounts of formic acid. The resulting sirup (12 gm) is dissolved in 120 ml of water and 3 gm of powdered calcium hydroxide is added. The mixture is slowly heated to boiling with good stirring and quickly filtered hot to remove a brown precipitate. On cooling calcium 3-O-benzyl D-glycerate separates. This is left standing for several hours at 5°, the precipitate filtered off, and recrystallized from hot water (110 ml). The pure salt crystallizes in long needles. Yield: 9.5 gm of air-dried material (60%). The salt contains one molecule of water of crystallization which can be removed by drying for 2 hr over P_2O_5 at 100° and 0.01 mm Hg. The anhydrous salt melts at 215–220° with slight decomposition; $[\alpha]_D^{22} = +20°$ ($c = 0.5$ in water). A 9 gm portion of the purified calcium salt (VII) is dissolved in 50 ml of 1 N HCl. The solution is extracted four times with 50-ml portions of ether. The combined ether extracts contain about 8 gm of 3-O-benzyl-D-glyceric acid. The extracts are dried over sodium sulfate and filtered. The dry filtrate is treated with an ether solution containing 2 gm of diazomethane. The yellow color of the mixture indicates a slight excess of diazomethane. After 30 min the solution is concentrated *in vacuo* to a sirup (8.5 gm and the latter freed from the remainder of the solvent by subjecting it to a high vacuum at 50°. The rotation of the undiluted methyl 3-O-benzyl-D-glycerate is $[\alpha]_D = -1.31°$. It is phosphorylated without further purification. The methyl ester (8 gm) is dissolved in 40 ml of dry pyridine and cooled to 5° with ice water. With exclusion of moisture, 10.8 gm of diphenylphosphoryl chloride is added from a dropping funnel over a period of 10 min. Pyridine hydrochloride separates. The dropping funnel is rinsed with 10 ml of dry pyridine. The stoppered solution is allowed to stand at 5–10° overnight. After 1 ml of water is added to destroy excess phosphorylating agent, the solution is allowed to stand for 30 min. Most of the pyridine is removed *in vacuo* at 50°, and the residue is taken up in 100 ml of chloroform and washed with 100-ml portions of water, cold 1 N HCl, cold 1 N $KHCO_3$ solution, and water. The chloroform layer is dried over sodium sulfate and concentrated at 50° *in vacuo* to a thick sirup. Yield: 16 gm (95%). The compound is used without purification.

A 5 gm portion of palladium chloride (5%) on activated charcoal (*22c*) in 100 ml of 95% ethanol is shaken with hydrogen. About 150 ml of hydrogen is taken up. The catalyst is freed from acid by suspending and centrifuging 4 or 5 times with 95% ethanol. The washed catalyst is suspended in 100 ml of absolute ethanol and 5 gm of methyl 3-O-benzyl-2-diphenylphosphoryl-D-glycerate added. The mixture is shaken with hydrogen at atmospheric pressure and room temperature. Absorption of hydrogen (about 280 ml) is finished in 10–15 minutes.

The subsequent removal of the phenyl groups requires a platinum catalyst, with which this reaction is completed in 1.5 hr at the most. With slower reactions (3–5 hr) up to 5% phosphate migration occurs and the product is difficult to crystallize. It is therefore necessary that the catalyst be freshly prepared and its activity checked with about 0.5 gm of the intermediate IX. The removal of the protective group by hydrogenation, together with the hydrolysis of the methyl ester should be finished in 2.5–3 hr.

The palladium catalyst is separated by centrifuging and the solution returned to the hydrogenation vessel; 1 gm of freshly prepared platinum oxide (*22d*) is added together with 1 gm of acid-washed activated charcoal. The mixture is shaken vigorously with hydrogen until the hydrogen uptake (2800 ml/hr) is finished. The catalyst is removed by centrifuging and the supernatant immediately mixed with 25 ml of 1 N NaOH. The cloudy solution is concentrated in a vacuum at 40° to a sirup, which is taken up in 10 ml of water, and treated with 10 ml of 1 N NaOH; then the solution is permitted to stand for 30 min at room temperature.

The solution, which now contains trisodium D-glyceric acid-2-phosphate, is mixed with some Filter-Cel and filtered through Whatman No. 50 paper (*22e*).

The flask is washed out with 10 ml of water and the rinsings poured over the residue on the filter. The combined filtrate is treated with methanol to cloudiness (about 50 ml). The solution is allowed to stand at room temperature and crystallization hastened by rubbing with a glass rod or inoculating. After standing overnight at 5°, the precipitate is centrifuged off, washed free of water with methanol, and finally washed with absolute ether and allowed to dry in air. Yield: 2.2–2.5 gm. To recrystallize, the material is dissolved in 15 ml of water, filtered with Filter-Cel, and treated with methanol to cloudiness. Long (5–10 mm) needles separate out in rosettes. The precipitate is isolated as described. The resulting trisodium D-glyceric acid 2-phosphate has a rotation of $[\alpha]_D^{22} = +3.6°$ ($c = 2$ in water); the free acid has $[\alpha]_D^{22} = 12.9°$ ($c = 1.8$ in 1 N HCl).

Analytical values indicate a pentahydrate. At 80° and 0.01 mm the water of crystallization is removed in 6 hr.

D-Glyceric Acid-3-Phosphate (3-Phosphoglyceric Acid)

In order to obtain D-glyceric acid-3-phosphate successfully, it is best nowadays to proceed from 2-benzyl-D-glyceraldehyde (I). Its preparation from a dimethylene-D-mannitol has been described in the preceding synthesis of D-glyceraldehyde-3-phosphate. In our first communication on the synthesis of D-glyceric acid-3-phosphate (23), we described the preparation of I from another starting material, 3,4-isopropylidene α-D-methylarabinoside. The details of the newer preparation will be published elsewhere shortly.

$$
\begin{array}{ccc}
\text{HC=O} & & \text{COOH} \\
| & \xrightarrow{\text{I}_2, \ ^{\ominus}\text{OH}} & | \\
\text{HCOCH}_2\cdot\text{C}_6\text{H}_5 & & \text{HCOCH}_2\cdot\text{C}_6\text{H}_5 \xrightarrow{\text{CH}_2\cdot\text{N}_2} \\
| & & | \\
\text{H}_2\text{COH} & & \text{H}_2\text{COH} \\
\text{I} & & \text{II}
\end{array}
$$

$$
\begin{array}{ccc}
\text{COOCH}_3 & & \text{COOCH}_3 \\
| & \xrightarrow[\text{Pyridine}]{(\text{C}_6\text{H}_5\text{O})_2\cdot\text{P=O}\cdot\text{Cl}} & | \\
\text{HCOCH}_2\cdot\text{C}_6\text{H}_5 & & \text{HCOCH}_2\cdot\text{C}_6\text{H}_5 \\
| & & | \\
\text{H}_2\text{COH} & & \text{H}_2\text{COPO}_3(\text{C}_6\text{H}_5)_2 \\
\text{III} & & \text{IV}
\end{array}
$$

$$
\xrightarrow[\substack{3.\ \text{NaOH} \\ 4.\ \text{Ba(OAc)}_2}]{\substack{1.\ \text{Pd}-\text{H}_2 \\ 2.\ \text{Pt}-\text{H}_2}}
\begin{array}{c}
\text{COO} \\
| \quad\searrow\text{Ba} \\
\text{HCOH} \quad\nearrow \\
| \\
\text{H}_2\text{COPO}_3\text{H} \\
\text{V}
\end{array}
$$

I is oxidized with iodine in alkaline bicarbonate solution to the acid II which is converted to its methyl ester (III) with diazomethane. III is converted to IV with diphenylphosphoryl chloride under the usual conditions. From IV, first the benzyl group in the 2-position is hydrogenated off with palladium and hydrogen, then the phenyl groups are removed from the phosphoric acid moiety with platinum oxide and hydrogen, and finally the methyl ester is hydrolyzed with dilute sodium hydroxide. The crystalline acid barium salt can be precipitated with barium acetate (24). The rotation of the free acid is $[\alpha]_D = -14.3°$ (in 1 N HCl) and $[\alpha]_D = -743°$ (in neutral molybdate). The corresponding values in the literature are $-14.5°$ and $-745°$ (25).

The unusually high rotation of the D-glyceric acid-3-phosphate in molybdate solution serves as a basis for its determination in the presence of the isomeric D-glyceric acid-2-phosphate (26). Since the rotation of both phosphates of glyceric acid have now been observed with pure synthetic preparations, the compounds can be estimated polarimetrically with considerable precision.

D-Glyceric acid-2-phosphate and D-glyceric acid-3-phosphate, when prepared chemically pure are, of course, excellent substrates for the study of the enzyme, phosphoglyceromutase (27). Similarly, the enzyme, enolase, has been studied in detail by F. Wold and C. E. Ballou, using synthetic D-glyceric acid-2-phosphate and phosphopyruvic acid (28). In this connection it appears to be of interest that the next higher analogs of D-glyceric acid-2- and 3-phosphate, namely D-erythro-2,3-dihydroxy-butyric acid monophates I and II, are converted into one another by

$$
\begin{array}{cc}
\text{COOH} & \text{COOH} \\
| & | \\
\text{HCOPO}_3\text{H}_2 & \text{HCOH} \\
| & | \\
\text{HCOH} & \text{HCOPO}_3\text{H}_2 \\
| & | \\
\text{CH}_3 & \text{CH}_3 \\
\text{I} & \text{II}
\end{array}
$$

means of phosphoglyceromutase, although much more slowly than the corresponding glyceric acid phosphates. In contrast, I is not a substrate for enolase—on the contrary it is a very effective inhibitor for this enzyme. Both the phosphates I and II have been prepared by Ballou by chemical synthesis utilizing methods similar to that for the D-glyceric acid phosphates and starting from derivatives of D-rhamose (29).

Phosphoenol Pyruvic Acid (Phosphoryl-enol Pyruvic Acid)

The last phosphorylated three-carbon compound in the Embden-Meyerhof scheme is phosphoenol pyruvic acid, which was discovered in fermentation mixtures by Meyerhof and Lohmann (30) in 1934. A year later it was prepared by Kiessling in 3–5% yield by the direct action of phosphorus oxychloride and quinoline on pyruvic acid (31). Baer and Fischer have described (32) an improved procedure which starts with β-chlorolactic acid (I); the preparation is shown in the following formulas:

$$
\begin{array}{l}
\text{CH}_2\text{Cl-CH-COOH} \quad \xrightarrow[\substack{\text{Dimethyl-}\\\text{aniline}}]{\text{POCl}_3} \quad \left[\begin{array}{l} \text{CH}_2\text{Cl-CH-COOH} \\ \quad\quad\quad | \\ \quad\quad\quad \text{OPOCl}_2 \end{array} \right] \quad \xrightarrow[\substack{90\%\\ \text{C}_2\text{H}_5\text{OH}}]{\text{KOH}}
\end{array}
$$

with (I) and (II) labels.

$$
\begin{array}{l}
\text{CH}_2=\text{C-COOK} \quad \xrightarrow{\text{Ba(OOCCH}_3)_2} \quad \text{CH}_2=\text{C-COO}^1/_2\text{Ba} \quad \xrightarrow{\text{AgNO}_3} \\
\quad\quad | \quad\quad\quad\quad\quad\quad\quad\quad\quad\quad\quad\quad\quad | \\
\quad\quad \text{OPO}_3\text{K}_2 \quad\quad\quad\quad\quad\quad\quad\quad\quad\quad \text{OPO}_3\text{Ba}
\end{array}
$$

$$
\begin{array}{l}
\text{CH}_2=\text{C-COOAg} \quad \xrightarrow[\text{HNO}_3]{\text{Ba(NO}_3)_2} \quad \text{CH}_2=\text{C-COOAg*}) \\
\quad\quad | \quad\quad\quad\quad\quad\quad\quad\quad\quad\quad\quad\quad\quad\quad | \\
\quad\quad \text{OPO}_3\text{Ag}_2 \quad\quad\quad\quad\quad\quad\quad\quad\quad\quad \text{OPO}_3\text{Ba} \\
\quad\quad (\text{III}) \quad\quad\quad\quad\quad\quad\quad\quad\quad\quad\quad\quad\quad (\text{IV})
\end{array}
$$

It is a high energy phosphate which is now frequently used in enzyme mixtures in place of adenosine triphosphate. Recently Cramer and Voges (32a) have described the preparation of phosphoenol pyruvic acid.

* The positions of silver and barium are arbitrary. Phosphoenol pyruvic acid is isolated as the silver–barium salt (IV).

D-Erythrose-4-phosphate (32b)

The results described above in the field of phosphorylated 3-carbon atom carbohydrates gave us the courage to begin with phosphorylation of 4-carbon atom carbohydrates (tetroses). Here the circumstances were as follows: in 1954 it became more and more evident that along with the glycolytic degradation according to Embden-Meyerhof, still another pathway of carbohydrate decomposition occurs in many tissues, the so-called glucose-6-phosphate shunt (33). Several sugars and sugar phosphates, to which no metabolic importance had previously been attributed, acquired significance in the new cycle. One of the postulated intermediates, which might play a central role in this and other enzymatic conversions of carbohydrates, was D-erythrose-4-phosphate.

This tetrose phosphate was for example, assumed to be a reaction product of the enzyme transaldolase with sedoheptulase-7-phosphate and D-glyceraldehyde-3-phosphate (34). A further indication of the existence of D-erythrose-4-phosphate as an intermediate was the isolation of sedoheptulose diphosphate after dihydroxyacetone phosphate and the enzyme aldolase had been added to the reaction mixture (35). Similarly, the formation of tetrose-phosphates was assumed during the reaction of transketolase with D-fructose-6-phosphate and D-glyceraldehyde-3-phosphate (36).

Investigation of the metabolic reactions of D-erythrose-4-phosphate was invariably hindered by the difficulty of isolating the new substance from enzyme mixtures. Our new chemical synthesis came at the right moment.

The method was in many ways similar to those used in the preparation of D-glyceraldehyde-3-phosphate (7). Naturally, D-erythrose ($\pm$) had to be available in convenient amounts: this was brought about using two different methods. In the first D-arabinose was transformed to its diethyl mercaptal form, which was oxidized to the disulfone; the sulfone was degraded with aqueous ammonia to D-erythrose (37). The second method involved degradation of 4,6-O-ethylidine-D-glucose (38) with sodium metaperiodate to 2,4-O-ethylidine-D-erythrose. The scheme shows the phosphorylation steps.

The sirupy D-erythrose (I) was mercaptalated with ethyl mercaptan and hydrochloric acid, and the mercaptal was tritylated and acetylated to give II. After II was deacetylated with barium methoxide, it was transformed to the corresponding dimethyl acetal with the aid of mercuric oxide and mercuric chloride in methanol, following the conditions recommended by Wolfrom and co-workers (39), and was obtained in crystalline form (III) after benzoylation. The trityl group in the

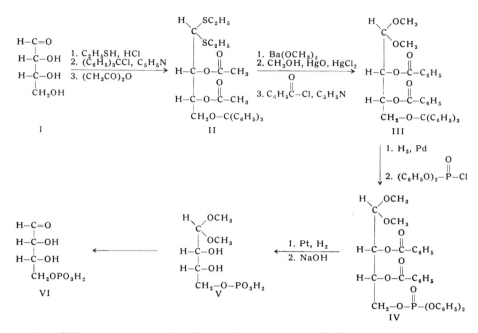

4-position was removed with hydrogen and palladium and the free hydroxyl group phosphorylated with diphenylphosphoryl chloride in the known manner (IV). To remove the protective groups from IV, it is only necessary to reduce off the phenyl groups with platinum oxide and hydrogen and to hydrolyze the benzoyl groups with alkali. The dimethyl acetal of D-erythrose-4-phosphate (V) is then obtained; it crystallizes in the form of its cyclohexylamine salt. As in the case of D-glyceraldehyde-3-phosphate, this is also the form in which D-erythrose-4-phosphate can be stored and is commercially available. To prepare an aqueous solution of the free acid (VI), the cyclohexylamine salt is treated in water with Dowex 50 (H⁺) and the solution of the free acid is maintained at 40° for 18 hr. Because of the acidity of the phosphoric acid group, the dimethyl acetal is hydrolyzed to the free aldehyde and thus a solution of the desired D-erythrose-4-phosphate (VI) is available for enzymatic experiments.

Like its acetal, the tetrose phosphate is optically inactive in neutral or acid solution. It is very similar to D-glyceraldehyde-3-phosphate in its behavior toward 1 N HCl at 100°.

METHOD OF PREPARATION

A 64 gm portion of 4,6-O-ethylidine-D-glucose (m.p. 175–180°) is oxidized to 2,4-O-ethylidine-D-erythrose with sodium metaperiodate

(*39a*). A colorless sirup is formed. This is dissolved with stirring in 140 ml of ethyl mercaptan, and the ice-cooled solution treated with 50 ml of concentrated hydrochloric acid. The mixture is shaken at 0° for 20 min, made slightly alkaline by careful addition of concentrated ammonium hydroxide solution, evaporated to dryness *in vacuo* and the residue freed from water by distilling absolute ethanol from it two or three times. Absolute alcohol is added, the undissolved NH_4Cl filtered off, the alcohol removed *in vacuo*, and the residue distilled azeotropically with benzene for further drying.

The product is dissolved in 400 ml of anhydrous pyridine, and 88 gm of triphenylmethyl chloride is added; the mixture is allowed to stand for 22 hr, cooled in ice, 200 ml of acetic anhydride is added, and the whole allowed to stand for ½ hr at 0°, and 10 hr at room temperature. The solution is ice-cooled, excess acetic anhydride is destroyed by adding 20 ml of water, and after standing for 30 min, the solution is brought to dryness *in vacuo*. The residue is taken up in 250 ml of chloroform, and the solution washed with 1 N sulfuric acid, 1 N K_2CO_3 solution, and water, and dried over sodium sulfate. The solvent is removed under reduced pressure, the remaining sirup taken up in 500 ml of hot methanol, treated with activated charcoal, and filtered hot. The 4-O-trityl-2,3-di-O-acetyl-D-erythrose diethylmercaptal crystallizes out and is recrystallized 3 times from methanol, giving a light yellow product, m. p. 105–6° Yield 78 mg (45% based on the ethylidene glucose). A further 2.5 gm of product of like purity is isolated from the mother liquors.

A 5 gm portion of the acetylated mercaptal is dissolved in 75 ml of warm, dry methanol in a 3-necked flask. The solution is quickly cooled to room temperature, treated with 2 ml of a 0.5 N barium methoxide solution, and left standing for 1 hr. The flask is equipped with a rapid stirrer and a condenser, and 7.5 gm of mercuric oxide is added to the solution, stirring vigorously enough to maintain the oxide in suspension, and 7.5 gm of mercuric chloride in warm, dry methanol is then added. The mixture is first stirred for 10 min at room temperature and then, boiling in the water bath, for 20 min. After cooling and filtering, the filtrate is evaporated to dryness *in vacuo*, in the presence of some mercuric oxide; the solid residue is extracted twice with 50-ml portions of chloroform, and the combined extracts washed three times with 100-ml portions of water (*39b*). After drying over sodium sulfate, the organic phase is concentrated *in vacuo* to a stiff sirup. Yield: 3.75 gm.

The sirup is dissolved in 20 ml of dry pyridine, and allowed to stand at room temperature for 18 hr with 5 ml of acetic anhydride, the excess acetic anhydride is destroyed with a small amount of water, the pyridine removed *in vacuo*, the residue taken up in 100 ml of chloroform and the solution washed with 100-ml portions of water, cold 1 N HCl, cold 1 M KHCO₃ solution, and water. The chloroform layer is dried over sodium sulfate, concentrated *in vacuo* to a sirup (5 gm), which crystallizes on addition of 5 ml of methanol. After standing for several hours at 5°, the crystals are filtered off and dried in air. Yield: 3.5 gm (79%). Recrystallization from a small volume of methanol gives 3.1 gm of granular crystals (m.p. 99–101°), $[\alpha]_D^{22} = +10.8°$ ($c = 2.4$ in chloroform).

Next, 3 gm of the acetylated acetal is dissolved in 50 ml of dry methanol, treated with 1 ml of a 0.5 N methanolic barium methoxide solution, and allowed to stand 1 hr. It is then concentrated *in vacuo* to a thick sirup, which is taken up in 15 ml of dry pyridine and treated with 3 ml of benzoyl chloride. This solution is allowed to stand for 18 hr at room temperature and worked up as described for the acetylated acetal. Yield: 3.5 gm (93%). After recrystallization from methanol, m.p. 122–4°, $[\alpha]_D^{25} = +18.3°$ ($c = 3$ in chloroform). The dibenzoate may be prepared directly after cleavage of the methylthio groups, but the yield is better, if one elects to go via the diacetate.

Next 3 gm of 4-O-trityl-2,3-di-O-benzoyl-D-erythrose dimethyl acetal is dissolved in 100 ml of absolute alcohol, mixed with 3 gm of catalyst produced from 5% palladium chloride on active charcoal (reduced) (*22, 22c*), and shaken with hydrogen at normal pressure for 16 hr. The hydrogen uptake (170 ml) is in excess of the calculated amount (110 ml). The catalyst is centrifuged off, and the solution brought to dryness *in vacuo*. Triphenylmethane crystals separate at this point. The residue, without separation of components, is dissolved in 10 ml of dry pyridine, cooled with ice water, and 2.5 gm of diphenylphosphoryl chloride is added dropwise, the mixture is allowed to stand at 5° for 18 hr, and then worked up as described for the acetylation of the dimethyl acetal. The yield of phosphorylated product contaminated with triphenylmethane is 3.7 gm.

The product is dissolved in 250 ml of absolute ethanol, 1 gm of platinum oxide catalyst is added and the mixture hydrogenated (hydrogen uptake in 10 hr is 1340 ml). The catalyst is centrifuged off, the ethanolic remainder treated with 30 ml of 1 N NaOH, allowed to stand for 18 hr, and the alcohol removed *in vacuo*. The residue is taken up in 100 ml of water and the solution extracted with ether in order to remove water-insoluble material. The aqueous phase is treated in portions with 50 ml of Dowex 50 (H⁺, 2 meq/ml) to remove cations, and again extracted with ether to remove cyclohexylcarboxylic acid. The aqueous solution is immediately adjusted to pH 9 (indicator paper) with cyclohexylamine, and brought to dryness *in vacuo*. The residue is dissolved in 5 ml of absolute ethanol, and the solution treated with ether until cloudy, and left at 5° for 18 hr; the precipitate formed is filtered through hardened filter paper, washed on the funnel with ether, air-dried and finally dried 1 hr over P_2O_5 under high vacuum. Yield: 0.6 gm (31%); m.p. 160–5°; $[\alpha]_D^{25} = 0 + 0.2°$ ($c = 5$ in water or $1 N$ HCl).

One hundred milligrams of the cyclohexylamine salt of the acetal is dissolved in 5 ml of water, stirred for 1 min with 2 ml of Dowex 50 (H^+, 2 meq/ml), the exchange resin filtered off, and the filtrate allowed to stand in a stoppered flask at 40° for 18 hr. Two-tenths of a milliliter of the solution is then used for an aldehyde determination, according to the Willstätter-Schudel method; this requires 0.018 meq of oxidant (theory is 0.02 meq). The reducing power of the solution does not increase on longer standing. The 1% solution of D-erythrose-4-phosphate thus obtained shows no measurable rotation in a 2-dm tube. After neutralization with sodium hydroxide, the $[\alpha]_D$ retains the value $0 + 1°$.

The well-known investigations (7) by B. L. Horecker of the condensation of D-erythrose-4-phosphate and dihydroxyacetone phosphate to give sedoheptulose-1,7-diphosphate under the influence of the enzyme aldolase obtained from rabbit muscle may be repeated elegantly with our two synthetic preparations (see above formulas).

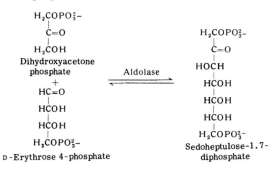

If D-erythrose-4-phosphate is reduced with $NaBH_4$, D-erythritol-4-phosphate is obtained, also as a beautifully crystalline cyclohexylamine salt (40). We were fortunately able to bring our synthetic results in the erythritol phosphate series into agreement with the biological results of Dr. Janet Shetter (41). Years ago Barker and Lipmann (42) had shown that erythritol is metabolized by *Propionibacterium pentosaceum*. The process plainly proceeds via a direct phosphorylation of the erythritol, and erythritol phosphate was assumed to be the first product. In the laboratory of Prof. Barker in Berkeley, J. Shetter was able to isolate the crystalline cyclohexylamine salt from a bacterial mixture; this proved to be identical with our synthetic preparation judging from its rotation and other properties. Here again is an instance where organic synthesis was able to prove unequivocally the constitution and configuration of an interesting natural product. Furthermore, using methods now adequately known to the reader, L-erythritol-4-phosphate was also synthesized. As was to be expected the compound showed the opposite optical rotation to that of the natural product (40).

The following enzyme experiment, which Srinivasan et al. (43) of Columbia University, New York, carried out with the synthetic carbohydrate phosphates prepared in our laboratory seems to be of especially far-reaching biological importance. These authors condensed D-erythrose-4-phosphate (I) with phosphoenol pyruvic acid (II) (44) under the influence of a cell-free extract of Escherichia coli (mutant 83–24) to form dehydroshikimic acid (IV) in a yield of 90%; 2-keto-3-deoxy-7-phospho-D-glucoheptonic acid was detected (45) as an intermediate.

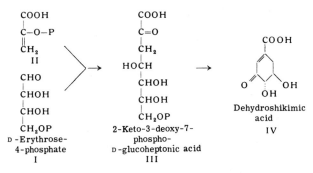

This enzymatic formation of a hydroaromatic plant acid from small straight chain carbohydrate phosphates seems to us to be an interesting model experiment. Proceeding from here one may reflect on how, perhaps, in the organic world the hydroaromatic substances, and from them the aromatic, could have been formed. It has always been conjectured that carbohydrates might serve as starting material for lignin, for example, but no one has been able to formulate the ring closure steps.

Moreover, shikimic acid (46), which occurs in plants, is transformed under very mild conditions into protocatechuic acid so that we have here a good pathway from carbohydrates to benzene derivatives.

Since according to Davis and co-workers (47), shikimic acid is an intermediate in bacterial metabolism for the formation of the aromatic amino acids, phenylalanine, tyrosine, tryptophan, and p-aminobenzoic acid, this points up further biological implications.

It affords satisfaction to the organic chemist that with the help of his synthetic products important reactions of biological metabolism can be verified or supported chemically.

REFERENCES

(1) H. A. Lardy and H. O. L. Fischer, *J. Biol. Chem.* **164**, 513 (1946).

(2) B. Helferich and W. Klein, *Ann. Chem. Liebigs* **450**, 219 (1926).

(3) P. Brigl and H. Müller, *Ber. deut. chem. Ges.* **72**, 2121 (1939).

(3a) J. E. Seegmiller and B. L. Horecker, *J. Biol. Chem.* **192**, 175 (1951).

(3b) M. Viscontini and C. Olivier, *Helv. Chim. Acta* **36**, 466 (1953).

(4) H. O. L. Fischer and E. Baer, *Ber. deut. chem. Ges.* **65**, 337, 1040 (1932).

(5) C. V. Smythe and W. Gerischer, *Biochem. Z.* **260**, 414 (1933).

(6) O. Warburg and W. Christian, *Biochem. Z.* **303**, 40 (1939); S. F. Velick and J. E. Hayes, Jr., *J. Biol. Chem.* **203**, 545 (1953).

(7) B. L. Horecker, in "Phosphorus Metabolism" (W. O. McElroy and B. D. Glass, eds.), Vol. 1, p. 117. Johns Hopkins Press, Baltimore, Maryland, 1951.

(8) C. E. Ballou and H. O. L. Fischer, *J. Am. Chem. Soc.* **77**, 3329 (1955).

(9) H. O. L. Fischer and E. Baer, *Naturwissenschaften* **25**, 589 (1937).

(10) W. T. Haskins, R. M. Hann, and C. S. Hudson, *J. Am. Chem. Soc.* **65**, 67 (1943).

(11) H. G. Fletcher, Jr. and H. W. Diehl, *J. Am. Chem. Soc.* **74**, 3797 (1952).

(12) J. C. Sowden and H. O. L. Fischer, *J. Am. Chem. Soc.* **63**, 3244 (1941); K. Freudenberg, W. Dürr, and K. Hochstetter, *Ber. deut. chem. Ges.* **61**, 1735 (1928).

(13) C. E. Ballou and H. O. L. Fischer, *J. Am. Chem. Soc.* **78**, 1659 (1956).

(14) H. O. L. Fischer. E. Baer, and L. Feldman, *Ber. deut. chem. Ges.* **63**, 1732 (1930); H. O. L. Fischer and E. Baer, *ibid.* **65**, 345 (1932).

(14a) C. E. Ballou, *Biochemical Prep.* **7**, 45 (1960).

(15) E. Fichter and B. Pfähler, *Ber. deut. chem. Ges.* **53**, 1608 (1920).

(16) O. Meyerhof and K. Lohmann, *Biochem. Z.* **271**, 89 (1934).

(17) W. Kiessling, *Ber. deut. chem. Ges.* **67**, 869 (1934).

(17a) The product is water soluble and hence the ether extracts should not be washed further with water.

(17b) Prepared from 50 gm of cyclohexylamine in 1 liter of absolute ethanol and 50 ml of 10 N sulfuric acid. The solution is cooled to 0°, the salt filtered off, washed on the funnel with absolute ethanol, and dried.

(18) C. E. Ballou and R. Hesse, *J. Am. Chem. Soc.* **78**, 3718 (1956).

(19) A. Ichihara and D. M. Greenberg, *Proc. Natl. Acad. Sci. U.S.* **41**, 605 (1955).

(20) H. O. L. Fischer and E. Baer, *Naturwissenschaften* **25**, 589 (1937); *J. Biol. Chem.* **128**, 491 (1939).

(21) H. O. L. Fischer and E. Baer, *Chem. Revs.* **29**, 287 (1941).

(21a) E. Baer and H. O. L. Fischer, *J. Biol. Chem.* **135**, 321 (1940).

(22) C. E. Ballou and H. O. L. Fischer, *J. Am. Chem. Soc.* **76**, 3188 (1954).

(22a) If the solution of dialdehyde is dried, a water-insoluble oil is formed which does not give the desired 3-O-benzyl-D-glyceric acid.

(22b) During the extraction the aqueous phase may become colored through the formation of free iodine. If this is the case, then more $Na_2S_2O_3$ is added.

(22c) H. Gilman and A. H. Blatt, *Org. Syntheses* **26**, 77 (1946).

(22d) H. Gilman and A. H. Blatt, *Org. Syntheses Coll. Vol.* **1**, 463 (1941).

(22e) The solution should be water clear. A gradual coloration, which appears during slower reduction, can lead to a product which crystallizes poorly.

(23) C. E. Ballou and H. O. L. Fischer, *Abstr. Papers 126th Meeting Am. Chem. Soc.* p. 7D (1954).

(24) O. Meyerhof and W. Kiessling, *Biochem. Z.* **276**, 239 (1935).

(25) O. Meyerhof and W. Schulz, *Biochem. Z.* **297**, 60 (1938).
(26) O. Meyerhof and P. Oesper, *J. Biol. Chem.* **179**, 1371 (1949).
(27) R. W. Cowgill and L. Pizer, *Federation Proc.* **14**, 198 (1955).
(28) F. Wold, Dissertation, Berkeley, California, 1956.
(29) C. E. Ballou, *J. Am. Chem. Soc.* **79**, 984 (1957).
(30) O. Meyerhof and K. Lohmann, *Biochem. Z.* **273**, 60 (1934).
(31) W. Kiessling, *Ber. deut. chem. Ges.* **68**, 597 (1935).
(32) E. Baer and H. O. L. Fischer, *J. Biol. Chem.* **180**, 145 (1949).
(32a) F. Cramer and D. Voges, *Chem. Ber.* **92**, 952 (1959).
(32b) C. E. Ballou, H. O. L. Fischer, and D. L. MacDonald, *J. Am. Chem. Soc.* **77**, 5967 (1955). Another method of preparation is given by J. N. Baxter, A. S. Perlin, and F. J. Simpson, *Can. J. Biochem. and Physiol.* **37**, 199 (1959).
(33) Literature: see e.g., S. S. Cohen, *in* "Chemical Pathways of Metabolism" (D. M. Greenberg, ed.), Vol. 1, p. 173. Academic Press, New York, 1954.
(34) B. L. Horecker and P. Z. Smyrniotis, *J. Am. Chem. Soc.* **75**, 2021 (1953); *J. Biol. Chem.* **212**, 811 (1955).
(35) B. L. Horecker, P. Z. Smyrniotis, H. H. Hiatt, and P. A. Marks, *J. Biol. Chem.* **212**, 827 (1955).
(36) E. Racker, G. de la Haba, and I. G. Leder, *Arch. Biochem. Biophys.* **48**, 238 (1954); *J. Biol. Chem.* **214**, 409 (1955).
(37) D. L. MacDonald and H. O. L. Fischer, *Biochim. et Biophys. Acta* **12**, 203 (1953); L. Hough and T. J. Taylor, *J. Chem. Soc.* p. 1212 (1955).
(38) R. C. Hockett, D. V. Collins, and A. Scattergood, *J. Am. Chem. Soc.* **73**, 599 (1951).
(39) M. L. Wolfrom, D. I. Weisblat, W. H. Zophy, and S. W. Waisbrot, *J. Am. Chem. Soc.* **63**, 201 (1941).
(39a) D. A. Rappaport and W. Z. Hassid, *J. Am. Chem. Soc.* **73**, 5524 (1951).
(39b) Decoloration with active charcoal and filtration through Celite may be necessary to remove an orange coloration. A single washing with 10% aqueous KI solution is also effective.
(40) D. L. MacDonald, H. O. L. Fischer, and C. E. Ballou, *J. Am. Chem. Soc.* **78**, 3720 (1956).
(41) J. K. Shetter, *J. Am. Chem. Soc.* **78**, 3722 (1956).
(42) H. A. Barker and F. Lipmann, *J. Biol. Chem.* **179**, 247 (1949).
(43) P. R. Srinivasan, M. Katagiri, and D. B. Sprinson, *J. Am. Chem. Soc.* **77**, 4943 (1955); cf. D. B. Sprinson, *in* "Essays in Biochemistry" (S. Graff, ed.), p. 267. Wiley, New York, 1956.
(44) E. Baer and H. O. L. Fischer, *J. Biol. Chem.* **180**, 145 (1949).
(45) D. B. Sprinson, *in* "Essays in Biochemistry" (S. Graff, ed.), p. 267. Wiley, New York, 1956.
(46) See among others, H. O. L. Fischer and G. Dangschat, *Helv. Chim. Acta* **20**, 705 (1937); *Naturwissenschaften* **26**, 562 (1938).
(47) B. D. Davis, *J. Biol. Chem.* **191**, 315 (1951); B. D. Davis, *in* "Amino Acid Metabolism" (W. D. McElroy and B. D. Glass, eds.), p. 799. Johns Hopkins Press, Baltimore, Maryland, 1955.

Amidomethylation[1]

H. HELLMANN

Chemisches Institut der Universität Tübingen

Definition and Importance of Amidomethylation

Whereas the substitution of a hydrogen atom by a dialkylamino-methyl group (Alk_2NCH_2—) is relatively easy to attain by the condensation of secondary amines with formaldehyde and nucleophilic or potentially nucleophilic compounds, substitution by a monoalkylamino-

$$Alk_2NH + OCH_2 + H-C\stackrel{/}{\diagdown} \xrightarrow{-H_2O} Alk_2N-CH_2-C\stackrel{/}{\diagdown}$$

methyl group ($AlkNH\overset{.}{C}H_2$—) succeeds less smoothly, and, finally, the replacement by an aminomethyl group (H_2NCH_2—) generally not at all, because in this case the remaining hydrogen atoms on the nitrogen also participate in the reaction. Accordingly the Mannich reaction with ammonia as the amine component leads almost always to tertiary amines:

$$NH_3 + 3\ OCH_2 + 3\ H-C\stackrel{/}{\diagdown} \xrightarrow{-3\ H_2O} N\left(-CH_2-C\stackrel{/}{\diagdown}\right)_3,$$

and only seldom to primary amines:

$$NH_3 + OCH_2 + H-C\stackrel{/}{\diagdown} \xrightarrow{-H_2O} H_2N-CH_2-C\stackrel{/}{\diagdown}$$

In general, the undesirable activity of the hydrogen atoms of amines and of ammonia is blocked temporarily by the introduction of a group, such as an acyl group, which is readily split off again. Therefore, it was reasonable to attempt the introduction of an aminomethyl group (H_2NCH_2—) by a two-step process of substitution by an acylamino-methyl group, followed by splitting off of the acyl group from the acylaminomethyl compound. There are several methods of amido-methylation; their preparative use will be described in the following sections.

Amidomethylation with N-Hydroxymethylamides

The easiest way to amidomethylate consists of the use of acylated ammonia—that is, an acid amide—as the amine component in a Mannich reaction; however, the question arises, whether such a condensation can still take place:

$$R-CO-NH_2 + OCH_2 + H-C\diagdown^{\diagup} \xrightarrow{-H_2O} R-CO-NH-CH_2-C\diagdown^{\diagup}$$

$$\downarrow + H_2O$$

$$R-COOH + H_2N-CH_2-C\diagdown^{\diagup}$$

The mechanism of the Mannich reaction about which much is known, is sketched to help answer this question (2). The formaldehyde unites first with the amine with the formation of a hydroxymethylamine (I), which, after taking on a proton, splits out water and goes over into a mesomeric carbonium–immonium ion (II). This ion, which is regarded as the true attacking agent in the Mannich reaction, aminomethylates a suitable nucleophilic condensation partner in an electrophilic substitution reaction:

$$R_2NH + OCH_2 + HC\diagdown^{\diagup} \longrightarrow R_2N-CH_2OH \quad \text{I}$$

$$\Big\downarrow + H^\oplus \quad -H_2O$$

$$R_2N-CH_2-C\diagdown^{\diagup} \xleftarrow{-H^\oplus} [R_2\overset{\frown}{N}-CH_2{}^\oplus \longleftrightarrow R_2\overset{\oplus}{N}=CH_2]$$

$$\text{II}$$

If the amine is replaced by an amide, which naturally possesses a substantially smaller nucleophilic potential, then appropriately, the formaldehyde is allowed first to react separately with the carboxamide to form the N-hydroxylmethylcarboxamide (III); in this manner the risk, inherent in a one-step reaction, of a primary addition of the formaldehyde to the second, probably stronger, nucleophilic condensation partner, is eliminated. It can be stated from the outset, that it requires a stronger acid catalyst to transform an N-hydroxymethylcarboxamide (III) into an acylaminomethylcarbonium–immonium ion (IV) than to form the aminomethylcarbonium ion (II). Further, the scope of reactivity of the condensing agent in amidomethylation is not completely identical with that in the aminomethylation reaction because of the stronger acid medium, be it that the acid suppresses too strongly the nucleophilic character of the reactant or because it changes profoundly the structure of its molecule.

$$R-CO-NH_2 + OCH_2 \longrightarrow R-CO-NH-CH_2OH \quad \text{III}$$

$$HC\diagdown^{\diagup}$$

$$\Big\downarrow + H^\oplus \quad -H_2O$$

$$R-CO-NH-CH_2-C\diagdown^{\diagup} \xleftarrow{-H^\oplus} [R-CO-\overset{\frown}{NH}-CH_2{}^\oplus \longleftrightarrow R-CO-\overset{\oplus}{NH}=CH_2]$$

$$\text{IV}$$

N-Hydroxymethylcarboxamides

The preparation of N-hydroxymethylcarboxamides ("methylolamides"), their use for acylaminomethylation and the hydrolysis of the acylaminomethylated products to primary amines had already been accomplished more than 50 years ago. In 1898 Sachs (3) prepared, as the first "methylolamide," N-hydroxymethylphthalimide (V) from formaldehyde and phthalimide. The readily crystallized compound holds the formaldehyde relatively loosely, but can be transformed nevertheless just as a more stable alcohol, to the ether (VI) by treatment with concentrated sulfuric acid (4):

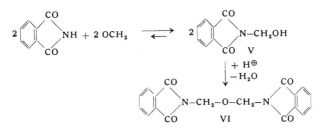

Later Einhorn succeeded in preparing corresponding hydroxymethyl compounds of primary carboxamides, not only by the addition of formaldehyde to the amide under the action of basic condensing agents such as potassium carbonate or sodium hydroxide (5), but also by the action of acids under mild conditions (6). The hydroxymethyl amides of this type (VII) retain the formaldehyde even less than V and readily change over to methylene bisamides (VIII) under the influence of mineral acids:

$$2 \ R-CO-NH_2 + 2 \ OCH_2 \ \rightleftarrows \ 2 \ R-CO-NH-CH_2OH$$
$$VII$$
$$\downarrow \begin{array}{l} + \ H^\oplus \\ -H_2O, \ -OCH_2 \end{array}$$
$$(R-CO-NH-)_2CH_2$$
$$VIII$$

Einhorn has described (7,8) more than 20 different N-hydroxymethylamides. Several additional ones have since been synthesized in other laboratories. Only the following are mentioned here: the monoamide derivatives, N-hydroxymethylbenzamide (7), -chloroacetamide (7), -trichloroacetamide (7), and -urethan (8); and the symmetrical dihydroxymethyl compounds of urea (8), succinamide (7), and oxamide (9).

Amidomethylation of Aromatics with N-Hydroxymethyl Amides

Soon after the preparation of N-hydroxymethylphthalimide (V), described by Sachs, Tscherniac (10) applied for a patent on the phthalimidomethylation of aromatic compounds by condensation with this hydroxymethylamide in concentrated sulfuric acid and the splitting of the condensation product to benzylamines.

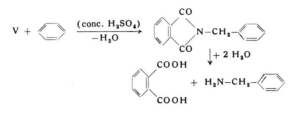

Since Tscherniac supported the view that the ether (VI) functions as an intermediate (because it is very easily formed from the hydroxymethylphthalimide in acid solution) he protected through another patent (11) the phthalimidomethylation of aromatic compounds by reaction with the ether VI in concentrated sulfuric acid. From the viewpoint of electronic theory one must regard a course of reaction via the ether VI as being highly improbable and therefore characterize the procedure protected by the second patent as a circuitous route.

One may assume that the oxonium ion IX, formed by the action of an acid on the hydroxymethylphthalimide, is converted by the loss of water to the phthalimidomethylcarbonium ion X, whose formation is promoted by mesomerism. As long as no other nucleophilic reactant is available to this ion, it adds to an unbound electron pair of the oxygen (of hydroxy-

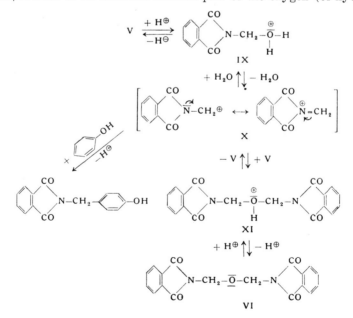

methylphthalimide) with the formation of the protonated form of bisphthalimidomethyl ether (XI). The oxonium ion XI can also split off a proton to form bisphthalimidomethyl ether (VI) as well as reverse to reform a phthalimidomethylcarbonium ion, since this splitting is also promoted by the mesomerism of the ion X.

However, the phthalimidomethylcarbonium ion is capable of undergoing other suitable electrophilic substitution reactions through contact with suitable reactants. Therefore it is not surprising that hydroxymethylphthalimide can be condensed with phenols in sulfuric acid solution; this is analogous to the alkylaminomethylation of phenols by the Mannich reaction, which was designated above as an electrophilic substitution reaction.

It is very noteworthy, however, that aromatic compounds which possess a nucleophilic potential inadequate for the Mannich reaction, such as unsubstituted benzene, benzoic acid, and others, are susceptible to the Tscherniac acylaminomethylation reaction. Acylaminomethylation with hydroxymethylamides in sulfuric acid solution is, therefore, to be compared with the other electrophilic substitution reactions which are so characteristic of the aromatic series, such as nitration, bromination, or the Friedel-Crafts reaction.

As Einhorn indicated, the methylol compounds of primary carboxamides (VII) may also be condensed (7, 8, 12) with aromatic compounds under acid conditions and the condensation products hydrolyzed to benzylamines.

The methylene bisamides (VIII) previously mentioned appear here only in minor amounts or not at all. That they are formed in good quantity when a carboxamide is heated alone with formaldehyde in mineral acid solution (13) is readily understandable. The urea-formaldehyde resins owe their formation to this reaction.

$$R-CO-NH-CH_2OH \xrightarrow{\ +H^{\oplus}\ } R\ CO-NH-CH_2-\overset{\oplus}{\underset{\overset{|}{H}}{O}}-H$$

$$\updownarrow \qquad\qquad\qquad\qquad +H_2O \uparrow\downarrow -H_2O$$

$$R-CO-NH_2 + OCH_2 \quad [R-CO-\overset{\frown}{NH}\overset{\oplus}{-}CH_2 \leftrightarrow R-CO-\overset{\oplus}{NH}=CH_2]$$

$$\downarrow -H^{\oplus}$$

$$R-CO-NH-CH_2-NH-CO-R$$

If another carboxamide is furnished as condensation partner to a hydroxymethyl amide in acid solution, the unsymmetrical methylene diamides are formed, e.g., in the condensation of N-hydroxymethylsalicylamide with benzamide (7) in alcoholic hydrochloric acid:

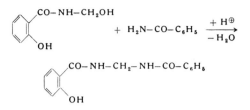

A survey reveals the isocyclic aromatic compounds which were amidomethylated by Tscherniac, Einhorn, and later workers. In these reactions the hydroxymethyl compounds of phthalimide, mono- and trichloroacetamide, urea, and succinamide were preferred. So far as the matter can be examined, the reaction proceeds much more easily and with much greater yield, the more nucleophilic the involved substance is under the reaction conditions. Mostly condensations on both hydroxymethylamide groups are obtained (*7, 9*) with the symmetrical dihydroxymethyl compounds; however, condensations on one side only have been described (*14*). With some phenols two or more amidomethyl groups enter the molecule, e.g., with veratrol (XII) (*15*) and with 1,5-dihydroxyanthraquinone (XIII) (*16*).

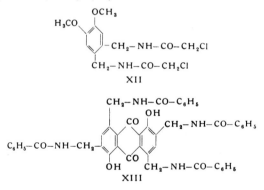

List of Acylaminomethylated Isocyclic Aromatic Compounds

Benzene (*10, 12*); benzoic acid (*7, 12*); benzenesulfonic acid (*10*); *m*-xylenesulfonic acid (*12*); nitrobenzene (*10*); *o*-, *m*-, *p*- nitrotoluene (*10*); dimethylaniline (*10*); acetanilide (*7, 12*); phenol (*10*); α-naphthol (*14*); β-naphthol (*7, 8, 12, 14*); thymol (*7*); salicylic acid (*7, 14*); α-naphthol-β-carboxylic acid (*14*); β-naphthol-3-carboxylic acid (*14*); pyrocatechol (*7*); resorcinol (*14*); hydroquinone (*7*); pyrogallol (*7*); mono- and dihydroxyanthraquinone (*16*); guaiacol (*7*); veratrol (*15*); pyrogallol trimethyl ether (*15*); hydroxyhydroquinone trimethyl ether (*15*); trimethyl ether of gallic acid (*15*); 2-methoxynaphthalene (*8*);

p-nitrophenol $(7, 10, 12, 14)$; p-nitrophenetol (7); 3-nitro-p-cresol (14); p-aminophenol (7); and phenacetin (7).

ACYLAMINOMETHYLATED HETEROCYCLIC AROMATICS

Many heterocyclic compounds having an aromatic character also have been condensed with hydroxymethylamides in acid solution. In the following summary of acylaminomethylated heterocycles the formula of the reaction product is presented from time to time in order to make clearer the place of entry of the acylaminomethyl group.

Esters of furoic acid with the hydroxymethyl compounds of phthalimide, benzamide, and chloroacetamide (17) and the symmetrical dihydroxymethyl compounds of urea and oxamide (9) lead to esters of 5-acylaminomethyl-2-furoic acid:

$$R-CO-NH-CH_2-\underset{O}{\boxed{}}-COOR$$

2-Thiophenecarboxylic acid with N-hydroxymethylchloroacetamide forms 5-chloroacetamidomethyl-2-thiophenecarboxylic acid (18):

$$Cl-CH_2-CO-NH-CH_2-\underset{S}{\boxed{}}-COOH$$

3-Methyl-1-phenyl-5-pyrazolone (7) and 2,3-dimethyl-1-phenyl-5-pyrazolone (19) with N-hydroxymethylchloroacetamide or benzamide are converted to 4-chloroacetamidomethyl-3-methyl-1-phenyl-5-pyrazolone and 4-benzamidomethylantipyrine:

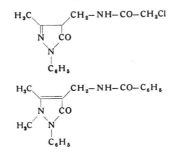

2-Hydroxyquinoline (7), 6- and 8-hydroxyquinoline, and 2-hydroxy-6-methoxyquinoline (20) have been reacted with hydroxymethylbenzamide; in these cases the authors did not determine the position of entry of the acylaminomethyl group.

4-Quinazolone and 2-methyl-4-quinazolone (21) were converted to the 3-acylaminomethyl derivatives (3-methyl- and 2,3-dimethyl-4-quinazolone do not react):

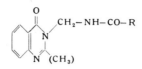

Acridine with hydroxymethylchloroacetamide and -benzamide formed to 9-acylaminomethylacridines (*22*):

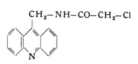

4-Methyl-2-thiouracil with hydroxymethylbenzamides, -phthalimide and -saccharin form the corresponding acylaminomethyl derivatives in which the condensation is said to have taken place, on analogous grounds, on the carbon and not on a nitrogen atom (*23*):

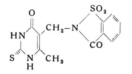

The same thiouracil was also condensed with sulfanilamide and formaldehyde in glacial acetic acid–hydrochloric acid to a sulfanilamido-methylthiouracil, and with *p*-acetamidobenzenesulfonamide to the acetyl derivative (*24*), in an unsymmetrical one-step condensation:

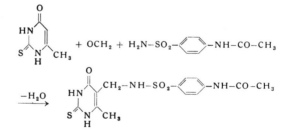

The condensation of the alkyl-substituted nitrogen heterocycles, α-picoline, quinaldine, 9-methyl- and ethylacridine as well as 2-methyl-4-quinazolone, with formaldehyde and sulfanilamide by heating at 130° (*25*) probably does not follow the course of a sulfonamidomethylation:

Amidomethylation of Methylene-active Compounds with N-Hydroxymethylcarboxamides

Aliphatic compounds containing an active methylene group can be amidomethylated with the aid of hydroxymethylamides, as long as they are not degraded by the acid condensing agent. Furthermore, the result is dependent upon the hydroxymethylamide introduced and the condensing agent. Acetylacetone, benzoylacetone, dibenzoylmethane, dihydroresorcinol, dimedone, and 3,5-dioxo-1,2-diphenylpyrazolidine condense smoothly with N-hydroxymethylphthalimide in the presence of concentrated sulfuric acid at room temperature with yields up to 85% (*25a*).

$$(CH_3CO)_2CH_2 + HOCH_2-N\underset{CO-}{\overset{CO-}{\diagup}} \xrightarrow[\substack{-H_2O \\ (85\%)}]{\text{conc. } H_2SO_4}$$

$$(CH_3CO)_2CH-CH_2-N\underset{CO-}{\overset{CO-}{\diagup}}$$

The corresponding condensations with N-hydroxymethylbenzamide are less productive (*19*). In this case boron trifluoride etherate is used advantageously as condensing agent; yields of 65% and 74% were obtained with dihydroresorcinol and dibenzoylmethane (*25a*). The hydrochloric acid hydrolysis of 2-phthalamidomethyldihydroresorcinol furnishes 7-amino-5-oxoheptanoic acid (*45*).

The adaptation of the method to cyanoacetic ester and nitriles with the object of amidomethylating the methylene-active center (*26,27*) is not possible, since the amidomethyl group enters the amido group produced by hydrolysis of the nitrile. Attempts to condense hydroxymethylbenzamide with malonic acid and malonic ester were unsuccessful (*27*).

Amidomethylation with N-Halomethylcarboxamides

Halomethylcarboxamides

N-Hydroxymethylcarboxamides may be converted to halomethylamides. Gabriel (*28*) obtained chloromethylphthalimide from hydroxymethylphthalimide and hydrochloric acid:

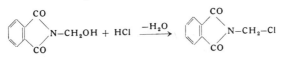

Cherbuliez and co-workers (*29,30*) prepared the chloromethylamide from N-hydroxymethylsuccinimide and N,N'-bis(hydroxymethyl)diketopiperazine by treatment with phosphorus pentachloride in an inert solvent:

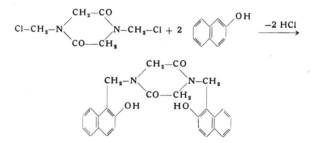

Böhme (*31*) recently has also prepared the N-halomethyl derivatives of primary acid amides (benzamide, 2,4-dichlorobenzamide, propionamide, acetamide, chloroacetamide, formamide) with the aid of phosphorus pentachloride. Cherbuliez and Feer (*29*) stress the fact that the N-chloromethylcarboxamides are as reactive as acid chlorides. The mobility of the halogen is understandable for in this instance, as in benzyl or allyl chloride, it is attached to a group which is mesomerically stabilized as a carbonium ion.

Amidomethylation of Aromatic Compounds with N-Halomethylcarboxamides

Cherbuliez (*30*) reacted the chloromethylcarboxamides which he prepared with aromatic compounds in a Friedel-Crafts reaction.

The condensation of 1,4-bis(chloromethyl)-2,5-dioxopiperazine with β-naphthol occurred especially well and with the best yields (*29*):

Very few examples of this type of reaction are known. Since, principally, one can arrive at the same results with the Tscherniac-Einhorn procedure, this would be given the preference, especially since the chloromethylcarboxamides must be prepared from the hydroxymethylcarboxamides. However, it is possible that the Cherbuliez procedure may lead to the desired result in some instances in which the Tscherniac-Einhorn method is unsuccessful.

Amidomethylation of Active Hydrogen (CH) Compounds with N-Halomethylcarboxamides

The high reactivity of the halogen in the halomethyl diacylimides (halomethylphthalimide or -succinimide) and the halomethyl derivatives of primary carboxamides (benzamide, 2,4-dichlorobenzamide, propionamide, acetamide, trichloroacetamide, formamide) was taken advantage of by Böhme (*31a*) in the amidomethylation of aliphatic compounds containing active hydrogen (C—H), in which he treated the halomethyl amide with the sodium compound. The monosubstituted β-diketones (dimedone, acetoacetonitrile) and monosubstituted methylene-active esters (malonic ester, acetoacetic ester, cyanoacetic ester, 1-carbalkoxy-2-cyclohexanone) can be amidomethylated quite smoothly.

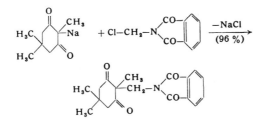

The monoamidomethylation of unsubstituted β-dicarboxyl compounds such as benzoylacetone, malonic ester, acetoacetic ester, and cyanoacetic ester also succeeds with the chloromethyl derivatives of benzamide, acetamide, and trichloroacetamide.

Thus, in the aliphatic series basic amidomethylation with halomethylcarboxamides is superior to acidic amidomethylation with hydroxymethylcarboxamides. Certainly the ability to amidomethylate with halomethylamides is not confined to active hydrogen (CH) compounds, but applicable to many other acidic hydrogen substances, whose amidomethylation by another procedure will be described in the following section.

Amidomethylation with N-Dialkylaminomethylcarboxamides and Their Quaternary Salts

The smooth course of the amidomethylation reaction with N-hydroxymethylamides in acid medium was interpreted in the foregoing as an electrophilic substitution reaction, in which the mesomeric amidomethylcarbonium ions of type X, which arise from the oxonium ions, IX, play a definite role.

Investigations of recent years have shown that quaternary ammonium salts could be used as outstanding alkylating agents for active-hydrogen substances, when the alkyl group to be transferred is mesomerically stabilized as a carbonium ion (*32*). Accordingly, active-hydrogen compounds, which are found chiefly in the aliphatic series, should be able to be amidomethylated with the aid of such quaternary ammonium salts which contain an amidomethyl group. This supposition was confirmed

(*33*). The quaternary ammonium salts may be easily prepared from methyl iodide and N-dialkylaminomethyl amides.

N-Dialkylaminomethyl Amides

After Sachs (*4*) had described the preparation of N-piperidino-methylphthalimide by the condensation of phthalimide with formaldehyde and piperidine, Einhorn (*7, 8*) obtained the corresponding dialkyl-aminomethyl derivatives of primary acid amides also by a condensation, which in principle resembled a Mannich reaction. Some additional representatives of this class of compounds have since been added; one might cite the derivatives of phthalimide (*4, 34, 35*), succinimide (*34, 36*), acetamide, benzamide (*7, 37*), urea (*8*), and benzenesulfonamide (*38*). Dimethylamine, diethylamine, piperidine or morpholine are most often used as the amine component, e.g.:

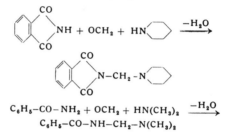

Amidomethylation of Acidic-hydrogen Compounds with Quaternary Salts of N-Dialkylaminomethylphthalimides

Phthalimidomethyltrimethylammonium iodide (XIV) (*34, 35*), easily obtained from N-dimethylaminomethylphthalimide and methyl iodide, contains a cation which, after splitting off trimethylamine, leaves behind the same mesomeric phthalimidomethylcarbonium ion (X) which was mentioned in the discussion of the phthalimidomethylation method of Tscherniac. However, since this ion is formed in a completely different series of reactions in an environment where it has available preformed or potential anions of acidic compounds as reaction partner, it is understandable that this condensation makes possible a different group of amidomethylated products than does the Tscherniac procedure. Thus the reaction of the quaternary salt, XIV, with sodium cyanide in dimethyl-formamide forms with a vigorous reaction phthalimidoacetonitrile (*33, 35*) (XV):

While in the condensation of XIV with sodiomalonic ester only a moderate yield of the disubstituted product was obtained (*33*), the reaction with formamidomalonic ester goes smoothly. Complete hydrolysis of the resulting phthalimidomethylformamidomalonic ester (XVI) gave 2,3-diaminopropionic acid in 85% over-all yield (*33*):

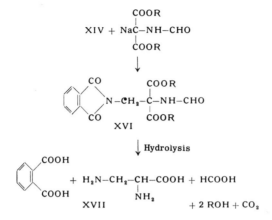

Besides these phthalimidomethylations on the C-atom, reactions involving the nitrogen were also described. The reactions with potassium carbazole or potassium phthalimide lead to N-phthalimidomethylcarbazole or diphthalimidomethane (*33*).

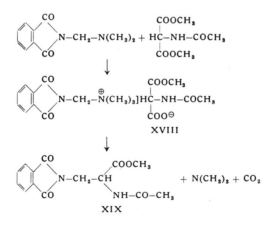

Phthalimidomethylations of this type can also occur when the phthalimidomethyltrimethylammonium ion is first formed as an intermediate in the reaction series. If, for example, dimethylaminomethylphthalimide is treated with dimethyl acetamidomalonate in boiling xylene, trimethylamine and carbon dioxide escape and methyl β-phthalimido-α-acetamidopropionate (XIX) (*39*) is formed as condensation product. The occurrence of the reaction can be freely interpreted by the assumption that dimethylaminomethylphthalimide and malonic ester react first to form the phthalimidomethyltrimethylammonium salt of the half ester of acetamidomalonic acid (XVIII) from which the quaternary ammonium ion, adapted for phthalimidomethylation, would be produced. This can condense with the malonic acid half-ester with trimethylamine elimination or, after its decarboxylation, with the corresponding carbanion. This variation will only rarely become of preparative importance.

The three methods of amidomethylation described represent substitution reactions, in which the mesomeric stabilization of the acylaminomethylcarbonium group (IV) obviously plays an important part.

$$[R'-CO-\overset{-}{N}R\overset{\frown}{-}\overset{\oplus}{C}H_2 \leftrightarrow R'-CO-\overset{\oplus}{N}R\underset{\frown}{=}CH_2]$$

A totally different reaction type is involved in the condensation of tertiary amines which contain an amidomethyl group.

Transaminomethylation of N-Dialkylaminomethyl Carboxamides Incapable of Condensation. (Pseudo-amidomethylation)

If condensation is attempted with dialkylaminomethylphthalimides themselves (i.e., not with their quaternary salts) with which the intermediate formation of quaternary ammonium ions (as described above), is impossible or hindered because the condensing partner is not an ester or does not contain such an ester group which can readily react with the tertiary amine, then the semblance of transaminomethylation is observed, that is an exchange of the dialkylaminomethyl group with a reactive hydrogen atom of the condensing partner. This is the case when, in the example cited above, the dimethylaminomethylphthalimide is replaced by piperidinomethylphthalimide and in place of the dimethyl ester of acylaminomalonic acid the corresponding diethyl ester is used. The isolable reaction products are phthalimide and piperidinomethyl acylaminomalonic ester (*33*):

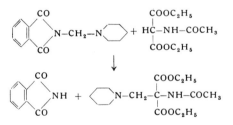

With the exchange of the piperidinomethyl group the reaction taking place comes to a standstill. On the other hand in the reaction of the same piperidinomethylphthalimide with indole a condensation to N-skatylphthalimide (XXI) follows the transaminomethylation (*33*), so that an amidomethylation with piperidinomethylphthalimide is assumed to have taken place if the course of reaction is ignored:

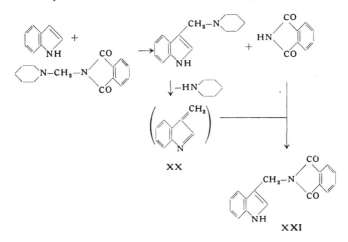

The different course of reaction is explained in the following manner. In the latter instance a tertiary amine is formed by transaminomethylation; it can react with phthalimide according to the elimination-addition mechanism (*32*). Then piperidinomethylindole can split off piperidine with formation of the methyleneindolenine (XX) (which is ready to act by addition). XX can react with phthalimide according to a Michael addition reaction. This mechanism is not available to the piperidinomethyl acylaminomalonic ester.

For the synthetic chemist the reactions described in the following section are of greater importance.

Amidomethylation with N-Dialkylaminomethyl Carboxamides

The dialkylaminomethyl derivatives of primary acid amides are also suitable for condensation reactions proceeding according to the elimination-addition mechanism. These compounds still possess a hydrogen atom on the amide nitrogen, which permits the splitting off of a secondary amine from the molecule with the formation of a methyleneamide (XXII) capable of addition:

$$R'-CO-NH-CH_2-NR_2 \rightleftarrows R'-CO-N=CH_2 + HNR_2$$
$$\text{XXII}$$

The condensation of N-dialkylaminomethylbenzamide with compounds containing an acidic hydrogen permits a large number of benzamidomethylations, which are not possible with the Tscherniac-

Einhorn method. By this means many compounds are simply prepared which are only otherwise accessible through the reaction of N-halomethyl carboxamides with the sodium compounds of acidic-hydrogen substances as described by Böhme.

The amine elimination, as pointed out above, is an equilibrium reaction, and condensation with substances containing an acidic hydrogen should proceed more readily, the more quickly the amine formed is removed from the equilibrium as an undesirable competitor. In practice, the dialkylaminomethylbenzamides react much better the lower the boiling point of the secondary amine which is removed in the condensation. Raising the temperature favors the elimination of the amine, but also favors the decomposition of the condensation product (reverse Michael addition). For most condensation reactions toluene, whose boiling temperature appears to be advantageous with reference to the reaction velocity and yields is selected as the solvent.

ATTACHMENT TO AMINES AND AMIDES

For evidence of the equilibrium sketched above, amine exchange experiments were utilized in which dimethylaminomethylbenzamide (XXIII) was heated in toluene to boiling with a slight excess of piperidine or tetrahydroquinoline and the passage of nitrogen. The escape of the dimethylamine set free, and thereby the course of the reaction, can be checked by titration with standard hydrochloric acid. In place of the escaping, readily volatile dimethylamine, piperidine or tetrahydroquinoline adds to the methyleneamide intermediate which is formed, to make piperidinomethylbenzamide (XXIV) or tetrahydroquinolinylmethyl-benzamide (37):

$$C_6H_5-CO-NH-CH_2-N(CH_3)_2 + HN\langle\rangle \underset{\longleftarrow}{\overset{\longrightarrow}{}}$$
XXIII

$$C_6H_5-CO-NH-CH_2-N\langle\rangle + HN(CH_3)_2$$
XXIV

The amine exchange goes almost quantitatively within a few hours.

With the addition of small amounts of powdered sodium hydroxide, all other conditions remaining fully the same, N-dimethylaminomethyl-benzamide (XXIII) was brought into reaction with the open-chain and cyclic amides, benzenesulfonamide, N-methyl-p-toluenesulfonamide, phthalimide, and isatin; whereby the unsymmetrical methylene diamides, N-benzoylaminomethylbenzenesulfonamide, N-benzoylaminomethyl-N-methyl-p-toluenesulfonamide (XXV), N-benzoylaminomethylphthalimide, and N-benzoylaminomethylisatin are formed in yields between 70 and 85% (38):

$$XXIII + HN-SO_2-C_6H_4-CH_3 \quad \xrightarrow{-HN(CH_3)_2}$$
$$\underset{CH_3}{|}$$

$$C_6H_5-CO-NH-CH_2-N-SO_2-C_6H_4-CH_3$$
$$XXV \qquad \underset{CH_3}{|}$$

It is to be remembered that unsymmetrical methylene diamides in certain cases can also be prepared with the help of hydroxymethyl amides in acid solution; in this case, however, the formation is based on another mechanism.

Indole and its derivatives, which cannot be considered for acylaminomethylation using the Tscherniac-Einhorn method because of their sensitivity towards strong acids, were also arylaminomethylated in the presence of nitrogen by boiling with dialkylaminomethylbenzamides in

$$C_6H_5-CO-NH-CH_2-N(CH_3)_2 + HN\langle\rangle \rightleftharpoons$$
$$XXIII$$
$$\underset{CH_2-NH-CO-C_6H_5}{}$$

toluene along with catalytic amounts of sodium hydroxide (40). The corresponding reaction with dialkylaminomethylphthalimide gives 3-phthalimidomethylindole (but here by way of a transaminomethylation and the skatylation of phthalimide through the initially formed 3-piperidinomethylindole).

ATTACHMENT TO MERCAPTANS AND SULFINIC ACIDS

Sulfur alkylations on sulfides, mercaptans, thioamides, sulfinates, and sulfites with the aid of condensable tertiary amines have been described often. It is not surprising therefore, that the reaction of dialkylaminomethyl derivatives of primary carboxamides with mercaptans and sulfinic acids leads smoothly to amidomethyl sulfides or amidomethyl sulfones (41).

$$C_6H_5-CO-NH-CH_2-N(C_2H_5)_2 + H-S-R \quad \xrightarrow{-HN(C_2H_5)_2}$$
$$XXVI$$

$$C_6H_5-CO-NH-CH_2-S-R \qquad R = C_4H_9, C_6H_5, C_7H_7 .$$

$$XXVI + HSO_2-R' \quad \xrightarrow{-HN(C_2H_5)_2}$$
$$C_6H_5-CO-NH-CH_2-SO_2-R' . \quad R' = C_6H_5, C_6H_4-CH_3, -\langle H\rangle ;$$

Since Knoevenagel (42) had already converted carboxamides and sulfonamides to acylamino- or sulfonamidomethanesulfonic acids with formaldehyde–bisulfite, the assumption could be made that amidomethyl-sulfones could be prepared from N-hydroxymethyl amides and sulfinic acids by the Tscherniac-Einhorn method. In fact benzamidomethyl phenyl sulfone is formed from sodium benzenesulfinate and N-hydroxymethylbenzamide under the influence of concentrated hydrochloric acid (43):

$$C_6H_5-CO-NH-CH_2OH + HSO_2-C_6H_5 \xrightarrow[-H_2O]{+ H^{\oplus}}$$

$$C_6H_5-CO-NH-CH_2-SO_2-C_6H_5$$

The yields with the acid-condensation are poorer, however.

ATTACHMENT TO COMPOUNDS CONTAINING ACIDIC HYDROGEN

The condensations of dialkylaminomethyl carboxamides with acidic-hydrogen–containing compounds is of considerable preparative interest (44). The result is greatly dependent upon the nature of the condensing partner containing the acidic hydrogen. Unsubstituted as well as monosubstituted malonic esters are especially suitable:

$$C_6H_5-CO-NH-CH_2-NR_2 + \overset{COOR'}{\underset{COOR'}{HC-R''}} \xrightarrow{-HNR_2}$$

$$C_6H_5-CO-NH-CH_2-\overset{COOR'}{\underset{COOR'}{C-R''}}$$

$$R'' = H, CH_3, C_2H_5, C_6H_5, C_7H_7, NH-COCH_3.$$

Similar favorable results were attained with substituted cyanoacetic esters. This is important since the corresponding amidomethylations of cyanoacetic esters by condensation with hydroxymethylamides in sulfuric acid solution by the Tscherniac and Einhorn method are not successful. Thus the reaction of diethylaminomethylbenzamide with diethyl α-cyanopimelate goes quite smoothly to the benzoylaminomethyl derivative with the reaction taking place on the carbon atom (XXVII), while the American authors, English and Clapp (26), seeking the same compound and using the Tscherniac-Einhorn method, obtained a conversion

$$C_6H_5-CO-NH-CH_2-N(C_2H_5)_2 + \overset{CN}{\underset{COOC_2H_5}{HC-(CH_2)_4-COOC_2H_5}}$$

$$\xrightarrow{-HN(C_2H_5)_2} C_6H_5-CO-NH-CH_2-\overset{CN}{\underset{COOC_2H_5}{C-(CH_2)_4-COOC_2H_5}}$$
XXVII

of the nitrile group to the amide, followed by acylaminomethylation on the amide nitrogen.

The amidomethylated malonic esters and cyanoacetic esters are important intermediates for the preparation of β-amino acids and β-acylamino acids (44). Boiling for 2 hr with concentrated hydrobromic acid brings about hydrolysis of the ester groups and decarboxylation to the β-acylaminocarboxylic acids, while continuation of the hydrolysis leads, after about 5 hr, to splitting off of the acyl group on the nitrogen with formation of the free β-amino acids.

$$
\begin{array}{c}
\text{(CN)} \\
\text{COOC}_2\text{H}_5 \\
|
\end{array}
$$

$$
\underset{\substack{|\\ \text{CO}\\ |\\ \text{C}_6\text{H}_5}}{\text{NH}-\text{CH}_2-}\underset{\substack{|\\ \text{COOC}_2\text{H}_5}}{\text{C}-\text{R}} \quad \xrightarrow[\text{2h, 126 °C}]{\text{conc. HBr}} \quad \text{C}_6\text{H}_5-\text{CO}-\text{HN}-\text{CH}_2-\underset{\substack{|\\ \text{R}}}{\text{CH}}-\text{COOH}
$$

$$
\downarrow \substack{\text{conc. HBr} \\ \text{6—8h, 126 °C}}
$$

$$
\text{R}=\text{CH}_3,\ \text{C}_6\text{H}_5,\ \text{C}_7\text{H}_7. \qquad \text{C}_6\text{H}_5\text{COOH} + \text{H}_2\text{N}-\text{CH}_2-\underset{\substack{|\\ \text{R}}}{\text{CH}}-\text{COOH}
$$

With dimethyl benzamidomethylacetamidomalonate the same hydrolysis furnishes, after only 2½ hr, 2,3-diaminopropionic acid, which can be easily prepared in an over-all yield of 85%.

$$
\underset{\substack{|\\ \text{COOCH}_3}}{\overset{\substack{\text{COOCH}_3\\ |}}{\text{C}_6\text{H}_5-\text{CO}-\text{NH}-\text{CH}_2-\text{C}-\text{NH}-\text{COCH}_3}} \xrightarrow[\text{2. 5 hr,126 °C}]{\text{conc. HBr}}
$$

$$
\text{H}_2\text{N}-\text{CH}_2-\underset{\substack{|\\ \text{NH}_2}}{\text{CH}}-\text{COOH}
$$

A similar productive synthesis of this diamino acid by condensation of dimethylaminomethylphthalimide methiodide with sodium acetamidomalonic ester was described above. The method of preparation just given is simpler, however.

Acetoacetic ester and nitroalkanes may also be amidomethylated with the aid of dialkylaminomethyl carboxamides, although not so easily (44). Condensation experiments with β-diketones, sulfones, benzyl cyanide, and cyclohexanone have not been satisfactory to date.

Summary and Outlook

Four methods are available for the substitution of a hydrogen atom by an amidomethyl group.

1. The condensation with N-hydroxymethylcarboxamides in acid medium. This method is applied primarily to aromatic compounds.

2. The condensation with N-halomethylamides using aluminum chloride as a Friedel-Crafts condensing agent. Used for the amido-

methylation of aromatics (the above-mentioned method is to be given preference), as well as for reaction with compounds containing acidic hydrogen, found in large numbers especially in the aliphatic series, in the presence of equimolar amounts of basic condensing agents.

3. The condensation with quaternary salts of N-dialkylaminomethyl-phthalimides. These react with about the same range of acidic-hydrogen–containing substances as in method 2. The reaction is carried out under similar conditions.

4. The condensation with N-dialkylaminomethyl derivatives of primary carboxamides. Used to advantage for the amidomethylation of acidic-hydrogen–containing compounds in the presence of catalytic amounts of a basic condensing agent.

The condensations cited under 1–3. are substitution reactions, in which the mesomeric stabilization of the amidomethylcarbonium ion obviously plays an essential part, while for the condensation named in 4. an elimination-addition mechanism is assumed.

Few examples are known of amidomethylation by condensation with formaldehyde and acid amide in a one-flask method. Also, the limit or overlapping of the range of application of the individual methods has not yet been fully investigated. Efforts to improve the amidomethylation process as a first step for the preparation of primary amines must be directed primarily to derivatives of amides whose acyl group can be easily removed from the amidomethylated product. The amides hitherto employed preferentially release their acyl group after condensation often only after being subjected to quite drastic hydrolytic conditions. Efforts in this direction are in progress in the author's laboratory.

Recently it has been shown that phthalimidomethyl derivatives of β-diketones such as dihydroresorcinol, dimedone, dibenzoylmethane, and acetylacetone condense with active methylene compounds such as malonic esters, acetoacetic esters, cyanoacetic esters, and nitrocyclohexane by elimination of phthalimide and formation of unsymmetrical products, which to some extent are not available in any other way (45). Preparative use of this fact is made when the corresponding Mannich bases, capable of condensation, cannot be introduced into a substance because of their instability.

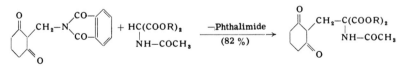

The acid hydrolysis of the condensation product from 2-phthalimido-methyldihydroresorcinol and the ester of acetamidomalonic acid leads to

4,5,6,7-tetrahydro-4-oxo-2-indolinecarboxylic acid and 2-carboxy-2-pyr-roline-5-butyric acid.

Experimental

N-Hydroxymethylbenzamide (*7*). A 70 gm portion of benzamide is gently warmed with a solution of 2 gm of potassium carbonate in 70 ml of water and 45 gm of a 40% formaldehyde solution until a clear solution is formed. On cooling crystallization begins. After 24 hr the major portion of N-hydroxymethylbenzamide has precipitated. The remainder is obtained by careful concentration. After recrystallization from very dilute alcohol the melting point is in the range of 104–6°. Yield: practically quantitative.

N-Hydroxymethylphthalimide (*3*) is prepared most easily by dissolving phthalimide in formalin. M.p. 141–2°.

1,4-Bis(hydroxymethyl)-2,5-dioxopiperazine (*29*). A 10 gm portion of powdered diketopiperazine in 60 gm of neutralized 40% formaldehyde solution is brought into solution on the water bath. After 24 hr in the ice box the hydroxymethylamide is filtered, washed with water, and recrystallized from alcohol. M.p. 178°. Yield: 90%.

Benzamidomethylation of p-nitrophenol with N-hydroxymethylbenzamide and concentrated sulfuric acid (*7*). The solution of 14 gm (0.1 mole) of p-nitrophenol in 50 gm of conc. sulfuric acid is treated with 15 gm (0.1 mole) of powdered N-hydroxymethylbenzamide with good cooling. With trituration complete solution occurs. After 2 days the reaction mixture is poured onto ice and the crystalline o-benzamido-methyl-p-nitrophenol precipitates. After filtering and washing with water it is recrystallized from acetone. M.p. 217–8°. Yield: 90%.

One hour's heating of the components with zinc chloride at 140° or using alcoholic hydrochloric acid as a condensing agent gives poor yields in this case.

The corresponding phthalimidomethylation of o-nitrophenol with N-hydroxymethylphthalimide and conc. sulfuric acid furnishes the condensation product in 95% yield (*10*).

The splitting off of the benzoyl group from the condensation product to obtain the primary amine is possible by boiling with alcoholic hydrochloric acid for 12 hr or more simply, without isolation of the condensation product, by boiling the reaction mixture, having previously diluted it with water.

Benzamidomethylation of β-naphthol with N-hydroxymethylbenzamide and alcoholic hydrochloric acid (*7*). The mixture of 4.3 gm (0.03 mole) of β-naphthol and 4.5 gm (0.03 mole) of N-hydroxymethylbenz-amide is dissolved in alcohol and treated with 2 ml of conc. hydrochloric

acid. Within 2 hr the major portion of the condensation product precipitates. The remainder is obtained by concentration under vacuum. Recrystallization is from ethyl acetate. M.p. 186°. Yield: Quantitative.

*Phthalimidomethylation of dihydroresorcinol with N-hydroxymethyl-
phthalimide and conc. sulfuric acid (25a).* To a cooled solution of 11.2
gm (0.1 mole) of dihydroresorcinol in 100 ml of conc. sulfuric acid, 17.7
gm (0.1 mole) of N-hydroxymethylphthalimide is slowly added in small
portions. After standing for 2 or 3 days at room temperature, the mixture
is poured onto ice, the precipitate filtered, stirred with water, again
filtered and washed with water. The 2-phthalimidomethyldihydrore-
sorcinol is extracted from the filter residue by boiling with alcohol and
obtained crystalline by cooling the alcohol extract. M.p. *ca.* 200° (dec.).
Yield: 18 gm (66%). Hydrolysis by boiling 5 hr with conc. hydrochloric
acid leads to 7-amino-5-oxoheptanoic acid hydrochloride, m.p. 116–8°.
Yield 75%.

1,4-Bis(chloromethyl)-2,5-dioxopiperazine (29). Six grams of phosphorus pentachloride, 5 gm of carbon tetrachloride and 5 gm of acetyl
chloride are ground together in a mortar and then treated with 2 gm of
bis(hydroxymethyl) dioxopiperazine in portions; warming, evolution of
HCl, and precipitation of the reaction product occur. After cessation of
HCl evolution, the mixture is cooled to −15° to complete the crystallization and then filtered. The product is recrystallized from chloroform.
M.p. 162° (dec.), with sintering at *ca.* 140°. Yield: 91%.

N-Chloromethylbenzamide (31a). A suspension of 15.1 gm of N-
hydroxymethylbenzamide in 25 ml of absolute ether is treated with 20.8
gm of phosphorus pentachloride under 15 ml of ether with cooling and
exclusion of moisture, shaken, and allowed to stand for 2 hr at room
temperature. The precipitated crystals are filtered, washed with small
amounts of ice cold ether and petroleum ether, and recrystallized from
a mixture of carbon tetrachloride and acetonitrile by the addition of
petroleum ether. The crystals decompose in air; m.p. 87–8°. Yield: 132
gm (78%).

*Amidomethylation of β-naphthol with bis(chloromethyl)dioxopipera-
zine (29).* A 1 gm (0.005 mole) portion of bis(chloromethyl)dioxopipera-
zine and 1.4 gm (0.01 mole) of β-naphthol are refluxed in 6 ml of benzene
until the evolution of HCl, after *ca.* 1 hr, stops. A portion of the product
crystallizes out during the reaction, the rest after cooling. After filtration
it is washed with alcohol and ether. M.p. 285–6°. Yield 89%.

*Benzamidomethylation of ethyl 2-cyclohexanonecarboxylate with N-
chloromethylbenzamide (31a).* A 7.7 gm portion of sodium wire under
350 ml of dioxane is treated with 57 gm of ethyl 2-cyclohexanonecar-
boxylate, 56.5 gm of N-chloromethylbenzamide added in portions, and

the mixture heated on the steam bath for 3 hr. The dark residue, after removal of sodium chloride and dioxane, is repeatedly extracted by boiling with water or ligroin. The melting point of ethyl 1-benzamido-methyl-2-cyclohexanone-1-carboxylate is 109°. Yield: 85 gm (84%).

N-Dimethylaminomethylphthalimide (34). A 14.7 gm (0.1 mole) portion of phthalimide is suspended in 10 ml of ethanol, treated with 8.25 ml (0.11 mole) of a 40% formaldehyde solution and 15 ml (0.1 mole) of a 33% dimethylamine solution, and then warmed on the water bath until a clear solution is obtained. After 1–4 days' standing in an open flask at room temperature dimethylaminomethylphthalimide precipitates as centimeter long, thick bars united in bunches, along with fine needles of N-hydroxymethylphthalimide. The crystalline mixture, after filtration and drying, is extracted by boiling with petroleum ether several times. On cooling the petroleum ether extract, long, thick needles of dimethylaminomethylphthalimide separate. M.p. 77–8°. Yield: 42%.

The N-hydroxymethylphthalimide, insoluble in petroleum ether, amounts to 38%.

Sometimes the dimethylaminomethylphthalimide, recognized by its stout crystalline form, separates before the N-hydroxymethylphthalimide, and isolation of the base is simplified.

N-Diethylaminomethylbenzamide (37). A 12.1 gm (0.1 mole) portion of benzamide is gently warmed with 20 ml of water, 7.3 gm (0.1 mole) of diethylamine, and 7.5 gm (0.1 mole) of 40% formaldehyde solution until the solution of benzamide takes place. After standing for 1 hr at room temperature the water is distilled off under vacuum on a water bath, whose temperature in the course of ½ hr is raised from 30 to 100°. The diethylaminomethylbenzamide which remains as residue is at first mostly oily, but soon crystallizes with rubbing. Purification by precipitation from benzene with petroleum ether, again gives the oil, which soon crystallizes. M.p. 62–4°. Yield: 73%.

N-Dimethylaminomethylbenzamide is also obtained in a similar good yield. M.p. 57–9°.

Phthalimidomethylation of cyanide with N-dimethylaminomethyl-phthalimide methiodide (33,35).—The methiodide of N-dimethyl-aminomethylphthalimide (XIV). A 2 gm (0.01 mole) portion of dimethylaminomethylphthalimide is dissolved in 6 ml of hot absolute alcohol and treated dropwise with 0.7 ml (0.01 mole) of methyl iodide. After 1 min spontaneous crystallization is evident. After filtration the crystalline material is extracted with boiling alcohol in which the methiodide is insoluble. M.p. 225–7° (dec.) Yield: 73%.

Conversion of the methiodide (XIV) with sodium cyanide to phthal-amidoacetonitrile. A 3.46 gm (0.01 mole) portion of methiodide and

0.5 gm (0.01 mole) of sodium cyanide are heated to boiling in 25 ml of dimethylformamide, which also was found very suitable as solvent in the condensations of quaternary salts of other Mannich bases, until the vigorous evolution of trimethylamine decreases, after 3–4 hr. The solvent is distilled under vacuum and the residue stirred with water, whereupon phthalimidoacetonitrile separates. It is recrystallized from water. M.p. 123°. Yield: 76%.

N-Benzamidomethylation of indole with N-dimethylaminomethylbenzamide (40). A mixture of 17.8 gm (0.1 mole) of N-dimethylaminomethylbenzamide, 23.4 gm (0.2 mole) of indole, and 0.01 gm of powdered sodium hydroxide is boiled in 500 ml of dry toluene for 7 hr under a small stream of nitrogen. By the end of this time about 80% of the dimethylamine has evolved, as determined by titration with standard hydrochloric acid. The greater portion of the reaction product crystallizes after cooling; a further amount is obtained by concentrating to 100 ml and the addition of 200 ml of petroleum ether. The crude product is recrystallized from xylene, and the methylene bisbenzamide which separates first must be filtered off from the still warm solution. By washing three times with 150 ml of 20% acetic acid the remainder of the methylene bisbenzamide can be removed. It is recrystallized once more from toluene. M.p. 130–1°. Yield: 57%.

S-Benzamidomethylation of butyl mercaptan with N-dimethylaminomethylbenzamide (41). A mixture of 0.9 gm (0.01 mole) of butyl mercaptan, 1.8 gm (0.01 mole) of N-dimethylaminomethylbenzamide, and 0.01 gm of powdered sodium hydroxide is heated to boiling in 80 ml of benzene in a stream of nitrogen. Within 6 hr about 90% of the dimethylamine is evolved. After this 60 ml of benzene is distilled off. On addition of petroleum ether to the concentrated solution the reaction product separates, at first mostly as an oil, which crystallizes, however, on rubbing. It is recrystallized from petroleum ether. M.p. 56°. Yield: 85%.

Benzamidomethylation of acetamidomalonic ester with N-dimethylaminomethylbenzamide; synthesis of 2,3-diaminopropionic acid (44). A mixture of 1.8 gm (0.01 mole) of N-dimethylaminomethylbenzamide and 1.9 gm (0.01 mole) of dimethyl acetamidomalonate with 0.05 gm of powdered sodium hydroxide is boiled in 30 ml of toluene in a stream of nitrogen. In 2–3 hr about 90% of the theoretical amount of dimethylamine is evolved. The dimethyl benzamidomethyl acetamidomalonate, which partly separates during the reaction, completely crystallizes after cooling. After filtration the residue is washed with water to remove the sodium hydroxide, dried, and recrystallized from toluene. M.p. 151°. Yield 87%.

To obtain the 2,3-diaminopropionic acid 2 gm of dimethyl benzamidomethyl acetamidomalonate is heated to gentle boiling for 2½ hr with 10 ml of constant boiling hydrobromic acid. After 30 min the separation of benzoic acid starts in the reflux condenser. The crystallized benzoic acid is filtered from the cooled reaction mixture and the 2,3-diaminopropionic acid hydrobromide precipitated with the addition of alcohol. Purification is by precipitation from aqueous solution with alcohol, three times. M.p. 237° (dec.). Yield: 94%.

Condensation of 2-phthalimidomethyldihydroresorcinol with dimethyl acetamidomalonate (45). A solution of 0.23 gm of sodium, 1.89 gm (0.01 mole) of dimethyl acetamidomalonate and 2.71 gm (0.01 mole) of 2-phthalimidomethyldihydroresorcinol in 20 ml of absolute methanol is refluxed for 8 hr, the methanol is distilled off, and the residue digested with 50 ml of water; about 1.3 gm of phthalimide remains undissolved. The solution is acidified and concentrated, and the dimethyl acetamido 2-dihydroresorcylmethylmalonate crystallizes. It is recrystallized from methanol. M.p. 184–5° (dec.). Yield: 2.55 gm (82%).

REFERENCES

(1) Compare H. Hellmann and G. Optiz, "α-Aminoalkylierung," 350 pp. Verlag Chemie, G.M.B.H., Weinheim-Bergstr., 1960.

(2) H. Hellmann and G. Opitz, *Angew. Chem.* **68**, 265 (1956).

(3) F. Sachs, *Ber. deut. chem. Ges.* **31**, 3230 (1898); German Patent 104,624; P. Friedländer, "Fortschritte der Teerfarbenfabrikation und verwandter Industriezweige," Vol. 5, p. 926. Springer, Berlin, 1901.

(4) F. Sachs, *Ber. deut. chem. Ges.* **31**, 1232 (1898).

(5) A. Einhorn, German Patent 157,355; P. Friedländer, "Fortschritte der Teerfarbenfabrikation und verwandter Industriezweige," Vol. 7, p. 616. Springer, Berlin, 1902–1904.

(6) A. Einhorn, German Patent 158,088; P. Friedländer, "Fortschritte der Teerfarbenfabrikation und verwandter Industriezweige," Vol. 7, p. 617. Springer, Berlin, 1902–1904.

(7) A. Einhorn, *Ann. Chem. Liebigs* **343**, 207 (1905).

(8) A. Einhorn, *Ann. Chem. Liebigs* **361**, 113 (1908).

(9) O. Moldenhauer, W. Irion, and H. Marwitz, *Ann. Chem. Liebigs* **583**, 37 (1953).

(10) J. Tscherniac, German Patent 134,979 (1902); P. Friedländer, "Fortschritte der Teerfarbenfabrikation und verwandter Industriezweige," Vol. 6, p. 143. Springer, Berlin, 1902.

(11) J. Tscherniac, German Patent 134,980 (1902); P. Friedländer, "Fortschritte der Teerfarbenfabrikation und verwandter Industriezweige," Vol. 6, p. 145. Springer, Berlin, 1902.

(12) A. Einhorn, German Patent 156,398 (1904); P. Friedländer, "Fortschritte der Teerfarbenfabrikation und verwandter Industriezweige," Vol. 7, p. 614. Springer, Berlin, 1904.

(13) G. Pulvermacher, *Ber. deut. chem. Ges.* **25**, 311 (1892).

(14) H. de Diesbach, O. Wanger, and A. v. Stockalper, *Helv. Chim. Acta* **14**, 355 (1931).

(15) L. Monti, *Gazz. chim. ital.* **60**, 777 (1930).

(16) H. de Diesbach and P. Gubser, *Helv. Chim. Acta* **11**, 1098 (1928); **13**, 120 (1930).

(17) G. B. Marini, *Gazz. chim. ital.* **69**, 340 (1939).

(18) R. O. Cinneide, *Proc. Roy. Irish Acad. Sect. B* **42**, 359 (1935); *Chem. Abstr.* **29**, 7326 (1935).

(19) L. Monti, *Gazz. chim. ital.* **60**, 39 (1930).

(20) L. Monti and G. Verona, *Gazz. chim. ital.* **62**, 878 (1932).

(21) L. Monti, A. Osti, and S. Piras, *Gazz. chim. ital.* **71**, 654 (1941).

(22) L. Monti, *Gazz. chim. ital.* **63**, 724 (1933).

(23) L. Monti and G. Franchi, *Gazz. chim. ital.* **81**, 191 (1951).

(24) L. Monti and G. Franchi, *Gazz. chim. ital.* **81**, 332 (1951).

(25) L. Monti and L. Felici, *Gazz. chim. ital.* **70**, 375 (1940).

(25a) H. Hellmann, G. Aichinger, and H. P. Wiedemann, *Ann. Chem. Liebigs* **626**, 35 (1959).

(26) J. P. English and R. C. Clapp, *J. Am. Chem. Soc.* **67**, 2262 (1945).

(27) S. R. Buc, *J. Am. Chem. Soc.* **69**, 254 (1947).

(28) S. Gabriel, *Ber. deut. chem. Ges.* **41**, 242 (1908).

(29) E. Cherbuliez and E. Feer, *Helv. Chim. Acta* **5**, 678 (1922).

(30) E. Cherbuliez and G. Sulzer, *Helv. Chim. Acta* **8**, 567 (1925).

(31) H. Böhme, *Angew. Chem.* **69**, 185 (1957); H. Böhme and F. Eiden, German Patent 1,025,883 (1955); *Chem. Abstr.* **54**, 9773 (1960).

(31a) H. Böhme, R. Broese, and F. Eiden, *Chem. Ber.* **92**, 1258 (1959); H. Böhme, R. Broese, A. Dick, F. Eiden, and D. Schünemann, *ibid.* **92**, 1599 (1959).

(32) H. Hellmann, *Angew. Chem.* **65**, 473 (1953).

(33) H. Hellmann, I. Loschmann, and F. Lingens, *Chem. Ber.* **87**, 1690 (1954).

(34) H. Hellmann and I. Loschmann, *Chem. Ber.* **87**, 1684 (1954).

(35) R. O. Atkinson, *J. Chem. Soc.* p. 1329 (1954).

(36) J. R. Feldman and E. C. Wagner, *J. Org. Chem.* **7**, 31 (1942).

(37) H. Hellmann and G. Haas, *Chem. Ber.* **90**, 50 (1957).

(38) W. J. Weaver, J. K. Simons, and W. E. Baldwin, *J. Am. Chem. Soc.* **66**, 222 (1944).

(39) H. Hellmann, unpublished data.

(40) H. Hellmann and G. Haas, *Chem. Ber.* **90**, 53 (1957).

(41) H. Hellmann and G. Haas, *Chem. Ber.* **90**, 444 (1957).

(42) E. Knoevenagel and H. Lebach, *Ber. deut. chem. Ges.* **37**, 4094 (1904).

(43) H. Hellmann and G. Haas, unpublished.

(44) H. Hellmann and G. Haas, *Chem. Ber.* **90**, 1357 (1957).

(45) H. Hellmann and G. Aichinger, *Chem. Ber.* **92**, 2122 (1959).

Selective Catalytic Oxidations with Noble Metal Catalysts

K. Heyns and H. Paulsen

Chemisches Staatsinstitut, Universität Hamburg

General Statements

Catalytic oxidation with molecular oxygen is carried out (*1*) with different products under the most varied conditions, particularly in industry. Metals, metal oxides, and salts are available as catalysts; nickel, copper, platinum, silver, the oxides of vanadium, zinc, aluminum, as well as the salts of cobalt and manganese, have proved especially effective. In most cases the readily controlled continuous catalytic oxidation in the gas phase is used technically, e.g. the oxidation of alcohols to aldehydes and acids or to ketones. In isolated cases the oxidation in heterogeneous liquid phase, in which the oxygen is blown through the reaction materials, has also attained technical importance, as in the oxidation of paraffins to fatty acids (*2*) or the oxidation of hydrocarbons to peroxides. Up to now catalytic oxidations as preparative methods have not been used as extensively as catalytic hydrogenations, which are very widely developed with various modifications as selective methods for the reduction of special functional groups in organic molecules. In what follows the process of catalytic oxidation, using a platinum catalyst in aqueous solution or in organic solvents at low temperature, will be described as an excellent practical preparative method for selective reactions in special cases. The methods of procedure and apparatus are similar to those of catalytic hydrogenation. Finely divided platinum is not only a special hydrogenation catalyst, but, with good effects, is also preparatively useful for the reverse reaction as oxidation or dehydrogenation catalyst for numerous types of reactions. Thus, primary alcohols may be oxidized to aldehydes and acids, as may secondary alcohols to ketones under such mild reaction conditions that the method is especially suitable for sensitive compounds. However, the actual value of the method lies in the fact that selective oxidations are possible. Polyhydroxy compounds which contain several oxidizable hydroxyl groups, such as the carbohydrates, can be oxidized at a definite group according to the conditions chosen. It has been shown that, in general, primary hydroxyl groups are attacked preferably before secondary hydroxyl groups. If only secondary groups are present, then the axial groups react preferentially to the equatorial. The selectivity of catalytic oxidation with platinum is so considerable that in certain cases, e.g. with cyclitols it may be paralleled throughout alongside the bacterial oxidations, which generally are distinguished by exceptional specificity.

Catalytic Oxidation as Dehydrogenation

The first observation that a platinum catalyst catalyzes oxidations in the presence of oxygen (air) was described by Strecker (3) in 1855 with the formation of cinnamic aldehyde from cinnamyl alcohol. Von Gorup-Besanez (4) and Dafert (5) stirred mannitol solutions in air with platinum black or allowed them to evaporate slowly, and determined the formation of reduced [sic] substances and acids, which they claimed were mannose and mannonic acid. Under similar conditions Grimeaux (6) observed the formation of glyceraldehyde from glycerine in aqueous solution in the presence of platinum black and air.

Exhaustive investigations were first begun by Wieland (7). Different simple alcohols yield the corresponding aldehydes in dilute aqueous solution with finely divided platinum and oxygen. Wieland designated these reactions as dehydrogenation in which the platinum activates the hydrogen of the alcohol. The molecular oxygen simply serves as acceptor for the activated hydrogen in that it oxidizes the hydrogen to water and thus removes it from the equilibrium. As support for this dehydrogenation theory there was considered the fact that this reaction, without any oxygen present, runs its course in the presence, for example, of methylene blue as acceptor for the platinum activated hydrogen whereby the dye goes over into a colorless leuco form. Accordingly the platinum catalyst was represented as a model of a dehydrase, whose reactions are said to correspond to dehydrogenation reactions which control the biological event. Müller and Schwabe (8) confirmed the Wieland dehydrogenation theory by quantitative investigation of the potential of the catalyst. They used apparatus which permitted them to measure, by means of a glass electrode, the potential of the platinum catalyst during oxidation. Figure 1 shows one such result of measurement of the oxidation of ethyl alcohol to acetic acid in the presence of an excess amount of sodium hydroxide.

Therefore, by the addition of alkali, the oxidation leads to acetic acid. Also potential differences brought about by a large change in hydrogen ion concentration can be avoided. The curve shows that the potential of the catalyst during oxidation lies strongly on the hydrogen side. The catalyst must be charged with hydrogen in a manner similar to an hydrogen electrode. Apparently the catalyst has detached the hydrogen from the adsorbed alcohol and has adsorbed the hydrogen while the desorbed portion reacts further with water to form the aldehyde. In a second reaction the activated hydrogen is oxidized by molecular oxygen. According to Macrae (*9*) this second oxidation step is said to proceed through an initial formation of hydrogen peroxide as intermediate, whose existence he had demonstrated by the formation of ceric peroxide, having carried out the oxidation in the presence of cerous hydroxide. The resulting hydrogen peroxide is very quickly decomposed by the effectual catalase activity of the platinum catalyst.

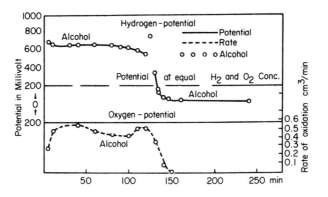

FIG. 1. Oxidation of ethyl alcohol to acetic acid in excess NaOH with platinum catalyst.

At the point at which no more oxygen consumption can be determined volumetrically (lower curve), the oxidation to acetic acid is thus ended; the potential of the catalyst shifts (upper curve) and lies strongly on the oxygen side. At this instance no hydrogen capable of being removed—such as is available in alcohol and aldehyde, but not in acetic acid—is placed at the disposal of the catalyst and it takes on the potential of the molecular oxygen which is available in excess. The view which considers catalytic oxidation with platinum to be a dehydrogenation may be widely confirmed.

Recently investigations with the oxygen isotope O^{18} were undertaken by Rottenberg and Baertschi (*10*). Ethyl alcohol was oxidized to acetic acid in two experiments: in the first the oxygen used was marked with O_2^{18}, in the second the aqueous solvent was marked with H_2O^{18}. In the first instance only 5% of O^{18} was found in the acetic acid formed, while in the second oxidation 70–80% of the O^{18} from water was taken up. This result also supports the dehydrogenation theory. This, however, is not a proof since the same isotope distribution could be caused also by the simple isotopic exchange of acetaldehyde, formed as an intermediate which, as is well known, exchanges with H_2O^{18} very rapidly. On the basis of exchange experiments in isopropyl alcohol with H_2O^{18} in the presence of hydrogen and platinum, Rottenberg and Thürkauf (10a) consider a reversible dehydrogenation as the initial step as improbable and discuss an activation of the oxygen or a modified dehydrogenation mechanism.

The Catalyst and the Conditions for Oxidation

A 5–10% platinum catalyst on active carbon is used as catalyst which is precipitated on the carbon by hydrogenation or reduction with formaldehyde or hydrazine sulfate; the catalyst prepared with formaldehyde is said to be more active in some reactions (11). In many cases, e.g. in the preparation of different uronides (12, 13, 13a) and cycloketoses (13b), a purer platinum catalyst, prepared by the hydrogenation of platinum dioxide according to Adams, furnishes better yields. In these cases it was recommended that the freshly hydrogenated catalyst be freed from adsorbed hydrogen by subjecting it to several evacuations (12, 13). A 0.5% platinum catalyst with aluminum oxide as carrier has been used successfully (16); it is especially suitable for the counter-current process.

For successful oxidation it is important that the solution of reaction material, in which the catalyst is suspended, is brought into quite intimate contact with the catalyst and the finely dispersed oxygen by stirring, taking care this does not occur too vigorously. Hydrogenation apparatus equipped with agitators or magnetic stirrers may be employed as reaction vessels, since they permit the observation of oxygen consumption in the closed systems. For oxidation at lower temperatures Kluyver's aeration flasks have proved useful, in which air is sucked through or oxygen is forced in with pressure through the fritted bottom, by means of which the gas is very finely dispersed. At higher temperatures three-necked flasks equipped with rapid stirrers to ensure thorough mixing, and in which a stream of oxygen is blown through, are mostly used. The desired temperature must be regulated by thermostats. If in this arrangement, a recycling apparatus (17) is used in which the oxygen is again introduced into the cycle, then the determination of oxygen consumption is also possible here. The oxidation, e.g. feasible for technical plants, may also be continuous, in which the reaction solution is allowed to flow through a column of catalyst (Al_2O_3 with 0.5% Pt) and oxygen is passed through in counterflow (16). The column length and the flow velocity are regulated in such a manner that the substrate in the emergent solution is completely oxidized. Reactions at higher temperature are attained by heating the column. Oxidation in the autoclave at higher oxygen pressure was also investigated (18). The method, however, offered no advantage since the equilibrium-determining step of dehydrogenation is apparently not accelerated.

Oxidation takes place advantageously in dilute solutions (about 2–7%). At concentrations over 10% the reaction rate is inhibited and the yields become poorer. Primarily water is considered the solvent for polyhydroxy compounds. Furthermore, oxidations in organic solvents such as ethyl acetate, acetone (19), benzine, and chloroform (17) have been undertaken with good results; although here the possibilities have been examined only to a small degree.

Investigations concerning catalyst poisons give no uniform picture. Hydrogen sulfide and tertiary amines (pyridine, quinoline) are generally strong inhibitors (20). According to some authors phenol (21) is a strong catalyst poison; others could not confirm the inhibition. A poisonous action by calcium and silicate ions was observed only in isolated oxidations (17). In all cases the oxidation solution must be completely homogeneous. If a second phase is present, e.g. a trace of oil droplets in water, then the catalyst clumps together and the oxidation comes to a standstill immediately.

In general primary alcohol groups in neutral to weakly acid solution are oxidized to the aldehyde stage and only in small amounts further to the acid stage. However, the yields of aldehyde are not always satisfactory. In the presence of alkali the acids which are formed are continuously trapped, the oxidation leading then to good yields of carboxylic acids. The addition of sodium bicarbonate has been shown to be quite effective since oxidation in almost neutral to weakly alkaline solution is then possible. Secondary alcohols are oxidized to the corresponding ketones in neutral to weakly acidic solution, addition of a neutralizing agent being unnecessary.

The most favorable reaction conditions for each special reaction are mostly determined by a series of experiments. Small temperature differences, alteration of the concentrations and the course of pH, the condition of the catalyst, and the attainment of a most favorable dispersion of the catalyst and oxygen can influence the success of the reaction decisively.

Oxidation of Simple Alcohols

Systematic investigations by Heyns and Blazejewicz (17) on the oxidizability of diverse types of alcohols under the optimum conditions give a general view of the range of application of the method. The results are summarized in Table 1.

All oxidations were carried out in a normal hydrogenation apparatus, which can be heated and which permitted the determination of oxygen consumption. Oxidations occurred fastest in polar solvents as water, or nonpolar as benzine and n-heptane. Acetone, butanone, and dioxane were

TABLE 1

Primary alcohols

a) Aliphatic, saturated, monohydroxy alcohols

Substrate	Solvent	Catalyst	Time hr	Temperature °C	Oxidation product	Yield %	Remarks
Ethanol	Water	Pt-C	0.5	20	Acetic acid	100	Alkaline
n-Propanol	Water	Pt-C	11	66	Propionic acid	98	Alkaline
n-Butanol	n-Heptane	PtO₂	5	41	Butyraldehyde	57	
	Glacial acetic acid	PtO₂	46	15	Buryraldehyde	33	
	Water	Pt-C	17	80	Butyric acid	100	Alkaline, dioxane
n-Pentanol	n-Heptane	Pt-C	5	60	Valeraldehyde	51	
	Dioxane	PtO₂	12	17	Valeraldehyde	29	79% O₂-conversion
	Glacial acetic acid	PtO₂	13	19	Valeraldehyde	39	
	Pivalic acid	PtO₂	68	61	Valeraldehyde	33	Very impure
n-Hexanol	Water	Pt-C	26	93 Boiling temperature	Caproic acid	99	Alkaline, dioxane
n-Heptanol	n-Heptane	PtO₂	1	60	Heptaldehyde	26	135% O₂-conversion
Dodecyl alcohol	n-Heptane	PtO₂	0.25	60	Lauraldehyde	77	
	Methyl ethyl ketone	PtO₂	42	40	Lauraldehyde	78	Preparative
	n-Heptane	PtO₂	2	60	Lauric acid	96	
Myristyl alcohol	n-Heptane	PtO₂	0.75	60	Myristaldehyde	91	
Cetyl alcohol	n-Heptane	PtO₂	7	59	Palmitaldehyde	95	
Stearyl alcohol	n-Heptane	PtO₂	0.5	60	Stearaldehyde	77	

b) Aliphatic saturated, polyhydroxy alcohols

Substrate	Solvent	Catalyst	Time	Temperature	Product	Yield	Remarks
Glycol	Water	Pt-C	11	Boiling temperature	Oxalic acid	51	Alkaline
	Water	Pt-C	6	Boiling temperature	Glycolic acid	100	1 Mole alkali
1,4-Butanediol	Water	Pt-C	32	Boiling temperature	Succinic acid	55	Alkaline
1,10-Decanediol	n-Heptane	PtO_2	1.5	60	Sebacaldehyde	54	

c) Aliphatic, unsaturated, monohydroxy alcohols

Substrate	Solvent	Catalyst	Time	Temperature	Product	Yield	Remarks
Tiglic alcohol	n-Heptane	PtO_2	2	60	Tiglicaldehyde	77	
Geraniol	n-Heptane	PtO_2	1.5	60	Citral	63	
Oleic alcohol	n-Heptane	PtO_2	3	60	Oleinaldehyde	47 (crude)	14% Pure aldehyde
Elaidic alcohol	n-Heptane	PtO_2	3	60	Elaidicaldehyde	73 (crude)	22% Pure aldehyde

d) Aromatic alcohols

Substrate	Solvent	Catalyst	Time	Temperature	Product	Yield	Remarks
Benzyl alcohol	n-Heptane	PtO_2	1	60	Benzaldehyde	78	Alkaline + toluenesulfonic acid
	Water	Pt-C	10	Boiling temperature	Benzoic acid	97	
Phenethyl alcohol	n-Heptane	PtO_2	1.5	60	Phenylacetaldehyde	34	
	Water	Pt-C	12	Boiling temperature	Phenylacetic acid	90	Alkaline + toluenesulfonic acid

Secondary alcohols

Substrate	Solvent	Catalyst	Time	Temperature	Product	Yield	Remarks
2-Propanol	n-Heptanol	PtO_2	0.5	17	Acetone	91	No alkali
	Water	Pt-C	1	60	Acetone	85	
	Dioxane	PtO_2	23	17	Acetone	63	
	Ethyl acetate	Pt-C	342	18	Acetone	76	Preparative

TABLE 1 (Continued)

Substrate	Solvent	Oxidation				Yield %	Remarks
		Catalyst	Time hr	Temperature °C	Oxidation product		
2-Pentanol	n-Heptane	PtO$_2$	1	17	2-Pentanone	77	
	Normal benzine	PtO$_2$	8.5	20	2-Pentanone	62	
	Dioxane	PtO$_2$	24	18	2-Pentanone	54	
3-Pentanol	n-Heptane	PtO$_2$	5.5	16	3-Pentanone	71	
	Acetic acid	PtO$_2$	120	32	3-Pentanone	70	
2-Hexanol	n-Heptane	PtO$_2$	6	17	2-Hexanone	56	
	Dioxane	PtO$_2$	24	20	2-Hexanone	75	
Methyl isobutyl carbinol	Dioxane	PtO$_2$	26	20	Methyl isobutyl ketone	56	
2-Octanol	n-Heptane	PtO$_2$	96	20	2-Octanone	80	
b) Alicyclic and aromatic alcohols							
Cyclopentanol	n-Heptane	PtO$_2$	0.75	20	Cyclopentanone	82	
Cyclohexanol	n-Heptane	PtO$_2$	1.5	20	Cyclohexanone	92	
	Normal benzine	PtO$_2$	4	18	Cyclohexanone	90	
	Normal benzine	Pt-C	24	48	Cyclohexanone	60	
	Ethyl acetate	PtO$_2$	8	20	Cyclohexanone	59	
α-Chlorocyclohexanol	Dioxane	PtO$_2$	—	18	Acetaldehyde	—	Is degraded
Cycloheptanol	n-Heptane	PtO$_2$	1	17	Cycloheptanone	99	
Benzhydrol	n-Heptane	PtO$_2$	23	37	Benzophenone	98	
2-Methylcyclohexanol	Ethyl acetate	PtO$_2$	18	20	2-Methylcyclohexanone	50	(19)

quite suitable. In benzene, ethyl acetate, and glacial acetic acid the oxidation proceeded very slowly. Solvent mixtures, with the exception of acetone-water, were less useful.

Water-soluble alcohols were oxidized well in water. The platinum-carbon catalyst in water, however, is sensitive to poisons especially calcium ions. Therefore it is advisable to use only freshly distilled water. Primary alcohols furnish aldehydes in neutral solution; however, through the partial formation of acids inhibition occurs soon so that the yields are low. On addition of 1 mole of alkali the carboxylic acids are formed smoothly. With dihydroxy alcohols, e.g. glycol, only one hydroxyl group is oxidized with 1 mole of alkali and the corresponding hydroxy acid, e.g. glycolic acid, is obtained. The reaction times increase within a homologous series with increasing chain length. Secondary alcohols furnish ketones; here the oxidation is not substantially influenced by the pH value.

All alcohols, especially those insoluble in water, are best oxidized in n-heptane or benzine with a platinum dioxide catalyst prepared according to Adams-Shriner (Degussa). The water of reaction, which partially deposits on the surface of the catalyst, appears to play an important part, for the oxidation proceeds only in a definite range of concentration. If the alcohol concentration is too large the catalyst clumps together completely because of the water of reaction, in which case the reaction comes very quickly to a standstill. Surprisingly, the oxidation is not successful in a too dilute solution. Oxidations in larger concentrations are possible in dioxane, butanone, or glacial acetic acid, in which the water of reaction can be taken up; however, the oxidation times are considerably longer.

Monohydroxy primary alcohols furnish aldehydes by oxidation in n-heptane after taking up $\frac{1}{2}$ mole of oxygen. The yields with the lower members lie at 40–60% and increase with longer chain alcohols to over 90%, while the reaction time sharply decreases. Thus dodecyl alcohol furnishes lauraldehyde in 15 min. On continuation of the oxidation another $\frac{1}{2}$ mole of oxygen is consumed and lauric acid is obtained in 2 hr. Accordingly the method offers a very simple means of preparing long-chain aldehydes in good yields.

Double bonds, in general, are not touched by catalytic oxidation. Unsaturated alcohols such as tiglic alcohol (2-methyl-2-buten-1-ol), may be oxidized catalytically to the aldehyde. With *cis-trans* isomerism, as in oleic or elaidic alcohol (octadecenyl alcohols), the configuration is retained upon oxidation to the aldehyde.

Cyclic secondary alcohols are easily converted to the ketones quantitatively. According to Sneeden and Turner (*19*) the alkyl-substituted cyclic alcohols behave similarly, though with increasing branching on the ring the yields decrease and the reaction times increase. Haloalcohols cannot be oxidized to ketones; they are fully degraded; thus in the oxidation of α-chlorocyclohexanol only acetaldehyde is found as the degradation product.

With aliphatic secondary alcohols the reaction time increases with the chain length. Alcohols with the hydroxyl group in the 2-position are the easiest to oxidize. Alcohols with branched chains give only very poor yields.

Oxidation of Primary Hydroxyl Groups

Oxidation of Aldoses

Aldoses are oxidized very easily, the aldehyde group going to the carboxyl group. Thus, according to Busch (22), D-glucose is oxidized to D-gluconic acid with palladium catalyst (precipitated on $CaCO_3$) even at room temperature and in the presence of the corresponding amount of alkali. The further oxidation of D-gluconic acid in alkaline solution with palladium catalyst furnishes, according to Poethke (23), the following degradation products: arabonic acid, erythronic acid, tartaric acid, tartronic acid, oxalic acid, and carbon dioxide. Accordingly, gluconic acid is not oxidized further to saccharic acid (with preservation of the carbon chain), but instead is degraded successively from carbon-1 with carbon dioxide splitting off to the formation of dicarboxylic acids beginning with tartaric acid.

Heyns and Heinemann (24) have described the preparation of D-gluconic acid by oxidation of D-glucose with the reasonably active platinum-charcoal catalyst in the presence of an equivalent amount of alkali. With the same method Heyns and Stöckel (25) have converted D-galactose, D-mannose, D-xylose, and L-arabinose to the aldonic acids. The pentoses were oxidized significantly more quickly. They required only 45 min at 22° for oxidation, while D-glucose, for example, required 5 hr.

Mehltretter (26) oxidized glucose with platinum-charcoal catalyst under rigorous conditions at 50° and found that the primary hydroxyl group at carbon-6 can then be oxidized specifically to a carboxyl group with the formation of saccharic acid. The determination of this fact is of importance for the synthesis of uronic acids (see below).

Oxidation of Ketoses

In ketoses the primary hydroxyl group on carbon-1 is so activated through the neighboring keto group, that it can be as easily oxidized as an aldehyde group in aldoses. It is, in every case, more readily attacked than the hydroxyl at carbon-6. Thus, according to Heyns (*20*), there is obtained from L-sorbose (I) by catalytic oxidation with platinum-charcoal catalyst at 30° in yields of over 60% 2-keto-L-gulonic acid (II) which can be rearranged to ascorbic acid (III). Sodium bicarbonate

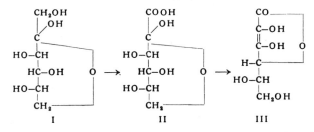

I   II   III

is added to trap the acid formed and to maintain a neutral medium. The 2-keto-L-gulonic acid can be obtained as the precursor of ascorbic acid in good yield by direct oxidation of L-sorbose, a blocking of the sensitive hydroxyl group being unnecessary, as, e.g. in the case of the permanganate oxidation of diacetone-sorbose according to Reichstein (*27*). Analogous to L-sorbose, D-fructose is also convertible to 2-keto-D-gluconic acid by oxidation (*20*).

Ascorbic acid itself, whose oxidation with oxygen is catalyzed by metal ions, e.g. iron or copper ions, is easily oxidized in the presence of platinum-charcoal catalyst under the mildest conditions. It is converted by the passage of air for 80 min at 0° to dehydroascorbic acid (*28*) quantitatively and without substantial by-products.

Blocked sorbose derivatives are catalytically oxidizable in high yields to the ketogulonic acids. Thus the quantitative catalytic oxidation of di-O-isopropylidene-L-sorbose to di-O-isopropylidene-2-keto-L-gulonic acid is reported (*29*). Methyl-α-L-sorboside can also be catalytically oxidized quantitatively (*30*). The methylglucoside of 2-keto-L-gulonic acid which is formed cannot be cleaved further without extensive destruction of the molecule. Trenner (*31*) has subjected 2,3-O-isopropylidene-L-sorbofuranose (IVa) to catalytic oxidation at higher temperature (60°) and obtained 2,3-isopropylidene-2-ketofuranosido-L-gulosaccharic acid (IVb), which he was able to transform with simultaneous splitting out of the isopropylidene group into an ascorbic acid derivative.

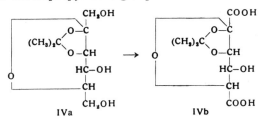

IVa   IVb

In addition to the primary hydroxyl group on carbon-1, the primary group on carbon-6 is also oxidized under these conditions. The reaction resembles the oxidation of glucose to saccharic acid.

Preparation of Uronic Acids

In this area catalytic oxidation has found a wide versatile field of application. Uronides are frequently required for metabolic investigations and D-glucuronic acid has become of therapeutic interest. There has been lacking for some time, however, a workable, practical synthesis.

A glucuronic acid synthesis was possible in which first of all the sensitive reducible group on carbon-1 of D-glucose was blocked in a suitable manner. In this manner methyl-α-D-glucoside can be catalytically oxidized at 60° to methyl-α-D-glucuronide in good yields (*32, 33*). Again the acid formed was neutralized by continuous addition of sodium bicarbonate.

Methyl-α-D-glucuronide can be split further only in moderate yields since a considerable part of the liberated D-glucuronic acid is destroyed by the necessarily strong acid conditions for hydrolysis. Therefore Fernández-García (*34*) and Mehltretter (*35*) started out with 1,2-O-isopropylidene-D-glucofuranose (V).

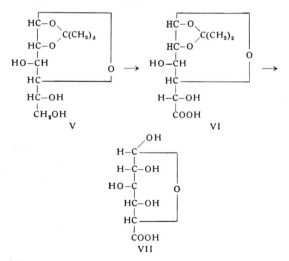

The 1,2-O-isopropylidene-D-glucuronic acid (VI) obtained by oxidation can be split to the free D-glucuronic acid (VII) with oxalic acid under mild conditions. The synthesis furnishes over 30% of crystalline D-glucuronic acid lactone. According to Mehltretter (*36*), 1,2-cyclohexylidene-D-glucofuranose, the acetal of cyclohexanone, can be used as starting material.

Later, glucosides of various types were oxidized catalytically to their uronides. A summarizing survey gives the following formulas.

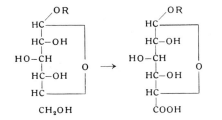

R = α-CH₃ *(16, 32, 33, 37, 38)*   α-*p*-Nitrophenyl *(38a)*
    β-CH₃ *(33)*   β-Mandelonitrile *(38c)*
    —C₂H₅ *(16, 38)*   β-*p*-Hydroxymandelonitrile *(38c)*
    β-CH₂CH₂OH *(16, 38)*   β-*p*-Methylmandelonitrile *(38c)*
    α-(−)-Menthyl *(21)*   β-*p*-Nitromandelonitrile *(38c)*
    β-(−)-Menthyl *(21)*   β-4-Methylumbelliferone *(38b)*
    α-Phosphate *(21, 33, 38d)*   α-Borneol *(38a)*
    β-Phosphate *(21)*   α-Fructose (Saccharose) *(38)*
    α-Phenyl *(38a, 38g)*   β-*p*-Biphenyl *(38f)*
    β-Phenyl *(13, 38e)*
    β-2-Naphthyl *(12)*

Also relatively sensitive compounds such as D-glucose-1-phosphate (α- and β-form) can be easily oxidized *(21)*. Moreover, the method has been applied also to the synthesis of uronides of other carbohydrates. Marsh *(21)* and Barker *(33)* oxidized methyl-D-galactopyranoside (α- and β-form) and methyl-D-mannopyranoside (α- and β-form) to the D-galacturonic and D-mannuronic acid derivatives.

Further, phenyl-α-(and β-)D-galactopyranoside and *o*-nitrophenyl-β-D-galactopyranoside can be oxidized to the corresponding uronides *(38a)*; in general, nitro groups *(38a, 38c)* and nitrile groups *(38c)* do not influence the reaction and are not changed.

Glucose derivatives blocked in various ways can often be catalytically oxidized to the corresponding blocked glucuronic acid derivatives in high yields. In order to favor the crystallization of uronic acids it is advantageous to introduce large lipophilic groups, e.g. benzyl groups, for blocking purposes, which are easily removed again. The water solubility of the compounds is thereby strongly decreased; generally, however, the substances can be oxidized in suspension. The uronic acid formed dissolves as the sodium salt. Numerous synthetic pathways were worked out by Wacek and co-workers *(38h)*, for the preparation of 4-methyl-D-glucuronic acid, which served as a comparison substance in the elucidation of polyuronic acids such as alginic acid and which is found to be a building unit in the hemicelluloses *(38i)*. Accordingly, benzyl-4-O-methyl-β-D-glucoside is oxidized to benzyl-4-O-methyl-β-D-glucuronide in 50% yield, whose reduction yields free 4-O-methyl-D-glucuronic acid. Substantially higher yields (93% or 85%) can be attained by the oxidation of methyl 2,3-di-O-benzyl-α-D-glucoside and benzyl 2,3-di-O-benzyl-β-D-glucoside. The methyl ester of the uronides obtained can be methylated to 4-methyluronides, from which methyl 4-O-methyl-α-D-glucuronide or free 4-O-methyl-D-glucuronic acid is available after splitting off the benzyl groups. With benzyl 2,3-di-O-benzyl-4-methyl-β-D-glucoside the oxidation takes a long time (24 hr) because of the low solubility of the compound; nevertheless, following hydrogenation 4-O-methyl-D-glucuronic acid is obtained in one step. According to Wacek (38h) glucose-dibenzylmercaptal and 4-methylglucose-dibenzylmercaptal are not oxidizable. Obviously the catalyst loses its activity in the presence of the mercapto groups.

Deoxycarbohydrates have been oxidized by Overend and co-workers (39): methyl 2-deoxy-α-D-glucopyranoside and methyl 2-deoxy-α-D-galactopyranoside to the uronides, 2-deoxy-D-glucose to 2-deoxy-D-saccharic acid. The oxidation times for the last reactions are extremely long (7–8 days), while the oxidation of glucose derivatives takes about 10–20 hr. The corresponding blocked derivatives of pentose are very much easier to oxidize catalytically than the glucose derivatives. According to Heyns and Lenz (39a) the oxidation of 1,2-O-cyclohexylidene-D-xylofuranose at 48° in 6 hr in the presence of 1 mole of sodium bicarbonate furnishes the corresponding uronic acid. D-Xyluronic acid is obtained by acid hydrolysis. The methyl-D-araburonide was also synthesized by catalytic oxidation (16); however, cleavage by hydrolysis takes place only with difficulty.

At first the oxidation of phenylglucosides presented difficulties. According to Marsh (21) phenol which has split off in small amounts acts as a catalyst poison. Kwan-Chung Tsou and Seligman (13) succeeded in making this oxidation go, for they employed another catalyst (purer platinum catalyst, according to Adams) and worked at 100°. In this manner they obtained 2-naphthyl-β-D-glucuronide (12) and phenyl-β-D-glucuronide (13).

According to Aspinall and co-workers (39b) polysaccharides are also catalytically oxidizable, in which case glucofuranosiduronic acid and glucopyranosiduronic acid groups can be introduced into the polysaccharide bond. The glycosidic bond of the uronides formed in this manner is considerably more difficult to split than those of simple glycosides. Therefore, aldobiuronic acids are obtained as cleavage fragments through selective hydrolysis of the oxidized compounds. From oxidized arabinoxylane, 3-D-xylose-L-arabinofuranosiduronic acid is isolated after hydrolysis, and from oxidized ε-galactan, 6-D-galactose-β-D-galactopyranosiduronic acid and 6-D-galactose-L-arabinofuranosiduronic acid were isolated. The method is of importance for the structure elucidation of the bonding of the nonreducing end groups, which possess CH_2OH groups and whose polysaccharide chain is bound favorably with a 1,6-bond, for the oxidation of the polysaccharides evidently proceeds satisfactorily when only few units with free CH_2OH groups are available. Polysaccharides with favorable 1,4-bonds, as for example, starches, in which every building unit possesses a free CH_2OH group, can be converted to polyuronic acids only to a limited degree according to Heyns and Beck (39c).

Oxidation of Amino Sugars

Catalytic oxidation is also suitable for amino sugars. According to Heyns and Koch (40), under mild conditions (30°) in the presence of sufficient amounts of potassium bicarbonate to bind the hydrochloric acid, D-glucosamine hydrochloride is oxidizable directly to D-glucosaminic acid, which is readily obtained because it crystallizes easily. This procedure is to be preferred to the oxidation method with mercuric oxide specified by Pringsheim and Ruschmann (40a). In the same manner L-glucosamine can be oxidized to L-glucosaminic acid. This reaction was used by Hardegger and Lohse (41) as the first stage in their muscarine synthesis.

In the preparation of the previously unknown D-glucosamineuronic acid (2-amino-2-deoxy-D-glucuronic acid) (X), aside from the blocking of the aldehyde group at carbon-1, further protection for the sensitive amino group at carbon-2 was necessary because of the necessarily more strenuous reaction condition for the oxidation of the hydroxyl group at carbon-6. Blocking with the N-carbobenzoxy group, which shows sufficient stability in the oxidation reaction, proved to be most suitable. The group bestows good crystallizability to the products and moreover can be easily removed by hydrogenation. Thus Heyns and Paulsen (42) oxidized α-methyl-N-carbobenzoxy-α-D-glucosaminide to uronic acid, from which free methyl-α-D-glucosamineuronide is obtained by hydrogenation. The splitting of this methylglycoside was impossible, however, so that the oxidation was carried out on α-benzyl-N-carbobenzoxy-α-D-glucosaminide (VIII). The quite difficultly soluble VIII could be oxidized in suspension at 95°, in which case the uronic acid (IX) went into solution continuously as the sodium salt. The α-benzyl-N-carbobenzoxy-α-D-glucosamineuronide (IX) formed may be converted into the beautifully crystalline, free D-glucosamineuronic acid (X) by simultaneously splitting off the benzyl and carbobenzoxy groups by hydrogenation.

An additional D-glucosamineuronic acid synthesis (*43*) shows the range of application of the catalytic method. D-Glucosamine is converted in liquid ammonia to 1-amino-D-glucosamine, which can be isolated as

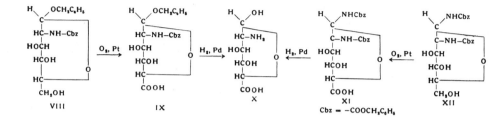

N,N'-bis(carbobenzoxy)-1-amino-D-glucosamine (XII). This compound, which still forms a N-glycoside, can also be oxidized in neutral solution at 90° to uronic acid (XI). The hydrogenation-cleavage and simultaneous hydrolysis furnishes D-glucosamineuronic acid again. Marsh and Lewy (*38a*) succeeded in catalytically oxidizing D-glucosaminide, whose amino group was protected only by an acetyl group. They obtained from α- and β-phenyl-N-acetyl-D-glucosaminide the corresponding uronides.

The D-galactosamineuronic acid (2-amino-2-deoxy-D-galacturonic acid) was obtained just recently by Heyns and Beck (*13a*), in which they oxidized benzyl-N-carbobenzoxy-α-D-galactosaminide to uronic acid, whose hydrogenolysis gave free D-galactosamineuronic acid. The isolation is somewhat unfavorable, since all compounds of D-galactosamine are significantly more easily soluble in water than those of D-glucosamine.

Weygand and Bergmann (*44*) investigated the oxidation of Amadori products, derivatives of isoglucosamine. They oxidized *p*-tolyl-isoglucosamine in ammoniacal solution (2 N) at 50° with platinum-charcoal and confirmed a degradation of the compound to D-arabonic acid. The following mechanism is assumed:

$$
\begin{array}{l}
\text{CH}_2\text{-NH-C}_6\text{H}_4\text{-CH}_3 \quad \text{CH-NH-C}_6\text{H}_5\text{-CH}_3 \\
\quad\text{C=O} \qquad\qquad\qquad \text{C-ONH}_4 \\
\text{HOCH} \xrightarrow{\text{NH}_4\text{OH}} \text{HOCH} \xrightarrow{\text{O}_2,\ \text{Pt}} \\
\text{OCH-NH-C}_6\text{H}_5\text{-CH}_3 \\
\quad + \\
\quad \text{COONH}_4 \\
\text{HOCH} \xrightarrow[\text{H}_2\text{O}]{\text{O}_2,\ \text{Pt}} \text{H}_2\text{N-C}_6\text{H}_5\text{-CH}_3 + \text{CO}_2 + \text{H}_2\text{O}
\end{array}
$$

The oxidation of the enolized Amadori compound should furnish D-arabonic acid and formyltoluide, which is cleaved and whose formaldehyde portion gives formic acid and carbon dioxide on further oxidation.

With p-anisyl- and p-phenethyl-D-isoglucosamine the same oxidation degradation to D-arabonic acid was possible.

Oxidation of Polyhydric Alcohols

In the hexitol series Glattfeld and Gershon (18) have investigated thoroughly the catalytic oxidation of mannitol and dulcitol in particular. Platinum oxide was used as catalyst, which was reduced to platinum along with the substrate. An equivalent amount, e.g., of mannitol, is oxidized at the same time to D-mannose. The main material was then catalytically oxidized with oxygen (80–90°). The operation was carried out in aqueous solution without the addition of alkali, thus under conditions in which aldehydes or ketones are formed preferably. From the catalytic oxidation of mannitol, which furnishes always only one sugar on oxidation irrespective as to whether the primary hydroxyl group on carbon-1 or carbon-6 is oxidized, there could be isolated 35% D-mannose as the phenylhydrazone or 20% methyl-α-D-mannoside. The further oxidation of D-mannose passes through D-mannonic acid, D-mannuronic acid, finally to D-mannosaccharinic acid, in which case all intermediates are in the mixture. Dulcitol, analogous to mannitol, gave a 30% yield of D,L-galactose as the phenylhydrazone. On the other hand dulcitol is oxidized smoothly with platinum-charcoal catalyst at 61° to mucic acid (38d) in the presence of 2 moles of sodium bicarbonate.

The catalytic oxidation of D-sorbitol in aqueous neutral solution with platinum-charcoal was thoroughly investigated by Heyns and Beck (45). In this L-gulose and D-glucose are obtained primarily along with L-sorbose and D-fructose and different polyhydroxycarboxylic acids. In glacial acetic acid and acetic acid–water as solvents the fraction of carboxylic acids and ketoses formed is significantly smaller; at the same time, however, the reaction velocity decreases. The carboxylic acids can easily be removed with ion exchange resins, D-glucose and D-fructose through fermentation. L-Gulose could be separated as benzylphenylhydrazone in 20% yield, based on sorbitol. Therefore a simple preparation of this sugar, usually difficult to obtain, has become possible.

In the presence of 1 mole of alkali 1,3-2,4-di-O-ethylidene-D-sorbitol can easily be oxidized catalytically to 3,5-4,6-di-O-ethylidene-L-gulonic acid (45, 46a) in yields of 60–70%. According to an American patent by D'Addieco (46a) this acid is oxidized with sodium hypochlorite in the presence of nickel (II) chloride to 3,5-4,6-di-O-ethylidene-2-keto-L-gulonic acid which, after splitting off the acetal groups, could be rearranged to L-ascorbic acid. This opened up a synthetic route to vitamin C which does not proceed through L-sorbose which generally is obtainable only through bacterial oxidation. The yield of 2-keto-L-gulonic acid was given at 33%; there was no elucidation concerning the isolation of the substance so that no statements concerning the utility of the method are possible.

L-Fucitol can be catalytically oxidized in alkaline solution to L-furonic acid (46b).

Pentaerythritol (XIIIa), which contains four equivalent primary hydroxyl groups, was catalytically oxidized in the presence of 1 mole of alkali at 35° to trimethylolacetic acid (XIIIb) [2,2-bis(hydroxymethyl)hydracrylic acid] by Heyns and Beck (46c). The reaction remains largely at this stage, since evidently the remaining hydroxyl groups are more difficult to oxidize as soon as a carboxyl group is present in the molecule. The attempt to oxidize further under more vigorous conditions leads to decomposition.

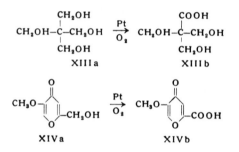

The monomethyl ether of kojic acid (XIVa) can be catalytically oxidized at a pH 5–6 at 65° to the methyl ether of comenic acid (XIVb), according to Heyns and Vogelsang (47). On the other hand free kojic acid is largely destroyed by catalytic oxidation and furnishes only small amounts of comenic acid. A poisonous action of the phenolic group of kojic acid on the catalyst was not observed (cf. 21).

Oxidation of Unsaturated Alcohols

The catalytic oxidation of unsaturated alcohols has been investigated only briefly up to this time. Aside from the work of Strecker (3), who oxidized cinnamic alcohol to cinnamaldehyde, Delaby (48) has concerned himself with the oxidation of α,β-unsaturated alcohols. Allyl alcohol was oxidized to acrolein with palladium black at 85° without a solvent.

A new, interesting possible application of catalytic oxidation of unsaturated compounds was recently discovered in the area of carotinoids by Karrer and Hess (48a). They oxidized vitamin A (XIVc) to retinin (vitamin A-aldehyde) (XIVd) with Adams' catalyst in glacial acetic acid at normal temperature.

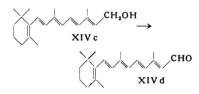

Oxidation of Secondary Hydroxyl Groups

Oxidation of Cyclitols

The first investigations on the selective catalytic oxidations of secondary hydroxyl groups to ketones was started by Heyns and Paulsen (*49*) with *myo*-inositol (*50*) (XVIa). It was shown that *myo*-inositol (XVIa) is catalytically oxidizable to a monoketone at 60° in an almost neutral solution with a platinum-charcoal catalyst. The reaction remains at the monoketone stage and yields further oxidized or ring-cleavage products only in minor quantities. In *myo*-inositol (XVIa) only the solitary axial hydroxyl group on carbon-2 is oxidized, in which case *myo*-inosose-2 (XVIb) (*51*) is formed, which may also be obtained by bacterial oxidation of *myo*-inositol with *Acetobacter suboxydans* (*52*). Catalytic oxidation attacks preferably the axial hydroxyl groups and in its selectivity is in complete accord with the bacterial oxidation. Also sequovitol (XVIIa) (*53*), a 5-O-methyl ether of *myo*-inositol, can be easily and readily oxidized at the axial hydroxyl group at carbon-2 to the *meso*-inosose-2 derivative (XVIIb) (*54*). The structure of laminitol, an inositol derivative from brown algae, could be elucidated by Lindberg and Wickberg (*55*) to be 4-C-methyl-*myo*-inositol on the basis of its behavior on catalytic oxidation, for catalytic oxidation furnished 4-C-methyl-*myo*-inosose-2 which could be converted by reduction to a mixture of laminitol and mytilitol.

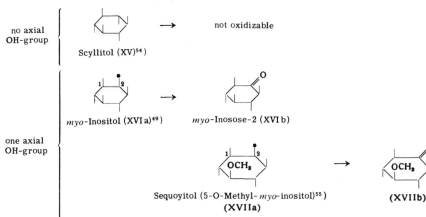

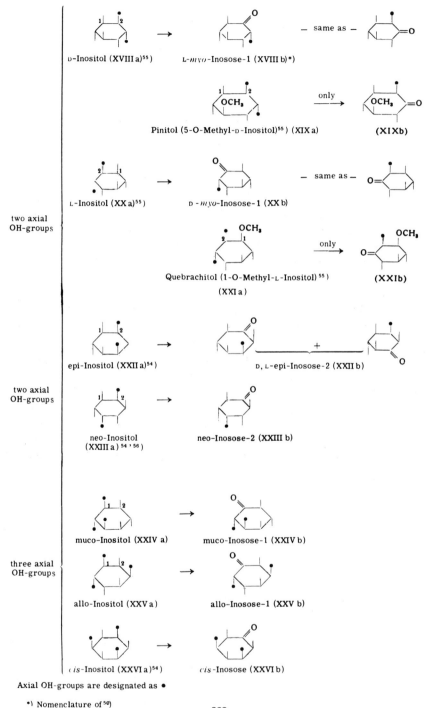

D-Inositol (XVIII a)[55]   L-*myo*-Inosose-1 (XVIII b)*)   — same as —

Pinitol (5-O-Methyl-D-Inositol)[55]) (XIX a)   only   (XIXb)

L-Inositol (XX a)[55]   D - *myo*-Inosose-1 (XX b)   — same as —

two axial
OH-groups

Quebrachitol (1-O-Methyl-L-Inositol) [55])   only   (XXIb)
(XXI a)

epi-Inositol (XXII a)[54]   D, L-epi-Inosose-2 (XXII b)   +

two axial
OH-groups

neo-Inositol
(XXIII a) [54 , 56]   neo-Inosose-2 (XXIII b)

muco-Inositol (XXIV a)   muco-Inosose-1 (XXIV b)

three axial
OH-groups

allo-Inositol (XXV a)   allo-Inosose-1 (XXV b)

cis-Inositol (XXVI a)[54]   *cis*-Inosose (XXVI b)

Axial OH-groups are designated as ●

*) Nomenclature of [50]

Further catalytic oxidations of almost all inositols, especially those by Angyal (*56*) as well as Anderson and Post (*54*), confirm the principle of selective oxidation of the axial hydroxyl groups. Only one axial hydroxyl group is oxidized so that even with the inositols having a number of axial hydroxyl groups only a monoketone is formed. In the inososes formed, which contain additional axial hydroxyl groups, plainly these are no longer susceptible to further oxidation.

If an inositol possesses two axial hydroxyl groups, then in general, these are equally oxidizable. So, according to Angyal (*56*), the racemic D,L-epi-inosose-2 (XXIIb) can be obtained from epi-inositol (XXIIa); and from neo-inositol (XXIIIa) only neo-inosose-2 (XXIIIb), since both oxidation possibilities furnish the same product. The latter oxidation was carried out also by Allen (*56*a) who, by hydrogenation of the phenylhydrazone of neo-inosose-2 (XIIIb) with platinum, could synthesize finally neo-inosamine-2, which Patrick and co-workers (*14*) isolated recently from an antibiotic similar to Hygromycin.

D-Inositol (XVIIIa) and L-inositol (XXa), each with two axial hydroxyl groups, give rise to only L-*myo*-inosose-1 (XVIIIb) or D-*myo*-inosose-1 (XXb) according to Anderson (*54*), since in both cases both axial groups are equivalent. In contrast the bacterial oxidation of L-inositol (XXa) and also of neo-inositol (XXIIIa) furnishes the diketones. On the other hand, in pinitol (XIXa) and in quebrachitol (XXIa), both methyl ethers of D- or L-inositol (XVIIIa, XXa), the two hydroxyl groups in each are no longer equivalent. Here then a new selectivity of catalytic oxidation is indicated, since of the two axial hydroxyl groups present in pinitol (XIXa) and quebrachitol (XXIa) only one is selectively oxidized and only the inososes XIXb and XXIb are obtained, according to Anderson and Post (*54*). In many cases, therefore, the method can be of significance for steric assignment of still unknown inositol derivatives. Quebrachitol is oxidized with difficulty with platinum-charcoal; on the other hand it is oxidized easily wth pure platinum catalyst (Adams') at low oxygen pressure.

Of the inositols having three axial hydroxyl groups the fully symmetrical *cis*-inositol (XXVIa) can be oxidized according to Angyal (*56*), only to the equally symmetrical *cis*-inosose (XXVIb). According to Angyal (*56*), the other two inositols, muco-inositol (XXIVa) and allo-inositol (XXVa) furnish the following monoketoses on catalytic oxidation: muco-inosose-1 (XXIVb) or allo-inosose-1 (XXVa). Therefore, with three axial hydroxyl groups, that group is oxidized which possesses an axial and an equatorial hydroxyl group in the vicinity. Scyllitol (XV) which possesses no axial, but only six equatorial hydroxyl groups is not attacked by catalytic oxidation under the usual conditions.

The oxidation of shikimic acid (XXXIX) to dehydroshikimic acid (XL), formed during the course of reaction in the biosynthesis of aromatic ring systems, and the oxidation of quinic acid (XXXVII) to dehydroquinic acid (XXXVIII) through *Acetobacter* are also feasible with catalytic oxidation (*56b, 57*). Quinic acid (XXXVII) possesses an axial hydroxyl on carbon-5, shikimic acid (XXXIX) in the half-chair form has a quasi-axial hydroxyl in the same position. According to Heyns and Gottschalck (*56b*) both hydroxyl groups can be selectively

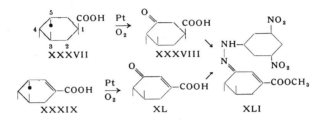

converted to keto groups by catalytic oxidation (Adams' catalyst). The stereospecificity of the reaction could be shown by the conversion of both oxidation products XXXVIII and XL into the 2,4-dinitrophenyl-hydrazone of methyl dehydroshikimate (XLI) which derivative is excellent for characterization. The quasi-axial hydroxyl group of shikimic acid (XXXIX) in this instance is much more easily oxidized at room temperature in 12 hr with Adams' catalyst, while the oxidation of the axial hydroxyl group of quinic acid (XXXVII) requires a reaction temperature of 50°.

Oxidation of Aminocyclitols

In contrast to inososes the aminocyclitols can be oxidized further, if they still possess axial hydroxyl groups. The principle of selectivity of catalytic oxidation with respect to axial hydroxyl groups is also realized here. The sensitive amino group must be protected during the oxidation; for this the carbobenzoxy group appears to be the most favorable. In this manner Heyns and Paulsen (*13b*) have catalytically oxidized N-carbobenzoxy-D,L-*myo*-inosamine-4 (XXXI) to N-carbo-benzoxy-D,L-2-keto-*myo*-inosamine-4 (XXXII) with Adams' platinum catalyst and so obtained a cyclic aminoketose for the first time (cf. *14*). This reaction is the most important intermediate step of the streptamine synthesis subsequently carried out by these authors.

In the nitric acid oxidation of *myo*-inositol (XXVII) to D,L-epi-inosose-2 (*58*) (XXVIII) the single axial hydroxyl group at carbon-2 remains untouched and is available for a later oxidation. The oxime

XXIX of this inosose furnishes by *trans* hydrogenation the inosamine (XXX) (*59*) whose carbobenzoxy derivative (XXXI) is catalytically oxidized, in which case the one axial hydroxyl group still available is specifically converted to the keto group. The oxime XXXIII of the aminoketose XXXII gives through *trans* hydrogenation, along with the abolition of the racemate, only one compound, the optically inactive streptamine XXXIV, which is identical with the cleavage product from streptomycin.

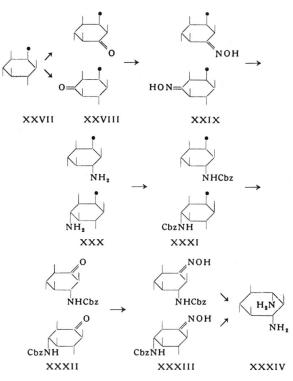

XXVII XXVIII XXIX

XXX XXXI

XXXII XXXIII XXXIV

Cbz = - COOCH$_2$C$_6$H$_5$; XXVIII-XXXIII are racemates, whose antipodes are shown. Axial OH-groups are designated with.

The investigations of Eugster and co-workers (*59a*) with the catalytic oxidations in the muscarine series are significant in this connection. They found that the cyclic alcohols of the tetrahydrofuran series with amino side chains can be readily oxidized catalytically when the amino group is present as a quaternary salt. The amino group then remains unchanged, while the alcohol group can be converted smoothly into the keto group. Thus the oxidation of muscarine (XLII) and epi-muscarine (XLIII) furnishes the same ketone, muscarone (XLIV), while from

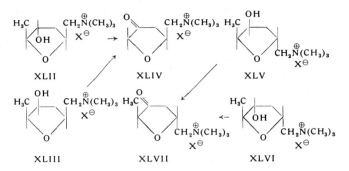

allo-muscarine (XLV) and epi-allo-muscarine (XLVI) the isomeric allo-muscarone (XLVII) is formed in both cases. Consequently, the reaction permits a correlation of the stereoisomeric muscarine derivatives. Differences in the oxidizability of the two isomers, in which the hydroxyl group stands in *cis* and *trans* position, were not observed. Such selectivity, in contrast to the six-membered ring, is not to be expected, since the five-membered ring is constructed almost flat and the hydroxyl groups are therefore only slightly differentiated in relation to the ring. Two further model reactions for the oxidation of XLVIII and XLIX to the corresponding ketones were devised by Eugster and Waser (*59a*):

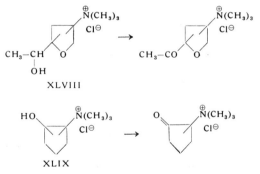

All oxidations were carried out with Adams' catalyst at room temperature in water, in some cases in 0.1 N acetic acid.

Oxidation of Steroids

Mannich and Siewert (*15*) undertook the first investigations of the catalytic oxidation of steroids with ouabagenine, although the reaction did not lead to clear, distinct products. Sneeden and Turner (*19,60*) have investigated these substances systematically and have oxidized first cholestanol and the ester of hydroxycholanic acid as model substances. They worked with an Adams' platinum catalyst in ethyl acetate as the solvent at room temperature. Cholestan-3α-ol and cholestan-3β-ol could be oxidized to 3-cholestanone without significant difference. Therefore it follows that with steroids the oxidation rates of axial and equatorial hydroxyl groups, certainly for the hydroxyl groups at carbon-3, are not as greatly differentiated as in the case of the cyclitols.

The oxidation of methyl 3α-hydroxycholanate, methyl 3α, 6α-dihydroxycholanate, and methyl 3α, 7α, 12α-trihydroxycholanate furnishes only the 3-keto compound in every case. The hydroxyl group at carbon-3, in contrast to the other hydroxyl groups, is distinguished by its exceptionally easy catalytic oxidizability. The reason could be the special position of this group at the outermost point of the molecule which appears to be favorable for dehydrogenation adsorption on the catalyst. In contrast to catalytic oxidation, the order of oxidizability of the hydroxyl groups is exactly reversed with chromic acid oxidation in glacial acetic acid. Not only in the AB-*cis*- but also in the AB-*trans*-joined steroids, the hydroxyl group at carbon-3 (axial and equatorial) is the slowest of the hydroxyl groups under consideration to be oxidized (*61*). Cholesterol cannot as yet be oxidized catalytically.

Sneeden and Turner (*60*) have found this selectivity of oxidation of the hydroxyl group at carbon-3 also in the cardiac poisons (cardenolids) dihydro-ouabagenine (XXXV) which they oxidized to the ketone (XXXVI). The position of the hydroxyl group at carbon-3 is so specially prominent that it is the first to be oxidized to the keto group, although a primary hydroxy group at carbon-19 in the molecule is still present, at which no attack takes place.

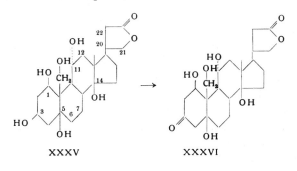

XXXV   XXXVI

Procedures

Preparation of the Catalyst

(a)   10% Platinum on charcoal by hydrogenation. In one liter of water and 10 ml of concentrated hydrochloric acid 45 gm of Carboraffin (Merck) is suspended and 50 ml of a solution which contains 5 gm of platinum as chloroplatinic acid is added. The mixture is hydrogenated in a 2 liter vessel. After the hydrogen uptake has stopped, the catalyst is washed well and dried at 50° *in vacuo*.

(b) 10% Platinum on charcoal by formaldehyde reduction. A 90 gm portion of Carboraffin (Merck) is stirred with a solution of 10 gm of platinum as chloroplatinic acid in 600 ml of water in a 1.5 liter container. The solution is neutralized with sodium bicarbonate, heated to 80°, and 55 ml of a 38% formaldehyde solution is added in portions over a 45 min period with mechanical stirring. At the same time sodium bicarbonate is added to neutralize the formic acid which is formed so that the solutions always remain weakly alkaline. The solution is maintained at 80° for another 2 hr with stirring. The solution is cooled and the catalyst filtered off, thoroughly washed and dried either in the air or at 50° *in vacuo*.

(c) Pure platinum catalyst. A 0.5 gm portion of platinum dioxide (Adams') is prehydrogenated in the solvent (10 ml) in which oxidation is to take place (e.g., water, ethyl acetate, benzine). After the completion of the hydrogenation the vessel is carefully evacuated several times after being filled with air, in order to remove as much hydrogen as possible. The catalyst is used and stored in the moist state.

2-Keto-L-gulonic Acid from L-Sorbose (19)

A 180 gm portion of L-sorbose is dissolved in 5 liters of distilled water, treated with 100 gm of sodium bicarbonate in 4 liters of water, and after 200 gm of catalyst is added (5% platinum on charcoal, prepared according to procedure a), is shaken for 54 hr in a 15 liter flask open to access of air. The conversion then comes to 62% of 2-keto-L-gulonic acid. To check the reaction it is best to determine quantitatively the 2-keto-L-gulonic acid formed (19). After the catalyst is filtered off the solution is brought to a pH of 8 with dilute sodium hydroxide solution and the oxalic acid precipitated with calcium acetate. The solution is concentrated *in vacuo* in which case the sodium salt of 2-keto-L-gulonic acid precipitates. The residual viscous sirup, permeated with crystals, crystallizes on standing. It is triturated with methanol-water (60:40), whereupon 118 gm of sodium salt (50%) can be separated. From the mother liquor, after clarification with charcoal and concentration, an additional 8–10 gm of sodium salt is obtained. Eight per cent of 2-keto-L-gulonic acid remains unisolated in the sirup which remains, which still contains 8% of L-sorbose. The sodium 2-keto-L-gulonate is recrystallized from water-alcohol, m.p. 145° (dec). It retains one molecule of water which is removed over phosphorus pentoxide. $[\alpha]_D^{24} = -24.4°$ (C = 1.8 water).

D-Glucuronic Acid from 1,2-O-Isopropylidene-D-glucofuranose (35)

A 60 gm portion of 1,2-O-isopropylidene-D-glucofuranose (V) and 6.3 gm of sodium bicarbonate are dissolved in 900 ml of water in a 3-necked flask. After 6.3 gm of catalyst is added (13% platinum on charcoal, prepared according to procedure b), the solution is vigorously mixed with a strong stirrer (3000 rpm) and a stream of compressed air is introduced (about 112 liter per hr) by means of an inlet tube, the air being first purified by washing with concentrated sulfuric acid. (The compressed air must be free from lubricants to avoid poisoning the catalyst. Such problems do not exist with the use of oxygen.) The reaction temperature of 50° is maintained constant with thermostat control. After 1.25 hr the pH of the solution has dropped to 7.5; again 6.3 gm of sodium bicarbonate is added. Altogether during a 7 hr period three 6.3 gm-portions of sodium bicarbonate are added to maintain the pH value. After 11.5 hr the reaction is stopped. The catalyst is filtered off, washed well, and the solution concentrated *in vacuo* to 200 ml, carefully brought to a pH of 2 with concentrated hydrochloric acid and extracted ten times with 200 ml of ethyl acetate. The extracts, dried over sodium sulfate, after concentration *in vacuo*, furnish 35 gm (53.5%) of crystalline 1,2-isopropylidene-D-glucuronic acid (VI) (m.p. 140–143°) as residue. The product recrystallized from ethyl acetate has a melting point of 145–146°, $[\alpha]_D^{25} = -7.4$ (C = 2.34 water). By hydrolysis with oxalic acid the free D-glucuronic acid is obtained (35).

Preparation of D-Glucosamineuronic Acid (42)

In a 2 liter 3-necked flask equipped with stirrer, reflux condenser, and inlet tube, 15 gm of α-benzyl N-carbobenzoxy-D-glucosaminide (VIII) and 6 gm of Adams' catalyst (prepared according to procedure c) are suspended in 1500 ml of water. Oxidation takes place by bubbling through an oxygen stream (5–10 bubbles per sec) with stirring (1800 rpm) at 80°. A solution of 4.1 gm of sodium bicarbonate in 50 ml of water is added continuously to maintain the pH of the solution between 7.0 and 8.0. Half of the sodium bicarbonate is used in about 2 hr. The insoluble glycoside (VIII) goes into solution as the sodium salt of the uronide (IX) as oxidation proceeds. After 12 hr the reaction is finished. A test sample should then no longer crystallize in a gel-like form. The reaction can be interrupted; 'this is often even an advantage. After the solution is separated from the catalyst and washed, it is concentrated to 300 ml. The slimy substance (starting material) which separates is brought into a suitable state for filtering or centrifuging by shaking with ammonium sulfate and quartz sand. The solution must remain slightly alkaline, otherwise the acid will precipitate. The uronic acid is precipitated from the filtrate with 6 ml of concentrated hydrochloric acid, recrystallized from 1 liter of hot water, and decolorized with animal charcoal; yield is 6 gm (40%), m.p. 186° (dec), $[\alpha]_D^{20} = +132.3°$ (C = 2.5 in pyridine). From this uronide (IX) the free D-glucosamineuronic acid (X) is obtained by hydrogenation using a palladium catalyst.

Trimethylolacetic Acid from Pentaerythritol (46c)

A 30 gm portion of pentaerythritol in 1.8 liters of water is treated with 20 gm of catalyst (10% platinum on charcoal, prepared according to procedure b) and the solution brought to a pH 6.2 with 40 ml of an 8% sodium bicarbonate solution. With vigorous stirring (3-necked flask) oxygen is bubbled through; the reaction temperature is 35°. The pH of the solution at the beginning drops rapidly and is maintained between 6 and 7 by the continuous addition of a sodium bicarbonate solution. In time the reaction velocity decreases so that the consumption of sodium bicarbonate becomes considerably slower. After 8 hr the reaction is interrupted; about 180–200 ml of sodium bicarbonate solution (that is, 65% of theory) has been used. After the catalyst is filtered, the solution is concentrated in vacuo to 100 ml and passed through a basic exchanger (Lewatit MN, OH-form). The trimethylolacetic acid [2,2-bis(hydroxymethyl)hydracrylic acid] is eluted from the exchanger with 30% acetic acid. The eluates are concentrated in vacuo. The residue crystallizes in a short time. It is recrystallized from isopropyl alcohol; however the acid crystallizes slowly; yield is 50% of theory, m.p. 210–213°.

myo-Inosose-2 from myo-Inositol (49, 62)

A 7.5 gm portion of myo-inositol in 500 ml water is oxidized in a 3-necked flask with vigorous stirring and the introduction of oxygen at 45°, using 4 gm of Adams' catalyst (prepared according to procedure c). The reaction can be followed by the determination of the reduction value by means of Fehling titration (49). After $3\frac{1}{3}$ hr the maximum reduction value, about 75–80% transformation, is reached. The same result is obtained with the platinum-charcoal catalyst (prepared according to procedure a) when oxidation takes place in a Kluyver's aeration flask with air sucked through at 70–75° for 8 hr. After the catalyst is removed the solution is concentrated to 20 ml in vacuo with cooling, treated with a solution of 8 gm of phenylhydrazine and 1 gm of sodium acetate in 15 ml of 50% acetic acid, and vigorously stirred with cooling for 40 min, whereby the thick mash which forms is diluted soon with water. To remove the color the red product (6 gm) is suspended in 15 ml of ethanol and washed further with ethanol. The remaining red phenyl-hydrazone (5 gm) is heated with 50 ml of ethanol, 5 ml of freshly distilled benzaldehyde, and 2 ml of glacial acetic acid for 5 min, until almost all has gone into solution or is finely suspended. After the addition of 250 ml of boiling water heating is continued for 3–5 min. The solution, extracted well with ether, is decolorized with animal charcoal and concentrated to about 5 ml *in vacuo*. Hot methanol (25 ml) is added until cloudiness sets in. One cooling *myo*-inosose-2 (2 gm) precipitates as beautiful prisms, m.p. 198° (dec).

Oxidation of Methyl 3α, 7α, 12α-Trihydroxycholanate (19)

A 200 mg portion of catalyst is prepared in ethyl acetate according to procedure c and suspended in a solution of 410 mg of methyl 3α, 7α, 12α-trihydroxycholanate in 25 ml of ethyl acetate. The mixture is vigorously stirred with a magnetic stirrer in an oxygen atmosphere contained in a closed hydrogenation apparatus. After 16 hr the uptake of oxygen is finished. The catalyst is removed and the solution concentrated. The crude residue is recrystallized from dilute ethanol and yields 290 mg of methyl 3-keto-7α, 12α-dihydroxycholanate (70%), m.p. 173–175°.

L-Gulose from D-Sorbitol (45)

A 40 gm portion of D-sorbitol is dissolved in 600 ml of water in a 3-necked flask equipped with a stirrer and gas inlet tube, and which is maintained at 40° with a thermostat. After 20 gm of platinum-charcoal (10% is added) (prepared according to procedure b), oxygen, having been passed through sulfuric acid contained in a wash bottle, is introduced for 8½ hr with stirring. After the catalyst is removed, the solution is concentrated to 250 ml and passed through a column containing 450 ml of exchanger (Lewatit MN, OH-form). The eluate is concentrated to 500 ml and after 3 gm of yeast and 400 mg of ammonium dihydrogen phosphate are added, is held at 38° for 2 days in the incubator. The yeast, after addition of a spatula-tip of activated charcoal, is centrifuged off; the fermentation solution is concentrated *in vacuo* to a thin sirup. The residue is taken up in 100 ml of methanol, filtered, and 14 gm of benzylphenylhydrazine hydrochloride and 9.8 gm of sodium acetate added. It is warmed slightly and kept for 24 hr in the ice box. Then 250 ml of water is added and after several hours the mixture is filtered, washed with water and ether. The yield is 14 gm of crude hydrazone, m.p. 125°. The light yellow-colored product is colorless after recrystallization from 180 ml of chloroform and 25 ml of methanol, m.p. 131°, $[\alpha]_D^{20} = +29.0°$ (C = 2.5 in methanol). The hydrazone is cleaved according to the method of Sowden and Fischer (63).

Lauraldehyde from Dodecyl Alcohol *(17)*

A 0.18 gm portion of Adam's catalyst (Degussa), 0.65 gm of dodecyl alcohol, and 20 ml of *n*-heptane are placed in the shaking vessel of a Theilacker hydrogenation apparatus. After the air has been displaced with hydrogen, the catalyst is hydrogenated (40 ml of hydrogen is taken up). The hydrogen is removed by evacuating the vessel three times and the apparatus is then filled with oxygen. After the vessel has been heated to the oxidation temperature of 60°, it is shaken with the oxygen. Uptake of oxygen in 15 min: 42 ml (104% of theory). The solution is diluted with 50 ml of isopropyl alcohol, treated with 100 ml of a 0.25% dinitrophenylhydrazine solution containing sulfuric acid, stirred for 1 hr, diluted with 300 ml of water, and the *n*-heptane layer allowed to evaporate. Yield of 1.27 gm of crude hydrazone, m.p. 92°; after recrystallization 0.97 gm (76%), m.p. 105°. If the oxidation is continued, then the reaction ends after 2 hr after an uptake of 82 ml of oxygen. The acid which is formed is extracted with alkali solution and after acidification extracted with ether. Yield is 0.65 gm of lauric acid (87%), m.p. 45°.

References

(1) J. Houben, T. Weyl, and E. Müller, "Methoden der organische Chemie," 4th ed., Vol. 4, Pt. 2, p. 344; Vol. 7, Pt. 1, p. 190; Vol. 8, p. 402. Thieme, Stuttgart, 1955; G. M. Schwab, ed., "Handbuch der Katalyse," Vol. 7, Pt. 1, p. 478. Springer, Vienna, 1943; A. Kutzelnigg, *Angew. Chem.* **50**, 353 (1937); W. Wolf, *Fette u. Seifen* **49**, 117 (1942); *Chem. Abstr.* **37**, 2335 (1943).

(2) F. Wittka, "Gewinnung der höheren Fettsäuren durch Oxidation der Kohlenwasserstoffe." J. A. Barth, Leipzig, 1940.

(3) A. Strecker, *Ann. Chem. Liebigs* **93**, 370 (1855).

(4) E. von Gorup-Besanez, *Ann. Chem. Liebigs* **118**, 259,273 (1861).

(5) F. W. Dafert, *Ber. deut. chem. Ges.* **17**, 227 (1884).

(6) M. Grimeaux, *Compt. rend. acad. sci.* **104**, 1276 (1887).

(7) H. Wieland, *Ber. deut. chem. Ges.* **45**, 484, 2606 (1912); **46**, 3327 (1913); **54**, 2353 (1921).

(8) E. Müller and K. Schwabe, *Z. Elektrochem.* **34**, 170 (1928); *Chem. Abstr.* **22**, 2307 (1928); *Kolloid-Z.* **52**, 163 (1930); *Chem. Abstr.* **24**, 5209 (1930).

(9) T. F. Macrae, *Biochem. J.* **27**, 1248 (1933).

(10) M. Rottenberg and P. Baertschi, *Helv. Chim. Acta* **39**, 1973 (1956).

(10a) M. Rottenberg and M. Thürkauf, *Helv. Chim. Acta* **42**, 226 (1959).

(11) G. B. Taylor, G. B. Kistiakowsky, and J. H. Perry, *J. Phys. Chem.* **34**, 799 (1930).

(12) K.-C. Tsou and A. Seligman, *J. Am. Chem. Soc.* **74**, 5605 (1952).

(13) K.-C. Tsou and A. Seligman, *J. Am. Chem. Soc.* **75**, 1042 (1953).

(13a) K. Heyns and M. Beck, *Chem. Ber.* **90**, 2334 (1957).

(13b) K. Heyns and H. Paulsen, *Chem. Ber.* **89**, 1152 (1956).

(14) J. B. Patrick, R. P. Williams, C. W. Waller, and B. L. Hutchings, *J. Am. Chem. Soc.* **78**, 2652 (1956); R. L. Mann and D. O. Woolf, *ibid.* **79**, 120 (1957).

(15) C. Mannich and G. Siewert, *Ber. deut. chem. Ges.* **75**, 750 (1942).
(16) Corn Products Refining Co., French Patent 1,044,563 (1953); D. G. Benjamin and S. W. Kapranos, U.S. Patent 2,627,520 (1953); *Chem. Abstr.* **48**, 710 (1954).
(17) K. Heyns and L. Blazejewicz, *Tetrahedron* **9**, 67 (1960).
(18) J. W. E. Glattfeld and S. Gershon, *J. Am. Chem. Soc.* **60**, 2013 (1938).
(19) R. P. A. Sneeden and R. B. Turner, *J. Am. Chem. Soc.* **77**, 190 (1955).
(20) K. Heyns, *Ann. Chem. Liebigs* **558**, 171, 177 (1947); compare also Canadian Patent 381,575; *Chem. Abstr.* **33**, 5416 (1939); German Patent 692,897 (1946); *Chem. Abstr.* **35**, 4396 (1941); U.S. Patent 2,190,377 (1940); *Chem. Abstr.* **34**, 4080 (1940).
(21) C. A. Marsh, *Nature* **168**, 602 (1951); *J. Chem. Soc.* 1578 (1952); *Biochem. J.* **50**, xi (1952).
(22) M. Busch, German Patent 702,729 (1941); *Chem. Abstr.* **35**, 7980 (1941).
(23) W. Poethke, *Pharmazie* **4**, 214 (1949).
(24) K. Heyns and R. Heinemann, *Ann. Chem. Liebigs* **558**, 187 (1947).
(25) K. Heyns and O. Stöckel, *Ann. Chem. Liebigs* **558**, 192 (1947).
(26) C. L. Mehltretter, C. E. Rist, and B. H. Alexander, U.S. Patent 2,472,168 (1949); *Chem. Abstr.* **43**, 7506 (1949).
(27) T. Reichstein and A. Grüssner, *Helv. Chim. Acta* **17**, 311 (1934).
(28) K. Heyns and H. Paulsen, unpublished.
(29) G. Görlich, German Patent 935,968 (1955); *Chem. Abstr.* **52**, 19972 (1958).
(30) Dr. Elder, Chicago, private communication.
(31) N. R. Trenner, U.S. Patent 2,428,438 (1947); *Chem. Abstr.* **42**, 924 (1948); U.S. Patent 2,483,251 (1949); *Chem. Abstr.* **44**, 3521 (1950).
(32) C. L. Mehltretter, U.S. Patent 2,562,220 (1951); *Chem. Abstr.* **46**, 3561 (1952).
(33) S. A. Barker, E. J. Bourne, and M. Stacy, *Chem. & Ind.* (*London*) p. 970 (1951).
(34) R. Fernández-García, L. Amorós, H. Blay, E. Santiago, H. Soltero-Díaz, and A. A. Colón, *El Crisol* **4**, 40 (1950); *Chem. Abstr.* **45**, 555 (1951).
(35) C. L. Mehltretter, B. H. Alexander, R. L. Mellies, and C. E. Rist, *J. Am. Chem. Soc.* **73**, 2424 (1951).
(36) C. L. Mehltretter, *Advances in Carbohydrate Chem.* **8**, 244 (1953).
(37) Corn Products Refining Co., British Patent 679,776 (1952); *Chem. Abstr.* **47**, 8325 (1953).
(38) Corn Products Refining Co., German Patent 886,305 (1953); *Chem. Zentr.* **125**, 9138 (1954).
(38a) C. A. Marsh and G. A. Lewy, *Biochem. J.* **68**, 617 (1958).
(38b) C. A. Marsh and G. A. Lewy, *Nature* **178**, 589 (1956).
(38c) E. T. Krebs and E. T. Krebs, Jr., British Patent 788,855 (1958); *Chem. Abstr.* **52**, 11913 (1958).
(38d) S. A. Barker, E. J. Bourne, J. G. Fleetwood, and M. Stacy, *J. Chem. Soc.* p. 4128 (1958).
(38e) G. N. Bollenback, J. W. Long, D. G. Benjamin, and J. A. Lindquist, *J. Am. Chem. Soc.* **77**, 3310 (1955).
(38f) M. Gee, F. T. Jones, and R. M. McCready, *J. Org. Chem.* **22**, 471 (1957).
(38g) According to a Japanese Patent [A. Katsushima, Japanese Patent SOH 33-1966 (1959); *Chem. Abstr.* **54**, 12010 (1960)]; N-phenylglucosamine is also oxidizable in an ammoniacal solution to the corresponding glucuronide, which can be easily hydrolyzed.

(38h) A. Wacek, W. Limontschew, F. Leitinger, F. Hilbert, and W. Oberbichler, *Monatsh. Chem.* **90**, 555 (1959); A. Wacek, F. Leitinger, and P. Hochbahn, *ibid.* **90**, 562 (1959).

(38i) F. W. Barth and T. E. Timmel, *J. Am. Chem. Soc.* **80**, 6320 (1958).

(39) W. G. Overend, F. Schafizadeh, M. Stacy, and G. Vaughan, *J. Chem. Soc.* p. 3633 (1954).

(39a) K. Heyns and J. Lenz, *Chem. Ber.* **94**, 348 (1961).

(39b) G. O. Aspinall, J. M. Cairncross, and A. Nicolson, *Proc. Chem. Soc.* p. 270 (1959); *J. Chem. Soc.* pp. 2503, 3998 (1960).

(39c) K. Heyns and M. Beck, unpublished.

(40) K. Heyns and W. Koch, *Chem. Ber.* **86**, 110 (1953).

(40a) P. Pringsheim and G. Ruschmann, *Ber. deut. chem. Ges.* **48**, 680 (1915).

(41) E. Hardegger and F. Lohse, *Helv. Chim. Acta* **40**, 2383 (1957).

(42) K. Heyns and H. Paulsen, *Chem. Ber.* **88**, 188 (1955).

(43) H. Paulsen, Dissertation, Universität Hamburg, 1955.

(44) F. Weygand and A. Bergmann, *Chem. Ber.* **80**, 261 (1947).

(45) K. Heyns and M. Beck, *Chem. Ber.* **91**, 1720 (1958).

(46a) A. A. D'Addieco, U.S. Patent 2,847,421 (1958); *Chem. Abstr.* **53**, 3084 (1959).

(46b) S. Okui, *J. Pharm. Soc. Japan* **47**, 1395 (1954).

(46c) K. Heyns and M. Beck, *Chem. Ber.* **89**, 1648 (1956).

(47) K. Heyns and G. Vogelsang, *Chem. Ber.* **87**, 13 (1954).

(48) R. Delaby, *Compt. rend. acad. sci.* **182**, 140 (1926).

(48a) P. Karrer and W. Hess, *Helv. Chim. Acta* **40**, 265 (1957).

(49) K. Heyns and H. Paulsen, *Chem. Ber.* **86**, 833 (1953).

(50) In this instance the nomenclature of H. G. Fletcher, Jr., L. Anderson, and H. A. Lardy, *J. Org. Chem.* **16**, 1238 (1951) and of S. J. Angyal and C. G. Mac-Donald, *J. Chem. Soc.* p. 686 (1952) generally used in the Anglo-Saxon literature is employed. The prefix, *myo-*, is equivalent to the syllable, *meso-*. Thus, *meso*-inositol is equivalent to *myo*-inositol, *meso*-inosose-2 to *myo*-inosose-2 and so forth. We thank Prof. Th. Posternak (Geneva) for the reference of the recommendation of the Nomenclature Commission of IUPAC who are in favor of the retention of *meso-inositol* [*Bull. soc. chim. biol.* **38**, 298 (1956)]. The views over questions of nomenclature are unfortunately not uniform.

(51) G. Hesse, B. Banerjee, and H. Schildknecht [*Experientia* **13**, 13 (1957)] suspected that the reductone form of inososes, described by Heyns and Paulsen (*49*) and isolated by H. v. Euler and A. Glaser [*Arkiv Kemi* **8**, 61 (1954)], or another inosose rearranged product, is present in stimulatory hormones of the Mimosoideae.

(52) A. J. Kluyver and A. G. J. Boezaardt, *Rec. chim. trav.* **58**, 956 (1939).

(53) L. Anderson, E. S. DeLuca, A. Bieder, and G. G. Post, *J. Am. Chem. Soc.* **79**, 1171 (1957).

(54) Also we are under special obligation to Prof. L. Anderson (Madison) for the transmission of his as yet unpublished results. See L. Anderson and G. G. Post, *Abstr. Papers Am. Chem. Soc. 134th Meeting*, p. 12D (1958).

(55) B. Lindberg and B. Wickberg, *Arkiv Kemi* **13**, 447 (1959); *Chem. Abstr.* **53**, 17913 (1959).

(56) We wish to thank Prof. S. J. Angyal (Sydney) for sharing with us so kindly his unpublished results and willingly giving his consent for their inclusion in this review. See S. J. Angyal and L. Anderson, *Advances in Carbohydrate Chem.* **14**, 135 (1959).

(56a) G. R. Allen, Jr., *J. Am. Chem. Soc.* **78,** 5691 (1956).

(56b) K. Heyns and H. Gottschalck, *Chem. Ber.* **94,** 343 (1961).

(57) Cf. also R. Grewe and J. P. Jeschke, *Chem. Ber.* **89,** 2080 (1956).

(58) T. Posternak, *Helv. Chim. Acta* **19,** 1333 (1936); **25,** 746 (1942).

(59) H. Straube-Rieke, H. A. Lardy, and L. Anderson, *J. Am. Chem. Soc.* **75,** 694 (1953).

(59a) C. H. Eugster and P. G. Waser, *Helv. Chim. Acta* **40,** 888 (1957); C. H. Eugster, F. Häflinger, R. Denss, and E. Girod, *ibid.* **41,** 205, 583, 705 (1958).

(60) R. P. A. Sneeden and R. B. Turner, *J. Am. Chem. Soc.* **77,** 130 (1955); cf. R. B. Turner and J. A. Mezchino, *ibid.* **80,** 4862 (1958) concerning the catalytic oxidation of 20,22-dihydrostrophantidine.

(61) L. Fieser and M. Fieser, "Natural Products Related to Phenanthrene," 3rd ed., p. 126. Reinhold, New York, 1949; J. Schreiber and A. Eschenmoser, *Helv. Chem. Acta* **38,** 1529 (1955).

(62) Improved variation of procedure.

(63) J. C. Sowden and H. O. L. Fischer, *J. Am. Chem. Soc.* **67,** 1713 (1945).

Alkylation of Phenols with Alkenes

R. Stroh, R. Seydel, and W. Hahn

Farbenfabriken Bayer A. G., Leverkusen

Introduction

Recently (*1*) a new preparative method for ring alkylation of aromatic amines was described. Alkenes are allowed to react with aromatic amines at higher temperatures in the presence of catalytic amounts of aluminum, which dissolves in aromatic amines with the formation of amides. In this manner the alkenes enter the ring as alkyl groups, predominantly *ortho* to the amino group in the ring.

It has been shown that this procedure may be extended to phenols; the aluminum phenolates, formed from phenol and aluminum, act as catalysts. Here, also, the alkenes enter as alkyl groups in an *ortho* position to the hydroxyl group in the ring (*2*).

The usual methods for the preparation of alkyl phenols are based upon the reaction of alcohols, alkyl halides, and alkenes with phenols in the presence of acid catalysts, that is both protonated acids, especially sulfuric acid, and Lewis acids ($AlCl_3$, BF_3) and silicates of the montmorillonite type (fuller's earth). A tabular review of the older literature is given by Price (*3*).

A compilation of the newer literature may be found in the summary (Annual Unit Processes Review) which appears annually in the journal "Industrial and Engineering Chemistry" (*4*).

Generally *o*- and *o,p*-substituted phenols are obtained from phenol by these hitherto known methods. If the *p*-position is occupied, the substituents enter *ortho* to the hydroxyl group of the phenol.

The addition of cyclohexene to phenol at 350° without a catalyst leads, according to Skraup (*5*), to *o*-cyclohexylphenol, although in very moderate yields, and to a dicyclohexylphenol which, however, was not identified as *o,o'*-dicyclohexylphenol. According to a patent of the Rheinische Campherfabrik (*6*) thymol (2-isopropyl-5-methyl phenol) along with starting material is obtained from propylene and *m*-cresol by heating in a pressure vessel, also without a catalyst, at 330–350° for 20–24 hr. Further, a patent of the N. V. de Bataafsche Petroleum Mij. should be mentioned (*7*) in which the reaction of phenols with alkenes having 7-22 carbon atoms with no catalyst is claimed. The structure of the resulting alkylphenols is not stated.

It was therefore surprising that aluminum phenoxide proved to be an excellent catalyst for the ring alkylation of phenols with alkenes (7a). Whereas in the alkylation of aromatic amines the ease of reaction of the alkenes decreases from ethylene to propylene, to butylene, the reverse order is true for the alkylation of phenols. Especially isobutylene reacts quite smoothly with phenols. The course of reaction of phenol alkylation is also more uniform with the higher alkenes.

Ethylation of Phenols

The aluminum phenoxide used as alkylating catalyst does not need to be isolated. It is prepared from aluminum and excess phenol in the high pressure autoclave before introducing the ethylene under pressure. Aluminum, 1 to 2% based on the weight of phenol, is used in the form of powder, turnings, or granules, which go into solution by heating at 120–140° with evolution of hydrogen and the formation of the aluminum phenoxide. With phenol derivatives, e.g. the cresols, the reaction does not begin before 150–180°. In order always to dissolve the aluminum smoothly, it can be activated by the addition of a small amount of mercuric chloride.

Ethylation of phenol. In an iron high pressure autoclave of about 700 ml capacity and equipped with a stirrer are placed 300 gm of pure phenol, whose water content is less than 0.1%, along with 3 gm of aluminum granules. After sweeping out the air with an inert gas or ethylene, the contents are heated at 150° for 1 hr. The hydrogen resulting from the formation of the phenoxide may remain in the autoclave or may be vented. Now the heating is continued at 320–340°. At this temperature ethylene is introduced to 200 atm pressure. The uptake of ethylene begins with a loss in pressure. From time to time ethylene is forced in, until 170 gm of ethylene is taken up after about 6 hr, which corresponds to about 2 moles of ethylene to 1 mole of phenol. After the contents of the autoclave have cooled to room temperature, the residual pressure is released. On addition of dilute hydrochloric acid or sulfuric acid the aluminum phenoxide, dissolved in the reaction product, is decomposed. The acid present in the oily layer, which has been separated, is washed out with water and the crude product is fractionated by vacuum distillation at 50 mm. The boiling curve shows four distinct steps:

1. B. p. 102°/50 mm	Phenol		25%
2. B. p. 119°/50 mm	Phenol + 1 ethylene		20%
3. B. p. 135°/50 mm	Phenol + 2 ethylene		30%
4. B. p. 155°/50 mm	Phenol + 3 ethylene		15%

The remaining 41.3 gm = 10% of the crude product is made up of low-polymer ethylene, intermediate fractions, residue, and distillation loss.

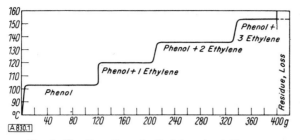

FIG. 1. Fractionation of ethylphenols at 50 mm.

Products of Phenol Ethylation

The first fraction consists of unreacted phenol and is always observed in this procedure.

The second fraction is *o*-ethylphenol. By oxidative fusion according to Graebe (*8*) salicylic acid is obtained. The phenylurethane melts at 141°, as given by Steinkopf (*9*).

The third fraction consists of a crystalline (at room temperature) product (85%) which still contains a liquid by-product (15%).

The former proves to be identical with 2,6-diethylphenol, which was described by Auwers and Wittig (*10*). It gives the well-crystallized 3,3′,5,5′-tetraethyl diphenoquinone on oxidation with chromic acid in glacial acetic acid or with potassium ferricyanide.

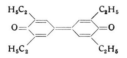

Such diphenoquinones result only from 2,6-disubstituted phenols. The phenylurethane and the infrared spectrum of the 2,6-diethylphenol obtained by ethylation of phenol are identical with the data for the phenol obtained from the boiling of the diazotized 2,6-diethylaniline (*11*).

The elementary analysis of the liquid portion (15%) of fraction 3. (b.p. 135°/50 mm) also gave values agreeable for a diethylphenol. The product was not identical, however, with the 2,4-, 2,5-, and 3,5-diethylphenols known in the literature. The compound takes up 2 atoms of bromine. Thus only an *o*- or *p*-position can be occupied. The infrared spectrum shows a definite "*ortho*-peak," so that a *p*-substitution is unlikely. Therefore a further ethylation of the ethyl group to a butyl group must have taken place. The known *p-sec*-butylphenol melts at 61–62°, while the *o-sec*-butylphenol of Read and co-workers (*12*) has the same properties as the product in question.

Further confirmation was provided by the identity of the compound

TABLE 1
RING ETHYLATED PHENOLS

Starting phenol	Alkylated product	B.p. (°C/mm)	M.p. (°C)	Phenylurethane M.p. (°C)	Diphenoquinone M.p. (°C)
Phenol	2-Ethylphenol	119°/50	Below −18	141°	—
Phenol	2,6-Diethylphenol	135°/50	38–39°	164°	143°
Phenol	2-sec-Butylphenol	135°/50	12°	86°	—
Phenol	2-sec-Butyl-6-ethylphenol	155°/50	—	132°	137°
o-Cresol	2-Ethyl-6-methylphenol	124°/50	—	147°	163°
o-Cresol	2-sec-Butyl-2-methylphenol	144°/50	—	111°	133°
m-Cresol	2-Ethyl-5-methylphenol	136°/50	—	154°	—
m-Cresol	2,6-Diethyl-3-methylphenol	150°/50	31.5°	164°	—
p-Cresol	2-Ethyl-4-methylphenol	134°/50	—	101°	—
p-Cresol	2,6-Diethyl-4-methylphenol	150°/50	48°	133°	—
p-Cresol	2-sec-Butyl-4-methylphenol	151°/50	44°	97–98°	—
p-Cresol	2-sec-Butyl-6-ethyl-4-methylphenol	173°/50	—	140°	—
sym m-Xylenol	3,5-Dimethyl-2-ethylphenol	146°/50	78–79°	144°	—
sym m-Xylenol	2,6-Diethyl-3,5-dimethylphenol	163°/50	86–87°	210–211°	—
sym m-Xylenol	2-sec-Butyl-3,5-dimethyl-6-ethylphenol	156°/10	—	140°	—
o-Isopropylphenol	2-Ethyl-6-isopropylphenol	141°/50	—	163°	147°
o-sec-Butylphenol	2-sec-Butyl-2-ethylphenol	155°/50	—	132°	137°
2-Cyclohexylphenol	2-Cyclohexyl-6-ethylphenol	199°/50	35–36°	149°	173°
2-Naphthol	1-Ethyl-2-naphthol	150°/2	104°	148.5°	—
Hydroquinone	2,3,5-Triethylhydroquinone	—	127°	—	—

with the *o-sec*-butylphenol formed by the butylation of phenol (see below). The boiling of diazotized *o-sec*-butylaniline also gave the same phenol.

In the ethylation of *o*-toluidine (*12a*) it was observed that 2-ethyl-6-propylaniline as well as 2-*sec*-butyl-6-methylaniline are formed; this can only be explained by the further addition of ethylene to the side chain. In analogous fashion *o-sec*-butylphenol is formed by the addition of ethylene to *o*-ethylphenol, although in low amounts.

The fourth fraction of b. p. 155°/50 mm conforms to a triethylphenol according to analysis. Since it takes up 1 mole of bromine and couples, the compound cannot be a symmetrical triethylphenol. That it is 2-*sec*-butyl-6-ethylphenol was demonstrated in the following way:

The phenylurethane of the phenol in question is identical with the phenylurethane of the phenol (m.p. 131–132°) obtained from the diazotized and boiled 2-*sec*-butyl-6-ethylaniline. Furthermore, the "triethylphenol" is identical with the butylated product of *o*-ethylphenol (see Table 3) and with the ethylated product of *o-sec*-butylphenol (see Table 1).

After taking into account the recovered phenol, the yields amount to 32.1% *o*-ethylphenol, 39.4% 2,6-diethylphenol, and 16.6% 2-*sec*-butyl-6-ethylphenol, collectively 88.1% of theory of ethylated phenols (see Table 1).

At the high temperature necessary for the ethylation of phenol an activation of ethylene occurs even without a catalyst, yielding the same alkylphenols, although somewhat less uniformly.

Ethylation of Substituted Phenols

The ethylation of cresols and xylenols occurs in a manner completely analogous to the methyl-substituted anilines. Thus 2-ethyl-6-methylphenol is formed along with 2-*sec*-butyl-6-methylphenol in the ethylation of *o*-cresol without the free *p*-position being occupied (see Table 1). The *m*-cresol furnishes 2-ethyl-5-methylphenol along with 2,6-diethyl-3-methylphenol (see Table 1).

Four products are formed in the ethylation of *p*-cresol: 2-ethyl-4-methylphenol, 2,6-diethyl-4-methylphenol, and two *sec*-butyl derivatives, 2-*sec*-butyl-4-methylphenol and 2-*sec*-butyl-6-ethyl-4-methylphenol (see Table 1).

The ethylation of symmetrical *m*-xylenol (3,5-dimethylphenol) proceeds very smoothly. 3,5-Dimethyl-2-ethylphenol and 2,6-diethyl-3,5-dimethylphenol are formed. The latter is produced as the main product in crystalline form having a melting point of 86–87°. A triethylated *m*-xylenol occurs as a by-product which, however, still takes up 1 mole of bromine so that here too the formation of a *sec*-butyl group must be assumed.

In the ethylation of *o*-cyclohexylphenol the cyclohexyl group is partially split off and replaced by an ethyl group with the formation of 2,6-diethylphenol. At the same time, however, 2-cyclohexyl-6-ethylphenol is formed. The entrance of the ethyl group into the second *o*-position is apparent from the easy formation of the corresponding diphenoquinone (m.p. 173°) on oxidation with chromic acid–glacial acetic acid.

Both naphthols also may be ethylated with the help of aluminum. From β-naphthol, of the seven possible isomers, the 1-ethyl-2-naphthol (which no longer couples) is formed. It has been prepared by the reduction of 1-acetyl-2-naphthol by Fries and Engel (*13*).

Under the same conditions α-naphthol takes up 2 moles of ethylene per mole of naphthol. The positions of the ethyl groups have not yet been established definitely.

In the ethylation of hydroquinone a triethylhydroquinone is obtained, which was identified as 2,3,5-triethylhydroquinone. Its properties are similar to those of the 2,3,5-trimethylhydroquinone described in the literature (*14*).

Propylation of Phenols

In the propylation of phenols the catalytic influence of aluminum or aluminum phenoxide is much more strongly pronounced than in ethylation. This becomes apparent in the significantly lower reaction temperature (at 100–150°), in the shortening of the reaction time and in the more uniform course of reaction. Propylene always enters the ring as an isopropyl group.

2,6-Diisopropylphenol

As in the case of the ethylation of phenol the aluminum phenoxide is not added as such, but is prepared from aluminum and excess phenol in the autoclave before the propylene is pumped in. The composition of the reaction products may be varied depending on the amount of propylene used and the reaction temperature.

If a dipropylated phenol is to be obtained as the main product, then the following procedure is used:

2,6-Diisopropylphenol. A 200 gm (2.12 moles) portion of pure phenol and 2 gm of aluminum granules are heated in a 700 ml high pressure autoclave, after the air has been expelled, for 1 hr at 150°. The hydrogen (about 10 atm) resulting from the formation of the phenoxide may remain in the autoclave. Now the mixture is heated to 220° and 187 gm (4.45 moles) of liquid propylene (2.1 moles propylene per mole of phenol) is pumped out of a storage pressure bottle with a high pressure pump in about 45 min. After stirring for 2–3 hr at 220° the initial pressure of about 65–70 atm has fallen to 10 atm and the reaction is finished. The work-up is similar to that in the ethylation of phenol.

The boiling curve of the reaction products (see Fig. 2) shows two distinct steps.

      1. B.p. 126°/50 mm Phenol + propylene 10%
      2. B.p. 144°/50 mm Phenol + 2 propylene 76.7%

The remaining 50 gm = 13.3% of the charge consists of fore- and last-fraction residue, and distillation loss.

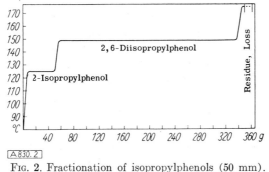

A830.2

Fɪɢ. 2. Fractionation of isopropylphenols (50 mm).

The course of the distillation curve of the reaction products reveals that propylation proceeds more completely than ethylation, since practically all of the phenol is converted. Predominantly a diisopropylphenol is formed, along with a small amount of monoisopropylphenol. The monoisopropylphenol is o-hydroxycumene (o-isopropylphenol), described in the literature (15). It proves to be identical with the isopropylphenol obtained from the diazotized o-isopropylaniline. The diisopropylphenol (2, 16) (freezing point + 18°) furnishes on oxidation a well crystallized diphenoquinone having a melting point of 199°, which verifies the occupation of the two positions *ortho* to the hydroxy group in this case also.

Based on phenol, the yields amount to 12.5% of theory as 2-isopropylphenol and 73% as 2,6-diisopropylphenol, collectively 85% of theory of propylated phenols. If smaller amounts of propylene are used, then the yield of o-isopropylphenol rises to over 50%.

With larger amounts a triisopropylphenol can be isolated from the last fractions, which is identical with the 2,4,6-triisopropylphenol described in the literature (17). It is formed by the action of isopropyl alcohol or propylene on phenol using acid catalysts. Here, by way of exception, p-substitution takes place after both o-positions are occupied.

The action of propylene on cresols in the presence of aluminum also leads to the expected occupancy of the free *o*-positions. Thus the already known 2-isopropyl-6-methylphenol (*18*) is obtained in good yield from propylene and *o*-cresol (200–220°).

Preparation of Thymol

The addition of propylene to *m*-cresol leads mainly to thymol (2-isopropyl-5-methylphenol) which is conveniently accessible by this method. According to a patent by the Rheinische Campherfabrik (*6*) the compound is formed at higher temperature without a catalyst in moderate yields.

Thymol(2-Isopropyl-5-methylphenol). A 250 gm (2.3 moles) portion of dry *m*-cresol together with 3 gm of aluminum granules are heated in a 700 ml high pressure autoclave after expelling the air. At about 180° the formation of aluminum cresolate begins (about 30° higher than for aluminum phenoxide formation). After 1 hr it is finished. The temperature is raised to 200° and 97 gm of propylene (1 mole of propylene for 1 mole of cresol) is forced in. After stirring for 3 hr at 200–220° the initial pressure of 80 atm has dropped to 12 atm and the reaction is ended. The work-up by washing and fractional distillation is carried out as for the ethylation of phenol. The main fraction (206 gm = 63% of the distillation charge) of b.p. 142–143°/50 mm is essentially thymol (m.p. 51°). From the forerun 52 gm (16%) of unreacted *m*-cresol can be separated. From the higher boiling portion 46 gm (14%) of a dipropylated *m*-cresol of b.p. 161°/50 mm is obtained; it is interpreted as being 2,6-diisopropyl-3-methylphenol. Calculated on the basis of recovered *m*-cresol the yield of thymol comes to 75%.

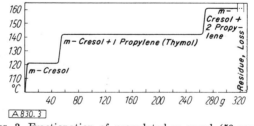

FIG. 3. Fractionation of propylated *m*-cresol (50 mm).

In the preparation of thymol on a larger scale an isomeric mono-isopropyl compound of *m*-cresol was isolated in small quantities from the mother liquors of thymol. It is not identical with the known 4- and 5-isopropyl-3-cresols. Probably 2-isopropyl-3-methylphenol is at hand (see Table 2).

TABLE 2

RING PROPYLATED PHENOLS

Starting phenol	Alkylated product	B.p. (°C/mm)	M.p. (°C)	Phenylurethane M.p. (°C)	Diphenoquinone M.p. (°C)
Phenol	2-Isopropylphenol	126°/50	8°	107°	—
Phenol	2,6-Diisopropylphenol	149°/50	18°	151°	199°
Phenol	2,4,6-Triisopropylphenol	175°/50	—	—	—
o-Cresol	2-Isopropyl-6-methylphenol	135°/50	—	156.5°	—
m-Cresol	2-Isopropyl-5-methylphenol (thymol)	143°/50	51.5°	107°	—
m-Cresol	2-Isopropyl-3-methylphenol	143°/50	—	120°	—
m-Cresol	2,6-Diisopropyl-3-methylphenol	161°/50	—	157°	—
p-Cresol	2-Isopropyl-4-methylphenol	140°/50	33.5°	97–98°	—
p-Cresol	2,6-Diisopropyl-4-methylphenol	160°/50	—	167°	—
sym m-Xylenol	3,5-Dimethyl-2-isopropylphenol	127°/10	—	143°	—
sym m-Xylenol	2,6-Diisopropyl-3,5-dimethylphenol	135°/10	93–94°	202°	147°
2-Ethylphenol	2-Ethyl-6-isopropylphenol	141°/50	—	163°	—
p-Isopentylphenol	4-Isopentyl-2-isopropylphenol	176°/50	—	123°	—
p-Isopentylphenol	2,6-Diisopropyl-4-isopentylphenol	184°/50	34–35°	132°	—
2-Cyclohexylphenol	2-Cyclohexyl-6-isopropylphenol	161°/50	—	139°	204°
2-Chlorophenol	2-Chloro-6-isopropylphenol	126°/50	—	117–118°	—
3-Chlorophenol	3-Chloro-2-isopropylphenol	105°/10	—	100–101°	—
3-Chlorophenol	5-Chloro-2-isopropylphenol	115°/10	—	157°	—
3-Chlorophenol	3-Chloro-2,6-diisopropylphenol	167°/50	36–37°	178°	—
3-Chlorophenol	3-Chloro-2,4,6-triisopropylphenol	186°/10	—	—	—
4-Chlorophenol	4-Chlorophenyl isopropyl ether	94°/10	—	—	—
4-Chlorophenol	4-Chloro-2-isopropylphenol	157°/50	46°	95°	—
4-Chlorophenol	4-Chloro-2,6-diisopropylphenol	175°/50	—	152°	—
Hydroquinone	2,5-Diisopropylhydroquinone	—	143°	—	—
Catechol	3,6-Diisopropylcatechol	173°/30	74–75°	—	—

Other Substituted Phenols

p-Cresol adds 1 and 2 moles of propylene in the position *ortho* to the hydroxyl group. Thereby the known compounds 2-isopropyl-4-methylphenol (hydroxy-*m*-cymene) (*19*) and 2,6-diisopropyl-4-methylphenol (*17*) are formed (see Table 2).

From the xylenols the symmetrical *m*-xylenol (3,5-dimethylphenol) was propylated at 220°. As was to be expected the 3,5-dimethyl-2-isopropyl- and the 2,6-diisopropyl-3,5-dimethylphenol were obtained.

The propylation of *o*-ethylphenol furnishes the same product as the ethylation of *o*-isopropylphenol. The 2-ethyl-6-isopropylphenol is formed (diphenoquinone, m.p. 147°).

Phenols with higher alkyl groups are also accessible with the new reaction. The smoothly proceeding propylation of 3-(*p*-hydroxyphenyl) pentane gave a mono- and diisopropyl compound. The latter does not take up bromine nor does it couple, so that a 3-(3-5-diisopropyl-4-hydroxyphenyl)pentane may be at hand.

In a similar manner the propylation of 2-cyclohexylphenols goes smoothly, and again the second position *ortho* to the hydroxyl group is occupied. The resulting 2-cyclohexyl-6-isopropylphenol furnishes a good crystalline diphenoquinone, m.p. 204°.

Propylated Chlorophenols

The propylation of chlorophenols goes more easily in the presence of phenol. Therefore the reaction temperature can be lowered to such an extent that a thermal decomposition of the chlorophenols is avoided. Care must be taken that the water content of the chlorophenols amounts to less than 0.1%; at higher water content the phenoxide formation is hindered.

A 300 gm (2.34 moles) portion of a chlorophenol together with 3 gm of aluminum granules and 6 gm of phenol are heated in a 700 ml high pressure autoclave at 200° for 1 hr; the aluminum goes into solution with the formation of aluminum phenoxide and aluminum chlorophenoxide. The hydrogen pressure of 13 atm is blown off and propylene is forced in, specifically about 100 gm for monoisopropylation and about 200 gm for diisopropylation. The initial pressure of about 55 atm begins to drop quickly at 165°. After 2 hr of heating to 200° the final pressure comes to only 2 atm and the reaction is ended. The reaction product is worked up by washing and fractionating as described in the ethylation of phenol.

2-Chloro-6-isopropylphenol is obtained from *o*-chlorophenol (see Table 2). Following this procedure a mono-, di-, or triisopropyl product is formed from *m*-chlorophenol (depending on the amounts of propylene used), by addition of 1 mole of propylene, 3-chloro-6-isopropylphenol; of 2 moles of propylene, 3-chloro-2,6-diisopropylphenol; and of 3 moles of propylene, 3-chloro-2,4,6-triisopropylphenol (see Table 2). The propylation of *p*-chlorophenol was also carried out according to the process given above. Whereas in the previously described ethylations and propylations mostly no or only slight formation of alkyl phenyl ethers is observed, in the propylation of *p*-chlorophenols a 12% yield of *p*-chlorophenyl isopropyl ether (*20*) could be isolated from the forerun along with starting material. In the main, however, the isopropyl group here also enters the ring in the position *ortho* to the hydroxyl group. 4-Chloro-2-isopropylphenol (*21*) and 4-chloro-2,6-diisopropylphenol are formed. Both products are identical with the substances obtained by the chlorination of *o*-isopropylphenol and 2,6-diisopropylphenol.

The propylation of hydroquinone (reaction temperature about 200°) leads to 2,5-diisopropylhydroquinone.

Alkylations with Butylene and Isobutylene

If butylene (a mixture of 42% 1-butene, 36% *trans*-2-butene, and 21% *cis*-2-butene) is used in place of propylene as alkylating agent then the addition of aluminum or aluminum phenoxide also brings about a preferred introduction to the position *ortho* to the hydroxy group of one or two secondary butyl groups. As in the case of the propylation of phenol, the addition of butylene begins at 190–200° (without a catalyst not until 340°). Either *o-sec*-butylphenol or 2,6-di-*sec*-butylphenol is formed as the main product, depending upon the amount of butylene added.

Butylation of Phenol. First aluminum phenoxide catalyst is formed from 300 gm of phenol and 3 gm of aluminum granules at 150° in 1 hr and remains dissolved in the excess phenol. After heating further to 190–220°, 350 gm of liquid butylene is pumped in with a high pressure pump in 45 min. The internal pressure, which in the beginning came to 45 atm, falls in about 6 hr to 5 atm; with this the reaction is stopped. The work-up is the same as for the ethylation of phenol. The boiling curve of the reaction product shows two distinct steps as in the case of the propylation of phenol:

1. 2-*sec*-Butylphenol b.p. 103°/10 mm 7%
2. 2,6-Di-*sec*-butylphenol b.p. 133°/10 mm 73%

If 0.9 mole of butylene is added to 1 mole of phenol under the above conditions, then a 41% yield of *o-sec*-butylphenol is obtained along with a 35% recovery of phenol.

TABLE 3

PHENOLS WITH *sec*-BUTYL GROUP

Starting phenol	Alkylated product	B.p. (°C/mm)	M.p. (°C)	Phenylurethane M.p. (°C)	Diphenoquinone M.p. (°C)
Phenol	2-*sec*-Butylphenol	135°/50	12°	86°	—
Phenol	2,6-Di-*sec*-butylphenol	169°/50	—	127°	201.5°
o-Cresol	2-*sec*-Butyl-6-methylphenol	144°/50	—	111°	133°
m-Cresol	2-*sec*-Butyl-5-methylphenol	154°/50	—	106.5°	—
m-Cresol	2,6-Di-*sec*-butyl-3-methylphenol	176.5°/50	—	112°	—
p-Cresol	2-*sec*-Butyl-4-methylphenol	151°/50	44°	97–98°	—
p-Cresol	2,6-Di-*sec*-butyl-4-methylphenol	177°/50	—	107°	—
2-Cyclohexylphenol	2-*sec*-Butyl-6-cyclohexylphenol	171°/10	—	133°	212°
2-Cyclopentylphenol	2-*sec*-Butyl-6-cyclopentylphenol	160°/10	—	—	—

The o-sec-butylphenol (*12*) is identical with the by-product of boiling point 150°/50 mm obtained in the ethylation of phenol.

The 2,6-di-sec-butylphenol (b.p. 133°/10 mm) has not yet been described in the literature. A diphenoquinone (m.p. 201.5°) is readily formed. The known 2,4-di-(sec-butyl)phenol has different constants (*22*). The sec-butylation of cresols and of cyclohexylphenol occurs as expected and furnishes the products presented in Table 3, which for the most part have not been described as yet.

Preparation of 2,6-Di-*tert*-butylphenol, 2-*tert*-Butylphenol, and 2,4,6-Tri-*tert*-butylphenol

Especially interesting is the action of isobutylene on phenols. With acid catalysts the p-*tert*-butylphenol (*23*) is readily obtained; however, the isobutylation can be extended to form 2,4-di-*tert*-butyl- and 2,4,6-tri-*tert*-butylphenol (*24*).

The preparation of o-*tert*-butylphenol (21%) along with the p-compound (70%) and 6% of di-*tert*-butyl compound is described in a patent of the Shell Development Company (*25*).

Ring alkylation of phenol with isobutylene begins at 80 to 100° with aluminum phenoxide present, and thus is significantly lower than propylation and sec-butylation. The 2,6-di-*tert*-butylphenol is obtained in good yield along with a small amount of o-*tert*-butylphenol. The former was prepared for the first time by *tert*-butylation of 4-bromophenol and the removal of the bromine by reduction (*26*).

On oxidation the 2,6-di-*tert*-butylphenol gives a well-crystallized diphenoquinone (see Table 4).

For the preparation of 2,6-di-*tert*-butylphenol, 2-*tert*-butylphenol or 2,4,6-tri-*tert*-butylphenol the alkylating catalyst is prepared in the same manner as for the ethylation or propylation of phenol. A 200 gm portion of phenol together with 2 gm of aluminum granules is stirred in a high pressure autoclave for 1 hr at 150°. After complete solution of the aluminum the contents of the autoclave are cooled to 80° Now the calculated amount (240 gm) of isobutylene (2 moles of alkene to 1 mole phenol) is pumped in with a liquid pump, over a period of about 1 hr, the heating being discontinued. The internal temperature climbs rapidly to 90° because of the heat of reaction. After all the isobutylene is pumped in, the mixture is stirred at 90–100° for about 2 hr longer to complete the reaction, in which case the internal pressure drops from a maximum of 18 atm to about 7–8 atm. The work-up of the reaction product proceeds as in the propylation of phenol. In order to avoid rearrangements, which are quite possible during the distillations which follow, the entrained traces of acid must be removed by thorough washing. The fractionation of the crude product gives 77% of 2,6-di-*tert*-butylphenol along with 8% of 2-*tert*-butylphenol and a small amount of a higher boiling constituent (2,4,6-tri-*tert*-butylphenol). If under similar conditions only-one-half of the above amount of isobutylene (120 gm) is pumped in, then 2-*tert*-butylphenol is obtained as the main product in 70% yield (based on unconverted phenol) along with unreacted phenol and some 2,6-di-*tert*-butylphenol. If the amount of isobutylene pumped in is increased to 400 gm and the reaction temperature increased to 200°, then after 6 hr an almost uniform crystalline crude product is obtained from which pure 2,4,6-tri-*tert*-butylphenol is obtained after recrystallization from 70% alcohol, m.p. 131° (70% of theory). This compound was also obtained by isobutylation with an acid catalyst, along with 4-*tert*-butylphenol and 2,4-di-*tert*-butylphenol (*27*).

The 2,6-di-*tert*-butylphenol, on heating, or on addition of catalytic amounts of acids, or fuller's earth, rearranges very quickly to 2,4-di-*tert*-butylphenol, in which case the *tert*-butyl group in the *ortho*-position is also partially split off. Under these conditions 2-*tert*-butylphenol also rearranges to form *p*-*tert*-butylphenol (*28*).

Therefore it is not surprising that at about 200° no 2,6-di-*tert*-butylphenol is formed, but mainly 4-*tert*-butylphenol and 2,4-di-*tert*-butylphenol along with small amounts of 2-*tert*-butylphenol.

While in the alkylation of phenols with ethylene ethyl phenyl ethers were not observed and with propylene only minor amounts were formed, isobutylene reacts with phenols in the presence of aluminum phenoxide to form *tert*-butyl phenyl ether (b.p. 70°/10 mm) smoothly even at room temperature. Natelson described this preparation from isobutylene and phenol in the presence of molar amounts of concentrated sulfuric acid at 0° (*29*).

The ring isobutylation of cresols also goes at relatively low temperatures (90–100°) and furnishes the expected *tert*-butylcresols (see Table 4).

o-Cyclohexylphenol is isobutylated best at 120° to 2-*tert*-butyl-6-cyclohexylphenol. This forms a diphenoquinone, m.p. 233°. At the same temperature 2-*tert*-butyl-6-chlorophenol is obtained predominantly from *o*-chlorophenol.

The isobutylation of hydroquinone requires higher temperatures than those for monohydroxy phenols. Thus with 2 moles of isobutylene at 220–240° 2,5-di-*tert*-butylhydroquinone is obtained, which is identical in its properties with the product described in the literature (*30*). The known mono-*tert*-butylhydroquinone is also formed (see Table 4). These substances are readily separated because of their different water solubilities.

TABLE 4

PHENOLS WITH tert-BUTYL GROUP

Starting phenol	Alkylated product	B.p. (°C/mm)	M.p. (°C)	Phenylurethane M.p. (°C)	Diphenoquinone M.p. (°C)
Phenol	tert-Butyl phenyl ether	70°/10	—	—	—
Phenol	2-tert-Butylphenol	136–137°/50	—	136°	—
Phenol	4-tert-Butylphenol	149°/50	99°	147°	—
Phenol	2,4-Di-tert-butylphenol	169°/50	57°	143°	—
Phenol	2,6-Di-tert-butylphenol	161°/50	39°	210°	239°
Phenol	2,4,6-Tri-tert-butylphenol	138°/10	131°	178°	—
o-Cresol	2-tert-Butyl-6-methylphenol	141°/50	—	194°	200–201°
o-Ethylphenol	2-tert-Butyl-6-ethylphenol	150°/50	—	—	—
m-Cresol	2-tert-Butyl-5-methylphenol	144°/50	23°	132–133°	—
p-Cresol	2-tert-Butyl-4-methylphenol	147.5°/50	54.5–55°	154°	—
p-Cresol	2,6-Di-tert-butyl-4-methylphenol	170°/50	70°	151°	—
2-Isopropylphenol	2-tert-Butyl-6-isopropylphenol	154°/50	—	—	—
2-sec-Butylphenol	2-sec-Butyl-6-tert-butylphenol	168°/50	—	—	—
2-Cyclohexylphenol	2-tert-Butyl-6-cyclohexylphenol	170°/10	—	192°	233°
2-Chlorophenol	2-tert-Butyl-6-chlorophenol	133°/50	—	145°	—
Hydroquinone	2-tert-Butylhydroquinone	—	129°	—	—
Hydroquinone	2,5-Di-tert-butylhydroquinone	—	212°	—	—
Hydroquinone	2,6-Di-tert-butylhydroquinone	—	102°	—	—
Catechol	3-tert-Butylcatechol	133°/10	—	—	—

TABLE 5

ALKYLATED PRODUCTS FROM PHENOLS WITH HIGHER ALKENES

Starting phenol	Alkylating agent	Alkylated product	B.p. (°C/mm)	M.p. (°C)	Phenylurethane M.p. (°C)	Diphenoquinone M.p. (°C)
Phenol	2-Methyl-2-butene	2-tert-Amylphenol	148°/50	—	124–126°	—
Phenol	Diisobutylene	2-(1,1,3,3-Tetramethylbutyl)phenol	150°/20	—	144–145°	—
Phenol	Diisobutylene	4-(1,1,3,3-Tetramethylbutyl)phenol	166°/20	87–88°	146–147°	—
Phenol	α-Methylstyrene	2-α,α-Dimethylbenzylphenol	160°/10	—	131°	—
Phenol	α-Methylstyrene	4-α,α-Dimethylbenzylphenol	184°/10	74–75°	—	—
Phenol	Cyclohexene	2-Cyclohexylphenol	145°/10	57°	110.5°	—
Phenol	Cyclohexene	2,6-Dicyclohexylphenol	205°/10	76–77°	160–161°	261–262°
o-Cresol	Styrene	2-Methyl-6-(1-phenylethyl)phenol	166°/10	—	72–74°	178–179°
o-Cresol	Styrene	2,4-Di-(1-phenylethyl)-6-methylphenol	183°/10	—	—	—
o-Cresol	α-Methylstyrene	2-α,α-Dimethylbenzyl-6-methylphenol	180°/10	—	136–137°	—
o-Cresol	Cyclohexene	2-Cyclohexyl-6-methylphenol	192°/50	70.5°	128°	215–216°
p-Cresol	Styrene	4-Methyl-2-(1-phenylethyl)phenol	172°/10	—	—	—
p-Cresol	Styrene	2,6-Di-(1-phenylethyl)-4-methylphenol	241°/10	—	—	—
p-Cresol	α-Methylstyrene	2-α,α-Dimethylbenzyl-4-methylphenol	171°/10	123°	127°	—
p-Cresol	α-Methylstyrene	2,6-Di-(α,α-dimethylbenzyl)-4-methylphenol	231°/10	—	—	—
p-Cresol	Cyclohexene	2-Cyclohexyl-4-methylphenol	156°/10	56°	145–146°	—
p-Cresol	Cyclohexene	2,6-Dicyclohexyl-4-methylphenol	268°/50	64°	165–166°	—

Alkylation with Higher and Cyclic Alkenes

Phenols can also be alkylated with higher alkenes. Thus 2-methyl-2-butene reacts with phenol in the presence of aluminum phenoxide at 120° with the introduction of an amyl group into the ring. In the reaction of phenol with diisobutylene p-substituted compounds are formed along with the o-substituted ones (see Table 5).

The alkylation of phenols with styrene and α-methylstyrene with aluminum phenoxide present is possible without pressure because of the higher boiling points of the alkenes. From o-cresols and styrene the 2-methyl-6-(1-phenylethyl)-phenol is formed; it gives on oxidation a diphenoquinone, m.p. 179°. At the same time a disubstituted cresol is formed which in all probability is 2-methyl-4,6-di-(1-phenylethyl)-phenol. A mono- and a disubstituted derivative were also obtained from p-cresol with styrene (see Table 5).

From α-methylstyrene and phenol the previously undescribed o-cumylphenol [2-α,α-dimethylbenzylphenol] (b.p. 160°/10 mm; phenylurethane, m.p. 131°) is obtained along with the known p-cumylphenol [4α,α-dimethylbenzylphenol].

The cresols react with α-methylstyrene under the same conditions as with phenol. The 2-cumyl-6-methylphenol, prepared from o-cresol, forms a diphenoquinone which in this instance also demonstrates that the introduction took place in the second position *ortho* to the hydroxyl group.

Whereas in the acid condensation of cyclohexene with phenol, o-cyclohexylphenol is obtained along with the p- and m-compounds, the cyclohexylation of phenol in the presence of aluminum phenoxide leads almost exclusively to 2-cyclohexyl- and to 2,6-dicyclohexylphenol. The latter furnishes a characteristic diphenoquinone (see Table 5).

In like manner p-cresol can be cyclohexylated to 2-cyclohexyl-4-methylphenol (free from m-compound) and to 2,6-di-cyclohexyl-4-methylphenol.

The results of alkylation with higher and branched alkenes show that the position *para* to the hydroxyl group is occupied to some extent, probably from steric considerations.

Properties of o-Alkyl Substituted Phenols

The solubility of the o-disubstituted phenols in dilute sodium hydroxide decreases with increasing size and branching of the alkyl groups. While 2,6-diethylphenol is still soluble in dilute sodium hydroxide, 2,6-di(*tert*-butyl)phenol is insoluble in aqueous alkali of every concentration and forms a sodium salt only with solid caustic soda, which is immediately hydrolyzed in water. It dissolves easily, however, in Claisen solution.* The behavior of o-alkylated phenols ("hindered phenols") having the p-position occupied was investigated with regard to the reactivity of the phenolic hydroxyl group by Stillson and co-workers (*24*). According to this publication the 2,6-di-*tert*-butyl-4-methylphenol is also insoluble in Claisen solution, which we could confirm in analogous cases. According to a patent of Esso Research (*31*) the potassium salt of di-*tert*-butyl-p-cresol may be obtained with solid alkali hydroxide by the azeotropic removal of water. The determination of active hydrogen by the Zerewitinoff procedure goes normally, while the determination of the hydroxyl number according to Verley-Bölsing fails.

The o-disubstituted phenols, and also 2,6-di-*tert*-butylphenol, couple normally with diazonium salts in the position *para* to the hydroxyl group.

Nitrosophenols are formed on nitrosation. The infrared spectrum of 2,6-diethyl-4-nitrosophenol indicates a pure nitroso compound; the isomeric quinone oxime present exists in equilibrium in the unsubstituted p-nitrosophenol (*32*).

The chlorination, sulfonation, and nitration of the o-disubstituted phenols occurs mostly in a normal manner and leads to the corresponding p-substituted derivatives. The strongly hindered phenols can behave abnormally. Thus, for example, the preparation of 2,6-di-*tert*-butyl-4-nitrophenol is not possible using the customary methods. In the nitration of 2,6-di-*tert*-butylphenol in glacial acetic acid a *tert*-butyl group is split off and 2-*tert*-butyl-4,6-dinitrophenol is formed (*32a*). On the other hand mononitration succeeds smoothly in the 4-position, as we found by the use of dilute nitric acid, in the presence of an inert hydrocarbon as solvent (*32*b). The procedure is as follows:

2,6-Di-tert-butyl-4-nitrophenol. In a 500 ml 3-necked flask equipped with a stirrer, dropping funnel, reflux condenser, and thermometer, 103 gm (0.5 mole) of 2,6-di-*tert*-butylphenol is dissolved in 100 ml of light petroleum (boiling range 60–95°). After heating the solution to 50°, 95 ml (106%) of nitric acid (30% by weight; d_{20} 1.180) is added dropwise with vigorous stirring over a period of 1 hr, during which the temperature is held between 50 and 55°. Along with the evolution of small amounts of nitrous gases, the reaction product precipitates as light ýellow crystalline mass, which is filtered by suction after an additional hour of stirring, covered with cold petroleum ether, washed with water until neutral and dried. Yield: 105 gm (83.7%) of 2,6-di-*tert*-butyl-4-nitrophenol, m.p. 156°.

---

* Claisen solution: 350 gm KOH in 250 gm of water, made up to 1 liter with methanol.

In the chlorination of 2,6-diethyl-4-nitrophenol a product is formed which contains 3 atoms of chlorine in addition to the nitro group and whose infrared spectrum suggests a dienone structure. Probably 2,6-diethyl-4-nitro-3,4,5-trichloro-1,4-dienone is at hand. Full chlorination of 2,6-diethylphenol also furnishes compounds with a dienone structure.

The action of thionyl chloride on 2,6-diethylphenol gives 4,4'-dihydroxy-3,3',5,5'-tetraethyldiphenyl sulfide along with 4-chloro-2,6-diethylphenol. This reaction of thionyl chloride which, in this instance acts as a chlorinating agent with simultaneous formation of a thioether, is unusual. Quite different is the behavior of dialkyl-substituted phenols in the reaction with thionyl chloride in the presence of aluminum chloride. In this reaction triarylsulfonium salts (33) are formed in excellent yields, probably via a 4,4'-dihydroxytetraalkyldiphenyl sulfoxide.

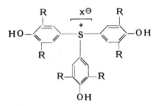

These sulfonium salts are almost insoluble in water, however, they pass into solution in an aqueous alkaline medium.

The "shielding effect" of the alkyl groups *ortho* to the phenolic hydroxyl group is also shown in that the Friedel-Crafts reaction is readily possible. Thus 3,5-diethyl-4-hydroxyacetophenone is formed in 70% yield from acetyl chloride and 2,6-diethylphenol.

The formation of diphenoquinones from phenols having the two *ortho* positions occupied and the *para* position free has already been noted. Normal quinones are readily formed when the oxidation is carried out after previous sulfonation (34). With 2,6-di-*tert*-butylphenol the quinone-formation also occurs with glacial acetic acid–chromic acid (35). Reduction furnishes 2,6-di-*tert*-butylhydroquinone, while the isobutylation of hydroquinone gives the 2,5-derivatives (see above).

Condensation with aldehydes takes place normally at the free *p*-position with the formation of the corresponding diphenylmethane derivatives.

If the condensation with aldehydes is carried out in the presence of alcohols in alkaline medium, then 3,5-dialkyl-4-hydroxybenzyl alkyl ethers are formed instead of diphenylmethanes (35a).

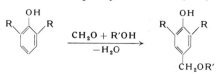

Mechanism of Reaction

In an attempt to explain the course of reaction of phenol alkylation and the action of the catalyst, aluminum phenoxide, a comparison with the analogous amine alkylation suggests itself. To explain the catalyst we had proceeded from the assumption (36) that the electron gap of aluminum plays a significant part since the reacton is inhibited by equimolecular amounts of alkali, calculated on the amount of aluminum added, probably because of the formation of the complexes, $[Al(NHC_6H_5)_4]MeI$, in which the electron gap of aluminum is filled.

The alkylation of phenol also occurs in the *ortho* position in the absence of aluminum, though less uniformly, while ring alkylation of amines without aluminum does not take place at all. Thus still another mechanism must play a part.

The acid character of the phenol may assist in the activation of the alkene at the high reaction temperature of phenol ethylation without a catalyst (350°). In the presence of aluminum phenoxide in phenol the acid character of the phenol is considerably increased. Analogous to the "alkoxo" acids described by Meerwein (37) the corresponding aluminum "phenoxo" acids of the type $[Al(OC_6H_5)_4]H$ are formed.

The formation of complex acids may be shown by a comparative pH determination of phenol and a solution of aluminum phenoxide in phenol.

Commercially pure phenol possesses a pH of 4.4–4.6 (measured with a glass electrode against a calomel electrode at 50°). With a 1% solution of aluminum phenoxide in phenol a pH value of 1.0 was obtained under the same conditions. Apparently a strong acid is present which makes the activation of the alkene understandable. Therefore the more facile activity of the branched alkenes in phenol alkylation is also explained in contrast to the alkylation of amines, since just these alkenes are more readily influenced by an acid activation.

The evidence for complex anions $[Al(OC_6H_5)_4]^-$ is also furnished by salt formation with metals analogous to the alkoxo acids. The corresponding salts are obtained by reaction with equimolecular amounts of aluminum and lithium or sodium.

The lithium salt, $[Al(OC_6H_5)_4]Li$ precipitates from the warm phenol solution and may be readily isolated. The pH value of a 1% solution of the lithium salt in phenol is 4.9 at 50°. A solution of aluminum phenoxide in phenol (pH 1 at 50°) shows a pH of 5.7 after the addition of an equivalent amount of sodium phenoxide. Corresponding to the alkoxide salts of Meerwein (38) the phenoxide salts also show a weak "phenolic" splitting, since the pH value of the commercially pure phenol is 4.4–4.6 (50°).

The above-mentioned complex salts in fact no longer show the catalytic activity of the aluminum phenoxide. Even the readily reactive isobutylene does not react with phenol under the ordinary conditions in the presence of the lithium and sodium salts of the aluminum phenoxo acids.

Aluminum phenoxide possesses, however, still a second specific property: the direction of alkyl substituents into the *ortho* position. If aluminum phenoxide is allowed to act upon *tert*-butyl phenyl ether at 100° in an open vessel, then rearrangement to *o-tert*-butylphenol takes place exclusively along with the splitting off of isobutylene. In a closed vessel the splitting off of isobutylene is diminshed in favor of an increased yield of *o*-substituted products.

The rearrangement of phenol ethers in the presence of sulfuric acid, for example, leads to *p-tert*-butylphenol from the *tert*-butyl ether, according to Natelson (*29*). According to our observations only traces of acids are necessary for the arrangement not only of the *tert*-butyl phenyl ether but also of the *o-tert*-butylphenol to the *p*-compound.

If *tert*-butyl phenyl ether is heated with lithium aluminum phenoxide instead of aluminum phenoxide under the same conditions, then the ether is recovered unchanged.

With these experiments the specific activity of aluminum phenoxide of favorably influencing *ortho*-substitution is confirmed. In the presence of excess phenol it may exist in equilibrium with the complex aluminum phenoxy acid.

For the explanation of the second phase of the reaction a similar interpretation as for the *o*-alkylation of aromatic amines is given, namely a reciprocal action of the alkene with the electron gap of aluminum (*39*). A decision as to whether phenol alkylation in the presence of aluminum phenoxide goes by way of the alkyl phenyl ether, cannot be made with certainty from the prevailing experimental results. The ether formation is undoubtedly favored by the strong acid character of the aluminum phenoxy acid and the readily activated isobutylene. Since a splitting off of isobutylene is observed on heating *tert*-butyl phenyl ether in an open vessel, the assumption of an alkyl phenyl ether as an intermediate is not conclusive.

Summary

Aluminum phenoxides act as catalysts at higher temperatures in the reaction of alkenes with phenols. In so doing the alkene as alkyl group enters the ring chiefly at the position *ortho* to the phenolic hydroxyl group.

The reactivity of the alkenes increases in the series: ethylene →
propylene → butylene → isobutylene.

With branched alkenes the reaction already begins at lower temperatures. Here phenyl ethers are also formed.

The strongly acidic aluminum phenoxo acids are formed from aluminum phenoxide and excess phenol, analogous to the alkoxo acids of Meerwein. The alkali salts of these complex acids prevent not only ring alkylation but also the formation of phenyl ethers.

A large number of o-alkylsubstituted phenols, which previously were generally difficult to obtain, have become readily accessible by the ring alkylation methods.

REFERENCES

(1) R. Stroh, J. Ebersberger, H. Haberland, and W. Hahn, *Angew. Chem.* **69**, 124 (1957).

(2) R. Stroh and R. Seydel, German Patent 944,014 (1956); *Chem. Abstr.* **53**, 321 (1959).

(3) C. Price, *Org. Reactions* **3**, 58 (1949).

(4) Latest review: L. F. Albright and R. N. Shreve, *Ind. Eng. Chem.* **53**, 492 (1961).

(5) S. Skraup, *Ber. deut. chem. Ges.* **60**, 1073 (1927).

(6) S. Skraup, German Patent 489,364 (1927); P. Friedländer, "Fortschritte der Teerfarbenfabrikation und verwandte Industriezweige," Vol. 16, p. 2870. Springer, Berlin, 1931; *Chem. Abstr.* **24**, 2145 (1930).

(7) British Patent 746,407 (1954); *Chem. Abstr.* **51**, 471 (1957).

(7a) See also work appearing in the meantime: A. J. Kolka, J. P. Napolitano, A. H. Filbey and G. G. Ecke, *J. Org. Chem.* **22**, 642 (1957).

(8) C. Graebe and H. Kraft, *Ber. deut. chem. Ges.* **39**, 794 (1906).

(9) W. Steinkopf and T. Höfner, *J. prakt. Chem.* **113**, 141 (1926).

(10) K. v. Auwers and G. Wittig, *Ber. deut. chem. Ges.* **57**, 1275 (1924).

(11) R. Stroh, J. Ebersberger, H. Haberland, and W. Hahn, *Angew. Chem.* **69**, 125 (1957).

(12) R. R. Read, C. A. Hewitt, and N. R. Pike, *J. Am. Chem. Soc.* **54**, 1194 (1932); F. Hawthorne and D. J. Cram, *ibid.* **74**, 585 (1952).

(12a) R. Stroh, J. Ebersberger, H. Haberland, and W. Hahn, *Angew. Chem.* **69**, 126 (1957).

(13) K. Fries and H. Engel, *Ann. Chem. Liebigs* **439**, 243 (1924).

(14) S. Goldschmidt and L. Strohmenger, *Ber. deut. chem. Ges.* **55**, 2465 (1922).

(15) M. Fileti, *Gazz. chim. ital.* **16**, 114 (1886).

(16) A. J. Kolka, J. P. Napolitano, and G. G. Ecke, *J. Org. Chem.* **21**, 712 (1956).

(17) F. J. Sowa, H. D. Hinton, and J. A. Nieuwland, *J. Am. Chem. Soc.* **55**, 3402 (1933).

(18) C. Guillaumin, *Bull. soc. chim. France* [4], **7**, 335 (1910).

(19) K. Fries and P. Moskopp, *Ann. Chem. Liebigs* **372**, 229 (1910).

(20) F. Bradfield and B. Jones, *J. Chem. Soc.* p. 1012 (1928).

(21) C. L. Moyle, U.S. Patent 2,623,907 (1949); *Chem. Abstr.* **47**, 2438 (1953).

(22) E. B. Reid and J. F. Yost, *J. Am. Chem. Soc.* **72**, 5232 (1950).

(23) H. Meyer and K. Bernhauer, *Monatsh. Chem.* **53/54**, 733 (1929).

(24) R. Wegler, *Chem. Ber.* **82**, 327 (1949); G. H. Stillson *et al.*, *J. Am. Chem. Soc.* **67**, 305 (1945).

(25) T. Evans and K. R. Edlund, U.S. Patent 2,051,475 (1933); *Chem. Abstr.* **30**, 6761 (1936).

(26) H. Hart and F. A. Cassis, *J. Am. Chem. Soc.* **73**, 3179 (1951); G. H. Stillson, U.S. Patent 2,459,597 (1949); *Chem. Abstr.* **43**, 3459 (1949).

(27) D. R. Stevens and W. A. Gruse, U.S. Patent 2,248,828 (1937); *Chem. Abstr.* **35**, 7176 (1941).

(28) P. M. Arnold, U.S. Patent 2,553,538 (1947); *Chem. Abstr.* **46**, 530 (1952).

(29) S. Natelson, *J. Am. Chem. Soc.* **56**, 1583 (1934); D. R. Stevens, *J. Org. Chem.* **20**, 1233 (1955).

(30) H. M. Crawford, M. Lumpkin, and M. McDonald, *J. Am. Chem. Soc.* **74**, 4087 (1952).

(31) C. Hale, U.S. Patent 2,745,882 (1953); *Chem. Abstr.* **51**, 1265 (1957).

(32) F. Klages, "Lehrbuch der organischen Chemie," Vol. 1, Part 2, p. 666. W. de Grutyer & Co., Berlin, 1953.

(32a) H. Hart and F. A. Cassis, *J. Am. Chem. Soc.* **73**, 3179 (1951).

(32b) Independent from us—as we learned later—the same observation was made by the Ethyl Corporation; cf. T. M. Coffield and M. E. Griffing, U.S. Patent 2,868,844 (1957); *Chem. Abstr.* **53**, 16064 (1959).

(33) W. Hahn and R. Stroh, German Patent 948,332 (1955); *Chem. Abstr.* **53**, 2159 (1959).

(34) G. Gollmer and R. Stroh, German Patent 1,022,209 (1954); *Chem. Abstr.* **54**, 2260 (1960).

(35) G. R. Yohe, J. E. Dunbar, R. L. Pedrotti, F. M. Scheidt, F. S. H. Lee, and E. C. Smith, *J. Org. Chem.* **21**, 1289 (1956).

(35a) Compare also M. S. Kharasch and B. S. Joshi, *J. Org. Chem.* **22**, 1435 (1957); also A. H. Filbey, U.S. Patent 2,838,571 (1955); *Chem. Abstr.* **52**, 13805 (1958).

(36) R. Stroh, J. Ebersberger, H. Haberland, and W. Hahn, *Angew. Chem.* **69**, 131 (1957).

(37) H. Meerwein and T. Bersin, *Ann. Chem. Liebigs* **476**, 113 (1929).

(38) H. Meerwein and G. Hinz, *Ann. Chem. Liebigs* **484**, 1 (1930).

(39) R. Stroh, J. Ebersberger, H. Haberland, and W. Hahn, *Angew. Chem.* **69**, 131 (1957).

Continuous Preparation of Phenylsodium

H. Ruschig*, R. Fugmann, and W. Meixner

Pharmazeutisch-Wissenschaftliche Laboratorien der Farbwerke Hoechst AG

The preparation of phenylsodium from chlorobenzene was discovered by G. Ehrhart in the years 1929–1931 and is described in patents of the IG-Farbenindustrie (*1*). The method is used in many laboratories without, however, being essentially changed. In place of sodium wire which was used initially, sodium dispersions were used when they became available (*2*), and these of course react substantially more energetically.

To the best of our knowledge, only batch preparations were made and found no technical application. The reason lay in the danger factor involved in the conversion to large amounts. Phenylsodium suspensions tend to spontaneous ignition on being stirred in air or in the presence of moisture. It is understandable that a kettle charged with 50 or 100 kg of phenylsodium presents a source of danger. Furthermore the sudden beginning of the strongly exothermic reaction is difficult to control with such large amounts and it may boil over and spatter. Therefore a continuous procedure for industry is desirable.

A procedure will be described in which phenylsodium suspensions can be prepared continuously and without danger. The method will be demonstrated with two pieces of apparatus of different size. The laboratory apparatus furnishes about 4 moles of phenylsodium per hour (*3*). The industrial apparatus produces ten times that amount.

The laboratory apparatus consists essentially of 3 parts (Fig. 1):

(a) a dosage device,
(b) two reaction loops,
(c) a collection vessel or reaction vessel for further reactions.

Initially the control of the dosage of sodium sand suspension was troublesome. The feeders and pumps in use failed to work because metallic sodium, on account of its ductility, smeared over or stopped up all the valves and movable joints so that it was not certain that a regulated addition of sodium sand was made to the reaction loop. Only one valveless feeder, developed for this purpose, worked satisfactorily; this was constructed like a bucket elevator.

The scoop mechanism, a cup-like receptacle made out of stainless steel, 1, is fastened with a plastic tube (impervious to benzene) to a rod,

* From an address given at a meeting of the German Chemical Society, held in Berlin on October 3, 1957; cf. *Angew. Chem.* **69**, 720 (1957).

2, which leads to a cam drive, 3, which moves the scoop up and down in a dipping vessel, 4, partially filled with sodium sand suspension. On the down-stroke the cup is filled with the sodium suspension. The scoop is so designed that in its movement it is tipped over on the side during the following up-stroke and can empty its contents into a connecting tube, 5, which leads to the first reaction loop.

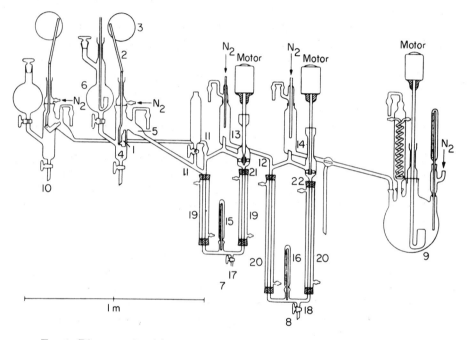

Fig. 1. Diagram of a laboratory unit for the preparation of phenylsodium.

The scoop mechanism is connected with the supply flask, 6, for the sodium sand suspension. The amount of sodium suspension transferred by the scoop is continuously restored from the supply flask as the result of automatic pressure equalization. The suspension in the supply flask is stirred constantly in order to prevent a settling of the sodium. The entire apparatus, including the reaction loops, 7, 8, and the collecting flask or reservoir, 9, is kept under nitrogen because of the sensitivity of sodium and of phenylsodium to the air.

The measured addition of chlorobenzene dissolved in a neutral solvent is made possible without difficulty with the help of customary dosage equipment. In order to make certain, however, that the equivalent amount of chlorobenzene is always included in the reaction loop, a similar scoop mechanism, 10, was chosen for the purpose on account of its simplicity.

The reaction of the sodium sand with chlorobenzene takes place in two similar reaction loops connected in series.

The first loop, 7 takes care of the main portion of the reaction. The second loop, 8, serves solely to make certain the reaction is carried to completion. The loops consist of a system of contiguous right-angled, self-enclosed glass tubes, 50 or 70 cm high, 30 cm wide, having a capacity of 175 or 250 ml. The glass tubes have a diameter of about 12 mm and are joined with ball joints. The loops each have an inlet, 11, 12, an overflow as an outlet 13, 14, a thermometer 15, 16, and a take-off stopcock, 17, 18. Both vertical tubes are encased in jackets and may be heated or cooled. Glycol monomethyl ether is used as the heat exchange liquid for safety reasons. In the right vertical tube of each loop a stainless steel stirrer, 21, 22, powered by rapid stirring motors, is built in, which permits the circulation of the contents of the loops at the rate of about 60 r.p.m. The overflow of the first loop, 13, is connected to the inlet of the second, 12. The phenylsodium suspension leaves the apparatus through the outlet of the second loop, 14, and flows into the collecting or reaction flask for further reaction. The laboratory apparatus described here permits the preparation of about 20 moles of phenylsodium per working day.

The industrial apparatus is a suitably scaled enlargement of the laboratory apparatus (Fig. 2). Only the spatial orientation of the reaction loops (diameter of the reaction tubes: 25 mm) was changed in order to conserve structural height.

The start of the reaction calls for some attention. Both loops are filled with toluene or benzene and heated to about 40°. Then about one-fifth of the volume is drained out of the first loop and it is then filled again with the help of the scoop mechanisms with sodium sand suspensions and chlorobenzene solution. After a short time, discoloration accompanied by a rise in temperature sets in the mixing zone. This indicates the start of the reaction. The stirrer and the scoop mechanisms are started again and additional sodium and chlorobenzene are added continuously. With external conditions remaining constant a definite reaction temperature is established after a short time, which remains quite constant to the end. It may be easily regulated by altering the rate of flow, by regulating the temperature of the heat exchanger, or, to a limited extent, by changing the rate of agitation.

The dark phenylsodium suspension collected in the collecting flask may be continuously used in further reactions. Its average yield runs at least 74%, determined by the weight of the corresponding amount of benzoic acid (formed by addition of CO_2). If the phenylsodium is used for the metallation of acidic methylene groups, then it is possible to add the starting material directly to the chlorobenzene solution as described on p. 365 for benzyldiethylacetonitrile (exactly as in the discontinuous procedure, see reference (1) German Patent 622,875—Example 7).

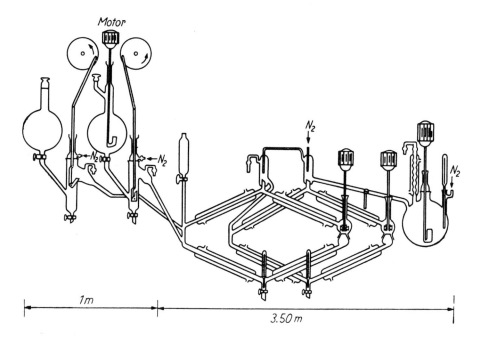

FIG. 2. Diagram of a technical apparatus for the preparation of phenylsodium. In building the apparatus care must be taken that the overflows in the left and right part show a suitable difference in elevation so that a constant flow of the phenylsodium suspension is assured.

Hitherto phenylsodium has found significant application in the metallation of substances with acidic methylene groups, in the introduction of phenyl groups as in a Grignard reaction, in the preparation of phenylmalonic acid (2), etc. Its importance as a synthetic agent seems to be heightened by the fact that in some cases it can replace the more expensive phenyllithium. If fluorobenzene is allowed to react with phenylsodium in the presence of triethylamine according to the method described by Wittig for the reaction of fluorobenzene with phenyllithium (4), it is possible to obtain diethylaniline in over 50% yield. This reaction leads one to the conclusion that phenylsodium may replace phenyllithium in reactions which go via the dehydrobenzene. For practical purposes this fact could be of considerable importance. An extension of the range of application of phenylsodium for preparative chemistry could well result.

Examples

Benzoic Acid

IN THE LABORATORY APPARATUS

With the help of the scoop mechanism 900 ml of a solution containing 226 gm of chlorobenzene (2 moles) in benzene and 900 ml of a suspension of 92 gm of sodium metal (4 moles) in benzene are brought together in the reaction loops at the same time over a period of 1 hr in the manner described above. The temperature of the heating mantle is regulated in such a manner that the temperature of the reaction chamber comes to 35–40°. A strong stream of carbon dioxide is introduced with vigorous stirring into the phenylsodium suspension. The resulting benzoic acid is isolated by extraction of the benzene phase with water, acidification, and crystallization. The total yield amounts to 184 gm (75.5% of theory) m.p. 120–121°.

IN THE INDUSTRIAL APPARATUS

Over a period of 1 hr 9 liters of sodium suspension in benzene, containing 900 gm of sodium (36 moles plus 10% excess), is allowed to react with 9 liters of a solution containing 2.034 kg of chlorobenzene (18 moles) in benzene. The reaction temperature in the first loop comes to 40–45° and in the second loop to 35–40°. Carbon dioxide is introduced into the phenylsodium suspension at 20° until saturated. Water is added to the reaction solution; the aqueous phase is separated and acidified with hydrochloric acid. The precipitated benzoic acid is filtered, washed, and dried. Yield: 1.625 kg (74.6% of theory) of m.p. 120–121°.

Benzyldiethylacetonitrile

With the help of the scoop mechanism 900 ml of a solution containing 226 gm of chlorobenzene (2 moles) and 194 gm of diethylacetonitrile (2 moles) in benzene is brought together in the reaction loops with 900 ml of a suspension of 92 gm of sodium powder (4 moles) in benzene simultaneously over a period of 1 hr. The temperature is regulated to 35–40°. The metallated nitrile which flows off continuously is collected in a flask equipped with a stirrer, dropping funnel, inlet tube for nitrogen, gas delivery tube, and thermometer. To this suspension is added dropwise 252 gm of benzyl chloride (2 moles), during which time the temperature should not exceed 60°, and the reaction is allowed to proceed at that temperature for 30 min. After cooling, washing with water, concentrating, distilling, and fractionating, 325 gm of benzyldiethylaceto-nitrile (87% of theory) is obtained having a b.p. 157–159°/10 mm.

REFERENCES

(1) German Patent 622,875 (1931); *Chem. Abstr.* **30**, 2991 (1936); German Patent 633,083 (1931); *Chem. Abstr.* **30**, 7582 (1936); German Patent 644,486 (1931); *Chem. Abstr.* **31**, 5381 (1937).
(2) J. F. Nobis and L. F. Moormeier, *Ind. Eng. Chem.* **46**, 539 (1954).
(3) German Patent 1,044,079 (1958); *Chem. Abstr.* **55**, 4433 (1961).
(4) G. Wittig, *Angew. Chem.* **69**, 246 (1957).

Newer Investigations on Oxidation with Lead Tetraacetate[1]

R. CRIEGEE

Institute für Organische Chemie der Technischen Hochschule Karlsruhe

The lead tetraacetate discovered by Jacquelin (*2*) in 1851 can be thought of as being a salt of quadrivalent lead, or better yet, as being a mixed anhydride of orthoplumbic and acetic acids, because it is soluble in many organic solvents. As is well known, hydrolysis to brown PbO_2 takes place instantaneously.

Dimroth, who introduced lead tetraacetate as a reagent into the organic laboratory in 1920 (*3*), looked upon the compound chiefly as being only a soluble lead dioxide and used it as such—in homogeneous solution, however,—for dehydrogenations. Not until three years later did he show in a fundamental paper with Schweizer (*4*) that with its help substitution of H by OH (protected by acetyl) as well as the addition of two OH groups (also protected by acetyl) to a double bond are also possible. These three modes of action correspond to those of the halogens and Dimroth looked upon lead tetraacetate as a mild halogen; the two acetoxyls released may indeed be considered pseudohalogens according to Birckenbach. Yet, the acetoxyl groups are not "ατομος," indivisible, in contrast to the halogen atoms; on this fact is based one of the differences in behavior.

The statement that lead tetraacetate yields two acetoxy groups in oxidations and thus is transformed into lead acetate is only a general description of the oxidation process, for this process can proceed in various ways. In the first place, two acetoxy radicals can be released; in the second place, an acetoxy anion and an acetoxy cation (in which case the latter is then the oxidative species) can be released; finally, two acetate anions can be given off by the addition of two electrons (which bring about the oxidation):

$$1. \quad Pb(OAc)_4 \qquad = Pb(OAc)_2 + 2\ AcO\cdot$$

$$2. \quad Pb(OAc)_4 \qquad = Pb(OAc)_2 + Ac\overline{O}^{\oplus} + AcO^{\ominus}$$

$$3. \quad Pb(OAc)_4 + 2^{\ominus} \quad = Pb(OAc)_2 + 2\ AcO^{\ominus}$$

All of these reactions can take place in one or two steps.

Certainly not all oxidations which will be discussed proceed according to one mechanism; the nature of the substrate and reaction conditions are much too different. Until now a deeper insight was gained in only a few cases; in many reactions conjectures were made or conclusions were drawn from analogy to similar systems.

In the following the reactions of lead tetraacetate with three different groups will be discussed: (1) with the hydroxyl group; (2) with certain CH groups; and (3) with the carbon-carbon double bond. This classification coincides partly, but not fully, with dehydrogenation, substitution, and addition.

Reactions with Hydroxyl Compounds

Alcohols, phenols, carboxylic acids, and hydroperoxides can be attacked by lead tetraacetate. In many cases the reaction results in a dehydrogenation. This occurs most easily when a suitable second hydroxyl group is still available and the molecule possesses the possibility of stabilization after the removal of the two hydrogen atoms bound to the oxygen.

This is particularly the case in compounds of the hydroquinone and pyrocatechol type. Quinones, diquinones (3), quinone imines (5), and quinoid dyestuffs are formed quantitatively in all cases under the mildest conditions. The high redox potential of the quadrivalent lead produces an equilibrium which always lies completely on the side of the quinoid compounds.

$$\text{HO} - \langle \rangle - \text{OH} + \text{Pb(OAc)}_4 \longrightarrow \text{O} = \langle \rangle = \text{O} + \text{Pb(OAc)}_2 + 2\text{HOAc}$$

Similar also in its course and its nature is the dehydrogenative splitting of α-glycols (6) and other classes of compounds which carry either two hydroxyl groups, one hydroxyl and one amino, or two amino groups in the α-position. The reaction is also carried out in dilute solution at low temperatures and occurs quantitatively and irreversibly, although with a different velocity dependent upon the structure of the glycol and the conditions of reaction.

$$\begin{array}{c} {>}\text{C--OH} \\ | \\ {>}\text{C--OH} \end{array} + \text{Pb(OAc)}_4 \longrightarrow \begin{array}{c} {>}\text{C=O} \\ \\ {>}\text{C=O} \end{array} + \text{Pb(OAc)}_2 + 2\text{ HOAc}$$

The characteristic feature of splitting a single carbon-carbon bond has lead to a comprehensive investigation of the mechanism.

The dehydrogenation of monohydroxy primary and secondary alcohols to aldehydes and ketones occurs on the other hand only at higher temperatures, where the reaction products themselves are readily oxidized further. Sometimes, however, the corresponding aldehydes or ketones can be obtained in good yields, as Mićović (7), for example, has shown with 3-pyridylcarbinols. In other cases, as with benzpinacolyl alcohol, Mosher (8) found rearrangements and the cleavage of molecules, which he explained with an ionic mechanism.

Whereas most carboxylic acids are, for the most part, stable towards lead tetraacetate (apart from the reversible formation of the corresponding tetravalent lead salts), formic acid is dehydrogenated smoothly and quantitatively to carbon dioxide.

Monohydric phenols do not possess a second hydrogen atom which can be given up. Consequently stabilization of the phenol dehydrogenated by one hydrogen atom is possible only through the reception of one acetoxy group. As Wessely (9) and others have shown, the reaction products are quinols, or in case of further oxidation, quinones respectively:

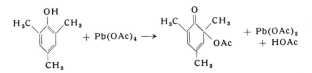

The common primary step in the preceding reactions seems to be a rapid, reversible alcoholysis of lead tetraacetate:

$$Pb(OAc)_4 + R–OH \rightleftarrows RO– Pb(OAc)_3 + HOAc$$

Such an alcoholysis product, $((AcO)_2Pb \underset{OH}{\overset{OCH_3}{\diagup}})$

could be isolated in one case (6). The rest of the reaction (in other words the real oxidation) takes place by the acceptance of the PbO electron pair by lead (caused by the strong electron affinity of quadrivalent lead), which in so doing is transformed into $Pb(OAc)_3^-$ and then into $Pb(OAc)_2 + OAc^-$:

$$RO \overset{\frown}{} Pb(OAc)_3 \longrightarrow RO^\oplus + Pb(OAc)_3^\ominus \longrightarrow Pb(OAc)_2 + OAc^\ominus$$

This electron shift is possible, however, only if the electron sextet of oxygen can be filled up at the same time. This becomes possible in the case of hydroquinone and α-glycols—ignoring the details—by a shift of the electron pair of the second OH bond. In monohydroxyl alcohols (more difficultly) and in formic acid it is realized by a shift in the electron pair of a CH bond. In monohydric phenols the sextet is restored by electrons from the ring:

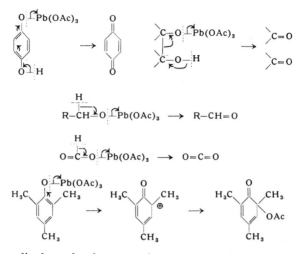

That a radical mechanism can play a part in the last named instance also is shown by the occasional appearance of dimerization products.

The oxidation of hydroperoxides is based on dehydrogenation with participation of an oxygen-bonded hydrogen atom (10). In contrast to all other classes of peroxides, these are attacked in the cold by lead tetraacetate, mostly with violent evolution of oxygen. Along with other methods this has become of importance for identification. The course of reaction is relatively smooth with primary and secondary monohydroperoxides as well as with ditertiary bishydroperoxides, while tertiary monohydroperoxides furnish various reaction products. Examples of the first two subgroups are the following reactions:

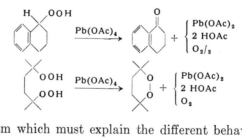

A mechanism which must explain the different behavior of sporadic hydroperoxides is not yet known, although the primary step appears to be similar to that for hydroxyl compounds (11).

Reactions with CH Groups

Some hydrogen atoms bound to carbon can be substituted by acetylated hydroxyl groups. Such acetoxylations are then—and only then—possible, when the carbon-hydrogen bond is adjacent to at least one activating group. Carbonyl groups of all kinds can function as such activating groups. There activity of activated groups increases in order from carboxylic acids (which accept an acetoxy group in the α-position only under extreme conditions) to acid anhydrides, to ketones.

$$R-CO-CH_3 + Pb(OAc)_4 = R-CO-CH_2OAc + Pb(OAc)_2 + HOAc$$

The β-diketones and the β-ketoacid esters react especially easily, as Dimroth (4) already found. The reaction is a first order reaction, just as is the halogenation of ketones, and therefore should occur via the enol form, according to Ichikawa (12) and Cavill (13). That the free enol of dimesitylacetaldehyde furnishes the corresponding oxidation product according to Fuson (14), was in agreement with this hypothesis. The mechanism is then the same as that for monohydric phenols. Occasionally, however, dimerization products appear here also (15).

Aromatic hydrocarbons with side chains also react in the same manner. Thus, toluene furnishes benzyl acetate (4), tetralin the acetate of ac-tetrahydronaphthol (11).

$$C_6H_5-CH_3 \rightarrow C_6H_5-CH_2OAc$$

Since substituents in the benzene ring exert a strong influence on the yields (between 6 and 60%) and dimerization products were never isolated, Cavill (16) rejects a radical mechanism (17).

The activating group, however, can also be a carbon-carbon double bond. Thus, alkenes of the allyl type, of which cyclohexene and α-pinene are examples (11, 18, 18a), can take on an acetylated hydroxyl group.

In both cases yields of 60–70% can be obtained; in other cases they are poorer, because alkenes can react quite differently as will be shown later on. The double bond can shift in the oxidation (18a); the stereospecific course argues against free radical formation. Acetylenes (19) of suitable structure can react in a similar manner under more strenuous conditions. The direct substitution of aromatically bound hydrogen by acetoxy succeeds only in unusual cases with exceptionally reactive ring hydrogen atoms, as is the case in benzanthracene or benzpyrene (20). An acetoxy group can also be introduced in the *para* position in anisole and other phenol ethers with moderate yields, according to Cavill (21).

In all of the examples cited the reactions proceed more smoothly and more uniformly and are therefore more efficient as preparative methods, the lower the temperature at which they can be carried out. Substances which are attacked by lead tetraacetate solution only with boiling, give mostly an abundance of oxidation products difficult to separate. All the more remarkable was the discovery of Fieser (22), that preparatively worthwhile methylations can be obtained in some cases under these conditions. Examples are the methylation of methylnaphthoquinone to dimethylnaphthoquinone or of trinitrobenzene to trinitrotoluene. With other aliphatic quadrivalent lead salts the corresponding alkylations are possible; with lead tetrabenzoate, phenylation occurred (23).

There is no doubt that here a pure radical reaction is involved.

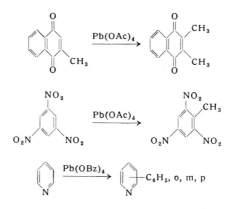

Lead tetraacetate decomposes under the reaction conditions into lead acetate and acetoxy radicals, which in turn furnish carbon dioxide and methyl radicals. In support of this mechanism is the completely similar action (not found with other lead tetraacetate oxidations) of diacyl peroxides, as well as the observation of an induction period which can be shortened in various ways.

Reaction at the Carbon-Carbon Double Bond

Addition of Two Acetoxy Groups

The "normal" reaction course of unsaturated compounds with lead tetraacetate consists in the addition of two acetoxy groups with the formation of the diacetate of α-glycols (4). However, this reaction with simple aliphatic or cyclic alkenes is less important than the above mentioned substitution in the alkyl position. In contrast, enol ethers (24), which are readily attacked at room temperature owing to the electron donating alkoxy groups, furnish the diacetates smoothly:

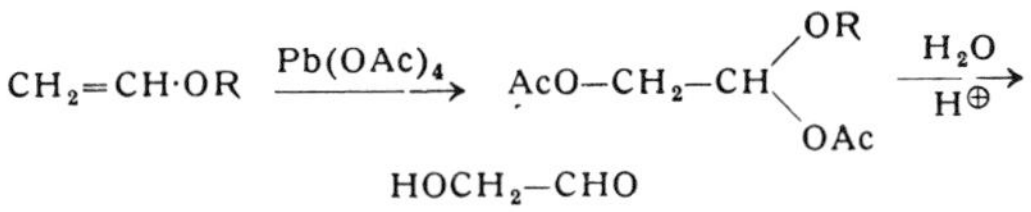

$$CH_2=CH\cdot OR \xrightarrow{Pb(OAc)_4} AcO-CH_2-CH \overset{OR}{\underset{OAc}{\big\langle}} \xrightarrow[H\oplus]{H_2O}$$

$$HOCH_2-CHO$$

In enol esters (*25*) the original acyl group present is frequently split off in the course of the reaction, so that free acetoxy ketones are formed; the course can be represented in the following manner:

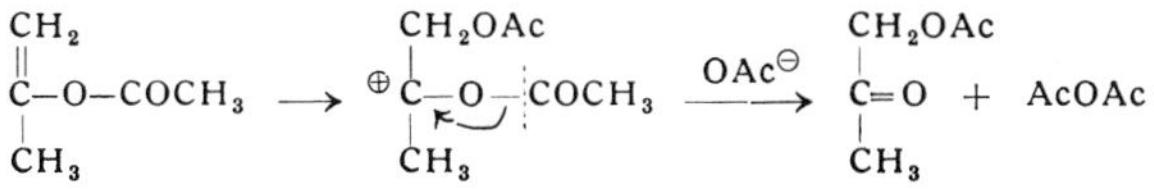

$$\underset{CH_3}{\overset{CH_2}{\underset{|}{\overset{||}{C}}}}-O-COCH_3 \longrightarrow \underset{CH_3}{\overset{CH_2OAc}{\underset{|}{\overset{|}{\oplus C}}}}-O \cdots COCH_3 \xrightarrow{OAc\ominus} \underset{CH_3}{\overset{CH_2OAc}{\underset{|}{\overset{|}{C}}}}=O + AcOAc$$

in which the formation of the cationic intermediate may proceed in such a manner as will be shown below with other alkenes.

With dienes, 1,2- or 1,4-addition can take place (*11, 26*). To all appearances the latter is exclusively the case with furan and α-acetoxy-furan (*27*), whose oxidations have found preparative applications. The oxidation of anthracene, according to Fieser and Putnam (*28*), is also a 1,4-addition in the first stage.

Addition of Methyl Acetate

We observed a combination of methylation and addition of acetoxy groups with styrene and with unsymmetrical diphenylethylene (*18*). The homologous alcohols, esterified with acetic acid, are formed in benzene solution in good yield under relatively mild conditions, at around 60°, thus, far below the decomposition point of lead tetraacetate.

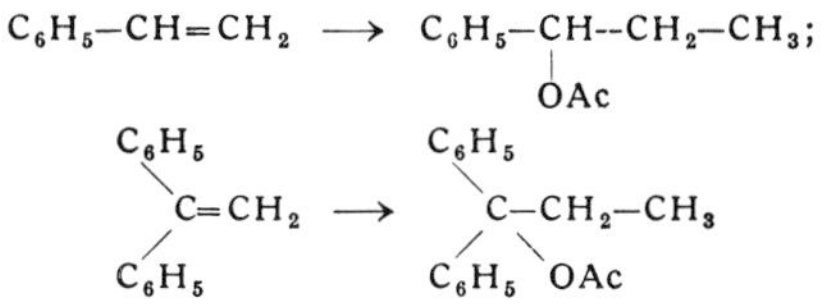

$$C_6H_5-CH=CH_2 \longrightarrow \underset{\overset{|}{OAc}}{C_6H_5-CH}-CH_2-CH_3;$$

$$\underset{C_6H_5}{\overset{C_6H_5}{\big\rangle}}C=CH_2 \longrightarrow \underset{C_6H_5}{\overset{C_6H_5}{\big\rangle}}C-CH_2-CH_3$$

The reaction, usually not encountered, is also applicable to lead tetrabenzoate (*29*): in this case phenyl and benzoxy are added.

In the case of styrene, polymerization of the hydrocarbon does not occur as a side reaction; the action of lead tetraacetate is thus completely different from that of diacetyl peroxide. Nevertheless, and in spite of the realtively mild conditions, a radical chain mechanism cannot be excluded with certainty; it could occur in somewhat the following manner:

$$C_6H_5-CH=CH_2 + CH_3{}^{\cdot} = C_6H_5-CH^{\cdot}-CH_2-CH_3$$
$$C_6H_5-CH^{\cdot}-CH_2-CH_3 + Pb(OAc)_4 = C_6H_5-CH(OAc)-CH_2-CH_3$$
$$+ Pb^{\cdot}(OAc)_3$$
$$Pb^{\cdot}(OAc)_3 = Pb(OAc)_2 + CO_2 + CH_3{}^{\cdot}$$

Oxidation with Rearrangement

The investigation of a styrene derivative, namely *p*-methoxystyrene (*24*), furnishes a deeper insight into the mechanism of the reaction. This example shows at the same time how seemingly very small changes in the structure of the substrate can lead to a fully altered course of reaction. *p*-Methoxystyrene was investigated in order to check if the activating influence of a methoxy group on a double bond (already mentioned) is transmitted through a benzene ring. Actually *p*-methoxystyrene reacts violently with the oxidizing agent even at room temperature; the expected reaction product was not obtained, instead the crystalline isomeric aldehyde diacetate of *p*-methoxyphenylacetaldehyde was obtained in 90% yield:

$$p-CH_3O \cdot C_6H_4 \cdot CH:CH_2 \ \longrightarrow \ p-CH_3O \cdot C_6H_4 \cdot CH(OAc) \cdot CH_2OAc$$
$$\longrightarrow \ p-CH_3O \cdot C_6H_4 \cdot CH_2 \cdot CH(OAc)_2$$

The same reaction took place also with *o*-methoxystyrene. That there is present in the reaction products a carbon skeleton altered in relation to the starting material is shown from the behavior of the styrene derivatives "tagged" in the *α*-position with a methyl group or with a second methoxyphenyl group: the "tagged" group was found in the reaction products in the *β*-position. Plainly then in all cases a methoxyphenyl group has shifted from the *α*- to the *β*-carbon atom.

Similar rearrangements in oxidations with lead tetraacetate were occasionally observed at one time or another. Thus a homocamphenilone is formed from camphene by ring enlargement, according to Hückel (*30*), while according to Hurd (*31*), tetrahydro-2-furanmethanediol diacetate is obtained from dihydropyran through ring contraction (*32*):

A hypothesis concerning the course of these rearrangement reactions as well as other oxidation reactions of lead tetraacetate was developed by Weis and Dimroth (*24*). According to them, lead tetraacetate acts in the first phase of the reaction by adding the fragments $Pb(OAc)_3^+$ OAc^- to the double bond, similar to the long-known case of mercuric acetate. The expected lead organic compound is not stable because of the great electron affinity of quadrivalent lead, but decomposes instantly with the extraction of an electron pair from the substrate into $Pb(OAc)_3^-$ (which in turn decomposes into $Pb(OAc)_2$ and OAc^-) and an organic cation in which the migration of the methoxyphenyl group takes place immediately. Final stabilization is achieved by the addition of an acetate anion:

$$CH_3O \cdot C_6H_4 \cdot CH=CH_2 \longrightarrow CH_3O \cdot C_6H_4-CH-CH_2-Pb(OAc)_3$$
$$\underset{OAc}{|} \quad \quad I$$

$$\longrightarrow CH_3O \cdot C_6H_4-CH-CH_2^{\oplus}$$
$$II \quad \underset{OAc}{|}$$

$$\longrightarrow CH_3O \cdot C_6H_4-CH_2-\overset{\oplus}{C}H \cdot OAc \longrightarrow CH_3O \cdot C_6H_4-CH_2 \cdot CH(OAc)_2$$

Consideration should be given to the fact that the intermediate II could arise directly from the styrene derivative by the action of an OAc$^+$ cation split out from lead tetraacetate, such as Mosher (*33*) has accepted as the reactive agent in certain oxidations. In this case, however, the OAc group must add to the β-carbon and not to the α-carbon atom (*33a*).

Reactions with Mercury Compounds

The above described mechanism utilizes organolead compounds of the type $RPb(OAc)_3$ as intermediates. Such compounds were first recently discovered by Panov and Kocheshkov (*34*) in which R was an aromatic group. Since I must be very short-lived—it never could be isolated—a great difference in the stability of the compound, $RPb(OAc)_3$ should exist depending upon the nature of R. We found in the reaction of diarylmercury compounds with lead tetraacetate (*35*) a way to prepare compounds of this type under mild conditions. In agreement with the presentation of the Russian authors the compounds proved to be completely stable.

$$R_2Hg + Pb(OAc)_4 \rightarrow RHgOAc + RPb(OAc)_3$$

If the reaction is applied to dialkylmercury compounds, then in place of $RPb(OAc)_3$ only its decomposition products, namely lead acetate and alkyl acetate, are obtained.

This decomposition should occur ionically and therefore furnish R^+ as intermediates. In agreement with this the neopentyl radical (known since the time of Whitmore (*36*) that it is unstable as a cation) undergoes a rearrangement to the *tert*-amyl group in the reaction of dineopentylmercury with lead tetraacetate and *tert-amyl* acetate is obtained instead of neopentyl acetate.

In order to decide whether the formation of the triacetoxylead compounds (stable aromatic or unstable aliphatic) takes place through the $Pb(OAc)_3^-$ ion or the $Pb(OAc)_3^+$ ion, the mixed mercury compound, benzylphenylmercury, was oxidized. It is known from the work of

Kharasch (37), that polar reagents cleave these compounds in such a way that the positive fragment adds to the phenyl, the negative to the benzyl. Thus, with hydrogen chloride, benzene and benzylmercuric chloride are obtained. Lead tetraacetate furnished phenyllead triacetate and benzylmercuric acetate which is explainable only by the appearance of the lead triacetate cation. This reacts as an electrophilic reagent at least in the case under discussion and also with respect to methoxystyrene. Many of the reactions previously considered can be explained by an electrophilic attack of the $Pb(OAc)_3^+$ cation (or also of the undissociated lead tetraacetate; in this case the OAc^- anion is removed in an intermediary step).

Investigations with Thallium(III) Acetate

We insert here some comment concerning the action of thallium(III) salts (38) which have not been investigated extensively. As is well known thallium stands between lead and mercury in the periodic system. Thus it was expected that thallium(III) acetate would react in a manner intermediate between that of mercuric acetate (which only adds on to double bonds under the mildest conditions) and lead tetraacetate (with which the corresponding adducts are assumed, but have never been isolated). Actually it was possible with the new reagent under mild conditions to isolate adducts which are transformed into the oxidation product of the substrate with the splitting off of thallium(I) acetate at higher temperature. An example of this is the reaction of styrene with thallic acetate in methanol:

$$C_6H_5-CH=CH_2 \xrightarrow[CH_3OH]{Tl(OAc)_3} \underset{\underset{OCH_3}{|}}{C_6H_5-CH-CH_2-Tl(OAc)_2} \xrightarrow{130\,°C}$$

$$\underset{\underset{OCH_3}{|}}{C_6H_5-CH-CH_2OAc} + C_6H_5-CH_2-CH\overset{OCH_3}{\underset{OAc}{\diagdown}} + Tl(OAc)$$

The decomposition of the adduct occurs in part with, in part without, rearrangement in the organic portion.

Formation of Esters of Glycolic Acid and of Glyoxylic Acid

As was indicated above, CH_3, CH_2, and CH groups are capable of undergoing substitution of a hydrogen atom by an acetoxy group under the influence of an activating neighboring group. A free or esterified carboxyl group does not bring about such activation below 100° (39).

Quite astonishing was the discovery that during the addition of two acetoxy groups to some alkenes, these groups themselves were substituted into the CH_3 group so that esters of glycolic acid or glyoxylic acid were obtained as final products depending upon whether one or two acetoxy groups entered the methyl group. These coupled oxidations occur generally at room temperature and often with excellent yields.

Cyclopentadiene (11) was a case known for some time; here, however, the results are somewhat complicated, since cis- and trans-addition occur as does addition in the 1,2- and 1,4-positions as well. A better example is furnished by isobutylene (40). If this is introduced into a suspension of lead tetraacetate in glacial acetic acid, then a glyoxylic acid derivative probably having the following structure is obtained:

$$(CH_3)_2C{=}CH_2 + 3\ Pb(OAc)_4 \rightarrow (CH_3)_2C{-}CH_2$$
$$AcO\quad O{\cdot}CO{\cdot}CH(OAc)_2$$

Brutcher (41) supplied the key to the understanding of this unexpected reaction with the discovery that the course of the reaction is completely altered by the addition of some water, and the monoacetate of a diol is formed in place of the complicated reaction product. With the use of his explanation, as well as the previous statements concerning the primary steps of the oxidation of methoxystyrene, the reaction sequence with isobutylene appears to be the following:

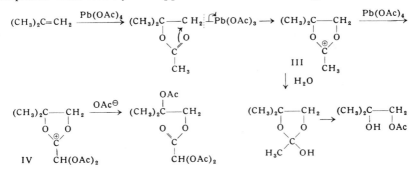

The crucial step is the "bridged" cation III in which the hydrogen atoms of the acetate-methyl group are substituted because of the positive charge on the acetate-carbon atom. The latter plays the part here of a strong activating group; much stronger than the grouping

$$-\overset{\|}{\underset{O}{C}}{-}CH_3 \longleftrightarrow -\overset{\oplus}{\underset{O\ominus}{C}}{=}CH_3$$

in methyl ketones. The stabilization of the newly formed cation IV occurs through the attachment of an acetate anion to the α-carbon of isobutylene.

Formation of Lactones from Alkenes

In conclusion an unusual side reaction should be mentioned which occurs in the oxidation of simple aliphatic alkenes. In the higher boiling fractions γ-lactones (40) are found which are formed by the addition of the group $OCOCH_2$ to the double bond. In the case of 4-octene the reaction product has the following structure confirmed through synthesis:

$$C_3H_7-CH{=}CH-C_3H_7 \longrightarrow C_3H_7-CH-CH-C_3H_7$$

Here also—as in the formation of esters of glycolic acid mentioned in the preceding section—the reactive $OCOCH_3$ group is altered in its methyl portion. Several mechanisms can be formulated for this reaction, but a positive decision is not yet possible.

Concluding Remarks

Once again an attempt should be made to bring order to the large body of factual material through a mechanistic approach. The following statements appear possible:

(1) In all cases in which lead tetraacetate reacts under mild conditions, the primary step of the reaction is an electrophilic attachment of $Pb(OAc)_3^+$ (or of $Pb(OAc)_4$ itself, followed or accompanied by the expulsion of an acetate anion) to the substrate. This can be:

   (a) a compound with a hetero atom to whose electron pair $Pb(OAc)_3^+$ attaches itself,
   (b) an alkene which adds $Pb(OAc)_3 \ldots OAc$,
   (c) an aromatic compound with strong electron donating groups,
   (d) an organometallic compound such as diphenylmercury.

(2) The resulting compounds are of the type $RPb(OAc)_3$ or $ROPb(OAc)_3$. The first of these types (with PbC bond) is stable only when R is an aromatic group (or perhaps also a vinyl type); the second (with PbO bond) only when R is part of a carboxylic acid (except formic acid) or a tert alkyl group. In all other cases the $Pb(OAc)_3$ group takes possession more or less easily, of the electron pair previously belonging to the substrate. In this frequently occurring case then, the oxidation with lead tetraacetate takes place only in the (indirect) removal of an electron pair. Consequently it falls into the large group of oxidation reactions of organic compounds, which Levitt (42) has assembled recently, having this feature in common.

(3) This acceptance of the electron pair by the OPb bond can occur

only if the oxygen atom simultaneously receives electrons from the substrate. The ease with which this is possible is crucial for the ease of oxidation.

(4) The carbonium ion formed from the CPb bond must be stabilized, and this is possible in several ways:

(a) by accepting an acetate anion, either from the $Pb(OAc)_3$ group or from the solvent with the formation of a "normal" diacetate,

(b) by forming a dioxolenium cation by ring closure with a $—O—C(CH_3)=O$ group already present. With sufficient stability of the new cation this can lead to the formation of esters of glycolic and glyoxylic acids.

(c) by rearrangement, followed by the addition of an acetate anion. The occurrence of the rearrangement depends upon the "ease of migration" of the substituents present.

(5) The methylation of aromatic compounds is a typical radical reaction. It requires temperatures at which lead tetraacetate begins to decompose, thus is observed only with substances which react only with difficulty with lead tetraacetate owing to a lack of nucleophilic positions.

(6) A number of oxidation reactions of lead tetraacetate are not yet classified in this scheme. Among these are: (a) substitution in the allyl position; (b) the addition of methyl acetate; (c) the formation of γ-lactones.

Predictions concerning the behavior of definite compounds with lead tetraacetate have only limited validity for the time being. The possibility of influencing the course of a reaction through choice of solvents or catalysts (43) e.g., BF_3 exists, but it has not yet been systematically investigated in most cases.

Otto Dimroth has demanded the renunciation of the empirical as a goal of organic chemistry. He wished to predict the course of a reaction from a knowledge of the energy parameters, from kinetic data, and from reaction mechanisms (all three of which are not independent of each other), and thus to be able to choose suitable reactants. The preceding view of quite a small branch of organic chemistry shows how far we still are today from this possibility. The close cooperation of experimenter and theoretician will be necessary in order to reconcile the disparity of data.

Supplement

Since the preceding article was written, some important contributions have appeared. They will be discussed in the same order as in the main article.

Reactions with Hydroxyl Compounds

W. von E. Doering (*44*) had shown in numerous investigations that 1,2-dicarboxylic acids could be transformed by decarboxylation with lead dioxide into alkenes. As Grob (*45a, 45b*) since then has discovered, the same degradation may be carried out with better reproducibility and with better yields using lead tetraacetate. The dicarboxylic acid is heated with lead tetraacetate in benzene, acetonitrile or, best, dimethylsulfoxide (*46*) solution with the addition of pyridine until the reaction begins with the evolution of carbon dioxide. The yields generally amount to 50–70%. Several examples may illustrate the application of the method:

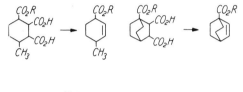

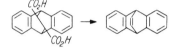

The following mechanism best satisfies the data:

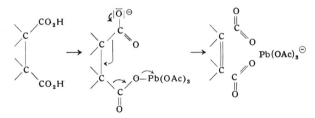

According to Jacques (*47*) β, γ-unsaturated acids are not only oxidized with lead tetraacetate but decarboxylated as well, in which case the double bond can be shifted at the same time. Probably the oxidizing agent attaches itself to the carboxyl group and not to the double bond:

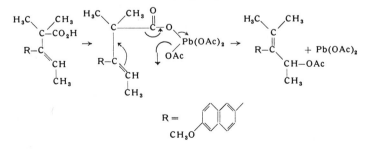

Reaction with CH Groups

Whereas normally only such CH groups which are activated by neighboring groups such as aryl radicals, carboxyl groups, or double bonds, are attacked by lead tetraacetate, there was discovered recently by a group of Swiss chemists (48) that a nonactivated methyl group can be oxidized under special steric conditions. The reaction product, a saturated cyclic ether, is formed in greater than 30% yield. The authors assume the formation of a tetravalent lead alkoxide as an intermediate and an electrophilic attachment to the methyl group after the splitting off of $Pb(OAc)_3^-$:

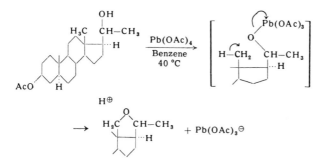

A new example of the dehydrogenation of a hydrocarbon by lead tetraacetate is furnished by Gardner and Thompson (49). It seems noteworthy that the dehydrogenation stops after the introduction of one double bond, whereas chloranil introduces the second double bond into the seven membered ring (although with poorer yield):

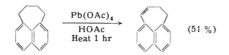

Reactions at the Carbon-Carbon Double Bond

Alder *et al.* (50) in a very careful piece of work investigated the reaction of lead tetraacetate on the double bond of the bicyclo [2.2.1] heptene system. In all cases the addition results in rearrangement. Noticeable is the strong influence of the solvent upon the nature of the reaction product. All reactions are in agreement with the view of an electrophilic attack of a $Pb(OAc)_3^+$ cation on the strained double bond as being the first reaction step. The following scheme gives a survey of the results (parentheses around the group denotes unknown steric arrangement):

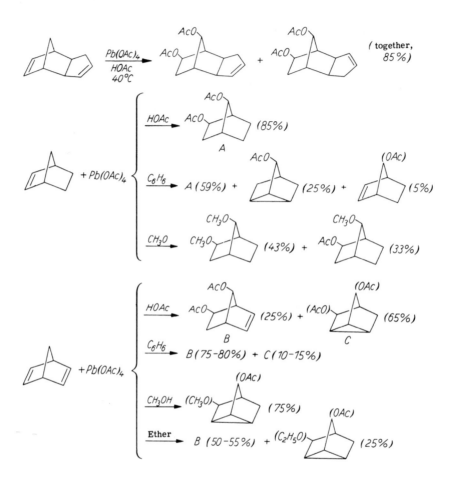

Miscellaneous

Lead tetraacetate not only attacks organomercuric compounds as an electrophile (51) but in certain cases it is possible also to convert aromatic compounds into organolead compounds through a "plumbation reaction." Panov and Kocheshkov (52) used lead tetraisobutyrate for this, with thiophene as the substrate. Dependent upon the proportion of reactants and the reaction conditions, compounds containing one or two thiophene radicals on the lead may be obtained:

According to Field and Lawson (53) mercaptans and thiophenols can be converted more or less smoothly into disulfides with lead tetraacetate.

The speed of this reaction is greater than that of the glycol cleavage of pinacol. Accordingly, monothioglycol is not cleaved oxidatively by lead tetraacetate, but on the contrary is converted to the corresponding disulfide (54). A lead tetramercaptide is considered as the intermediate.

Noteworthy and of preparative importance is the discovery of Horner (55), that tertiary amines can be dealkylated on treatment with lead tetraacetate in acetic anhydride (just as with N-bromosuccinimide) with excellent yields. Thus, dimethylaniline gives 83% of acetylmethylaniline and diethylaniline 90% of the corresponding acetyl compound. The mechanism of this reaction is still unknown.

Selected Preparations

Pyridinealdehyde (7)

In a 1 liter three-necked flask fitted with a dropping funnel, reflux condenser, and stirrer, 53.2 gm (0.12 mole) of lead tetraacetate (dried over P_2O_5) and 200 ml of absolute benzene are placed. The mixture is heated to boiling with stirring; then—after removing the source of heat— a solution of 13.1 gm (0.12 mole) of freshly distilled pyridinecarbinol in 50 ml of absolute benzene is added dropwise from the dropping funnel in 3–5 min. After the brown solution boils for several minutes, it becomes light yellow or colorless and the resulting lead acetate precipitates. Heating is continued for another 45 min and then any excess lead tetraacetate is removed by the addition of a few drops of glycol. The cooled solution is suction filtered, and the lead salt is then washed twice with benzene. The combined benzene solutions are shaken with a solution of 20 gm of potassium carbonate in 200 ml of water to remove acetic acid, the aqueous layer is then extracted five times with chloroform or ether.

The combined solutions are dried and the solvent removed. The aldehydes remaining are fractionated *in vacuo*.

2-Pyridinealdehyde b.p. 70–73°/13mm, yield 65.4%
3-Pyridinealdehyde b.p. 86–89°/13mm, yield 77.8%
4-Pyridinealdehyde b.p. 90–91°/20mm, yield 68.4%

3,3,6,6-Tetramethyl-o-dioxane (10)

A 14.6 gm portion of technical 1,1,4,4-tetramethyl-1,4-butanediol is stirred with 57 ml of 50% hydrogen peroxide ($d^{18} = 1.200$) and after cooling with vigorous stirring is decomposed with 45.5 ml of 70% sulfuric acid. Stirring is continued for 40 min at 25–30°, and a volume of ice water three times the total volume of the mixture is added. The mixture is filtered by suction and washed well with ice water and some sodium bicarbonate solution; yield, after drying in desiccator, is 10.5 gm (59%), m.p. 105° (from benzene).

A 17.8 gm portion of bishydroperoxide in 150 ml of glacial acetic acid is added dropwise to a vigorously stirred suspension of 45 gm of lead tetraacetate in 200 ml of glacial acetic acid at 25–30°. When oxygen is no longer evolved the mixture is neutralized with $2N$ NaOH and extracted with ether. Vacuum distillation gives 6.8 gm (47%) of tetra-methyl-o-dioxane with a b.p. 48–49°/14mm: n_D^{20} 1.4251.

Trans-Verbenol Acetate (18)

A 20 gm portion of α-pinene in 450 ml of absolute benzene is oxidized with 64 gm of lead tetraacetate with vigorous stirring at 70° for 2 hr. The cooled solution is filtered from the lead acetate and the residue washed with some benzene. The benzene is distilled off from the filtrate at about 100 mm at a bath temperature of 30–40° and utilizing a small column; some more lead acetate separates. Once again it is filtered and the reaction product is distilled *in vacuo*. After a forerun consisting of glacial acetic acid and 3 gm of unreacted pinene is obtained, 18.5 gm (74%) of verbenol acetate is obtained, b.p. 70–71°/2.5mm; n_D^{23} 1.4730; $[\alpha]_D^{20}$ −11.2°. Saponification gives *trans*-verbenol, b.p. 56–57°/0.7mm, p-nitrobenzoate, m.p. 82°. If the oxidation of α-pinene takes place in glacial acetic acid as solvent, then only 34% of verbenol acetate is obtained, along with verbenes and sorbrerol diacetate.

2,3-Dimethyl-1,4-naphthoquinone (22)

A solution of 0.86 gm of 2-methyl-1,4-naphthoquinone and 0.6 gm of malonic acid (as catalyst) in 15 ml of glacial acetic acid is treated with 5 gm of lead tetraacetate and warmed in the water bath first for 1 hr at 50–60°, then for an additional hour at 70°. A precipitate (a lead malonate?) which first forms then disappears. At the same temperature 2 gm portions of lead tetraacetate are added 2–3 times, until upon further addition gas is no longer evolved. The excess oxidizing agent is destroyed with several drops of glycerol. The reaction mixture is poured into water and the yellow precipitate is crystallized from methanol; m.p. 122–124°; yield 0.45 gm (49%).

Ethoxy-1,2-ethanediol Diacetate (18, 24)

A 30 gm portion of freshly distilled ethyl vinyl ether is added drop-wise over a 40 min period to a vigorously stirred suspension of 185 gm of lead tetraacetate in 600 ml of absolute benzene. After cooling the temperature is kept at 30°. The workup is like that for verbenol acetate. Distillation gives 72 gm (89%) of the diacetoxy compound, b.p. 76–77°/2mm, n_D^{25} 1.4133.

On shaking with an aqueous solution of semicarbazide hydrochloride the semicarbazone of acetylglycolaldehyde is obtained, m.p. 170°.

2,5-Dihydro-2,5-furandiol Diacetate (27)

In a 1 liter three-necked flask fitted with a stirrer, thermometer, and reflux condenser are placed 580 ml of glacial acetic acid and 230 ml of acetic anhydride and with vigorous stirring there is added in 10–20 gm portions a total of 300 gm of lead oxide (Pb_3O_4). The temperature is maintained at 50°. After about 3.5 hr the reaction is finished. Then 29.8 gm of furan is added, the temperature rises to 60° and the heating bath is removed. In the next 10 min the temperature rises to 65°. A temperature of 60–65° is maintained for 75 min, first through cooling, then by heating; then the major portion of the solvent is removed at 10 mm with the water bath at 60–65°, and 400 ml of absolute ether is added to the paste-like residue. After shaking and stirring the precipitated lead acetate (415 gm) becomes filterable. The yellow-brown filtrate is freed from ether and distilled *in vacuo*. The major portion (56 gm, 69%) has a b.p. 89–93°/0.5 mm, n_D^{25} 1.4536. The substance is a mixture of the *cis* and *trans* forms, from which the isomer of m.p. 51–52° may be obtained by crystallization from methanol at −20°. Hydrolysis of both forms leads to malealdehyde.

Acetate of Ethylphenylmethanol (18)

A 23.5 gm portion of freshly distilled styrene in 500 ml of absolute benzene is oxidized with 100 gm of lead tetraacetate with stirring at a bath temperature of 75–80°; workup as for verbenol acetate. On distillation 30 gm (82%) of the acetate of ethylphenylmethanol is obtained, b.p. 103–110°/12mm (redistillation: b.p. 77–78°/2mm). Alkaline saponification furnishes a 90% yield of ethylphenylmethanol, b.p. 105–106°/16mm, n_D^{20} 1.5208; *p*-nitrobenzoate, m.p. 56°.

p-Methoxyphenylacetaldehyde Diacetate (24)

A 15 gm portion of freshly distilled *p*-methoxystyrene is added with vigorous stirring to a suspension of 52 gm of lead tetraacetate in 80 ml of glacial acetic acid; the temperature is maintained at 25° by external cooling. When the reaction is finished (verified with leucomalachite green), the mixture is poured into 400 ml of water. The precipitated yellow oil solidifies after a time and after filtration is dried in the desiccator. The crude product (23.5 gm; 94%) is recrystallized from petroleum ether (b.p. 40–60°); m.p. 52°. The substance is not infinitely stable in the laboratory atmosphere (acidic), therefore it is sealed up in an appropriate fashion.

1-Carbethoxy-Δ^2-bicyclo[2.2.2]octene (45b)

In a 1 liter flask fitted with stirrer, condenser, and gas inlet tube 27 gm (0.1 mole) of 1-carbethoxy-Δ^2-bicyclo [2.2.2] octane-2,3-dicarboxylic acid is treated with 150 ml of absolute benzene and 12 ml (0.15 mole) of absolute pyridine. After the addition of 46.6 gm (0.1 mole) of about 95% lead tetraacetate the mixture is warmed on the steam bath in a current of nitrogen and with stirring until a clear solution is formed and a somewhat vigorous reaction sets in. After the evolution of carbon dioxide has subsided, the mixture is refluxed for 2 hr longer. Then the precipitated lead acetate is filtered and the benzene solution is washed successively with water, 2 N sodium carbonate, 2 N hydrochloric acid, and finally again with water. After drying over sodium sulfate the solution is concentrated using a column. Distillation of the oily residue in a stream of nitrogen furnishes 11.3 gm of a bicyclooctene derivative of b.p. 95–96°/10mm.

The crystalline distillation residue furnishes 3 gm of the anhydride of the starting material after two recrystallizations from ether-petroleum ether. Considering this amount of recovered material, the total yield of the unsaturated compound is 71%.

Demethylation of Dimethylaniline (55)

To a mixture of 6.0 gm (50 mmole) of dimethylaniline in 25 ml of chloroform and 10 ml of acetic anhydride, which is contained in three-necked flask fitted with a stirrer, a solution of 22.15 gm (50 mmole) of lead tetraacetate in 50 ml of chloroform is added dropwise over a period of 30–40 min at room temperature in an atmosphere of nitrogen. The reaction, after an initial green coloration, proceeds with a strong evolution of heat. With occasional cooling with water, stirring is continued for 1 hr. The precipitated lead acetate is filtered, the chloroform solution is extracted with 200 ml of water, and the layers are separated. The chloroform layer is concentrated, the acetic acid and acetic anhydride removed *in vacuo* and the remaining N-methylacetanilide is recrystallized from water; m.p. 102°; yield 6.1 gm (83%).

REFERENCES

(1) See R. Criegee, *Angew Chem.* **53**, 321 (1940).

(2) A. Jacquelin, *J. prakt. Chem.* **53**, 151 (1851).

(3) O. Dimroth, O. Friedemann, and H. Kämmerer, *Ber. deut. chem. Ges.* **53**, 481 (1920); O. Dimroth and V. Hilcken, *ibid.* **54**, 3050 (1921).

(4) O. Dimroth and R. Schweizer, *Ber. deut. chem. Ges.* **56**, 1375 (1923).

(5) R. Adams and co-workers, numerous publications in *J. Am. Chem. Soc.* (1950–1957).

(6) R. Criegee and co-workers, e.g., *Ann. Chem. Liebigs* **507**, 159 (1933); *ibid.* **599**, 81 (1956).

(7) V. M. Mićović and M. L. Mihailović, *Rec. trav. chim.* **71**, 970 (1952).

(8) W. A. Mosher and H. A. Neidig, *J. Am. Chem. Soc.* **72**, 4452 (1950).

(9) F. Wessely and F. Sinwel, *Monatsh. Chem.* **81**, 1055 (1950); see further, F. Wessely and co-workers, *ibid.* **83**, 902 (1952); *ibid.* **85**, 69 (1954); H. Schmid and H. Burger, *Helv. Chim. Acta* **35**, 928 (1952); A. Ebnöther, T. F. Meijer, and H. Schmid, *ibid.* p. 910; G. W. K. Cavill and co-workers, *J. Chem. Soc.* p. 2785 (1954); R. R. Holmes and co-workers, *J. Am. Chem. Soc.* **76**, 2400 (1954).

(10) R. Criegee, H. Pilz, and H. Flyare, *Ber. deut. chem. Ges.* **72**, 1799 (1939); R. Criegee and G. Paulig, *ibid.* **88**, 712 (1955).

(11) Concerning the dehydrogenation of hydrocarbons and heterocyclics to aromatic systems which only seldom goes smoothly, see R. Criegee, *Ann. Chem. Liebigs* **481**, 263 (1930) as well as reference (1); see also H. Meerwein, *Ber. deut. chem. Ges.* **77**, 227 (1944).

(12) K. Ichikawa and Y. Yamaguchi, *J. Chem. Soc. Japan* **73**, 415 (1952); *Chem. Abstr.* **47**, 10474 (1953); for other preparative examples of ketone oxidation see also R. Criegee and K. Klonk, *Ann. Chem. Liebigs* **564**, 1 (1949); L. F. Fieser and R. Stevenson, *J. Am. Chem. Soc.* **76**, 1728 (1954).

(13) G. W. K. Cavill and |D. H. Solomon, *J. Chem. Soc.* p. 4426 (1955).

(14) R. C. Fuson and co-workers, *J. Am. Chem. Soc.* **79**, 1938 (1957).

(15) W. Cocker and J. C. P. Schwarz, *Chem. & Ind. (London)* p. 390 (1951); *Chem. Abstr.* **46**, 435 (1952).

(16) G. W. K. Cavill and D. H. Solomon, *J. Chem. Soc.* p. 3943 (1954); see also G. W. K. Cavill, A. Robertson, and W. B. Whalley, *ibid.* p. 1567 (1949)

(17) Further examples: W. S. Johnson and co-workers, *J. Am. Chem. Soc.* **66**, 218 (1944); *ibid.* **78**, 6312 (1956).

(18) C. Weis, Dissertation, Karlsruhe, 1953.

(18a) G. H. Wilham, *J. Chem. Soc.* p. 2232 (1961).

(19) V. Franzen, *Chem. Ber.* **87**, 1478 (1954); see also Marktscheffel, Diplomarb., Karlsruhe, 1952.

(20) L. F. Fieser and E. B. Hershberg, *J. Am. Chem. Soc.* **60**, 1893 (1938); *ibid.* **61**, 1565 (1939).

(21) G. W. K. Cavill and D. H. Solomon, *J. Chem. Soc.* p. 1404 (1955); H. E. Barron and co-workers, *Chem. & Ind. (London)* p. 76. (1954).

(22) L. F. Fieser and F. C. Chang, *J. Am. Chem. Soc.* **64**, 2043 (1942); L. F. Fieser, R. C. Clapp, and W. H. Daudt, *ibid.* p. 2052; see also J. W. Cornforth and E. Cookson, *J. Chem. Soc.* p. 1085 (1952).

(23) D. H. Hey, J. M. Stirling, and G. H. Williams, *J. Chem. Soc.* p. 2747 (1954); *ibid.* p. 3963 (1955).

(24) R. Criegee, P. Dimroth, K. Noll, R. Simon, and C. Weis, *Chem. Ber.* **90**, 1070 (1957); see also M. Levas, *Ann. chim. (Paris)* [12] **7**, 697 (1952); *Chem. Abstr.* **48**, 1243 (1954).

(25) R. Simon, Dissertation, Karlsruhe, 1951; W. S. Johnson, B. Gestambide, and R. Pappo, *J. Am. Chem. Soc.* **79**, 1991 (1957).

(26) T. Posternak and H. Friedli, *Helv. Chim. Acta* **36**, 251 (1953).

(27) N. Elming and N. Clauson-Kaas, *Acta Chem. Scand.* **6**, 535 565 (1952); the oxidation of 2,5-diarylfurans goes quite differently: Ch.-K. Dien and R. E. Lutz, *J. Org. Chem.* **22**, 1355 (1957).

(28) L. F. Fieser and S. T. Putnam, *J. Am. Chem. Soc.* **69**, 1038 (1947).

(29) S. Goldschmidt and E. Stöckl, *Chem. Ber.* **85**, 630 (1952).

(30) W. Hückel and H. G. Kirschner, *Chem. Ber.* **80**, 41 (1947).

(31) C. D. Hurd and O. E. Edwards, *J. Org. Chem.* **19**, 1319 (1954).

(32) A further interesting case is that of longifolen: P. Naffa and G. Ourisson, *Bull. soc. chim. France* p. 1115 (1954).

(33) W. A. Mosher and C. L. Kehr, *J. Am. Chem. Soc.* **75**, 3172 (1953).

(33a) Remark by the referee: the lead tetraacetate oxidation of bicyclo[1.2.2] heptene and -heptadiene occurs in complete agreement with this concept: K. Alder, F. H. Flock, and H. Wirtz, *Chem. Ber.* **91**, 609 (1958).

(34) E. M. Panov and K. A. Kocheshkov, *Doklady Akad. Nauk S.S.S.R.* **85**, 1037 (1952); *Chem. Abstr.* **47**, 6365 (1953).

(35) R. Criegee, P. Dimroth, and R. Schempf, *Chem. Ber.* **90**, 1337 (1957). Compounds of the type $R_2Pb(OAc)_2$ were prepared already in this manner by M. M. Nad' and K. A. Kocheshkov, *Zhur. Obshchei Khim.* **12**, 409 (1942); *Chem. Abstr.* **37**, 3068 (1943); as well as by A. N. Nesmeyanov, R. K. Friedlina, and A. Kochetkov, *Izvest. Akad. Nauk S.S.S.R. Otdel Khim. Nauk* p. 127 (1948); *Chem. Abstr.* **43**, 1716 (1949).

(36) E. g., F. C. Whitmore, E. L. Wittle, and A. P. Popkin, *J. Am. Chem. Soc.* **61**, 1586 (1939).

(37) M. S. Kharasch and A. L. Flenner, *J. Am. Chem. Soc.* **54**, 674 (1932).

(38) H.-J. Kabbe, Dissertation, Karlsruhe, 1958; *Ann. Chem. Liebigs* **656**, 204 (1962).

(39) M. S. Kharasch, H. N. Friedlander, and W. H. Urry, *J. Org. Chem.* **16**, 533 (1951).

(40) E. Hahl, Dissertation, Karlsruhe, 1958.

(41) F. V. Brutcher, Jr. and F. J. Vara, *J. Am. Chem. Soc.* **78**, 5695 (1956).

(42) L. S. Levitt, *J. Org. Chem.* **20**, 1297 (1955).

(43) M. Finkelstein, *Chem. Ber.* **90**, 2097 (1957).

(44) W. von E. Doering, M. Farber, and A. Sayigh, *J. Am. Chem. Soc.* **74**, 4370 (1952); W. von E. Doering and M. Finkelstein, *J. Org. Chem.* **23**, 141 (1958).

(45a) C. A. Grob, M. Ohta, and A. Weiss, *Angew. Chem.* **70**, 343 (1958).

(45b) C. A. Grob, M. Ohta, E. Renk, and A. Weiss, *Helv. Chim. Acta* **41**, 1191 (1958).

(46) Private communication from Prof. C. A. Grob.

(47) J. Jacques, C. Weidmann, and A. Horeau, *Bull. soc. chim. France* p. 424 (1959).

(48) G. Cainelli, M. L. Mihailović, D. Arigoni, and O. Jeger, *Helv. Chim. Acta* **42**, 1124 (1959).

(49) P. D. Gardner and R. J. Thompson, *J. Org. Chem.* **22**, 36 (1957).

(50) K. Alder, F. H. Flock, and H. Wirtz, *Chem. Ber.* **91**, 609 (1958).

(51) The reaction, $Ar_2Hg + Pb(OAc)_4 \rightarrow ArPb(OAc)_3 + ArHgOAc$, which was not known to us at the time, had already been carried out by E. M. Panov, V. J. Lodochnikova, and K. A. Kocheshkov, *Doklady Akad. Nauk S.S.S.R.* **111**, 1042 (1956); *Chem. Abstr.* **51**, 9512 (1957).

(52) E. M. Panov and K. A. Kocheshkov, *Doklady Akad. Nauk S.S.S.R.* **123**, 295 (1958); *Chem. Abstr.* **53**, 7133 (1959).

(53) L. Field and J. E. Lawson, *J. Am. Chem. Soc.* **80**, 838 (1958).

(54) How lead teraacetate acts upon such thioglycols, which contain the OH and SH group in small rings in the *cis*-position, is not known. It is quite conceivable that in such cases the glycol cleavage is the quicker reaction.

(55) L. Horner, E. Winkelmann, K. H. Knapp, and W. Ludwig, *Chem. Ber.* **92**, 288 (1959).

Author Index

The numbers in parentheses are footnote numbers and are inserted to enable the reader to locate a cross reference when the author's name does not appear at the point of reference in the text.

Buc, S. R., 285(27), *302*
Buchkremer, J., 145(118), *159*
Buchner, B., 198(82), *211*
Buchta, E., 112(68a), 114(74b), *128*
Buchwald, H., 194(113), 202(113), *211*
Buckler, S. A., 195(75f), *210*
Bühler, W., 20, *29*
Büntgen, C., 59(29), 62(29), 76(50), 77
(50), 87(50), 88(50), *98, 99*
Bueren, H., 6(34), 8(47), *27*
Bundesmann, H., 228(2), *252*
Bunge, W., 12(62), *28*
Burg, A. B., 199, *211*, 213(7), 214(7), 218
(7), *224*
Burger, H., 369(9), *387*
Burkhard, E. B., 136(35), 137(35), *157*
Burmistrova, M. S., 64(34c), 71(34c), 88
(34c), *98*, 106(114), *130*
Burness, D. M., 3(7, 18), 9(55, 56), 13, 17
(93), 19(93), 20(93), *26, 27, 28, 29*
Burson, S. L., 104(34), *127*
Burton, J. F., 138(51), *157*
Busch, M., 312, *333*
Buu-Hoi, N. P., 119(88a, 88b), *129*

C

Cahill, W. M., 138(50, 51), *157*
Cahours, A., 164, *208*
Cainelli, G., 381(48), *388*
Cairncross, J. M., 316(39b), *334*
Caldwell, J. R., 148(145, 151, 152), 149
(145, 152, 156, 159), *160*
Canet, M., 103(117), 107(117), 113(117),
130
Cantor, S. M., 136(31), 137(31), *157*
Cardwell, H. M. E., 108(130, 131), *131*
Case, F. H., 104(20), 116(20), *126*
Casper, J., 174(32), 198(32), 201(32), *209*
Cassis, F. A., 349(26), 354(32a), *359*
Castells, J., 112(65, 66a), 123(66a), *128*
Cavallito, C. J., 224(68), *226*
Cavill, G. W. K., 369(9), 371, *387*
Cerrito, L., 150(169), *161*
Chaikin, S. W., 214(18, 21), 218(18, 21),
219(21), *224, 225*
Chakrabarty, N. K., 115(77a), 123(77a),
128
Challenger, F., 177(37), 178(43), *209*
Chandra, K., 115(77a), 123(77a), *128*
Chang, F. C., 372(22), 384(22), *387*

Chatt, J., 193(68), *210*
Chatterjee, D. N., 106(106, 107), 112(70),
128, 130
Chatterjee, N. N., 105(48), *127*
Chen, C., 104(34), *127*
Cherbuliez, E., 285, 286, 297(29), 298(29),
302
Chick, F., 140, 142(70), 143, 147(70), *158*
Chipman, H. R., 17(97), *29*
Chiurdoglu, G., 104(22), *126*
Chizhov, O. S., 21(114), *30*
Cholak, J., 135(25), *157*
Christian, W., 256(6), *275*
Chute, W. J., 145(112), *159*
Cinneide, R. O., 283(18), *302*
Claborn, H. V., 136(43), *157*
Claisen, L., 1, 12, 19, 20(107), *26, 29*, 57
(25), *98*
Clapp, R. C., 285(26), 294, *302*, 372 (22),
384(22), *387*
Clark, E. R., 101(13a), 107(13a), *126*
Clark, J., 63(36a), *98*
Claus, C. J., 219(29b), *225*
Clauson-Kaas, N., 373(27), 385(27), *387*
Clemo, G. R., 116(79a, 79b), 117(79a,
79b), *128*
Cliffe, W. H., 118, *129*
Coats, R. R., 120, *129*
Cochran, P. B., 135(23), *157*
Cocker, W., 371(15), *387*
Coe, D. G., 191, *210*
Coenen, M., 59(28, 29), 61(36), 62(28,
29), 87(49, 50), 96(38), 97(49), 65, 67
(38), 75(38), 76(49, 50), 77(49, 50),
79(36), 80(38), 83(38), 87(36, 38), 88
(50), 93(49), *98, 99*
Coffield, T. M., 355(32b), *359*
Cohen, L. A., 217(29a), *225*
Cohen, S. S., 269(33), *276*
Coleman, G. H., 139(69), *158*
Collie, N., 200(101), *211*
Collie, W., 196(75g), *210*
Collins, D. V., 269(38), *276*
Colón, A. A., 314(34), *333*
Colonge, J., 106(113), 121(113), *130*
Conover, L. H., 223(58), *226*
Constam, E. J., 240(11), *252*
Cook, H. G., 39(17), *50*
Cook, J. W., 114(74), 117, 120, *128, 129*
Cookson, E., 372(22), 384(22), *387*

Müller, R., 8, *27*
Müller-Schiedmayer, G., 194(75b), *210*
Mugdan, M., 147(134), *160*
Mukherji, S. M., 9(53), *27*
Murray, M. A., 214(12), *224*
Mychajlyszyn, V., 121(97b), *130*
Mylius, G., 119(89), *129*

N

Naber, A. D., 105(104), *130*
Nad', M. M., 375(35), *388*
Naffa, P., 374(32), *388*
Nagel, K., 216(27), *225*
Nandi, B. L., 113(72), *128*
Napolitano, J. P., 338(7a), 343(16), *358*
Nargund, K. S., 105(52), 113, 123(52), *127*
Natelson, S., 350, 357, *359*
Naves, Y. R., 121(97d), *130*
Nazarov, I. N., 64(34c), 66(39), 67(39), 71(34c), 88(34c), *98, 99,* 105(103), 106(114), *130*
Neidig, H. A., 369(8), *386*
Nelles, J., 3(9,19), *26*
Nelson, J. F., 145(113), *159*
Nesmeyanov, A. N., 3(20), 7(38,42,43), 13(66,67,70,71), 18(99), 20(104,105), 21(71,111,112,113), *26, 27, 28, 29,* 375(35), *388*
Neuberger, A., 140(76), *158*
Neunhoeffer, O., 101, 109, *126*
Neuse, E., 15, *28*
Nevenzel, J. C., 105(104), *130*
Newman, M. S., 105(104), *130*
Newton, A., 243(12), *252*
Newton, L. W., 144(99), *159*
Nickel, H., 181(49), 182(49,50), 203(50), *210*
Nicolaus, B. J. R., 218(32), *225*
Nicolson, A., 316(39b), *334*
Nieuwland, J. A., 343(17), 346(17), *358*
Nifant'ev, E. E., 8, 13(66,67), *27, 28*
Nightingal, D. A., 136(33), 137(33,40), 140(78), *157, 158*
Nikles, E., 15, *28*
Nippe, B., 172(27), *209*
Nobis, J. F., 361(2), 364(2), *366*
Nodzu, R., 136(39), 137(39), *157*
Noll, K., 374(24), 384(24), 385(24), *387*

Nonaka, M., 23(119), *30*
Nordwig, A., 221, *225*
Northrop, J. H., 138(56), *158*
Nunn, J. R., 104(35,38), 111, *127*
Nystrom, R. F., 214(13,15,16,18), 218 18), 220(16), 223(60,64,65), *224, 226*

O

Oberbichler, W., 315(38h), 316(38h), *334*
Obermeier, F., 37(12), *50*
Oediger, H., 173(30), 187(30), 191(65a), 192(65d), 206(30), *209, 210*
Oesper, P., 267(26), *276*
Ogard, A. E., 213(5), 214(5), 216(5), 222 (5), *224*
Ohta, M., 380(45a,45b), 386(45b), *388*
Okui, S., 320(46b), *334*
Olivier, C., 255, *275*
Olszewski, W. F., 179(47a), *209*
Oppegard, A. L., 200(98), *211*
Oppelt, M., 220(42), *225*
Optiz, G., 277(1), 278(2), *301*
Orchard, W. M., 145(112), *159*
Orttmann, H., 101(10a), *126*
Osburn, J. M., 145(116), *159*
Osti, A., 283(21), *302*
Ostrowski, W., 144(98), *159*
Ourisson, G., 374(32), *388*
Ouschakoff, M.,. 112(66), *128*
Overend, W. G., 316, *334*
Owen, L. N., 119, *129*

P

Packendorff, K., 145(115), *159*
Padgham, D. M., 139(65), *158*
Pakendorf, K. G., 119, *129*
Panouse, J. J., 224(68), *226*
Panov, E. M., 375, 382, *388*
Pappalardo, J. A., 3(10), *26*
Pappo, R., 373(25), *387*
Parvin, K., 200(93), 201(93), 202(93), *211*
Paschke, P., 101, 109, *126*
Pascual, J., 102(15c), 112(65,66a,68b), 123(66a), *126, 128*
Pass, F., 194(106), 201(106), 202(106), *211*

Subject Index

6-Butyryl-2-methylpyridine, 15
6-Butyryl-2-propylpyridine, 15

C

ε-Caprolactone, 144
N-Carbethoxyalanine ethyl ester, 34
1-Carbethoxy-Δ^2-bicyclo[2.2.2]octene, 386
2-Carbethoxycyclopentanone, 101, 121
  alkylation at 1-C, 122
  cleavage to acids, 109, 123
    to ketones, 109, 122
  condensation with
    amines, 116
    halides, 103
    phenols, 118
  cyanohydrins, 113
  enol salt, 102, 122
  Grignard reaction with, 114
  potassium salt, 122
  reaction at carbon-3, 121
  reaction with hydrazine, 124
  reduction, 111
  Reformatsky reaction with, 114
N-Carbobenzoxy-α-L-diglutamylglu-
    tamic acid tetraethyl ester, 45
Carbobenzoxy-L-glutamyl-α,γ-bisglycine
    ethyl ester, 35
Carbobenzoxyglycine, 35, 43
Carbobenzoxyglycyl-β-alanine ethyl
    ester, 44
Carbobenzoxyglycylglycine, 36
  ethyl ester, 35, 42
Carbobenzoxyglycyl-DL-phenylalanine
    ethyl ester, 46
Carbobenzoxytetraglycine ethyl ester,
    36, 44
Carbobenzoxypeptide ester, 43
Carbodiimides, 189
Carbohydrate metabolism, chemical syn-
    thesis of intermediates of, 253ff.
Carbonyl compounds
  alkylation of 1,3-cyclohexanedione
    with, 61
  reaction with ketene, 145
  reduction with hydrides, 213ff.
    to hydrocarbons, 223
Carbonyl group, protection of, 217
DL-N-Carbonylalanine ethyl ester, 33
N-Carbonylamino acids, esters, 32
N-Carbonylamino acids, ethyl esters, 33

L-N-Carbonylaspartic diethyl ester, 34
N-Carbonylglycine ethyl ester, 35, 36
4-Chloroacetamidomethyl-3-methyl-1-
    phenyl-5-pyrazolone, 283
5-Chloroacetamidomethyl-2-thio-
    phenecarboxylic acid, 283
Chloroacetyl chloride, 142
1-Chloro-1-buten-3-one, 3
β-Chlorocrotonaldehyde, 3
2-Chloro-6-ethylaniline, 233
3-Chloro-2,6-diethylaniline, 233
3-Chloro-2,6-diisopropylphenol, 347
4-Chloro-2,6-diisopropylphenol, 347
2-Chloro-6-isopropylphenol, 346
3-Chloro-6-isopropylphenol, 347
4-Chloro-2-isopropylphenol, 347
N-Chloromethylbenzamide, 298
4-Chloro-2-nitrophenylmercaptoacetyl
    chloride, 142
3-Chloro-2,4,6-triisopropylphenol, 347
β-Chlorovinyl methyl ketone, 3
Chromones, 118
Cinnamylcyclopentanone, 121
Comenic acid, methyl ester, 320
m-Cresotic acid, 13
Cumarins, 118
2-Cyanamino-4-methylpyrimidine, 17
3-Cyano-2,6-dimethylpyridine, 15
3-Cyano-2-hydroxy-6-methylpyridine, 14
Cyclitols, oxidation of, 321
Cyclobutanone, 145
1,3-Cyclohexanediones
  alkylation with
    carbonyl compounds, 61
    organic halogen compounds, 55
  cleavage to acids, 70
  cleavage and reduction to acids, 74
  long-chain acids from, 51ff.
  Michael addition with, 65
  miscellaneous addition methods, 68
  preparation, 52
  2-substituted, 55ff., 62
6-Cyclohexylhexanoic acid, 79
Cyclopentanecarboxylic acids, 2-substi-
    tuted, 115
1,2-Cyclopentanedione monoxime, 120
Cyclopentanone
  α,α-dialkylated, 110
  O-substituted, 109
2-Cyclopentanonecarboxamides, 117

Valokonis